ADVANCES IN

GEOPHYSICS

VOLUME 28

Issues in Atmospheric and Oceanic Modeling

Part A

Climate Dynamics

Joseph Smagorinsky

Advances in

GEOPHYSICS

VOLUME 28

Issues in Atmospheric and Oceanic Modeling

Part A
Climate Dynamics

Edited by

BARRY SALTZMAN

Department of Geology and Geophysics
Yale University
New Haven, Connecticut

Volume Editor

SYUKURO MANABE

Geophysical Fluid Dynamics Laboratory/NOAA
Princeton University
Princeton, New Jersey

1985

ACADEMIC PRESS, INC.
Harcourt Brace Jovanovich, Publishers

Orlando   San Diego   New York   Austin
London   Montreal   Sydney   Tokyo   Toronto

Dedicated to Joseph Smagorinsky on his retirement
from the Geophysical Fluid Dynamics Laboratory
of NOAA, January 31, 1983.

ACADEMIC PRESS, INC.
Orlando, Florida 32887

United Kingdom Edition published by
ACADEMIC PRESS INC. (LONDON) LTD.
24–28 Oval Road, London NW1 7DX

LIBRARY OF CONGRESS CATALOG CARD NUMBER: 52–12266

ISBN 0–12–018828–7
ISBN 0–12–000002–4 (paperback)

PRINTED IN THE UNITED STATES OF AMERICA

85 86 87 88   9 8 7 6 5 4 3 2 1

CONTENTS

Climate Sensitivity

ROBERT E. DICKINSON

CO$_2$ and Hydrology

SYUKURO MANABE AND RICHARD T. WETHERALD

Modeling of Paleoclimates

JOHN E. KUTZBACH

The Southern Oscillation and El Niño

S. GEORGE PHILANDER AND EUGENE M. RASMUSSON

Part II. The Middle Atmosphere

Some Aspects of Stratospheric Dynamics

Dennis L. Hartmann

Wave–Mean-Flow Interaction in the Middle Atmosphere

David G. Andrews

Radiative–Dynamical Interactions in the Middle Atmosphere

Stephen B. Fels

Mechanistic Interpretation of Stratospheric Tracer Transport

J. D. Mahlman

Part III.   Planetary Atmospheres

The General Circulation of Mars: Models and Observations

CONWAY B. LEOVY

Atmospheric Circulation of Venus

WILLIAM B. ROSSOW

Jovian and Comparative Atmospheric Modeling

GARETH P. WILLIAMS

Part IV.   Ocean Dynamics

Modeling Ocean Circulation

KIRK BRYAN AND JORGE L. SARMIENTO

Tropical Oceanography

S. GEORGE PHILANDER

Simulation of Mesoscale Ocean Variability
in Mid-Latitude Gyres

WILLIAM R. HOLLAND

Modeling Circulation and Mixing in Estuaries
and Coastal Oceans

ALAN F. BLUMBERG AND LI-YAUW OEY

Modeling Sea-Ice Dynamics

W. D. HIBLER, III

CONTRIBUTORS

Numbers in parentheses indicate the pages on which the authors' contributions begin.

DAVID G. ANDREWS, *Department of Atmospheric Physics, Clarendon Laboratory, Oxford University, Oxford OX1 3PU, United Kingdom* (249)

ALAN F. BLUMBERG,* *Dynalysis of Princeton, Princeton, New Jersey 08540-1512* (525)

KIRK BRYAN, *Geophysical Fluid Dynamics Laboratory/NOAA, Princeton University, Princeton, New Jersey 08542* (433)

ROBERT E. DICKINSON, *National Center for Atmospheric Research, Boulder, Colorado 80307* (99)

STEPHEN B. FELS, *Geophysical Fluid Dynamics Laboratory/NOAA, Princeton University, Princeton, New Jersey 08542* (277)

DENNIS L. HARTMANN, *Department of Atmospheric Sciences, University of Washington, Seattle, Washington 98195* (219)

ISAAC M. HELD, *Geophysical Fluid Dynamics Laboratory/NOAA, Princeton University, Princeton, New Jersey 08542* (3)

W. D. HIBLER, III, *U.S.A. Cold Regions, Research and Engineering Laboratories, Hanover, New Hampshire 03755* (549)

WILLIAM R. HOLLAND, *National Center for Atmospheric Research, Boulder, Colorado 80307* (479)

BRIAN J. HOSKINS, *Department of Meteorology, University of Reading, Reading RG6 2AU, England* (3)

JOHN E. KUTZBACH, *IES, Center for Climatic Research, University of Wisconsin — Madison, Madison, Wisconsin 53706* (159)

N.-C. LAU, *Geophysical Fluid Dynamics Laboratory/NOAA, Princeton University, Princeton, New Jersey 08542* (33)

CONWAY B. LEOVY, *Department of Atmospheric Sciences and Graduate Program of Geophysics, University of Washington, Seattle, Washington 98195* (327)

J. D. MAHLMAN, *Geophysical Fluid Dynamics Laboratory/NOAA, Princeton University, Princeton, New Jersey 08542* (301)

* Present address: HydroQual, Inc., Mahwah, New Jersey 07430.

SYUKURO MANABE, *Geophysical Fluid Dynamics Laboratory/NOAA, Princeton University, Princeton, New Jersey 08542* (131)

LI-YAUW OEY,* *Geophysical Fluid Dynamics Program, Princeton University, Princeton, New Jersey 08542* (525)

ABRAHAM H. OORT, *Geophysical Fluid Dynamics Laboratory/NOAA, Princeton University, Princeton, New Jersey 08542* (75)

S. GEORGE PHILANDER, *Geophysical Fluid Dynamics Laboratory/NOAA, Princeton University, Princeton, New Jersey 08542* (197, 461)

EUGENE M. RASMUSSON, *Climate Analysis Center, National Meteorological Center, National Weather Service/NOAA, Washington, D.C. 20233* (197)

WILLIAM B. ROSSOW, *NASA Goddard Space Flight Center, Institute for Space Studies, New York, New York 10025* (347)

JORGE L. SARMIENTO, *Geophysical Fluid Dynamics Program, Princeton University, Princeton, New Jersey 08542* (433)

J. M. WALLACE, *Department of Atmospheric Sciences, University of Washington, Seattle, Washington 98195* (33)

RICHARD T. WETHERALD, *Geophysical Fluid Dynamics Laboratory/NOAA, Princeton University, Princeton, New Jersey 08542* (131)

GARETH P. WILLIAMS, *Geophysical Fluid Dynamics Laboratory/NOAA, Princeton University, Princeton, New Jersey 08542* (381)

* Present address: Skidaway Institute of Oceanography, Savannah, Georgia 31416.

FOREWORD

A general scientific revolution was taking place in the mid-1940s, no small part of which was being played by research meteorologists. At the successful urging of John von Neumann, a computer of incomparable capacity for its time was being built, with improved weather forecasting as one of its main justifications. Within a few short years, the practice of theoretical meteorological research would be transformed from one characterized only by highly individualistic efforts to one in which a major role would be played by teams of co-workers using commonly shared high-speed computers to model and experiment with the workings of the atmosphere and its larger climatic system setting.

It was Joseph Smagorinsky who emerged as one of the pioneer, prototypical leaders of the new mode of research engendered by this revolution. Already an accomplished individual researcher who had made significant contributions to dynamical meteorology, especially regarding the effects of heating and moisture fields on weather and climate patterns, Smagorinsky realized early that the ultimate nonlinear theory of the detailed climatic state of the atmosphere and oceans would rest on large-scale numerical modeling, and he set about to create an institutional structure for accomplishing the long-term process of model building that would be necessary. In essence, Smagorinsky inaugurated a new style of creative scientific endeavor in which the contributions of a group of outstanding theorists and computer specialists are "orchestrated" to produce new, otherwise unobtainable, results and insights relevant to extremely complex problems.

This organic model-building process is now more alive than ever, with major general circulation modeling (GCM) groups active at many locations. These parallel efforts are, in fact, necessary to provide the only source of "reproducibility" possible in this kind of work; unlike the classic "pencil-and-paper" theories, no single individual can replicate the reported results of a GCM experiment. It is now widely recognized that the GCM solutions represent the most complete deductive explanation obtainable of the statistical equilibrium state of the atmosphere and its lower surface boundary layer. As such, they provide the basis for our most credible predictions of the climatic consequences of prescribed external changes and of prescribed changes in some of the slower response parts of the climatic system. In addition, the numerical models are just beginning to come to the fore as an experimental tool used to understand the dynamics of the atmosphere and oceans to the degree necessary to parameterize the time-average fluxes of mass, momentum, and energy by the synoptic-scale motions. This role is bound to increase in the future. Under the leadership of Joseph Smagorinsky, the Geophysical Fluid Dynamics Laboratory (GFDL) became a pacesetter in all these areas.

It is also true that it is to the GCM that we must continually turn to obtain information about the likely consequences of the actions of humanity on the global environment. Our understanding of the consequences of increasing CO_2 on climatic conditions largely derive from GCMs. Questions about the possible decrease of the ozone content of the stratosphere as a result of the release of chemicals in that region of the Earth's atmospheric envelope are illuminated by computations with GCMs. Our concerns with the effects of a nuclear exchange on the general circulation of the atmosphere can be treated only through the computations of general circulation models. The ability to extend the time range of weather forecasts is fundamentally dependent on the refinement of general circulation models and the acquisition of the necessary observational data required for their application. In recent years in the United States, Europe, and other regions of the world, significant advances have been made in long-range weather forecasting as a result of the development of these models.

Smagorinsky was not only a creative scientist and a leader of teams of scientists, he was a remarkably able administrator, at home within the administrative currents of government organizations as well as within the intellectual give and take of a scientific laboratory. The history of the Geophysical Fluid Dynamics Laboratory is indeed the reflection of his career. After leaving Princeton and returning to the Weather Bureau in Washington, D.C., he became the focus for the predecessor laboratory of the Geophysical Fluid Dynamics Laboratory. The General Circulation Laboratory of the Weather Bureau was housed in a storefront building on Pennsylvania Avenue in the shadow of the U.S. Capitol. On display there were the computers of whose basic necessity Smagorinsky had been able to convince governmental officials. People walked back and forth observing the curious phenomenon of scientists placing tapes on machines and deciphering the incredible volume of numbers produced.

It was clear that a storefront building on Pennsylvania Avenue, however choice the location, was not the best environment for Smagorinsky's dreams. He wanted a laboratory on a university campus, in which the intellectual stimulation of the scientific community in a university could be melded with the resources and facilities provided by the government. It would be a place where scientists from his laboratory, cooperating with others invited from all parts of the world, could work in a stimulating environment totally focused on the key problems of geophysical fluid dynamics. It was a mark of his administrative ability that he persuaded the Weather Bureau to move the General Circulation Laboratory to the campus at Princeton University to be housed in a building exclusively devoted to geophysical fluid dynamics research.

From its inception the laboratory bore the imprint of Smagorinsky's insistence on high standards in every aspect of work. It became and continues to be a mecca for scientists from many countries for the study of numerical approaches to a variety of atmospheric and oceanographic problems. Perhaps no single laboratory has had the worldwide influence of Smagorinsky's GFDL. It became a model for many other groups and countries throughout the world.

It has been our great pleasure to observe and admire "Smag's" efforts and the monumental achievements of the GFDL. We have enjoyed and benefited greatly from our long years of association with him as friends and colleagues. It is a privilege now to introduce this Festschrift volume dedicated to him. Rich in excellent review papers and ably edited by Syukuro Manabe and his GFDL colleagues, the contents give ample testimony to Joe Smagorinsky's seminal influence on theoretical meteorology and its practitioners.

BARRY SALTZMAN
ROBERT M. WHITE

PREFACE

This book is dedicated to Joseph Smagorinsky in commemoration of his retirement as Director of the Geophysical Fluid Dynamics Laboratory (GFDL) of the National Oceanic and Atmospheric Administration (NOAA) and to celebrate his lifelong achievements in the atmospheric and oceanic sciences.

Joe Smagorinsky pioneered the development of mathematical models of the atmosphere, beginning in the 1950s with his construction of a general circulation model of the atmosphere based on the primitive equations and continuing over the next two decades with the evolution of more comprehensive models. In addition, he promoted the application of the modeling technique to a wide variety of phenomena, both large and small in scale, basic and applied in form, and to a wide variety of systems, both oceanic and atmospheric, terrestrial and extraterrestrial. From the beginning he recognized the enormous potential of the computer for the atmospheric and oceanic sciences and throughout his term as Director of the GFDL, he succeeded in obtaining the most advanced machines made or conceived of for his laboratory's use and in creating a research environment that optimized their potential.

Joe Smagorinsky also made a major contribution in the planning and execution of the Global Atmospheric Research Program (GARP), first as a member and then as the Chairman of the Joint Organizing Committee of the World Meteorological Organization (WMO) and the International Council of Scientific Union (ICSU). His imaginative leadership and absolute commitment were indispensable to the success of GARP and its First Global GARP Experiment (FGGE). His scientific expertise was invaluable in the design and realization of GARP's major modeling studies of atmospheric variations on both the weather and climate scales.

The main objective of this book is to assess the current state of atmospheric and oceanic modeling and of related theoretical and diagnostic studies and to pinpoint outstanding problems of immediate and future concern. A wide range of topics is discussed; for convenience, the book is split into two parts according to scale. The first part, "Climate Dynamics," contains articles on climate, the middle atmosphere, planetary atmospheres, and ocean dynamics. The second part, "Weather Dynamics," covers numerical weather prediction, mesoscale dynamics, tropical dynamics, turbulence, and convection. Each essay presents a topic in historical perspective, discussing its present status and assessing the future prospect for research.

Another objective of the book is to give some measure of the progress made during the past 30 years and of Joe's role in that achievement. The authors were thus chosen from among his friends and students, both at the GFDL and elsewhere, and were encouraged—mainly because of space limitations—to present their own views of their topic rather than to attempt a comprehensive review. We regret any omissions or bias that this selectivity has caused and beg the forebearance of the many people who have contributed to the science and of the many friends of Joe who could not be included in these volumes.

It is hoped that this book will give some indication of the enormous power and future potential of mathematical modeling and that it will stimulate further interest in its application to atmospheric and oceanic problems. If we achieve this aim, we will have begun to repay the great debt we owe to Joe Smagorinsky.

The publication of this book would not have been possible without the help and enthusiasm of the associate editors—K. Bryan, Y. Kurihara, J. D. Mahlman, G. L. Mellor, K. Miyakoda, A. H. Oort, I. Orlanski, G. Philander, and G. P. Williams—who participated in planning the book and editing its various sections.

Barry Saltzman, the regular editor of *Advances in Geophysics* gave me the privilege of serving as the guest editor of this two-part volume. His thoughtful guidance and assistance made this book possible.

Robert White, who gave his wholehearted support to the GFDL during his term as Administrator of the NOAA, kindly agreed to write the Foreword in collaboration with Barry Saltzman. J. D. Mahlman, the current director of the GFDL has given us constant encouragement and support and has made the resources of the GFDL available for this large effort.

Finally, it is a great pleasure to acknowledge all those, especially the authors, who set aside many other pressing commitments to contribute with insight and enthusiasm to these two volumes.

SYUKURO MANABE

ADVANCES IN

GEOPHYSICS

VOLUME 28

Issues in Atmospheric and Oceanic Modeling

Part A

Climate Dynamics

Part I

CLIMATE

LARGE-SCALE EDDIES AND THE GENERAL CIRCULATION OF THE TROPOSPHERE

Isaac M. Held

Geophysical Fluid Dynamics Laboratory/NOAA
Princeton University
Princeton, New Jersey

AND

Brian J. Hoskins

Department of Meteorology
University of Reading
Reading, England

1. Introduction

Our theoretical understanding of the general circulation of the atmosphere, and of the role of large-scale eddies in maintaining that circulation, is primitive but rapidly evolving. There exist several interesting ideas relevant to closure schemes for mid-latitude eddies generated by baroclinic instability, but none is so well founded in theory as to be convincing, and systematic tests against eddy-resolving numerical models are as yet very limited. There is a substantial body of work on weakly nonlinear baroclinic waves, but its relevance for the atmosphere remains obscure. A host of competing theories have been proposed recently to explain the distinctive structure of the low-frequency variability of the atmosphere. Analyses of observations and general circulation models are evolving particularly rapidly and complementing each other as they focus on the most dynamically interesting budgets and statistics. And new global data sets are making possible meaningful studies of dynamical balances in the tropics and of planetary wave propagation between the tropics and mid-latitudes. Our reaction to this turbulent state of

3

affairs is to present our own idiosyncratic views on how different parts of the system fit together and on what some of the outstanding problems are. If there is any theme to be found beneath the surface of this essay, it may be the following: in developing general circulation theory and eddy flux closures, we must move beyond speculation followed by qualitative comparison with the atmosphere in all its complexity, toward formulating hypotheses that can be quantitatively tested against idealized numerical models designed for the purpose. As evidence that this approach is feasible, we have the remarkable success of numerical general circulation models (GCMs) of the atmosphere, to which Dr. Smagorinsky has made such a decisive contribution. We are delighted to contribute this essay to a book honoring his achievements.

2. THE HADLEY CELL

Until stated otherwise, we consider an atmosphere with zonally symmetric lower boundary conditions and external forcing and, therefore, a zonally symmetric climate. Fortunately, experiments with GCMs indicate that the climate of such an atmosphere does not differ greatly from the zonal average of the climate produced by realistic Earth-like asymmetries in the lower boundary. We begin by asking what form the general circulation might take in the absence of "large-scale" eddies, keeping in mind that if one somehow suppresses the baroclinic and barotropic instabilities primarily responsible for cyclone- and planetary-scale eddies, small-scale eddies will still be generated in the surface boundary layer and by gravitational and, perhaps, inertial or Kelvin–Helmholtz instabilities in the free atmosphere.

Take the vertical temperature and moisture structures as given for the moment, so as to isolate problems associated with horizontal temperature gradients and vertical wind shears. In the absence of any time-mean flow, suppose that radiation plus convection produce the temperature field $T_E(\theta, p)$. In a rapidly rotating atmosphere, one is tempted to set $T = T_E$ as a first approximation, assume thermal wind balance,

$$f[\partial u/\partial \ln(p)] = (R/a)(\partial T/\partial \theta) \qquad (2.1)$$

and then obtain the wind field by assuming that surface drag is sufficient to maintain $u \approx 0$ near the surface. Unless one is so fortunate that $\partial T_E/\partial\theta$ is identically zero at the equator, this procedure is clearly inadequate, since the resulting wind will be infinite at the equator. Difficulties remain even if T_E happens to be symmetric about the equator, as the following heuristic model [based on Held and Hou (1980)] demonstrates. The model also suggests how axisymmetric large-scale flow in the tropics (the Hadley cell) corrects these deficiencies.

Assume that the meridional flow is confined (as it is in the Hadley cell) to two boundary layers at the surface, $p = p_S$, and at the tropopause, $p = p_T$, of pressure thicknesses δ_S and δ_T. Define a mass transport velocity $V = v_T \delta_T / \Delta p = -v_S \delta_S / \Delta p$, where v_S and v_T are the meridional velocities averaged over each layer and $\Delta p = p_S - p_T$. A thermodynamic equation adequate for our purposes is

$$0 = -\nabla \cdot (m\boldsymbol{v}) - c_P(T - T_E)/\tau \qquad (2.2)$$

where m is the moist static energy, $c_P T + gz + Lr$, τ is a radiative relaxation time, and $\boldsymbol{v} = (v, \omega)$. Vertically integrating, we have

$$[T] = [T_E] - \frac{\tau}{a\cos(\theta)}\frac{\partial}{\partial\theta}(\cos(\theta)SV) \qquad (2.3)$$

where

$$[T] \equiv \frac{1}{\Delta p}\int_{p_T}^{p_S} T\,dp \qquad (2.4)$$

while

$$S \equiv [m(p_T) - m(p_S)]/c_P \qquad (2.5)$$

is a measure of the gross moist stability of the atmosphere. Here $[T]$ can be related to $u(p_T) = U$ by vertically integrating (2.1) and assuming that $u(p_S)$ is negligibly small,

$$fU = -\frac{R}{a}\frac{\partial}{\partial\theta}\int T\,d\ln(p) \qquad (2.6)$$

$f\,2u = \frac{R}{a}\frac{2T\,2\ln(p)}{2\theta} \quad p+s(\theta)$

$= \frac{R}{a}\frac{2}{2\theta}(T\ln(p))$

Assuming further that the vertical profile of T is independent of latitude, $T = [T](\theta) + t(p)$, then

$$fU = -\frac{R\chi}{a}\frac{\partial[T]}{\partial\theta} \qquad (2.7)$$

where χ is the depth of the troposphere in scale heights. A relation between U and V must be obtained from the zonal angular momentum budget. In the spirit of constructing a simple heuristic model, we assume that angular momentum is conserved following a horizontal streamline at the top of the Hadley cell, except for linear damping:

$U = u(p_T)$

$$\kappa U = (f + \zeta)V = -\frac{V}{a^2\cos(\theta)}\frac{\partial M}{\partial\theta} \qquad (2.8)$$

where $M = \Omega a^2 \cos^2(\theta) + Ua\cos(\theta)$, ζ is the relative vorticity, and κ is a constant. We now have three equations [(2.3), (2.7), and (2.8)] in the three

$M = \Omega a^2 \cos^2(\theta) + Ua\cos(\theta)$

$U = 0$ AT POINT OF MAXIMUM ANGULAR MOMENTUM

$M \leq \Omega a^2$ AT ALL LATITUDES

unknowns U, V, and $[T]$. The only nonlinearity results from the advection of relative vorticity in (2.8). Similar models have been discussed by Hou (1984) and Schneider (1983).

Assuming that $\kappa \neq 0$, (2.8) implies that $U = 0$ at the point of maximum angular momentum. Therefore, $M \leq \Omega a^2$ at all latitudes. Equivalently, $U(\theta) \leq U_M(\theta) = \Omega a \sin^2(\theta)/\cos(\theta)$. Returning to (2.8), we see that as $\kappa \to 0$, either V or $f + \zeta$ must vanish. But in regions where $V \to 0$, we also must have $[T] \to [T_E]$ and $U \to U_E$ where U_E is the wind field in balance with $\partial[T_E]/\partial\theta$. Therefore, wherever $U_E > U_M$, $f + \zeta$ must vanish as $\kappa \to 0$. Figure 1a shows the zonal winds produced by this model for several values of the parameter $S\kappa\tau$. (U is a function of κ, S, and τ only through the combination $S\kappa\tau$.) Also plotted are U_E and U_M. Here $[T_E]$ is symmetric about the equator; its form and the values of the other model parameters are given in the figure caption. Figure 1b shows the absolute vorticities corresponding to the winds in Fig. 1a. As analyzed in Held and Hou (1980), the region in which the absolute vorticity vanishes as $\kappa \to 0$ is somewhat larger than that in which $U_E > U_M$. The results are qualitatively similar if the forcing is asymmetric about the equator; the region within which $f + \zeta \to 0$ is then asymmetric as well.

If large-scale eddies were suppressed, what processes would result in significant stress on the upper-tropospheric flow in the Hadley cell? It has been

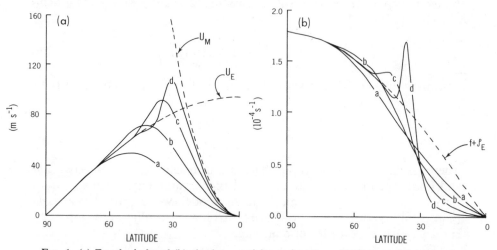

FIG. 1. (a) Zonal wind and (b) absolute vorticity as function of latitude predicted by the idealized Hadley cell model of Section 2. The radiative equilibrium temperature $[T_E]$ is set equal to $T_0\{1 - \Delta_H P_2[\sin(\theta)]\}$ with $\Delta_H = \frac{2}{3}$. T_0 is chosen so that $R\chi T_0/g = 15$ km, and P_2 is the second Legendre polynomial. The curves a–d correspond to the four values of the parameter $\kappa S\tau = (0.3, 0.075, 0.015, 0.003)T_0$. Also shown are the angular momentum conserving wind U_M and the radiative equilibrium wind U_E.

suggested [e.g., Holton and Colton (1972), Schneider and Lindzen (1976), Chang (1977)] that momentum fluxes in cumulus convection are significant in this regard. Our view at present is that such fluxes are unlikely to be important for the planetary-scale flow since (1) there is little deep convection in regions of large vertical shear where the mixing would have relatively large effects on the flow field [see Thompson and Hartmann (1979)], (2) GCMs that do not include this "cumulus friction" are not grossly in error in their climate simulations [e.g., Manabe *et al.,* (1974)], (3) it is not clear that the momentum fluxes would be systematically of one sign — if the convection is organized two-dimensionally, linear theory leads one to expect countergradient momentum fluxes [see Lemone (1983) for an interesting observational study of the momentum fluxes due to a tropical squall line], and (4) diagnosis of the upper-tropospheric vorticity budget from data collected at the European Centre for Medium Range Weather Forecasts (ECMWF) does not suggest a large residual in the frictionless vorticity equation [Sardeshmukh and Hoskins (1984); also Section 5 below]. Our hypothesis is that the limit of small κ is appropriate in (2.8).

The important implication of these arguments is that a very strong and sharp subtropical jet would exist if large-scale eddies were suppressed. One of the most important roles played by these eddies is, therefore, that of providing stresses that prevent the poleward flow in the Hadley cell from conserving angular momentum. Furthermore, in the absence of these stresses, the absolute vorticity equatorward of the jet would be small (Fig. 1b). It appears that the large-scale eddies help to maintain the tropical upper-tropospheric vorticities and vorticity gradients, and since these gradients are essential for the propagation of extratropical planetary waves into the tropics, the potential for interesting wave–mean flow interaction certainly exists.

The vertical structure of the tropical atmosphere enters the model [(2.3), (2.7), (2.8)] through the tropopause height and the stability parameter S. Of these, the former is the easier to understand to a first approximation. Indeed, a simple way of estimating the tropical tropopause height is to couple the rule that $S \approx 0$, i.e., that the moist static energy in the upper branch of the Hadley cell is comparable to that in the surface layer, with a radiative–convective model with prescribed clouds and relative humidity [e.g., Manabe and Wetherald (1967)]. The radiative–convective model provides one relation between the tropospheric lapse rate and the tropopause height, and the rule $S \approx 0$ another [see Held (1982) for details]. Of course, this scheme should ideally be replaced by a theory for the vertical distribution of the convective heating, as well as of relative humidity and cloudiness.

In our simple tropical model, the key dynamical quantity is the stability parameter S, which may be small but must be positive if the Hadley cell is to carry energy poleward. The factors that control S, or the closely related

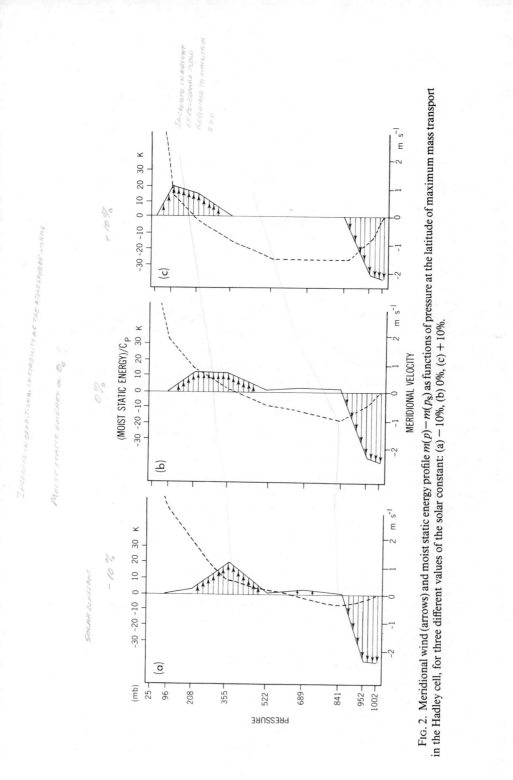

FIG. 2. Meridional wind (arrows) and moist static energy profile $m(p) - m(p_s)$ as functions of pressure at the latitude of maximum mass transport in the Hadley cell, for three different values of the solar constant: (a) -10%, (b) 0%, (c) $+10\%$.

degree of compensation between the oppositely directed horizontal fluxes of dry static energy and latent heat in the Hadley cell, remain obscure to us. Figure 2 describes some preliminary results from an idealized numerical general circulation model, forced by annual mean insolation and with a "swamp" (flat, zero heat capacity, water-saturated surface) as lower boundary. Three experiments were performed — one with the standard value of the solar constant and two others with the solar constant increased and decreased by 10%. Surface albedos and cloud amounts were held fixed. There are nine levels in the vertical, and convection is treated with Manabe's convective adjustment scheme. The figure shows the vertical profile of moist static energy $m(p)$ (subtracting off the value of m at the lowest model level) and of meridional velocity $v(p)$ in the three cases, at the latitude of maximum mass transport in the Hadley cell (12° latitude in each case). Clearly evident is the increase in conditional instability of the atmosphere as it warms and the increase in height of the poleward flow required to maintain $S > 0$. While the changes in mass transport are small (the mass transport is set equal to $\int v \, dp$, with the integral from the surface to the level at which v changes sign), the dry static energy flux increases dramatically with increasing insolation because of the increased height of the poleward flow. However, there is greater compensation between dry static energy and latent heat fluxes: $-$(latent heat flux)/(dry static energy flux) $= (0.67, 0.72, 0.83)$ in the $(-10\%, 0, +10\%)$ calculations. As a result, S remains almost constant: $S =$ (moist static energy flux)/($c_P \times$ mass flux) $= (13.3, 15.9, 13.4 \text{ K})$. We have no arguments at present for the constancy of S or of its value of ≈ 15 K in these calculations. The dependence of S on the convective parameterization and boundary layer schemes in GCMs deserves careful examination.

The problem is complicated further by the importance of the latitudinal dependence of S for the structure of the flow. From Eq. (2.3), we see that if V is to have sharp gradients, as it must at an Intertropical Convergence Zone (ITCZ), then S must also have sharp gradients, for $[T]$ is constrained to be smooth by (2.7) and (2.8). These sharp gradients in S can only come from the low-level moisture field. That structure in the moisture field is of such importance makes the construction of idealized Hadley cell models particularly challenging.

3. Rossby Wave Radiation

The dynamics of the stratosphere and mesosphere is controlled to a great extent by planetary waves excited in the troposphere. Much has been learned by specifying the tropospheric sources and concentrating instead on the wave propagation into the middle atmosphere and on the ultimate fate, or "dissipation" of these waves, with particular regard to the irreversible mixing induced in the process [e.g., Matsuno (1971), Holton and Lindzen (1972), McIntyre and Palmer (1984)]. While there are limitations to this approach if the stratospheric dynamics feeds back significantly on the wave source [as in Plumb's (1981) idealized sudden warming model, for example], it has certainly proven to be fruitful. We believe that a similar approach is fruitful when analyzing large-scale tropospheric dynamics, important wave sources being baroclinic instability in the lower troposphere in middle and high latitudes, and deep convective heating in the tropics.

The basic assumption of this approach when applied to baroclinic instability is that irreversible mixing due to these instabilities can be divided into two distinct parts: that in the source region near the surface in mid-latitudes and that in the region where the planetary waves are "dissipated." This picture is suggested by the calculations of baroclinic wave "life cycles" described in Simmons and Hoskins (1978, 1980) and further discussed by Edmon *et al.* (1980), Hoskins (1983), and Hoskins and McIntyre (1985). Having specified a zonal flow on the sphere, the most unstable normal mode for a particular wave number M is determined. An integration of a nonlinear model including zonal wave numbers M, $2M$, $3M$, etc., is then initialized with the zonal flow plus a small amplitude normal mode. We confine the discussion here to the $M = 6$ mode for the basic flow of Simmons and Hoskins (1980), as the behavior is typical of that obtained for long wavelengths. Linear theory applies for the first few days, with eddy energy levels growing approximately exponentially at all heights. As the low-level temperature wave amplitude becomes large, there is a tendency to frontogenesis and a decrease in growth rate of the low-level energy, until at day 5–6 the eddy occludes and low-level growth ceases. It is during this period that the most significant low-level heat transfers occur. The westward tilt in the troposphere is maintained and the upper-level energy continues to grow until about day 7.5. At this stage, the upper-level troughs develop a large SW to NE tilt on their equatorward side. There are very large poleward transports of westerly momentum, and the eddy kinetic energy is almost completely converted into zonal kinetic energy.

The same baroclinic wave life cycle can be described, following Edmon *et al.* (1980), by using wave propagation and potential vorticity concepts. For a small-amplitude perturbation to a zonal flow the linearized, frictionless quasi-geostrophic potential vorticity equation may be written

$$\frac{\partial q'}{\partial t} = -\bar{u}\frac{\partial q'}{\partial x} - v'\frac{\partial \bar{q}}{\partial y} \qquad (3.1)$$

Multiplying by q', taking the zonal average and dividing by $\partial \bar{q}/\partial y$ gives

$$\frac{\partial A}{\partial t} = -\overline{v'q'} = -\nabla \cdot \mathbf{F} \qquad (3.2)$$

where

$$A = \frac{1}{2} \frac{\overline{q'^2}}{\partial \overline{q}/\partial y} = \frac{1}{2} \overline{\eta'^2} \frac{\partial \overline{q}}{\partial y} \tag{3.3}$$

is a measure of the wave activity, $\eta' = -q'/(\partial \overline{q}/\partial y)$ is the meridional particle displacement, and

$$\mathbf{F} = (-\overline{u'v'}, \frac{f_0}{N^2} \overline{v'\Theta'}) \tag{3.4}$$

is the Eliassen–Palm (EP) flux vector (Andrews and McIntyre, 1976; Edmon et al., 1980). When the concept of group velocity is applicable and when waves having only one value of the group velocity $\mathbf{c_g}$ are present, $\mathbf{F} = \mathbf{c_g} A$. For $\partial \overline{q}/\partial y$ positive, it follows from (3.2) that net propagation of wave activity into a region as shown by convergence of the EP flux implies a down-gradient potential vorticity flux, an increase in the q variance along a line of latitude, and increased latitudinal dispersion of fluid particles originally located at that latitude. In the absence of dissipation, the sign of all of these quantities is reversed as the wave activity propagates out of the region. The mean flow potential vorticity equation reduces to

$$\frac{\partial \overline{q}}{\partial t} = -\frac{\partial}{\partial y} \overline{v'q'} \qquad \begin{array}{l} \text{\small{AVERAGE OF}} \\ \text{\small{FLUCTUATIONS}} \\ \text{\small{IS IN MEAN FLOW EQT.}} \end{array} \tag{3.5}$$

Boundary temperature equations of the forms (3.1) and (3.5), with Θ' replacing q', are then needed to complete the eddy and mean flow problems.

The applicability of quasi-geostrophic theory to a situation in which the static stability varies greatly across a sloping tropopause and in which the relative vorticity is comparable with the Coriolis parameter in some regions is dubious; however, (3.1) is valid for the Ertel potential vorticity perturbation on isentropic surfaces and analogs of (3.2)–(3.4) exist. For nonlinear large-amplitude waves the simplicity of the preceding equations is lost; we assume that they may still be used as guidance in the diagnosis of the dynamical processes involved. The following discussion is a shortened version of that given in Hoskins and McIntyre (1985).

A schematic picture of the EP flux $\mathbf{F}$ at three different stages in the life cycle is given in Fig. 3. The detailed pictures for this and $\partial \overline{q}/\partial y$ are given in Hoskins (1983). Initially $\mathbf{F}$ is almost vertical and confined to low levels. As the low-level growth decreases, the arrows become large in the middle troposphere and have strong convergence at upper-tropospheric levels, implying vertical propagation of wave activity. By day 8 this process is complete and the arrows now point quasi-horizontally beneath the sloping tropopause; there is divergence near 50°N and 350 mb where before there had been convergence, and strong convergence near 30°N and 150 mb. The picture in

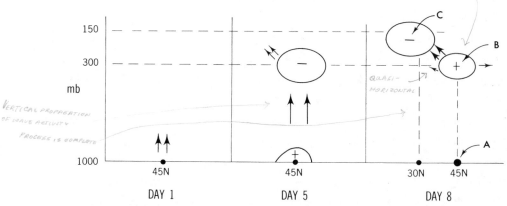

FIG. 3. Schematic of the Eliassen–Palm flux (arrows) and divergence of this flux (contours with plus or minus sign) at three times during the baroclinic eddy life-cycle calculation described in Section 3. The points A (45°, 1000 mb), B (45°, 300 mb), and C (30°, 150 mb) are referred to in the text and in Fig. 4.

this stage is of quasi-horizontal propagation from mid-latitudes into the subtropics.

To add substance to this picture, estimates of particle dispersion have been computed for the three points shown in Fig. 3. For point A, near the surface at 45°N, vertical advection is negligible in the thermodynamic equation and η' can be obtained from the temperature distribution. We define $\bar{\eta}$ to be the maximum latitudinal excursion of the temperature contour centered at the latitude of interest. Curve A in Fig. 4 shows the time evolution of $\bar{\eta}$ at point A. The temperature field at this level on day 6, following several days of almost exponential growth in $\bar{\eta}$, is shown in Fig. 5a. The frontogenesis and occlusion process have left only a very narrow region of warm air at 45°N. This region is eroded by the term representing sub-grid-scale mixing in the model until, by day 8, the isotherm displacement is near zero. Because of the mixing processes that have come into play, however, $\bar{\eta}$ cannot be used as a measure of particle dispersion beyond day 6.

The curves for points B and C are both obtained from the maximum latitudinal excursions on isentropic surfaces of the Ertel potential vorticity contour centered at the point of interest. At point B, the growth of $\bar{\eta}$ lags that at A. It reaches a maximum soon after day 7 and declines to negligible values at day 10. Analysis shows the dynamics here to be nearly reversible, with fluid particles returning to their initial latitudes. The growth of $\bar{\eta}$ at C slightly lags that at B but continues until day 8. The Ertel potential vorticity on the 350-K isentropic surface (which passes close to C) is illustrated in Fig. 5b. The potential vorticity field is being wrapped around a large subtropical gyre. This wrapping, or "wave breaking," continues and generates small-scale structures that are eventually dissipated. There is a marked similarity between these processes and those noted by McIntyre and Palmer (1984) as occurring in the stratosphere.

A simple model that provides a hint of the wave behavior responsible for the last stage of this life cycle is the <u>nondivergent</u> barotropic vorticity equation on the sphere, linearized about a zonal-mean zonal flow $\bar{u}$:

$$\frac{\partial \zeta'}{\partial t} = -\frac{\bar{u}}{a\cos(\theta)}\frac{\partial \zeta'}{\partial \lambda} - \frac{\gamma}{a\cos(\theta)}\frac{\partial \psi'}{\partial \lambda} + \nu\nabla^2\zeta' \tag{3.6}$$

where $\gamma = a^{-1}\,\partial(f+\bar{\zeta})/\partial\theta$. The resulting mean flow accelerations can be computed from

$$\frac{\partial \bar{u}}{\partial t} = \overline{v'\zeta'} = -\frac{\partial}{\partial t}\frac{\overline{\zeta'^2}}{2\gamma} - \nu\frac{\overline{|\nabla\zeta'|^2}}{2\gamma} \tag{3.7}$$

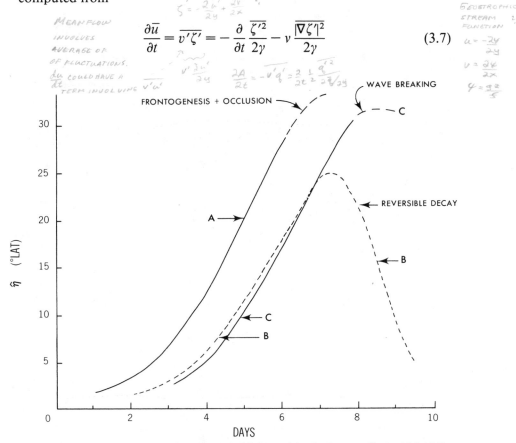

FIG. 4. Maximum meridional displacement of fluid particles (in degrees of latitude) initially at the points A, B, and C of Fig. 3, for the baroclinic eddy life-cycle calculation, estimated as described in the text.

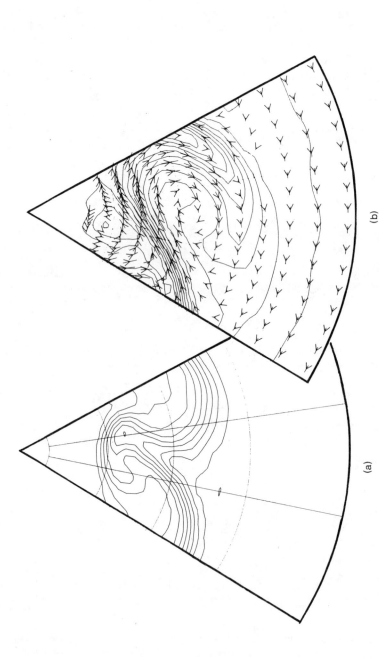

(a)

(b)

FIG. 5. (a) Temperature field on the lowest sigma-surface (0.967) at day 6 of the life cycle calculation and (b) Ertel potential vorticity field on the 350-K isentropic surface at day 8. The contour intervals are 5 K and 0.8 × 10⁻⁶ m² s⁻¹ K kg⁻¹ and the arrows in (b) are the flow field on this isentropic surface, in a frame of reference moving with the phase speed of the wave.

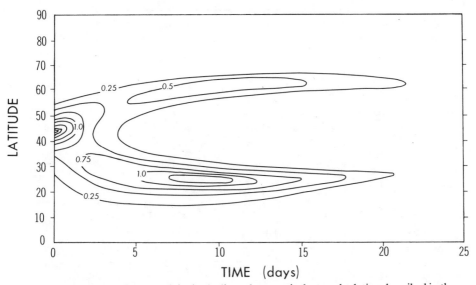

FIG. 6. Evolution of wave activity in the linear barotropic decay calculation described in the text. Contour interval is 0.25 m s⁻¹.

but we do not take these changes in mean wind into account in the linear model described here. In Figs. 6 and 7 we show the result of integrating (3.6) from the initial condition

$$\zeta'(\theta,\lambda) = C \cos(\theta) \cos(M\lambda) \exp\{-[(\theta - 45°)/10°]^2\} \qquad (3.8)$$

with $M = 6$ and $C = 5.0 \times 10^{-5}$ s⁻¹. Plotted in Fig. 6 is the evolution of the wave activity

$$A = \frac{\overline{\zeta'^2} \cos(\theta)}{2\gamma} \qquad (3.9)$$

assuming a wind profile typical of that in the wintertime upper troposphere, given by

$$\bar{u}(\theta) = (18 \quad \text{m s}^{-1}) \sin\{(3\pi/2)[1 + \sin(\theta)]\} + (14 \quad \text{m s}^{-1}) \cos^2(\theta) \quad (3.10)$$

and setting $\nu = 10^4$ m² s⁻¹. As can be seen from (3.7), the domain integral of A is conserved in the absence of dissipation. Choosing a time T large enough that the eddy activity at this time is negligible, we can compute from (3.7) the net change in mean zonal wind induced by the eddy propagation and decay as

$$[\bar{u}(T) - \bar{u}(0)] \cos(\theta) = A(t = 0) - \frac{\nu}{2\gamma} \int_0^T \overline{|\nabla \zeta'|^2} \, dt \, \cos(\theta) \quad (3.11)$$

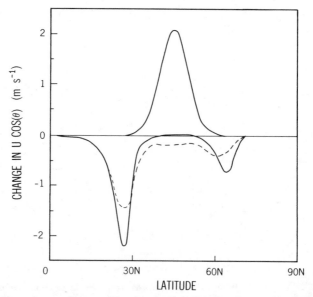

FIG. 7. Final zonal-mean flow modification predicted by linear barotropic model of Fig. 6 for two different diffusivities. The solid line above the axis is the mean flow acceleration due to the radiation of wave activity out of the region where it was initially located [the first term on the right-hand side of (3.11)]; the lines below the axis are the mean flow decelerations (for the two values of v) due to the dissipation of wave activity [the second term on the right-hand side of (3.11)]. (——, $v = 10^4$ m² s⁻¹; ------, $v = 10^5$ m² s⁻¹.)

The two terms on the right-hand side, and their sum, are plotted in Fig. 7 for $v = 10^4$ as well as for the larger value of 10^5.

In the case of solid body rotation (not shown), the eddy activity spreads more or less uniformly over the sphere. The mean flow is accelerated in the region in which the initial wave activity is large, while the compensating deceleration, determined by the dissipation of wave activity, occurs over a wide range of latitudes. For the typical wintertime profile, however, the wave drag is focused in subtropical and, to a lesser extent, subpolar latitudes. This behavior can be understood qualitatively by thinking of the initial disturbance as being made up of a number of wave packets with different dominant meridional wave numbers and, therefore, different phase speeds c. For $M = 6$, all of these wave packets have critical latitudes where $\bar{u} = c$ and are absorbed as they approach these latitudes [see, e.g., Yamagata (1976)]. (For longer waves, $M = 1-3$, the initial condition would also contain wave packets with phase speeds that are westward with respect to the mean flow at all latitudes; the evolution of this part of the initial condition would resemble more closely that found in the case of solid body rotation.) The linear model generates a cascade to small meridional scales near where the dominant wave packets in the initial disturbance reach their critical latitudes and near where one also expects the fully nonlinear model to wrap the vorticity contours so as to ultimately dissipate enstrophy.

This linear model captures the basic mechanism, Rossby wave dispersion out of mid-latitudes, that generates the eddy momentum fluxes in the atmosphere. These eddy momentum fluxes determine the surface stress and, therefore, the surface wind distribution outside of the deep tropics, since the convergence of the eddy flux in these regions can only be balanced in the time mean by surface drag. We say *determine* rather than simply *balance* the surface stress, since it is difficult to see how the small surface winds have a significant back effect on the wave sources if the surface is uniform. (In the presence of surface orography there are significant feedback possibilities of this sort, however.) Note also that the initial condition in this calculation has no meridional phase tilt. If we loosely think of baroclinic instability as creating the initial disturbance, it is evident that the momentum fluxes generated by the wave dispersion need bear no close resemblance to the momentum fluxes associated with the structure of the unstable wave.

It is clear from linear results such as these, as well as the life-cycle studies and observational analyses, that the tropical upper troposphere is a graveyard for planetary wave activity. The mixing induced by this wave dissipation is, as we have argued in Section 2, crucial in determining the zonal wind and vorticity gradient profiles in low latitudes. Since there does seem to be a region (point B in Fig. 4) where the dynamics is nearly linear and reversible, we believe that much can be done in studying this upper-tropospheric mixing by ignoring the complexities of the mixing in the source region and instead specifying the wave sources. Simplification of this sort is needed to help make sense of the complex of questions associated with the interaction of equatorward propagating planetary waves with the zonal flow, the Hadley cell, and moist convection in the tropics.

4. Eddy Flux Closure

One can conceive of an eddy flux closure scheme based on the ideas of the preceding section as consisting of two parts: a theory of finite amplitude baroclinic instability that provides not only the irreversible mixing in the source region in mid-latitudes near the surface but also the space–time spectrum of planetary waves radiating out of this region, plus a theory of mixing induced by these waves after their propagation into the subtropics or the middle atmosphere. Whether or not this separation of the mixing into two distinct parts is useful, our view is that nearly all of the mixing is the end result of a cascade process, with the rate of dissipation of potential enstrophy in the interior (or temperature variance near the lower boundary) controlled by the large scales themselves, as in fully developed turbulence. This "strongly nonlinear" picture should be contrasted with "weakly nonlinear" theories in which this rate of dissipation is determined by the strength of radiative damping, Ekman pumping, or thermal interchange with the surface.

Specifically, the time-averaged quasi-geostrophic potential enstrophy budget reads $\{v'q'\ \partial\bar{q}/\partial y\} = \{$dissipation$\}$, where braces denote a horizontal average and the overbar a time mean. The mean flow modification resulting from the eddy potential vorticity flux is thus intimately related to the enstrophy dissipation. In a "weakly nonlinear" theory, one has, schematically, $\{$dissipation$\} = \mu\{q'^2\}$, with μ independent of the large-scale flow, and the potential enstrophy production and dissipation both occur on the same large scales. Examples of "weakly nonlinear" theories can be found in several papers by Pedlosky (1970, 1979). The simple scaling arguments of Stone (1972) and Held (1978) for the magnitude of the transient fluxes in the source region should be thought of as "strongly nonlinear," since the claim made is that these magnitudes can be understood to first approximation without explicit reference to the strength of radiative damping, Ekman pumping, etc., and this is only possible if dissipation rates are determined by cascade rates.

This issue could, in theory, be settled by observational analyses, although the difficulty of obtaining a well-balanced potential enstrophy budget for transient eddies in the tropospheric interior or for temperature variance near the surface suggests that GCMs may be required for this purpose. It may well be that compromise is necessary, with cascades to small scales and dissipation on the large scale both being of importance. We suspect that such a compromise is more likely to be needed near the surface; on the one hand, the cascade of temperature variance is evident in the occlusion and frontal formation processes; on the other hand, it is likely that air-mass modification through heat exchange with the surface also plays a significant role, particularly over the oceans.

A proposal for mixing by baroclinic instabilities in the source region that has attracted considerable attention is that of "baroclinic adjustment" (Smagorinsky, 1963; Stone, 1978). In analogy with the well-known treatment of mixing due to gravitational instability, it is proposed that baroclinic instabilities "neutralize" the atmosphere. In the framework of the two-layer model, the instabilities are thought of as preventing the isentropic slope from increasing beyond the critical slope provided by Phillip's criterion. The similarity of the observed mid-tropospheric isentropic slopes poleward of the subtropical jet to this critical slope has been taken as confirmation of the basic idea.

The natural procedure for constructing the analogous neutralized state in a continuously stratified atmosphere is to satisfy the Charney–Stern criterion by destroying the temperature gradient at the surface and by destroying the potential vorticity gradient in a layer adjacent to the surface so as to avoid destabilizing vertical curvature at the top of the layer (Lindzen and Farrel, 1980; Held, 1982). In this continuous case it is considerably more difficult to argue that the eddies are successful in neutralizing the flow, since this state bears no particular resemblance to the observed mean flow. Is the aforementioned agreement between the two-layer model's critical isentropic slope and the observed extratropical slope simply a coincidence?

When the isentropic slopes in Charney's continuously stratified model drop below the critical slope in the two-layer model, the horizontal wavelengths and vertical scale of the unstable modes begin to decrease. One possibility then is that these small eddies are relatively inefficient at mixing, so that the flow is effectively neutralized if the isentropic slopes drop much below this point (Held, 1978). Because the changes in eddy scales as the mean flow parameters change are quite gradual, however, this argument does not seem adequate. Alternatively, one can use radiative–convective models of the vertical temperature profile (Manabe and Wetherald, 1967) to show that for any reasonable tropospheric static stability the dynamic heating of the troposphere must extend at least a scale height from the surface. One can then argue that an atmosphere dominated by shallower eddies is inconsistent; the static stability would decrease until deeper eddies were generated that could maintain a consistent radiative–convective equilibrium, and this requires isentropic slopes at least comparable to the two-layer model's neutralizing slope. [See Branscome (1983) and Gutowski (1985) for related arguments.]

In light of all of these untested speculations, it is probably wise to retreat and to ask how well the baroclinic adjustment concept or other closure ideas explain the results from idealized numerical models. A logical starting point might be a two-layer model with radiative relaxation toward a baroclinically unstable temperature gradient, Ekman pumping in the lower layer, and scale-selective horizontal mixing to accept the enstrophy cascade. For what range of radiative equilibrium temperature gradients, widths of the unstable region, and radiative and frictional relaxation times is baroclinic adjustment a useful concept? Are mixing length ideas useful when the meridional width of the unstable region is large compared with the radius of deformation, as argued in Haidvogel and Held (1980)? Under what conditions does a "life-cycle" experiment (in which one finds the most unstable modes on the time-averaged flow, then initializes with the mean flow plus a small amplitude normal mode, and watches the mode equilibrate) provide useful information about the statistically steady state? At what point do multiple zonal jets emerge as the unstable region is widened [see Williams's (1978) Jupiter simulations]? How does the partition of the enstrophy dissipation between small-scale mixing and large-scale damping (radiative relaxation, Ekman pumping) depend on the various model parameters? Careful numerical experiments aimed at questions such as these are needed if we are to make progress on the difficult eddy flux closure problem, even if results for such an idealized, dry, two-layer model are not directly relevant to the atmosphere.

5. STATIONARY EDDIES AND THEIR INTERACTION WITH TRANSIENTS

5.1. Extratropical Stationary Eddies

Given all of these obstacles standing in the way of an adequate theory for the climate of an atmosphere with zonally symmetric lower boundary, it may seem presumptuous to consider an atmosphere with as complex a lower boundary as the Earth's. However, much progress can be made by considering the zonal-mean flow as given and analyzing the deviations from zonal symmetry in the context of linear wave theory. Indeed, the pioneering work of Charney and Eliassen (1949) and Smagorinsky (1953) on topographic and thermal forcing, respectively, held out the promise that linear stationary wave theory might be of quantitative as well as qualitative value in explaining the asymmetries. The goal of a quantitative theory receded somewhat for a number of years, as the calculations became more detailed but did not improve systematically. In retrospect, this seems to have been due to the fact that nearly all calculations were performed on a mid-latitude beta-plane with reflecting walls, thus seriously distorting the meridional propagation of planetary waves and introducing potentially unphysical resonances. More recent work with linear primitive equation models on the sphere has again raised the possibility of quantitatively useful linear theories.

Linear inviscid stationary wave theory breaks down in low latitudes, where the phase speed of the wave (zero) is comparable to the zonal flow speed. There is little doubt that this breakdown results in at least partial absorption. The simplest indication of this is that the stationary eddy momentum flux is nearly always directed from low latitudes to mid-latitudes. Assuming that the theory of planetary waves on a slowly varying basic state is relevant, this immediately translates into the statement that the equatorward propagating waves are of larger amplitude than any poleward propagating waves. While partial reflections are a possibility, as suggested by steady-state nonlinear theories, we are aware of no observational studies that indicate that reflection is occurring in the troposphere; indeed, it will take a careful analysis to distinguish between a reflected wave and a wave forced directly by tropical heating or, perhaps, by convection generated by the incident wave. It seems to us to be the appropriate working hypothesis that low-latitude absorption is sufficient to prevent stationary wave resonance. This leads us to the position that most of the work on multiple equilibria for stationary waves interacting with zonal flows, depending as it does on resonantlike behavior of the stationary waves, is not likely to be applicable to the troposphere, unless the zonal winds happen to be configured in such a way that they do not allow propagation into the tropics.

An additional problem that stands in the way of quantitative tests of linear stationary wave theory is our lack of information on the observed diabatic heating distribution. One way of trying to circumvent this difficulty is to use the heating distribution produced by a GCM and compare the resulting stationary waves with those produced by the same GCM. Figure 8 shows one result from a study of this sort carried out by Nigam (1983) and Nigam *et. al.* (1986). It compares the deviations from zonal symmetry of the 300-mb meridional velocity predicted by a linear model with that produced by the GCM for the Northern Hemisphere winter. A large Rayleigh friction is introduced in the tropics of the linear model to make it strongly absorbing. This damping not only absorbs the waves incident on the tropics, but also controls the strength of the response (both tropical and extratropical) to the tropical diabatic heating. The results are reasonably good at this level, some of the more serious discrepancies being off the west coast of North America and in the immediate vicinity of the Tibetan plateau. The solution deteriorates significantly in extratropical latitudes as one moves to lower levels. The value of such a linear simulation of the stationary wave field is that it can be easily dissected into the responses to different parts of the forcing. Such a dissection shows that the response in the Northern Hemisphere extratropical upper troposphere during winter is a rather complicated superposition of the response to extratropical diabatic heating (mainly latent heating in the oceanic storm tracks), tropical latent heating, and flow over the major mountain complexes, the last being dominant in the meridional velocity and geopotential height field, but with all three of importance for the zonal wind maximum off Japan.

We should not expect too much from linear theory. Transient eddy heat fluxes undoubtedly grow in importance as one approaches the surface. At 850 mb in NH winter, they damp the standing eddy temperature variance with an e-folding time of ≈5 days (Lau, 1979). Furthermore, observational studies of the vorticity budget indicate that transient eddy fluxes are as important as the mean fluxes of vorticity in balancing the vorticity loss at the surface in the Aleutian and Icelandic lows (Lau, 1979). In the upper troposphere, on the other hand, linear theory may be better than one might expect at first glance. In quasi-geostrophic theory, for a linear stationary wave in a

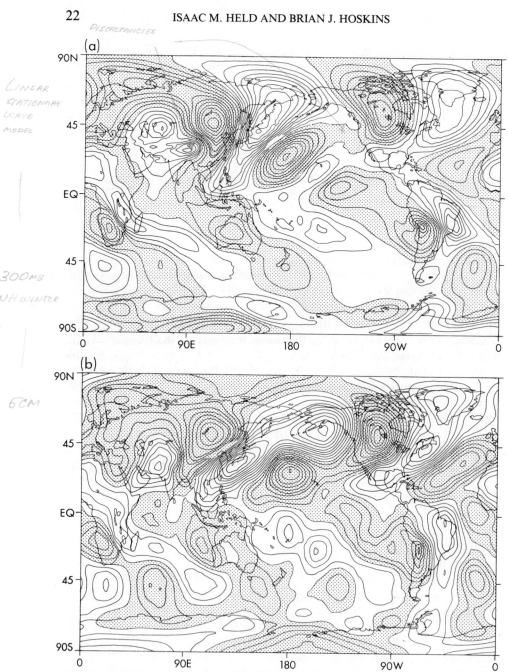

FIG. 8. Deviation of 300-mb meridional velocity from its zonal mean in (a) the linear stationary wave model of Nigam *et al.* (1986), which utilizes the GCM's zonal flow and diabatic heating field and (b) a GCM simulation of NH winter. Contour interval is 1 m s^{-1} and shaded areas are negative.

source-free region,

$$\bar{u}\,\frac{\partial q'}{\partial x} = -v'\,\frac{\partial \bar{q}}{\partial y} \tag{5.1}$$

In the special case that $\bar{u}$ and $\partial\bar{q}/\partial y$ are independent of y (but with arbitrary z dependence), we have $J(\psi', q') = 0$, implying that the linear solution satisfies the fully nonlinear equation. If $\bar{u}^{-1}\,\partial\bar{q}/\partial y$ is slowly varying, $J(\psi', q')$ will be nonzero but still much smaller than a naive scaling would indicate. Perhaps the deterioration of the forced wave solution as one descends in the troposphere is in part a consequence of diabatic heating and transient eddy fluxes destroying the balance (5.1) and thereby creating nonnegligible mean-flow nonlinearity.

5.2. Tropical Stationary Eddies

Progress in developing an understanding of large-scale stationary eddies in the tropics has been slowed by a variety of problems: the absence of a strong mean zonal flow about which to linearize, uncertainty as to the importance of small-scale momentum transport, and the absence of adequate observations. To help focus the discussion, we begin by considering the following steady vorticity, divergence, and thermodynamic equations, which have been linearized about a uniform zonal flow $\bar{u}$:

$$\bar{u}\,\frac{\partial\zeta'}{\partial x} + \beta v' = -fD' \tag{5.2}$$

$$f\zeta' - \beta u' = \nabla^2\phi' \tag{5.3}$$

$$\bar{u}\,\frac{\partial^2\phi'}{\partial x\,\partial z} + N^2 w' = Q' \tag{5.4}$$

We denote the characteristic length scales in the zonal, meridional, and vertical directions by L_x, L_y, and H. The other relevant length scales are $L_\beta = (\bar{u}/\beta)^{1/2}$ and the Rossby radius of deformation $L_R = NH/f$, where we take $f \approx \beta L_y$. Consistent with observations we assume that $L_\beta \approx L_y \ll L_x$. The vorticity equation then gives $\zeta'/D' \approx L_x/L_y$. In (5.3) the advection of divergence is found to be negligible, and this equation gives $\phi' \approx \beta L_y^3\zeta'$. Finally, taking $w' \approx D'H$, the ratio of horizontal to vertical advection terms in (5.4) is found to be $f^2 L_\beta^2/(N^2H^2) = L_\beta^2/L_R^2$. For tropical motions with $f \approx 2 \times 10^{-5}\ \mathrm{s}^{-1}$, $L_\beta \approx 500$ km, $N^2 \approx 10^{-4}\ \mathrm{s}^{-2}$, and $H \approx 5$ km, this ratio is equal to 1/25 so that the horizontal advection of temperature is negligible. We are left with the interesting situation that the thermodynamic equation gives the divergent flow (assuming that Q is given), the vorticity equation then gives the rotational flow, and the divergence equation determines the temperature structure.

From the Southeast Asian summer monsoon data of Krishnamurti (1971), Holton and Colton (1972) found that (5.2) was totally unable to model the correct position of the upper-level Tibetan anticyclone unless strong damping of vorticity was included, thereby moving this anticyclone from west of the upper-level divergence (as implies by $\beta v \approx -fD$) to almost coincident with it. This addition of strong vorticity damping has proven to be quite useful in constructing qualitative linear models of the zonally asymmetric mean tropical flow [e.g., Gill (1980)]. The possibility that this upper-tropospheric "damping" is crudely accounting for neglected nonlinearity is, we believe, strongly supported by the analysis of a GCMs tropical vorticity budget (Sardeshmukh and Held, 1984) and the vorticity budget of observed, analyzed, and initialized fields routinely constructed at ECMWF (Sardeshmukh and Hoskins, 1984). The GCM had no sub-grid-scale vertical mixing of momentum in the upper troposphere and a biharmonic horizontal diffusion had little effect on the vorticity budget, and yet the model produced a fairly realistic Tibetan anticyclone and monsoonal rainfall. The vorticity balance was found to be strongly nonlinear, with horizontal advection of relative vorticity playing the dominant role in balancing the stretching. A problem with the GCM analysis was that terms in the vorticity budget averaged over one month had considerable structure on the smallest scales resolved by the model, particularly near the Tibetan plateau. The ECMWF-analyzed fields for the anomalous El Niño–Southern Oscillation NH winter of 1982–1983 used by Sardeshmukh and Hoskins were considerably smoother, but the conclusion as to the importance of nonlinearity was the same.

Important features of the upper-tropospheric vorticity balance are well illustrated by the 150-mb absolute vorticity, divergence, and stream-function contours for the more normal NH winter of 1983–1984, shown in Fig. 9. The simplest balance, $\beta v = -fD$, is clearly inadequate. The regions of strong convection with large $D > 0$ (indicated by stippling) tend to be associated with small absolute vorticity ζ_a, so the generation of anticyclonic vorticity $\zeta_a D$ is smaller than would be obtained from the linearization fD. Comparison of the mean stream function with the mean vorticity suggests that outside regions of intense convection, vorticity is nearly conserved following the flow. Twisting and vertical advection are found to be negligible, and transient terms are generally smaller than the mean flow terms, although not entirely negligible. The relatively small residual found in the budget does not suggest the presence of large friction in the tropical upper troposphere.

The foregoing discussion suggests that a useful model of the tropical

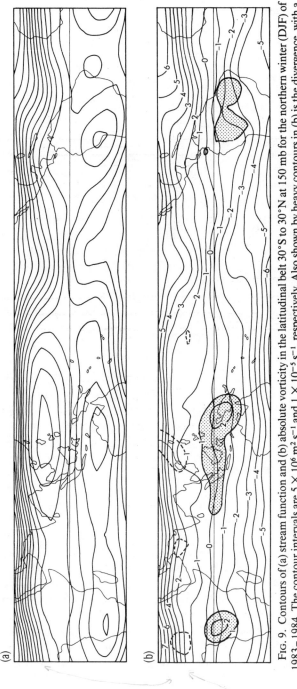

Fig. 9. Contours of (a) stream function and (b) absolute vorticity in the latitudinal belt 30°S to 30°N at 150 mb for the northern winter (DJF) of 1983–1984. The contour intervals are 5×10^6 m^2 s^{-1} and 1×10^{-5} s^{-1}, respectively. Also shown by heavy contours in (b) is the divergence, with a contour interval of 3×10^{-6} s^{-1}. Positive values greater than 3×10^{-6} s^{-1} are stippled and negative contours are dashed.

upper-tropospheric, long-wave pattern corresponding to specified heat sources is

$$\frac{\partial \zeta_a}{\partial t} + \nabla \cdot (v \zeta_a) = 0 \qquad (5.5)$$

Here $v = v_\zeta + v_D$, where v_D is the specified divergent wind associated with $D = \partial(Q/N^2)/\partial z$. Advection by the divergent flow v_D is essential; otherwise an anticyclonic vorticity source within a closed stream-function contour of the Tibetan anticyclone, say, could only be balanced by transients or dissipation. Determination of Q is the remaining formidable problem. It should be noted that if the entire Q field is specified, then the flow field at a given level can be determined independent of the flow at other levels. However, in a simple tropical model, one should at a minimum write $Q = Q_{convective} - T/\tau$ (separating latent heat release from radiative cooling) so as to allow the model to predict the pattern of downward motion that compensates the ascent in the convective regions. The dependence of the radiative cooling on $T\alpha \, \partial\phi/\partial z$ provides vertical coupling and thereby greatly complicates the problem.

While nonlinearity in the vorticity equation evidently plays a dominant role in the tropical upper troposphere, near the ground the flow is weaker due to surface friction, and the balance appears to be

$$\beta v \approx -fD - \kappa\zeta \qquad (5.6)$$

where, once again, $v = v_\zeta + v_D$ with v_D determined by the heating; the final term represents the effects of stresses in the planetary boundary layer. Both evaporation and moisture transport are strongly controlled by the low-level flow, so one can conceive of estimating $Q_{convective}$ without reference to the nonlinear upper-tropospheric flow. However, it seems that the pattern of radiative cooling and the low-level divergence field outside of the convecting regions must be affected by the upper-level nonlinearity.

5.3. Zonally Asymmetric Transients

All transient eddy statistics of interest (heat, momentum, and moisture fluxes, eddy kinetic energies, etc.) are observed to be strongly zonally asymmetric. The "synoptic-scale" transients, in particular, are organized into well-defined storm tracks that tend to be located downstream and poleward of the mean jet maxima. Frederiksen's (1979, 1980) calculations have shown that storm track position can be understood to first approximation from the baroclinic instability of the time-mean zonally asymmetric flow. Thus, it appears that the asymmetry of the lower boundary controls the storm tracks through its control of the stationary eddy pattern and not primarily through direct thermal or orographic forcing. In particular, "lee-cyclogenesis" (which we take to refer to the direct interaction of cyclones and topography) may be of importance in some regions but does not seem to be an important cause of the major oceanic storm tracks. Based on these instability analyses and observational studies such as that of Hoskins *et al.* (1983), a three-dimensional extension of the baroclinic wave life cycle described in Section 3 is suggested: wave activity is generated by baroclinic instability at low levels off the east coasts of the NH continents, propagates downstream and vertically to upper-tropospheric levels, and then propagates equatorward into regions where the wave activity is dissipated.

The effects of transient eddies on the time-mean zonal asymmetries in mid-latitudes is a complex problem, many facets of which have yet to be explored. Budget studies [i.e., Lau (1979)] indicate a rather modest (but not negligible) role for transient eddies in the structure of the upper-tropospheric stationary waves, and the simulation of a GCMs stationary eddies with a linear model by Nigam *et al.* (1986) seems to confirm this for the NH winter. (We are thinking here of the zonal-mean flow as being given; the transients do exert strong control of the upper-tropospheric wave pattern through their control of the zonal-mean flow on which the waves propagate and of the low-level zonal winds that determine the strength of the orographic forcing.) At lower levels, thermal damping of stationary waves by transients is substantial, and the combined effect of the heat and vorticity fluxes in the storm tracks is to accelerate the low-level westerlies at the start and middle of the track and generate cyclonic (anticyclonic) vorticity north (south) of these westerlies (Lau and Holopainen, 1984; Hoskins *et al.,* 1983). Thus, the transients do appear to help maintain the Icelandic Low – Azores High couplet, as an example. Upstream of these vorticity centers, the low-level equatorward flow of cold continental air and the poleward flow of moist subtropical air have a frontogenetic effect, increasing the low-level baroclinicity in the storm track. The implication is that transients may feed back positively onto their organization into storm tracks. Direct calculations of the effects of the observed transients on linear stationary wave models have been performed by Youngblut and Sasamori (1980) and Opsteegh and Vernekar (1982).

Examination of the wind or temperature tendencies due to observed transients can be misleading. In particular, the effects of transients can be very nonlocal. As an example, consider the idealized situation in which transient mixing is confined to a small region through which pass mean streamlines that then traverse a much larger region where the mean flow is conservative; mixing in the localized region can set the value of potential vorticity conserved along each streamline in the larger region and thereby control the structure of the flow. As another extreme example, one can conceive of transients as diffusively mixing some quantity (potential vorticity, say) so as to effectively destroy any gradients in some region; but once the gradients have been destroyed, the transient diffusive fluxes of that quantity also disappear. While the role of transients would be clear as one watched the flow evolve toward equilibrium, a budget analysis of the final steady state would not provide this information. These examples are meant only to emphasize that the effects of transient eddies must be studied in the context of a consistent mean flow dynamics.

There are also circumstances in which the formal separation between the time-mean flow and transient eddies itself obscures the underlying dynamics. Consider an atmosphere that cools at the rate $Q(y) = \mu y, 0 \le y \le L$, and suppose that our idealized thermodynamic equation reads

$$\frac{\partial \Theta}{\partial t} = -v \frac{\partial \Theta}{\partial y} - Q \tag{5.7}$$

Let the meridional velocity v be zero except for short bursts in which a uniform southerly wind $V > 0$ advects air poleward. Let T be the interval between bursts and $\tau \ll T$ the duration of a burst, and set $V = L/\tau$ so that by the end of each burst the atmosphere from $y = 0$ to L is nearly isothermal. The time-mean temperature gradient will then be $\approx -\mu T/2$, and the time-mean flow $V\tau/T = L/T$, implying a warming due to this mean flow of $\approx \mu L/2$. Therefore, at $y = L$ the diabatic cooling μL is half balanced by mean heating and half by transients. At $y = 0$, on the other hand, the diabatic cooling is zero, and the mean flow heating $\mu L/2$ is balanced by transient *cooling*. One is tempted to deduce from this formally correct analysis that the mean flow is the important ingredient in maintaining the warmth in the region, an inference totally at variance with the underlying dynamics. In order to understand the time-mean temperature gradient in such a system, one might try to understand what controls the time interval T between bursts rather than to focus on the transient eddy flux as the quantity of prime interest.

Whether or not analogs of this last scenario are of relevance to the stationary eddy pattern, it does seem suggestive of problems encountered in analyses of blocking episodes in terms of a time-mean (or low-pass-filtered) flow and higher-frequency transients. Conventional analyses of this sort in Hoskins *et al.* (1983) and later unpublished work almost always show the vorticity flux convergence associated with synoptic eddies to be in the direction of increasing the anomalous vorticity in the block; however, the heat flux convergence does not usually appear to be in the right sense. This does not agree with synoptic experience, which is that the poleward flux of warm air ahead of elongated cold fronts seems to reamplify blocks. The example discussed in the preceding paragraph suggests that this contradiction may be only apparent, the confusion resulting from the inclusion in the mean flow of part of the synoptician's "transience."

Despite the many potential pitfalls, we are optimistic that the developing cross-fertilization among theory, numerical general circulation modeling, and observational studies will result in rapid advances in our understanding of the large-scale flow in the atmosphere. While we do not expect this understanding to be readily translatable into closure schemes and simple models that could usefully compete with GCMs in simulating the time-mean flow in the atmosphere, the most important test of our understanding will remain the ability to distinguish between the essential and the inessential and thus to model aspects of the general circulation in as simple a way as possible.

ACKNOWLEDGMENTS

We would like to thank Peter Phillips and Steve Lyons of the GFDL for assisting with some of the calculations described herein. The influence of Prashant Sardeshmukh and Michael McIntyre on some of the ideas presented here·is also gratefully acknowledged. The former also produced Fig. 9 from ECMWF data.

REFERENCES

Andrews, D. G., and McIntyre, M. E. (1976). Planetary waves in horizontal and vertical shear: The generalized Eliassen-Palm relation and mean flow acceleration. *J. Atmos. Sci.* **33**, 2031–2048.

Branscome, L. E. (1983). A parameterization of transient eddy heat flux on a beta-plane. *J. Atmos. Sci.* **40**, 2508–2521.

Chang, C.-P. (1977). Some theoretical problems of the planetary scale monsoons. *Pure Appl. Geophys.* **115**, 1087–1109.

Charney, J. G., and Eliassen, A. (1949). A numerical method for predicting the perturbations of the middle latitude westerlies. *Tellus* **1**, 38–54.

Edmon, H. J., Jr., Hoskins, B. J., and McIntyre, M. E. (1980). Eliassen-Palm cross-sections for the troposphere. *J. Atmos. Sci.* **37**, 2600–2616; see also corrigendum: *Ibid.* **38**, 1115 (1981).

Frederiksen, J. S. (1979). The effects of long planetary waves on regions of cyclogenesis: Linear theory. *J. Atmos. Sci.* **36**, 195–204.

Frederiksen, J. S. (1980). Zonal and meridional variations of eddy fluxes by long planetary waves. *Q. J. R. Meteorol. Soc.* **106**, 63–84.

Gill, A. E. (1980). Some simple solutions for heat-induced tropical circulations. *Q. J. R. Meteorol. Soc.* **106**, 447–462.

Gutowski, W. J., Jr. (1985). A simple model for the interaction between vertical eddy heat fluxes and static stability. *J. Atmos. Sci.* **42**, 346–358.

Haidvogel, D. B., and Held, I. M. (1980). Homogeneous quasi-geostrophic turbulence driven by a uniform temperature gradient. *J. Atmos. Sci.* **37**, 2644–2660.

Held, I. M. (1978). The vertical scale of an unstable baroclinic wave and its importance for eddy heat flux parameterization. *J. Atmos. Sci.* **35**, 572–576.

Held, I. M. (1982). On the height of the tropopause and the static stability of the troposphere. *J. Atmos. Sci.* **39**, 412–417.

Held, I. M., and Hou, A. Y. (1980). Nonlinear axially symmetric circulations in a nearly inviscid atmosphere. *J. Atmos. Sci.* **37**, 515–533.

Holton, J. R., and Colton, D. E. (1972). A diagnostic study of the vorticity balance at 200 mb in the tropics during northern summer. *J. Atmos. Sci.* **29**, 1124–1128.

Holton, J. R., and Lindzen, R. S. (1972). An updated theory of the quasi-biennial cycle of the tropical stratosphere. *J. Atmos. Sci.* **29**, 1076–1080.

Hoskins, B. J. (1983). Modelling of the transient eddies and their feedback on the mean flow. *In* "Large-Scale Dynamical Processes in the Atmosphere" (B. J. Hoskins and R. Pearce, eds.), pp. 169–199. Academic Press, New York.

Hoskins, B. J., and McIntyre, M. E. (1986). In preparation.

Hoskins, B. J., James, I. N., and White, G. H. (1983). The shape, propagation, and mean flow interaction of large-scale weather systems. *J. Atmos. Sci.* **40**, 1595–1612.

Hou, A. Y. (1984). Axisymmetric circulations forced by heat and momentum sources: a simple model applicable to the Venus atmosphere. *J. Atmos. Sci.* **41**, 3437–3455.

Krishnamurti, T. N. (1971). Observational study of the tropical upper troposphere motion field during the Northern Hemisphere summer. *J. Appl. Meteorol.* **10**, 1066–1096.

Lau, N. C. (1979). The observed structure of tropospheric stationary waves and the local balances of vorticity and heat. *J. Atmos. Sci.* **36**, 996–1016.

Lau, N. C., and Holopainen, E. O. (1984). Transient eddy forcing of the time-mean flow as identified by geopotential tendencies. *J. Atmos. Sci.* **41**, 313–328.

Lemone, M. A. (1983). Momentum transport by a line of cumulonimbus. *J. Atmos. Sci.* **40**, 1815–1834.

Lindzen, R. S., and Farrell, B. (1980). The role of the polar regions in global climate; and a new parameterization of global heat transport. *Mon. Weather Rev.* **108**, 2064–2079.

McIntyre, M. E., and Palmer, T. N. (1984). The "surf zone" in the stratosphere. *J. Atmos. Terr. Phys.* **46**, 825–850.

Manabe, S., and Wetherald, R. T. (1967). Thermal equilibrium of the atmosphere with a given distribution of relative humidity. *J. Atmos. Sci.* **24**, 241–259.

Manabe, S., Hahn, D. G., and Holloway, J. L. (1974). The seasonal variation of the tropical circulation as simulated by a global model of the atmosphere. *J. Atmos. Sci.* **31**, 43–83.

Matsuno, T. (1971). A dynamical model of the stratospheric sudden warming. *J. Atmos. Sci.* **28**, 1479–1494.

Nigam, S. (1983). On the structure and forcing of tropospheric stationary waves. Ph.D. Thesis, Princeton University, Princeton, New Jersey.

Nigam, S., Held, I. M., and Lyons, S. (1986). Simulation of the stationary eddies in a GCM with a linear model. (In preparation.)

Opsteegh, J. D., and Vernekar, A. D. (1982). A simulation of the January standing wave pattern including the effects of transient eddies. *J. Atmos. Sci.* **39**, 734–744.

Pedlosky, J. (1970). Finite amplitude baroclinic waves. *J. Atmos. Sci.* **27**, 15–30.

Pedlosky, J. (1979). Finite-amplitude baroclinic waves in a continuous model of the atmosphere. *J. Atmos. Sci.* **36**, 1908–1924.

Plumb, R. A. (1981). Instability of the distorted polar night vortex: A theory of stratospheric warmings. *J. Atmos. Sci.* **38**, 2514–2531.

Sardeshmukh, P. D., and Held, I. M. (1984). The vorticity balance in the tropical upper troposphere of a general circulation model. *J. Atmos. Sci.* **41**, 768–778.

Sardeshmukh, P. D., and Hoskins, B. J. (1985). Vorticity balance in the tropics during the

1982–83 El-Niño–Southern Oscillation event. *Q. J. R. Meteorol. Soc.* **111,** 261–278.

Schneider, E. K. (1983). Martian great dust storms: Interpretive axially symmetric models. *Icarus* **55,** 302–331.

Schneider, E. K., and Lindzen, R. S. (1976). A discussion of the parameterization of momentum exchange by cumulus convection. *JGR, J. Geophys. Res.* **81,** 3158–3160.

Simmons, A. J., and Hoskins, B. J. (1978). The life cycles of some nonlinear baroclinic waves. *J. Atmos. Sci.* **35,** 414–432.

Simmons, A. J., and Hoskins, B. J. (1980). Barotropic influences on the growth and decay of nonlinear baroclinic waves. *J. Atmos. Sci.* **37,** 1679–1684.

Smagorinsky, J. (1953). The dynamical influence of large-scale heat sources and sinks on the quasi-stationary mean motions of the atmosphere. *Q. J. R. Meteorol. Soc.* **79,** 342–366.

Smagorinsky, J. (1963). General circulation experiments with the primitive equations. I. The basic experiment. *Mon. Weather Rev.* **91,** 99–164.

Stone, P. H. (1972). A simplified radiative-dynamical model for the static stability of rotating atmospheres. *J. Atmos. Sci.* **29,** 405–418.

Stone, P. H. (1978). Baroclinic adjustment. *J. Atmos. Sci.* **35,** 561–571.

Thompson, S. L., and Hartmann, D. L. (1979). "Cumulus friction": Estimated influence on the tropical mean meridional circulation. *J. Atmos. Sci.* **36,** 2022–2026.

Williams, G. P. (1978). Planetary circulations. 1. Barotropic representations of Jovian and terrestrial turbulence. *J. Atmos. Sci.* **25,** 1399–1426.

Yamagata, T. (1976). On trajectories of Rossby wave packets released in a lateral shear flow. *J. Oceanogr. Soc. Jpn.* **32,** 162–168.

Youngblut, C., and Sasamori, T. (1980). The nonlinear effects of transient and stationary eddies on the winter mean circulation. Part I. Diagnostic analysis. *J. Atmos. Sci.* **37,** 1944–1957.

ON THE ROLE OF BAROTROPIC
ENERGY CONVERSIONS
IN THE GENERAL CIRCULATION

J. M. WALLACE

Department of Atmospheric Sciences
University of Washington
Seattle, Washington

AND

N.-C. LAU

Geophysical Fluid Dynamics Laboratory/NOAA
Princeton University
Princeton, New Jersey

1. INTRODUCTION

In the ongoing quest for an understanding of the atmospheric general circulation, two of the central problems are (1) to identify the source or sources of nonseasonal temporal variability and (2) to understand how this temporal variability feeds back on the seasonally varying, time-averaged circulation. These problems are recurrent themes in the modern general circulation literature dating back to the works of Rossby, Starr, and Charney in the 1940s.

As a result of the collective efforts of many investigators, it has become widely accepted that baroclinic instability is the main source of transient variability in the general circulation, and that in the later stages of their life cycle, baroclinic waves feed energy into the time-mean zonally averaged flow and planetary-scale low-frequency transients by barotropic exchange processes. This view is exemplified by Smagorinsky's (1972) juxtaposition of the

33

terms "barotropic stability" and "baroclinic instability" as section headings for one of his major review articles on general circulation research.

Among the more important pieces of evidence in support of this interpretation are

(1)   the rapid growth rates associated with baroclinic instability of realistic atmospheric flows (Charney, 1947; Eady, 1949; Frederiksen, 1982);

(2)   the fact that the structure and evolution of extratropical disturbances on daily weather maps strongly resemble those of baroclinic waves as simulated in nonlinear integrations based on a primitive equation model (Simmons and Hoskins, 1978; Hoskins, 1983a); these simulated waves give up much of their kinetic energy to the mean flow during the later stages of their life cycle [see Held and Hoskins (this volume)];

(3)   the dominance of the baroclinic conversion terms C_A and C_E in the Lorenz (1955) kinetic energy cycle as deduced from observations [e.g., Oort (1964) and Oort and Rasmusson (1971)] and general circulation model (GCM) simulations [e.g., see Phillips (1956) and Smagorinsky (1963)], together with the prevailing countergradient eddy transport of westerly momentum, which is evidence of a conversion of kinetic energy from the eddies into the zonally averaged flow;

(4)   the theoretical arguments of Onsager (1949), Fjortoft (1951), and others that two-dimensional turbulence should be characterized by a "de-cascade" of kinetic energy from the scale of the forcing (presumably baroclinic instability) toward larger scales; the predicted "de-cascade" has been verified in a number of observational studies [e.g., see the reviews of Saltzman (1970) and Holopainen (1983)].

The preceding evidence in favor of baroclinic instability/barotropic stability as a conceptual model for interpreting the energetics of large-scale atmospheric motion is based on theoretical analyses, modeling studies, and observational diagnostics that either explicitly or implicitly ignore the strong stationary wave patterns induced by the major mountain ranges and land–sea thermal contrasts. That the stationary waves might conceivably influence the structure and energetics of the transient eddies has long been recognized [e.g., see Saltzman (1963)], but it has only been within the past decade that this problem has attracted widespread interest.

The works of Blackmon (1976), Blackmon et al. (1977), and Lau (1978, 1979) established that the transient eddy variance and covariance statistics for fluctuations with periods on the order of a week or less are organized in terms of elongated "storm tracks" that lie slightly poleward of the climatological mean jet-exit regions over the oceanic sectors of the Northern Hemisphere during wintertime. Frederiksen (1979, 1982) was able to simulate many of the features in these distributions in a linear stability analysis of the longitudinally dependent climatological mean flow. The effects of these transient eddy fluxes on the time-mean flow have been investigated by Hoskins (1983b) and by Lau and Holopainen (1984).

From the studies cited above it is evident that the stationary waves tend to organize baroclinic disturbances into preferred longitudinal sectors but do not fundamentally alter their wavelength, their meridional and vertical structure, their evolution, their fluxes in the meridional plane, or their energetics. Results of Hoskins (1983b) and Hoskins *et al.* (1983) indicate that in addition to their predominantly countergradient meridional fluxes of zonal momentum, longitudinally localized baroclinic waves produce a systematic westward flux of zonal momentum that is also countergradient, since the major storm tracks lie in the exit regions of westerly jetstreams. This westward flux enhances the barotropic energy conversion from the baroclinic waves into the time-mean flow as they evolve through their life cycle.

Fluctuations with periods longer than about 10 days exhibit a structure and evolution quite different from their higher-frequency counterparts. On these longer time scales the presence of the stationary waves is felt through their influence on the dispersion of trains of Rossby waves (Branstator, 1983) and through their role in organizing a significant fraction of the low-frequency variability into standing oscillations with geographically fixed nodes and antinodes (frequently referred to as "teleconnection patterns"). The first effect is most evident at intermediate time scales (10–30-day periods), while the second is most evident at long time scales (periods longer than a month and in the interannual variability of wintertime means) (Blackmon *et al.*, 1984a,b).

The specific dynamical mechanism(s) responsible for organizing the low-frequency variability into teleconnection patterns are not yet well understood, but Simmons *et al.* (1983) have shown evidence that barotropic instability of the climatological mean flow plays a role in several of the observed patterns. In terms of structure and evolution, the normal modes associated with this "two-dimensional barotropic instability" are fundamentally different from the modes associated with the classic zonally symmetric barotropic instability problem (Kuo, 1949). The primary mechanism by which they extract kinetic energy from the zonal flow is through the eastward (downgradient) flux of zonal momentum in the jet-exit regions. If this process proves to be important, then there will be a need for a reinterpretation of the role of barotropic conversion processes in the atmospheric general circulation.

In this chapter we will be concerned with the interactions between the transient eddies and the longitudinally dependent time-mean flow. After a brief review of the structure of the eddies, we will examine the barotropic conversion term in the Earth's atmosphere for both hemispheres and both seasons. For the Northern Hemisphere winter we will show results based on three different observational data sets. We will contrast the observational results with comparable results based on three different GCM experiments carried out at the Geophysical Fluid Dynamics Laboratory (GFDL): one for an Earth-like planet; one for a planet with a land–sea distribution like the Earth's, but with no mountains; and one for a planet with neither mountains nor oceans. Throughout the chapter we will be contrasting the behavior of high-frequency (periods less than 10 days) fluctuations and lower-frequency fluctuations, which appear to play very different roles in the general circulation.

2. STRUCTURE OF THE TRANSIENT EDDIES

Following Hoskins *et al.* (1983), the velocity correlation tensor can be divided into isotropic and anisotropic (trace-free) components

$$\begin{bmatrix} K & 0 \\ 0 & K \end{bmatrix} + \begin{bmatrix} M & N \\ N & -M \end{bmatrix} \tag{2.1}$$

where

$$K = (\overline{u'^2} + \overline{v'^2})/2, \qquad M = (\overline{u'^2} - \overline{v'^2})/2, \qquad N = \overline{u'v'} \tag{2.2}$$

Here the overbars represent climatological (time) means and the primes represent deviations from them. The principal axis of the velocity correlation tensor is oriented at an angle

$$\theta = \tfrac{1}{2} \tan^{-1}(N/M) \tag{2.3}$$

relative to the x axis. In coordinates $(\hat{x}, \hat{y})$ aligned with the major and minor axes,

$$\hat{M} = (\overline{\hat{u}'^2} - \overline{\hat{v}'^2})/2, \qquad \hat{N} = 0 \tag{2.4}$$

Since K and $\hat{M}$ are invariant under the rotation of the axes, it is possible to define a coefficient of anisotropy

$$\alpha = \hat{M}/K \tag{2.5}$$

which lies between zero and one, where $\alpha \rightarrow 1$ as $\overline{\hat{v}'^2} \rightarrow 0$.

The line segments in Fig. 1 depict the minor axes of the velocity correlation tensor, calculated by applying the preceding relationships to National Meteorological Center (NMC) operational 300-mb height analyses for eight Northern Hemisphere winter seasons (November 15–March 14, 1966–1967 to 1968–1969 and 1970–1971 to 1974–1975). Data processing procedures are as described by Lau *et al.* (1981). We have chosen to display minor rather than major axes because observational results by Blackmon *et al.* (1984b) indicate that over much of the hemisphere the group velocity associated with Rossby-wave dispersion tends to be eastward relative to the ground and parallel to the minor axes wherever it has a substantial zonal component. The length of the line segments is proportional to the coefficient of anisotropy.

The loops in Fig. 1 represent the 0.3 contour on selected one-point correlation maps for wintertime 500-mb height, as computed in Blackmon *et al.* (1984a). In most cases they resemble ellipses with minor axes corresponding closely to those associated with the velocity correlation tensor. The degree of ellipticity is related to the coefficient of anisotropy; where α is small, as indicated by short line segments, the loops tend to be more or less circular, whereas as α becomes larger, they become more like closed slits.

Figure 1a shows results based on unfiltered data, which exhibit only a modest amount of anisotropy, with α reaching values of 0.4 over the western United States. Even where α is small, there is a generally good agreement between the orientation of the closed curves and the minor axes of the velocity correlation tensor. Results for filtered data, shown in Fig. 1b,c, indicate a somewhat higher degree of anisotropy, with α reaching values of 0.55 over some regions in the low-pass filtered data.

Transient eddies in the 2.5- to 6-day period range [isolated by subjecting the wind and geopotential height data to the bandpass filter described by Blackmon (1976)] tend to be organized as east–west wave trains, in which individual disturbances have longer meridional scales than zonal scales. There is a prevailing tendency for a WNW–ESE orientation of the minor axes, particularly at the lower latitudes, which is indicative of an equatorward component of the group velocity. The bands of long line segments with similar alignment extending across the North Pacific and North America and across the North Atlantic and western Europe are suggestive of waveguides.

Eddies with periods longer than 10 days [isolated using the low-pass filter described by Blackmon (1976)] tend to be elongated in the east–west direction, as evidenced by the prevailing north–south orientation of their minor axes in Fig. 1c. Their anisotropy is particularly large over the oceanic sectors of the hemisphere. Over North America and parts of Eurasia there is evidence of the NW–SE Rossby-wave dispersion documented by Blackmon *et al.* (1984b).

3. A Vectorial Representation of the Barotropic Conversion

In Cartesian coordinates, the barotropic energy conversion from the transients into the time-mean flow is given by

$$C = \overline{u'^2}(\partial \bar{u}/\partial x) + \overline{v'^2}(\partial \bar{v}/\partial y) + \overline{u'v'}(\partial \bar{v}/\partial x + \partial \bar{u}/\partial y) \tag{3.1}$$

(a)

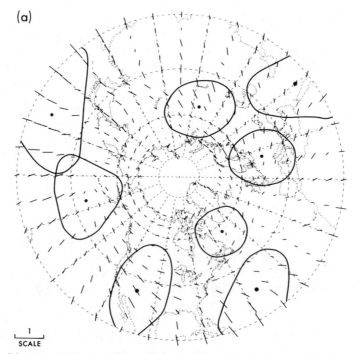

```
 ⌞___⌟
 SCALE
```

FIG. 1. Line segments indicate orientation of minor axes of local eddy correlation tensors; lengths are proportional to $\alpha = \hat{M}/K$, the coefficient of anisotropy. Scale given at lower left. Calculations based on eight winters of 300-mb NMC wind analyses, as described in text. Closed loops represent 0.3 contours of one-point correlation maps for 500-mb height at selected grid points, indicated by dots, based on data used in Blackmon *et al.* (1984a). (a) Unfiltered, twice-daily data; (b) bandpass (2.5–6-day period) filtered data; (c) low-pass (> 10-day period) filtered data. Except for Figs. 5, 6c, and 6d, the outermost latitude circle for all polar stereographic plots in this chapter is 20°N. Latitude circles and meridians are drawn at intervals of 20°.

To an accuracy of about 10%, it can be assumed that the time-mean flow in extratropical latitudes is nondivergent, and $\partial \bar{v}/\partial x$ is negligible in comparison to $\partial \bar{u}/\partial y$, so that

$$C \cong (\overline{u'^2} - \overline{v'^2})(\partial \bar{u}/\partial x) + \overline{u'v'}(\partial \bar{u}/\partial y) \tag{3.2}$$

or, following Hoskins *et al.* (1983) and Simmons *et al.* (1983),

$$C \cong -\mathbf{E} \cdot \nabla \bar{u} \tag{3.3}$$

where

$$\mathbf{E} = -(\overline{u'^2} - \overline{v'^2}, \overline{u'v'}) \tag{3.4}$$

$\frac{\partial \bar{u}}{\partial x} + \frac{\partial \bar{v}}{\partial y} = 0$

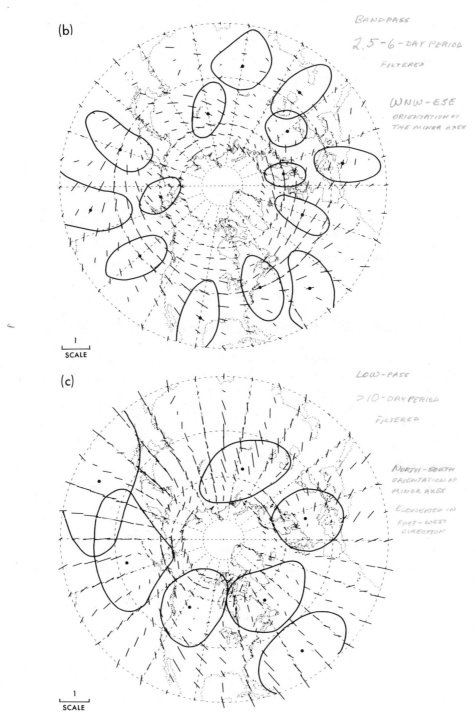

(b)

BANDPASS

2.5 – 6 – DAY PERIOD

FILTERED

WNW – ESE
ORIENTATION OF
THE MINOR AXES

1
SCALE

(c)

LOW – PASS

> 10 – DAY PERIOD

FILTERED

NORTH – SOUTH
ORIENTATION OF
MINOR AXES

ELONGATED IN
EAST – WEST
DIRECTION

1
SCALE

FIG. 1. *(Continued)*

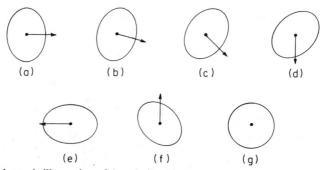

FIG. 2. Schematic illustration of the relationship between the eddy correlation tensor, indicated by the ellipses, and the **E** vector [calculated with reference to the usual (x, y) coordinates], indicated by the arrows. (a) $M < 0$, $N = 0$; (b) $M < 0$, $N = -M/2$; (c) $M < 0$, $N = -2M$; (d) $M = 0$, $N > 0$; (e) $M > 0$, $N = 0$; (f) $M = 0$, $N < 0$; (g) $M = 0$, $N = 0$.

In defining **E**, we have followed the sign convention established by Hoskins *et al.* (1983), which is motivated by the Eliassen–Palm flux formulation of Edmon *et al.* (1980). With this definition, the **E** vector tends to be in the direction of the relative group velocity, and the effective transient eddy flux of westerly momentum is directed in the opposite sense as **E**.

For $M \gg N$, **E** assumes a nearly zonal orientation. If $\overline{v'^2} > \overline{u'^2}$, **E** is directed eastward, and since

$$\tan^{-1}(N/2M) \cong \tfrac{1}{2} \tan^{-1}(N/M) \tag{3.5}$$

it almost exactly coincides with the minor axis of the velocity correlation tensor, as indicated in Fig. 2a,b. Such a relationship is observed throughout most of temperate latitudes in the bandpass filtered data (Fig. 1b). For $M \gg N$ and $\overline{u'^2} > \overline{v'^2}$, **E** is directed westward, and for the same reason, it almost exactly coincides with the major axis of the velocity correlation tensor, as in Fig. 2e. Such a relationship is observed over the oceanic sectors in the low-pass filtered data (Fig. 1c). These situations were emphasized by Hoskins *et al.* (1983). It should be noted that if N is larger than $M/2$, **E** will not be parallel to the axes of the eddy correlation tensor; e.g., see Fig. 2c,d,f.

In contrast to the axes of the velocity correlation tensor, which are invariant under rotation of the coordinate system, **E** is a pseudovector whose orientation depends on the coordinate system in which it is computed; e.g., the **E** field computed in natural coordinates oriented relative to the local absolute vorticity contours is noticeably different from that computed in conventional latitude–longitude coordinates [see Hoskins *et al.* (1983)].

4. OBSERVATIONAL RESULTS

4.1. NMC Analyses; Northern Hemisphere Winter

Figure 3a shows the distributions of E and $\bar{u}$ based on the same data set as Fig. 1. It is evident that the distribution of E and its relation to the zonal wind field is rather complicated and exhibits a strong regional dependence. Large conversions of kinetic energy from the time-mean flow to the transient eddies, as evidenced by E vectors directed up the gradient of $\bar{u}$, occur in the jet-exit region over the central Pacific and to the north of the jet-entrance regions over the southern United States and North Africa. Conversions in the reverse sense occur over much of the Atlantic. These areas correspond to extrema in the distribution of $E \cdot \nabla \bar{u}$, shown in Fig. 4a.

In the bandpass (2.5- to 6-day period) filtered data, shown in Fig. 3b, the most striking features are the bundles of eastward E vectors, directed down the gradient of $\bar{u}$ in the major storm tracks located slightly poleward of the jet-exit regions over the oceanic sectors of the hemisphere. Blackmon *et al.* (1977, 1984a) and Lau (1979) have argued that the structure of the high-frequency transient eddies within these storm-track regions can be identified with baroclinic wave activity. As in the unfiltered pattern, E is directed up the gradient of $\bar{u}$ over much of the United States. The pattern of $E \cdot \nabla \bar{u}$, shown in Fig. 4b, is dominated by regions of strong conversion of kinetic energy from the transient eddies into the mean flow over the oceanic sectors that are not so apparent in the unfiltered data (Fig. 4a). In these regions, the eddies with short time scales transport westerly momentum westward, toward the jet streams, thereby increasing the kinetic energy of the time-mean flow at the expense of the transient eddies.

Figure 3c shows a sharply contrasting picture for the low-frequency component of the transient eddies, which corresponds to fluctuations with periods longer than 10 days. Throughout most of the hemisphere, the E vectors have a westward component consistent with the east–west elongation of the low-frequency eddies in Fig. 1c. The longest E vectors in Fig. 3c are located in the jet-exit region over the central Pacific, where they are directed up the gradient of $\bar{u}$. An analogous but weaker region of westward E vectors is located over the Atlantic jet-exit region. The same features show up with greater clarity in monthly mean data (Fig. 3d), which emphasize transient fluctuations with periods on the order of 60 days or longer and the interannual variability of wintertime means. The westward E vectors in the jet-exit regions are indicative of a barotropic energy conversion from the time-mean flow into the low-frequency transient eddies. These features are evident in the corresponding distributions of $E \cdot \nabla \bar{u}$, shown in Fig. 4c,d,

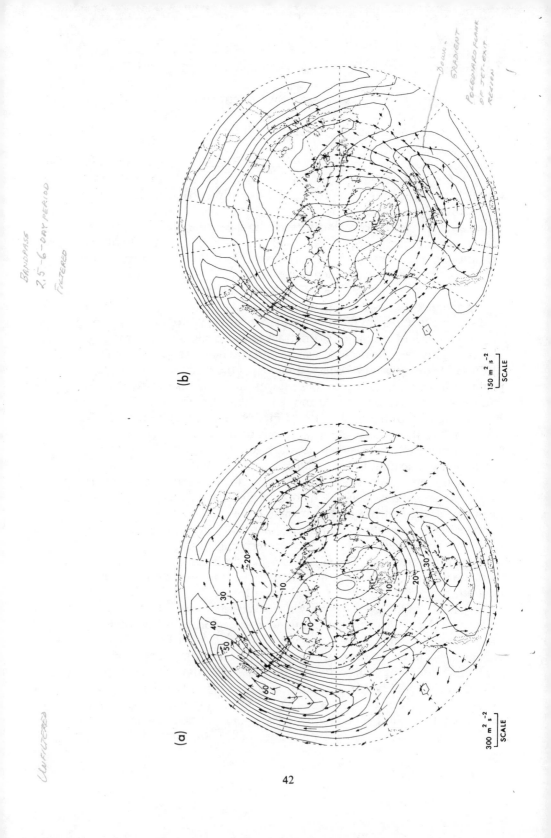

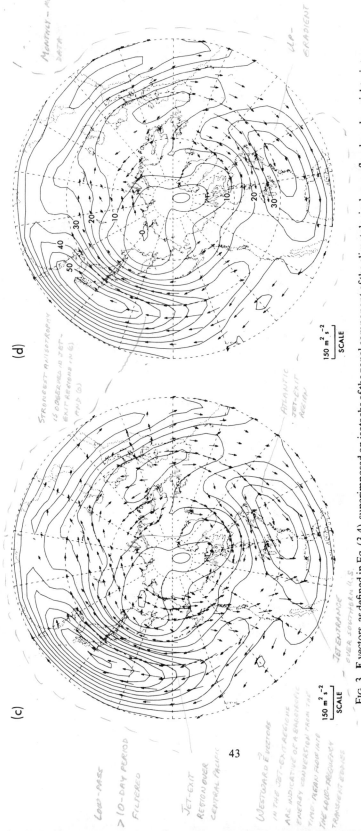

43

(c)

(d)

SCALE

150 m² s⁻²

SCALE

150 m² s⁻²

Fig. 3. **E** vectors, as defined in Eq. (3.4), superimposed on isotachs of the zonal component of the climatological mean flow based on eight winters of NMC 300-mb data for Northern Hemisphere winter. Contour interval for zonal wind 5 m s⁻¹; scales for **E** vectors given at lower left. (a) Unfiltered data, (b) bandpass (2.5–6-day period) filtered data, (c) low-pass (> 10-day period) filtered data, and (d) monthly mean data. Scale for (b)–(d) is one-half that of (a). Panels (a), (b), and (c) are based on data for November 15–March 14; (d) is based on data for November, December, January, February, and March (i.e., 5-month winters, 40 months altogether).

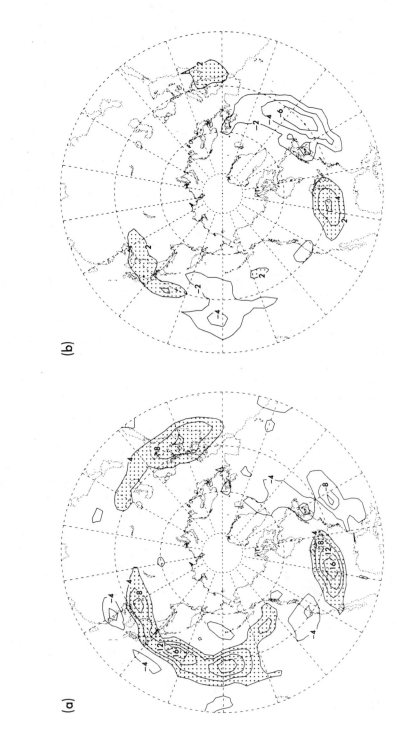

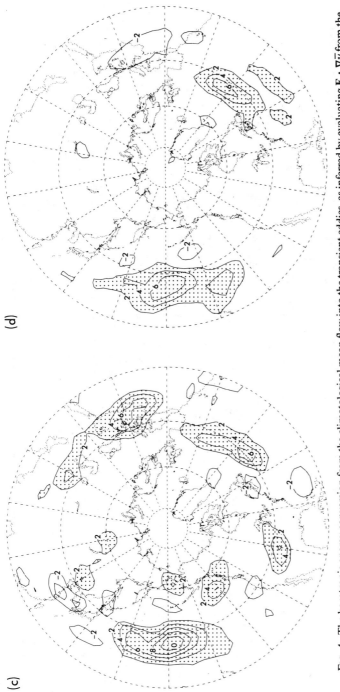
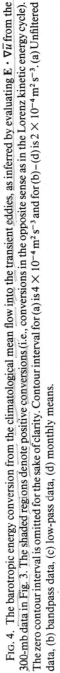

(c)

(d)

FIG. 4. The barotropic energy conversion from the climatological mean flow into the transient eddies, as inferred by evaluating $\mathbf{E} \cdot \nabla \bar{u}$ from the 300-mb data in Fig. 3. The shaded regions denote positive conversions (i.e., conversions in the opposite sense as in the Lorenz kinetic energy cycle). The zero contour interval is omitted for the sake of clarity. Contour interval for (a) is $4 \times 10^{-4} \, \text{m}^2 \, \text{s}^{-3}$ and for (b)–(d) is $2 \times 10^{-4} \, \text{m}^2 \, \text{s}^{-3}$. (a) Unfiltered data, (b) bandpass data, (c) low-pass data, (d) monthly means.

45

and they are responsible for some of the main features in the unfiltered data (Fig. 4a).

It is interesting to note the similarity between the distribution of **E** in Fig. 3d and the theoretically calculated distribution for the fastest-growing normal mode associated with barotropic instability of the climatological mean January 300-mb flow from Simmons *et al.* (1983), which is reproduced in Fig. 5. The strong correspondence supports their contention that two-dimensional barotropic instability is an energy source for low-frequency transient fluctuations in Northern Hemisphere winter. As further evidence,

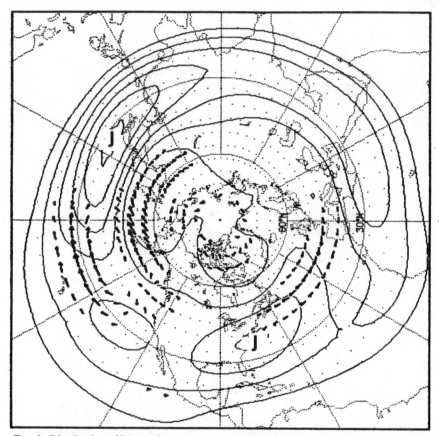

FIG. 5. Distribution of **E** in the fastest-growing normal mode associated with the climatological mean January 300-mb flow. Contours show the distribution of $\bar{u}$. [After Simmons, Wallace, and Branstator (1983). Reproduced with permission from *Journal of the Atmospheric Sciences*, a publication of the American Meteorological Society.]

Simmons *et al.* (1983) note that

(1) the fastest-growing normal mode associated with barotropic instability resembles two observed teleconnection patterns, as illustrated in Fig. 6;

(2) the "centers of action" in the stream function of this same fastest-growing normal mode correspond closely to the regions of strongest low-frequency variability of the geopotential height field, which lie over the northern oceans [e.g., see Blackmon *et al.* (1984a)];

(3) the normal modes associated with barotropic instability of the time-mean flow are characterized by much-lower-frequency oscillatory components than those associated with baroclinic instability; e.g., the fastest-growing normal mode has a period on the order of 50 days. This frequency separation between the barotropic and baroclinic normal modes is consistent with the distinctions between Fig. 3b and Fig. 3c,d.

Table I shows the hemispheric average (poleward of 20°N) of the conversion of kinetic energy from the transient eddies into the climatological mean flow, as defined in Eq. (3.1) and including the terms associated with the earth's spherical geometry, at the 300-mb level. There is a strong compensation between the high- and low-frequency fluctuations, as evidenced by the fact that the conversions for the time-filtered eddies are about an order of

TABLE I. BAROTROPIC ENERGY CONVERSIONS AT THE 300-MB LEVEL FOR NORTHERN HEMISPHERE WINTER[a]

| | NMC Data | | |
	Bandpass (2.5–6-day period)	Low pass (> 10-day period)	Unfiltered
C	3.8	−3.7	−0.3
K_T	16	43	108
C_K	0.5	1.4	3.5
	Mountain GCM Experiment		
C	2.2	−1.2	3.0
K_T	13	26	49
C_K	0.6	0.4	1.4

[a] C is as defined in Eq. (3.1) including the terms associated with the earth's spherical geometry, and K_T represents the kinetic energy of the transient eddies. C_K is the conversion of kinetic energy from the eddies into the zonally averaged flow, as defined in the Lorenz (1955) kinetic energy cycle. Kinetic energy (per unit mass) is given in units of square meters per square second; conversions in units of 10^{-5} m^{2}s^{-3} (approximately equivalent to square meters per square second per day).

[Handwritten margin notes:]
EQT. 3.1, C =
BAROTROPIC ENERGY CONVERSION FROM THE TRANSIENTS INTO THE TIME-MEAN FLOW

C_K =
CONVERSION OF KINETIC ENERGY FROM THE EDDIES INTO THE ZONALLY AVERAGED FLOW (LORENZ KINETIC ENERGY CYCLE)

TELECONNECTIONS USING NMC
MONTHLY MEAN 500-MB HEIGHT
DATA FOR THE N. H. WINTER
(FROM WALLACE AND
GUTZLER)

(a)

(b)

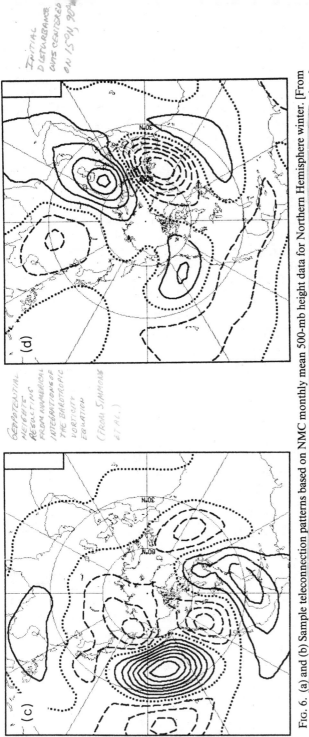

FIG. 6. (a) and (b) Sample teleconnection patterns based on NMC monthly mean 500-mb height data for Northern Hemisphere winter. [From Wallace and Gutzler (1981). Reproduced with permission from *Monthly Weather Review*, a publication of the American Meteorological Society.] (c) and (d) Sample geopotential height patterns obtained by Simmons *et al.* (1983) in numerical integrations based on the barotropic vorticity equation, perturbed about the 300-mb January climatological mean flow. [From Simmons, Wallace, and Branstator (1983). Reproduced with permission from *Journal of the Atmospheric Sciences*, a publication of the American Meteorological Society.] In both cases the flow was perturbed by inserting a local disturbance of very small amplitude into the initial conditions; the maps shown here represent the simulated 300-mb height perturbations 6 days later. In (c) the initial disturbance was centered on 30°N, 120°E, and in (d) it was centered on 15°N, 90°W. Patterns similar to (a) and (b) can be obtained from day 6 of the integrations onward in experiments with the initial disturbance placed in a wide variety of different locations.

49

magnitude larger than the net rate of conversion for the transient eddies as a whole. Comparing the top two rows of Table I, it is evident that the high-frequency transients feed energy into the mean flow at the jet-stream level at a rate sufficient to exhaust themselves on a time scale of 4 to 5 days on a hemispheric basis. However, it should be borne in mind that the conversion rates in Table I represent averages over regions of contrasting sign. Locally, in the storm tracks, the barotropic decay time is on the order of 1 to 2 days, and over the central United States the barotropic amplification time is equally short. On a hemispheric basis, roughly half the high-frequency barotropic conversion is due to the meridional term $u'v'\, \partial\bar{u}/\partial y$ in Eq. (3.2) and the other half is due to the term $(\overline{u'^2} - \overline{v'^2})\, \partial\bar{u}/\partial x$.

The low-frequency transients extract energy from the mean flow at a rate sufficient to replenish themselves on a time scale of about 2 weeks. It is evident from Figs. 3c and 4c that most of this conversion takes place in the jet-exit regions, but the poleward flanks of the jet-entrance regions over the central United States and the Mediterranean also make significant contributions to the hemispheric average. The term $(\overline{u'^2} - \overline{v'^2})\, \partial\bar{u}/\partial x$ dominates the low-frequency barotropic conversion.

4.2. Station Data

Over data sparse regions where the NMC wind fields are influenced by the procedures employed in interpolating irregularly spaced station data to grid-point fields, it is reasonable to question the validity of the features in the **E** and $\bar{u}$ fields described in Figs. 3 and 4. Following the approach in an investigation by Lau and Oort (1981), we present in Fig. 7a distributions of **E** and $\bar{u}$ based on a 10-winter (1963–1964 through 1972–1973) station data set compiled by Oort (1983) at the GFDL. The variances and covariances in Oort's data set are based on deviations from means for individual year/months, and therefore the contribution from the very-low-frequency variability is missing from these statistics. Nevertheless, they should be roughly comparable to the unfiltered results in Fig. 3a. Figure 7b shows **E** and $\bar{u}$ fields derived from monthly mean wind statistics for selected stations tabulated in *Monthly Climatic Data for the World* (World Meteorological Organization, 1963–1973), the counterpart of Fig. 3d. To the extent that they can be compared, Figs. 3 and 7 appear to be at least qualitatively consistent with respect to the major features in the **E** field. In particular, Fig. 7 provides a confirmation of the westward-directed **E** vectors associated with low-frequency transient disturbances in the jet-exit regions in the oceanic sectors and the southeastward-directed arrows on the poleward flanks of the jet-entrance regions over the United States and the Mediterranean region. Hence there can be little doubt concerning the reality of these features.

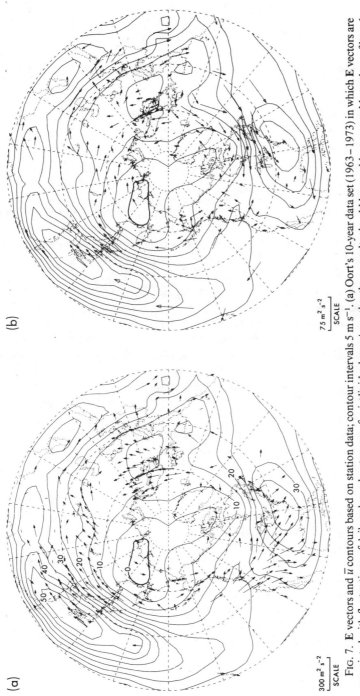

$\overline{300 \text{ m}^2 \text{ s}^{-2}}$
SCALE

$\overline{75 \text{ m}^2 \text{ s}^{-2}}$
SCALE

(a)

(b)

Fig. 7. **E** vectors and $\overline{u}$ contours based on station data; contour intervals 5 m s^{-1}. (a) Oort's 10-year data set (1963–1973) in which **E** vectors are associated with fluctuations of daily values about means for individual year/months; these results should be roughly comparable to the unfiltered results in Fig. 3a. (b) Selected station data extracted from *Monthly Climatic Data for the World* (World Meteorological Organization) also for the period 1963–1973, comparable to the monthly mean results in Fig. 3d. The scale for the arrows in (b) is expanded by a factor of two relative to that of Fig. 3d. The contours of $\overline{u}$ are based on Oort's 10-winter (1963–1973) analysis.

4.3. Analyses from the Global Weather Experiment

A major task carried out at the GFDL in connection with the Global Weather Experiment was the production of the "level III-B data set" consisting of analyzed fields based on the full set of satellite and ground-based observations taken during the experiment and transmitted to the World Data Centers, either in real time or in the months that followed the experiment [see Ploshay *et al.* (1983) for details].

Fields of **E** and $\bar{u}$ derived from this data set for December–February 1978–1979 and June–August 1979 are shown in Figs. 8 and 9. The field for Northern Hemisphere winter (Fig. 8a) exhibits all the major features described in the preceding section. Hence a single year's data should be sufficient for describing the relation between **E** and $\bar{u}$ on a global basis. In comparison to their wintertime counterparts, the summertime **E** vectors and the gradients of $\bar{u}$, shown in Fig. 8b, are weaker and there is less large-scale organization in the **E** field. The eastward-directed arrows across northern Europe and Asia are suggestive of a storm track. There are westward directed arrows in the shear zones to the south of the mid-latitude jet streams.

The distributions for the Southern Hemisphere, shown in Fig. 9, both exhibit a considerable amount of structure. Prominent features in the wintertime distribution (Fig. 9b) are the eastward-directed bundle of **E** vectors emerging from the exit of the high-latitude jet stream over the Indian Ocean and the equatorward vectors on the poleward flank of the jet-entrance region over and to the west of Australia. Comparison with results of Hoskins *et al.* (1983) (their Fig. 11), based on the 1980 winter, tends to confirm the existence of these features. The former appears to be associated with the primary storm track in the hemisphere and the latter is perhaps an analog to the wintertime jet-entrance regions over the southern United States and North Africa.

The summertime distribution (Fig. 9a) is dominated by a ring of eastward-directed **E** vectors that coincides with the strongest westerlies, near 50°S. At a number of different longitudes, bundles of arrows peel off from the equatorward flank of the jet and curve northward into the subtropics.

It is interesting to note that of the four distributions shown in Figs. 8 and 9, only the Northern Hemisphere winter (Fig. 8a) shows evidence of westward **E** vectors in the jet-exit regions. There are several examples of bundles of eastward-pointing vectors that curve equatorward on the poleward flanks of jet-entrance regions. Apparently, such regions account for most of the observed poleward flux of westerly momentum in the 30 to 40° latitude belt.

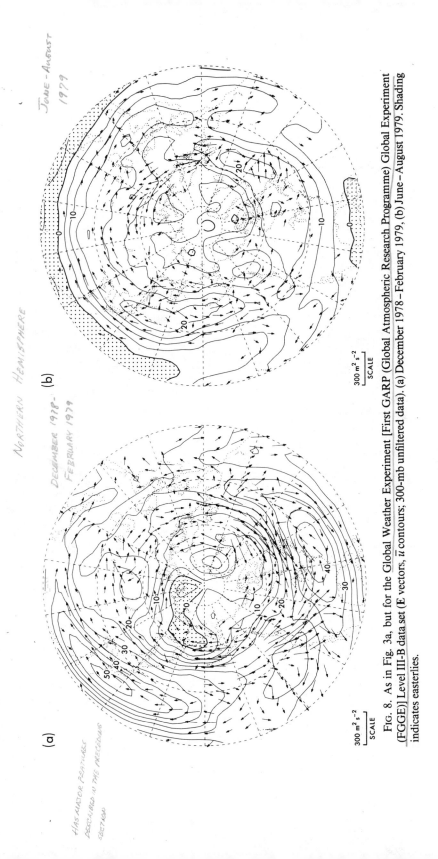

JUNE–AUGUST
1979

DECEMBER 1978–
FEBRUARY 1979

(a)

(b)

HAS MAJOR FEATURES
DESCRIBED IN THE PRECEDING
SECTION

300 m² s⁻²
SCALE

300 m² s⁻²
SCALE

FIG. 8. As in Fig. 3a, but for the Global Weather Experiment [First GARP (Global Atmospheric Research Programme) Global Experiment (FGGE)] Level III-B data set (E vectors, $\bar{u}$ contours; 300-mb unfiltered data). (a) December 1978 – February 1979, (b) June – August 1979. Shading indicates easterlies.

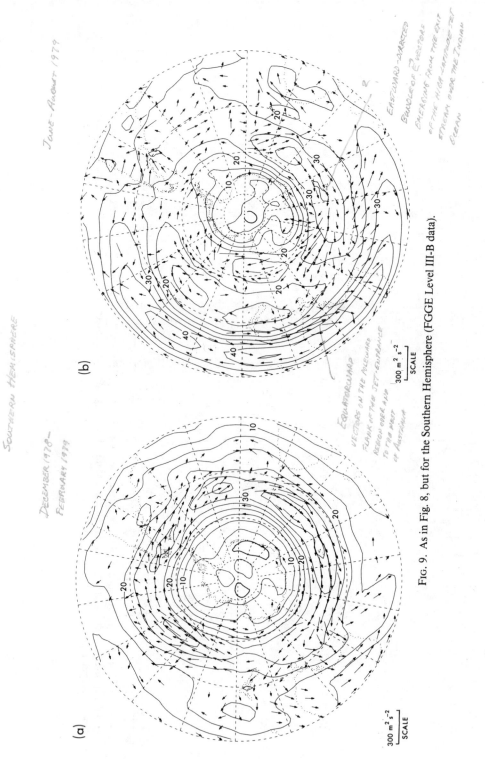

SOUTHERN HEMISPHERE

DECEMBER 1978 – FEBRUARY 1979

JUNE – AUGUST 1979

(a)

(b)

300 m² s⁻²
SCALE

300 m² s⁻²
SCALE

EQUATORWARD VECTORS ON THE POLEWARD FLANK OF THE JET-ENTRANCE REGION OVER AND TO THE WEST OF AUSTRALIA

EASTWARD-DIRECTED BUNDLE OF E VECTORS EMERGING FROM THE EXIT OF THE HIGH-LATITUDE JET STREAM OVER THE INDIAN OCEAN

FIG. 9. As in Fig. 8, but for the Southern Hemisphere (FGGE Level III-B data).

5. Results Based on GCM Simulations

In 1978–1980 the Climate Dynamics group at the GFDL carried out a pair of 15-year integrations with a low-resolution spectral model. [For details of the model formulation, see Gordon and Stern (1982).] Following the experimental strategy used by Manabe and Terpstra (1974), one of the integrations was carried out with realistic boundary conditions at the Earth's surface, and the other was identical but for the fact that the orography was removed. The two integrations are referred to as the "mountain (M)" and the "no mountain (NM)" experiments, respectively. In this section we shall describe results for the Northern Hemisphere during winter only. The results described in this section are averages based on the first 10 years of 15-year integrations.

From an inspection of the hemispherically averaged energetics statistics shown in Table I, one might easily conclude that the M experiment did not produce a very good simulation of the observed kinetic energy cycle. The transient eddy kinetic energy is too small by more than a factor of two, and the conversion between the transient eddies and the climatological mean flow is an order of magnitude larger than the observed and in the opposite direction. Even the term $(\overline{u'^2} - \overline{v'^2})(\partial\overline{u}/\partial x)$ (not shown) is from the eddies into the mean flow, whereas in the NMC data it is strong and in the reverse sense. However, a comparison of the distributions of E and $\overline{u}$, shown in Fig. 10, and $E \cdot \nabla\overline{u}$, shown in Fig. 11, with the corresponding distributions based on NMC data shown in Figs. 3 and 4, respectively, gives rather convincing evidence that the GCM is capable of simulating the barotropic interactions between the mean flow and the eddies at the jet-stream level at least qualitatively, if not in quantitative detail. This conclusion is reinforced by a comparison of Figs. 12 and 1, which shows that the horizontal structures of the transient eddies in the GCM simulation are realistic in terms of scale and shape. The marked differences in the hemispherically averaged barotropic energy conversions between the M experiment and the NMC data in Table I are evidently a reflection of the differing relative strengths of the various regional features.

The "no mountain" experiment yielded a jet-stream structure more reminiscent of the Southern Hemisphere. The E vectors shown in Fig. 13 are predominantly eastward in the latitude belt of the jet stream. Equatorward of the jet stream they peel off equatorward and weaken. Within the primary jet-entrance region over Eurasia, the E vectors stream southeastward on the poleward flank of the jet, where they cross the isotachs toward higher values of $\overline{u}$. A similar but weaker region of southeastward pointing E vectors occurs over eastern Canada, poleward of the weak secondary jet maximum off

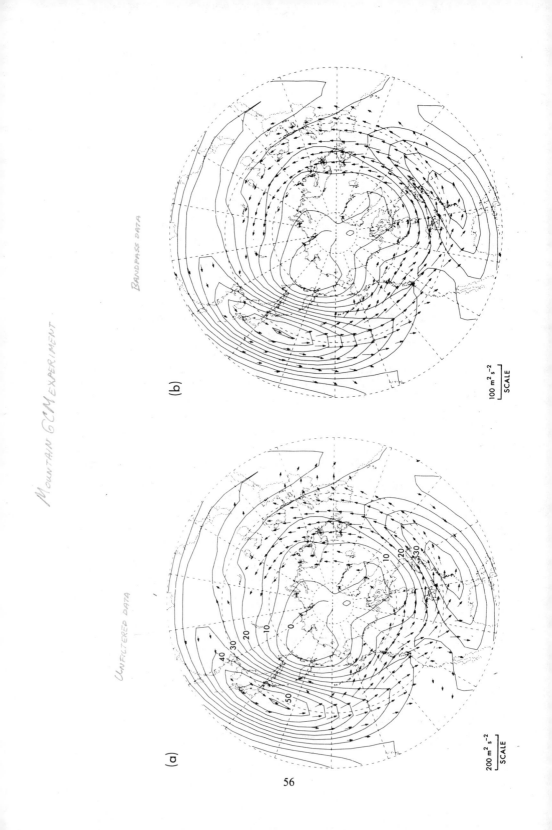

MOUNTAIN GCM EXPERIMENT

UNFILTERED DATA

BANDPASS DATA

(a)

(b)

SCALE
200 m² s⁻²

SCALE
100 m² s⁻²

56

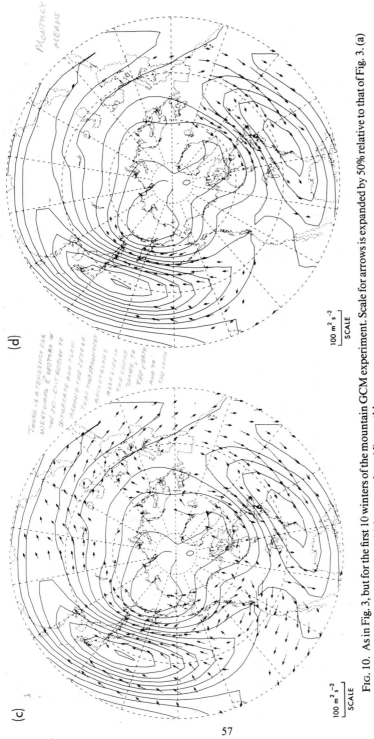

(c)

(d)

LOW-PASS
DATA

MONTHLY
MEANS

THERE IS A TENDENCY FOR
WESTWARD Ē VECTORS IN
THE JET-EXIT REGION TO
BIFURCATE AND FLOW
AROUND THE "ISTHE
THAT THE STRONGEST
ANTISTREAM
ALSO LIES IN
THE STRONG
"FLANKS"?? TO
THE NORTH
AND TO
THE SOUTH

100 m² s⁻²
SCALE

100 m² s⁻²
SCALE

FIG. 10. As in Fig. 3, but for the first 10 winters of the mountain GCM experiment. Scale for arrows is expanded by 50% relative to that of Fig. 3. (a) Unfiltered data, (b) bandpass data, (c) low-pass data, (d) monthly means.

BAROTROPIC ENERGY CONVERSION FROM THE CLIMATOLOGICAL $\vec{E} \cdot \vec{\nabla}_{u}$

MEAN FLOW INTO THE TRANSIENT EDDIES

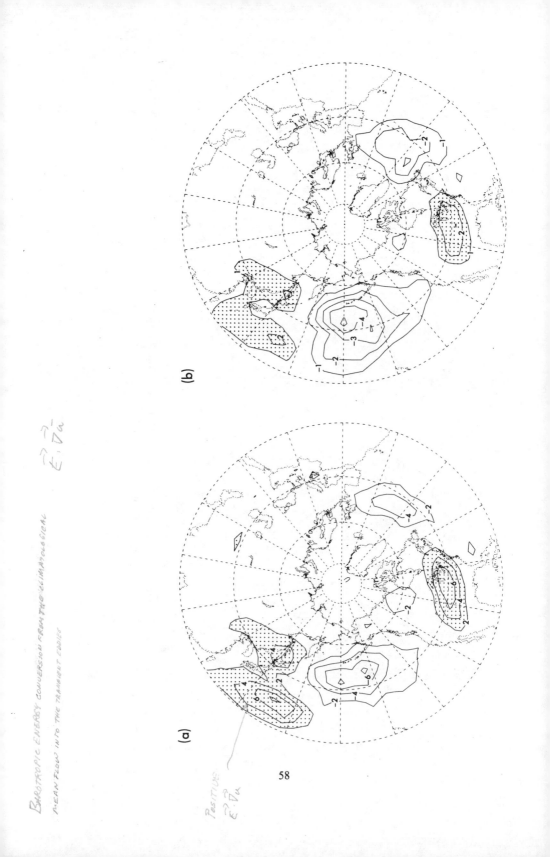

(a)

(b)

POSITIVE
$\vec{E} \cdot \vec{\nabla}_{u}$

58

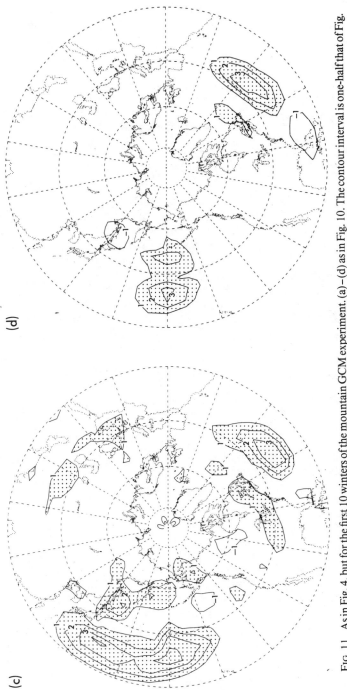

(c)

(d)

Fig. 11. As in Fig. 4, but for the first 10 winters of the mountain GCM experiment. (a)–(d) as in Fig. 10. The contour interval is one-half that of Fig. 4, i.e., (a) 2×10^{-4} m^2 s^{-3}, (b)–(d) 1×10^{-4} m^2 s^{-3}.

(a)

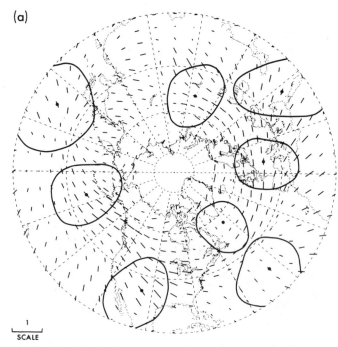

FIG. 12. As in Fig. 1, but for the first 10 winters of the mountain GCM experiment. (a)–(c) as in Fig. 1.

Nova Scotia. These regions are characterized by strong poleward, down-gradient fluxes of westerly momentum.

The very-low-frequency variability, as represented by monthly mean data shown in Fig. 13b, contributes very little to the poleward flux of westerly momentum. The main form of anisotropy at these very low frequencies is the prevailing westward sense of the arrows, which indicates that $u'^2 > v'^2$ and that the disturbances are elongated in the east–west direction. The strongest anisotropy is observed, not in the jet-exit regions, as in Fig. 3c,d, but in the shear zones to the north and south of the jet throughout most of the western half of the hemisphere. In the mountain experiment (Fig. 10c,d), there is a tendency for the westward **E** vectors in the jet-exit regions to bifurcate and flow around the jets so that the strongest anisotropy also lies in the shear zones, to the north and to the south. This tendency is particularly pronounced in the Atlantic sector.

The anisotropy in the shear zones is related to the distribution of telecon-

(b)

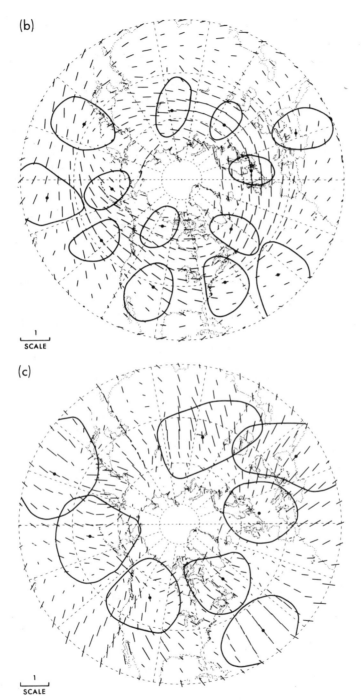

1
SCALE

(c)

1
SCALE

Fig. 12. *(Continued)*

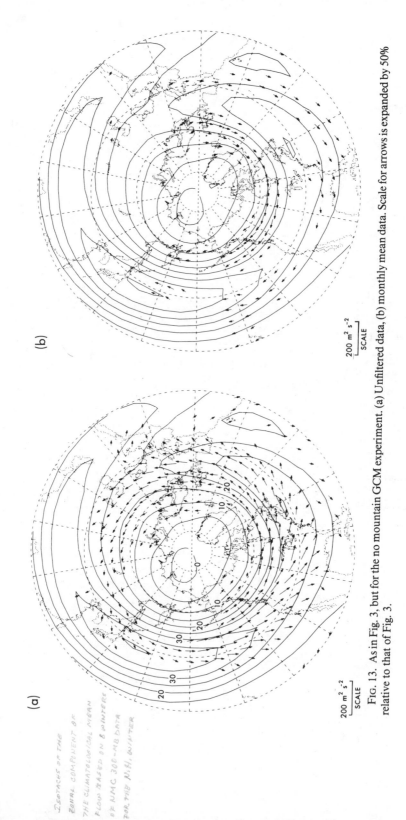

FIG. 13. As in Fig. 3, but for the no mountain GCM experiment. (a) Unfiltered data, (b) monthly mean data. Scale for arrows is expanded by 50% relative to that of Fig. 3.

(a)

(b)

200 m² s⁻²
SCALE

200 m² s⁻²
SCALE

nectivity* shown in Fig. 14c, which is characterized by an elongated maximum extended along the axis of the jet stream, in sharp contrast to the dipole patterns straddling the jet-exit regions suggested by the NMC data shown in Fig. 14a. In teleconnection patterns with centers of action centered on the axis of the jet stream, the fluctuations in zonal wind have odd symmetry about the axis of the jet stream; i.e., positive deviations of $\bar{u}$ to the north of the jet axis are accompanied by negative deviations to the south of the jet axis and vice versa. Note that the pattern of teleconnectivity in the M experiment (Fig. 14b) also shows a tendency for maxima centered on the axis of the jet stream, rather than along the flanks of it as in the NMC data over the Atlantic (Fig. 14a). These differences are also reflected in the distributions of $\mathbf{E} \cdot \nabla \bar{u}$ (compare Figs. 4d and 11d).

A third GCM experiment was conducted with the same spectral model in which the lower boundary was prescribed to be a flat, moist land surface, and the solar flux was prescribed to be constant and equal to its annual mean value rather than to be seasonally varying as in the M and NM experiments. The history tapes from a 48-month integration with this "flat land" (FL) model integration have not yet been fully analyzed, but I. M. Held of the GFDL has kindly provided us with monthly mean data. The mean zonal wind distribution, indicated by the contours in Fig. 15, is nearly zonally symmetric. The small departures from zonal symmetry are a result of the finite sampling interval. Because of the annual mean radiative forcing, the jet stream is weaker and more diffuse than in the NM experiment, which was based on wintertime forcing. Maximum wind speeds are only on the order of 25 m s^{-1}. The distribution of $\mathbf{E}$ based on monthly mean data, indicated by the arrows in Fig. 15, differs from that in the NM experiment (Fig. 13b): whereas the anisotropy vanishes in the core of the jet stream in the NM experiment, $\mathbf{E}$ reaches its largest values in the jet stream in the FL experiment. Throughout the hemisphere $\overline{u'^2} > \overline{v'^2}$, and the low-frequency eddies produce a weak poleward flux of westerly momentum.

In addition to the distributions of $\mathbf{E}$ and $\bar{u}$ displayed in Figs. 10 and 13, we have examined distributions for the Southern Hemisphere summer from both the M and NM experiments, which provide further examples of the kinds of structures described in this section. Results for the M experiment (not shown) resemble the pattern in the data from the Global Weather Experiment (Fig. 9a).

---

* The teleconnectivity at a given grid point is defined as the largest negative correlation coefficient that appears on the one-point correlation map for that grid point. It may also be defined as the column matrix whose elements are comprised of the largest negative correlation coefficients in each row (or column) of the Hermitian matrix whose elements are the correlation coefficients between the variable in question (in this case 500-mb height) at each grid point and each other grid point. For further details and examples, see Wallace and Gutzler (1981).

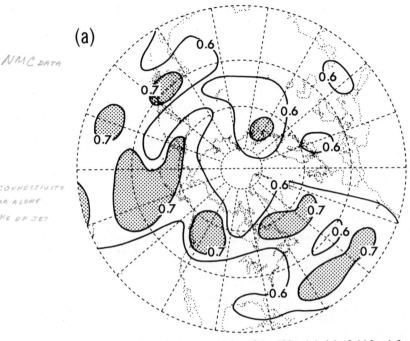

NMC data

Teleconnectivity maxima along flanks of jet axis

FIG. 14. The distribution of teleconnectivity of the 500-mb height field [as defined by Wallace and Gutzler (1981)] for the Northern Hemisphere winter, based on monthly mean data. (a) NMC data, (b) the mountain GCM experiment, and (c) the no mountain GCM experiment. Contour interval 0.1. Only values greater than 0.6 are contoured. Shading indicates values greater than 0.7.

6. Net Transient Eddy Forcing of the Mean Flow

It is of interest to determine whether the signature of any of the dynamical processes described in the previous sections is recognizable in the net forcing of the time-mean flow by the transient eddies. Lau and Holopainen (1984) have shown that the quasi-geostrophic tendency equation for the time-mean flow provides a convenient framework for inferring the net effect of the horizontal eddy fluxes of momentum and heat, taking into account the ageostrophic circulations that they induce. In this formulation, the convergence of the eddy fluxes plays a role analogous to the advection terms in the instantaneous tendency equation.

Figure 16, from Lau and Holopainen (1984), shows the tendencies in 300-mb geopotential height induced by the vorticity fluxes associated with high- and low-frequency fluctuations as defined earlier. The contour interval between solid contours is roughly equivalent to 5 m (of 300-mb height) per

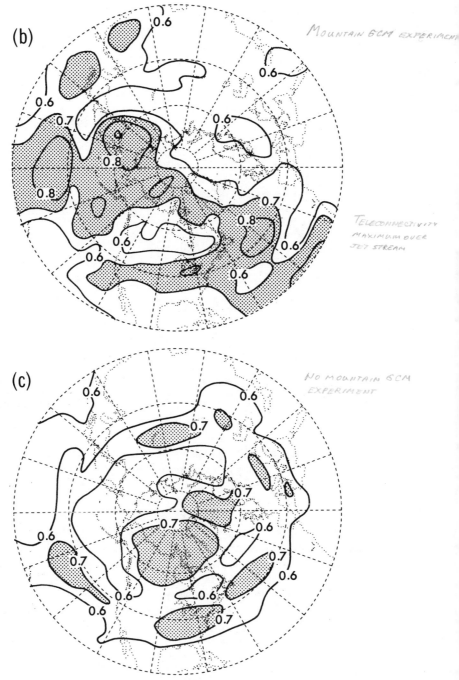

(b)

MOUNTAIN GCM EXPERIMENT

TELECONNECTIVITY
MAXIMUM OVER
JET STREAM

(c)

NO MOUNTAIN GCM
EXPERIMENT

FIG. 14. *(Continued)*

FLAT LAND
GCM EXPERIMENT

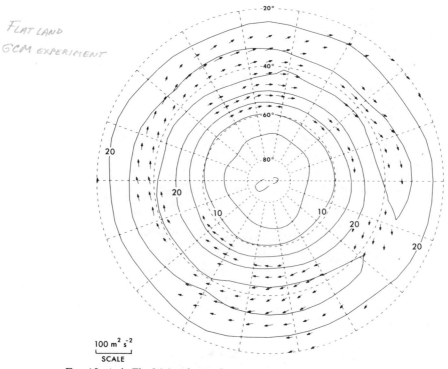

FIG. 15. As in Fig. 3d, but for the flat land GCM experiment. Pressure level 202 mb. Scale for arrows is expanded by 50% relative to that of Fig. 3d.

day. Calculations are based on the NMC data set for Northern Hemisphere winter. The vorticity fluxes by the high-frequency transients (Fig. 16a) tend to accelerate the climatological mean jet streams along their northern flanks. Throughout the Pacific and American sectors of the hemisphere, the eddies produce westerly accelerations in the 40 to 50°N latitude belt. The low-frequency eddies (Fig. 16b) produce stronger accelerations of the mean flow, particularly over the eastern oceans. They tend to weaken the longitudinal contrasts in jet stream structure, accelerating the zonal flow where it is weak over the eastern Pacific and Europe, decelerating the Asian jet stream southeast of Japan, and shifting the jet streams over the western United States and North Africa poleward, bringing them more closely into line with the other jets. The total 300-mb height tendency induced by the transient eddies, shown in Fig. 17, closely resembles that associated with the vorticity flux induced by the low-frequency eddies (Fig. 16b). Hence, low-frequency barotropic processes dominate the wave–mean-flow interaction at the jet stream level.

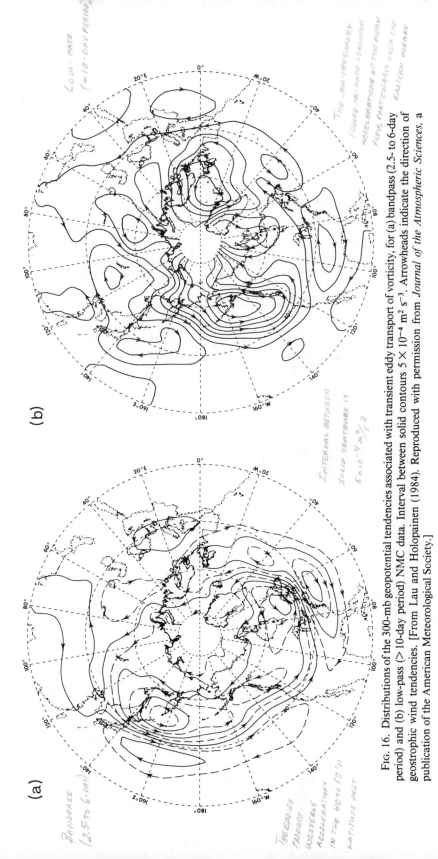

Fig. 16. Distributions of the 300-mb geopotential tendencies associated with transient eddy transport of vorticity, for (a) bandpass (2.5- to 6-day period) and (b) low-pass (>10-day period) NMC data. Interval between solid contours 5×10^{-4} m^2 s^{-3}. Arrowheads indicate the direction of geostrophic wind tendencies. [From Lau and Holopainen (1984). Reproduced with permission from *Journal of the Atmospheric Sciences*, a publication of the American Meteorological Society.]

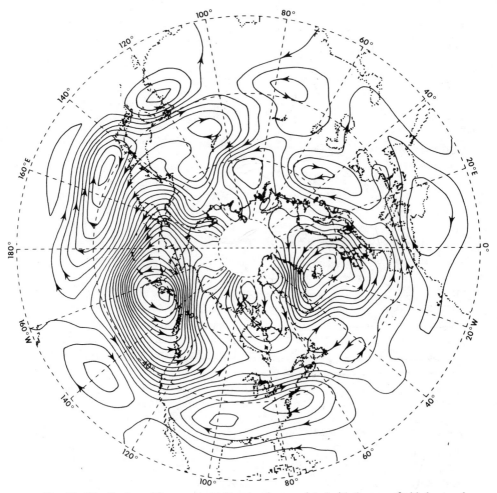

FIG. 17. Distribution of the geopotential tendencies associated with the sum of eddy heat and vorticity fluxes at 300 mb. The eddy forcings are computed by using unfiltered NMC data. Contour interval 5×10^{-4} m^2 s^{-3}. Arrowheads indicate the direction of the geostrophic wind tendencies. [From Lau and Holopainen (1984). Reproduced with permission from *Journal of the Atmospheric Sciences,* a publication of the American Meteorological Society.]

Hoskins *et al.* (1983) have shown that to within about 10%, the barotropic component of the eddy forcing of the mean zonal flow is given by $\nabla \cdot \mathbf{E}$. From a comparison of Figs. 3 and 16 it can be seen that all the features described in the preceding paragraph correspond to well-defined regions of divergence or convergence in the $\mathbf{E}$ field. Hence the patterns in the $\mathbf{E}$ vectors are helpful in interpreting the net eddy forcing of the mean zonal flow at the jet stream level.

7. FURTHER INTERPRETATION

All the distributions that we examined showed a tendency for eastward-directed **E** vectors at the high frequencies and westward-directed **E** vectors at the low frequencies, consistent with results of Hoskins *et al.* (1983) and Blackmon *et al.* (1984a,b). Hence, the filtered data exhibit considerably more anisotropy than do the unfiltered data. Much of this "polarization" of transient eddy structure in the frequency domain is due to differential doppler shifting associated with the time-mean flow and differential westward Rossby-wave propagation associated with the β effect.

To describe the doppler-shifting phenomenon, let us consider the hypothetical situation of a horizontal wind field corresponding to homogeneous, isotropic turbulence superimposed on a mean zonal flow that, for the sake of argument, can be presumed to be a pure superrotation. For the present, let us ignore the influence of the β effect in retarding or reversing the eastward advection of the larger-scale eddies. In such a flow, eddies of any given two-dimensional scale that are elongated in the east–west direction will require a longer time to be advected past fixed reference points than do eddies of the same scale that are elongated in the north–south direction. Alternatively, it can be argued that spherical harmonics of any given two-dimensional wave number n that are elongated in the east–west direction will exhibit lower frequencies at fixed reference points than those elongated in the opposite sense, even though all the harmonics are subject to the same eastward advective phase speed.

The argument can be extended to include the influence of the β effect as follows. For any given superrotation, there is a corresponding eddy scale or two-dimensional wave number n for which the westward phase propagation induced by the β effect just balances the eastward advection by the mean flow so that the wave is stationary relative to the ground. Surrounding this stationary wave number there exists a finite band of two-dimensional wave numbers for which the zonal phase speeds relative to the ground are smaller than any prescribed lower limit. It is these slow-moving waves that account for the patterns in the low-pass filtered and monthly mean data. However, it is not the phase speed alone that determines the ground-based frequency of the waves: it is the product of the phase speed and the zonal wave number. Hence, waves of a given two-dimensional wave number n that are elongated in the zonal direction have lower ground-based frequencies than those that are elongated in the meridional direction. It follows that low-pass filtered data should contain a disproportionately large share of waves or eddies that are zonally elongated, and vice versa.

Apart from the FL experiment, all the other distributions of **E** described in the preceding section exhibit spatially dependent anisotropy with distinctive horizontal structures that are evident even in the unfiltered data. These regional features give rise to local convergence and divergence in the E field, which is indicative of eddy forcing of the time-mean flow. They are associated with at least four distinct types of organization of the transient eddies:

(1) Bands of baroclinic wave activity, evident in the high-frequency component of the transient eddies: In the Northern Hemisphere winter, where the climatological mean jet streams have well-defined entrance and exit regions, baroclinic activity tends to be concentrated on the poleward flank of the jet-exit regions, where the E vectors exhibit a diffluent pattern as they stream eastward, down the gradient of $\bar{u}$, indicating that the eddies are giving up their kinetic energy to the mean flow (e.g., see Fig. 3b).

(2) The signature of two-dimensional barotropic instability characterized by westward, up-gradient E vectors in the jet-exit regions at the low frequencies: This phenomenon occurs regularly in the Northern Hemisphere winter (Figs. 3d and 8a) and less strongly in the M experiment (Fig. 10d), but not in the Southern Hemisphere nor in the Northern Hemisphere summer nor in the NM or FL experiments; apparently it is important only in the presence of rather strong zonal gradients of the time-mean flow. When it occurs, it is capable of producing barotropic energy conversions comparable to (1), but in the reverse sense.

(3) Locally strong equatorward Rossby-wave dispersion on the poleward flanks of the jet-entrance regions as evidenced by the curving of the E vectors and the orientations of the wave trains for the high- and intermediate-frequency transient eddies: The equatorward dispersion is indicative of a locally strong poleward momentum flux. Lau et al. (1978) found local maxima in the distribution of $\overline{u'v'}$ in the same regions. These fluxes are down the gradient of westerly momentum, and thus they are indicative of a conversion of kinetic energy from the climatological mean flow into the transient eddies. The magnitude of the conversion appears to be comparable to that associated with (2), and this phenomenon appears to be more widespread than (2) (e.g., see Figs. 3a, 9a, 10a, and 13a). The only example of a jet-entrance region where there is not a strong conversion in this sense is over China and Mongolia during wintertime, and that is at least partially due to the low eddy kinetic energy levels in that region. Comparison of panels (b) and (c) in Figs. 1, 3, and 10 suggests that the equatorward refraction of the Rossby-wave trains is more pronounced for the low-frequency than for the high-frequency eddies, but it is evident from Figs. 4 and 11 that eddies with a broad range of frequencies contribute to the barotropic energy conversion in these regions; hence, the signature of this process is clearly evident in the unfiltered data. Poleward of 30° latitude, most of the poleward flux of zonal momentum appears to be associated with these longitudinally dependent signatures. In contrast, there appears to be more widespread equatorward Rossby-wave

dispersion equatorward of 30°N on the anticyclonic side of the major jet streams.

(4)   Bands of low-frequency zonal wind fluctuations centered in the shear zones to the north and south of elongated jet streams: This form of organization, in and of itself, produces little barotropic energy conversion, since the **E** vectors tend to be parallel to the $\bar{u}$ contours. It is most evident in the NM experiment, but there are hints of it in some of the other distributions, e.g., in the M experiment (Fig. 10), in the fastest-growing mode of barotropic instability (Fig. 5), and in the data from the Global Weather Experiment for the Northern Hemisphere summer (Fig. 8b). Teleconnection patterns in the geopotential height field associated with (2) are characterized by dipole structures straddling the jet-exit regions, whereas those associated with (4) are centered on the jet stream, with u' showing a negative correlation between the poleward and equatorward flanks of the jet stream. From a synoptic point of view, (2) can be interpreted as an alternating lengthening and retraction of the jet streams in the downwind direction, whereas (4) can be interpreted as a north–south translation of the jets.

The preceding results in no way negate the importance of the conversion of kinetic energy from baroclinic waves into the climatological mean flow. The predominance of the pattern (1) in the high-frequency transient eddies is evidence that this process plays an important role in the general circulation. However, it is clear that the barotropic energy conversion involves more than a single dynamical process. The patterns (2) and (3) represent other kinds of interactions between the eddies and longitudinally dependent mean flows that involve energy conversions from the mean flow into the transient eddies; two-dimensional barotropic instability (2) involves the very low frequencies and equatorward wave dispersion (3) involves a wide range of frequencies.

It is evident that the process (1) contributes to the maintenance of the climatological mean jet streams and to the general poleward flux of zonal momentum from the subtropics into the middle latitudes. However, it should be emphasized that these contributions are small. In contrast, the net effect of the processes (2) and (3), which dominate the eddy forcing of the mean flow at the jet-stream level, is to reduce the longitudinal contrasts in the time-mean flow pattern: (2) by reducing the zonal gradients in zonal wind speed across the jet-exit regions and (3) by extracting westerly momentum from the jet-entrance regions, near 30°N, and depositing it farther poleward in regions of relatively weak zonal winds. Hence, in accord with the results presented in Fig. 17, the eddies are tending to create a more zonally symmetric flow pattern with a westerly jet stream poleward of its observed position.

The demonstrated importance of these low-frequency processes in the interactions between the transient eddies and the time mean flow supports the case for broadening our conceptual understanding of the general circulation to encompass not only the time-mean flow and baroclinic waves, but also a third entity or group of entities, labeled "low-frequency fluctuations," that might well exist even in the absence of baroclinic instability. In contrast to baroclinic waves, which give up much of their kinetic energy to the barotropic component of the time-mean flow, these low-frequency fluctuations apparently feed on the time-mean flow and thereby serve to damp the longitudinally dependent, climatological-mean features at the jet-stream level.

Acknowledgments

We would like to thank Isaac M. Held, Eero O. Holopainen, and Abraham H. Oort for reviewing the paper and offering helpful suggestions; the GFDL Scientific Illustration Group for drafting the figures; and John Conner for supplying the photography. This work was supported by the Climate Dynamics Program of the National Science Foundation under Grant ATM 78-06099 and by the Geophysical Fluid Dynamics Program under NOAA Grant 04-7-022-44017.

References

Blackmon, M. L. (1976). A climatological spectral study of the 500 mb geopotential height of the Northern Hemisphere. *J. Atmos. Sci.* **33**, 1607–1623.

Blackmon, M. L., Wallace J. M., Lau, N.-C., and Mullen, S. L. (1977). An observational study of the Northern Hemisphere wintertime circulation. *J. Atmos. Sci.* **34**, 1040–1053.

Blackmon, M. L., Lee, Y.-H., and Wallace, J. M. (1984a). Horizontal structure of 500 mb height fluctuations with long, intermediate and short time scales. *J. Atmos. Sci.* **41**, 961–979.

Blackmon, M. L., Lee, Y.-H., Wallace, J. M., and Hsu, H.-H. (1984b). Time variations of 500 mb height fluctuations with long, intermediate, and short time scales as deduced from lag-correlation statistics. *J. Atmos. Sci.* **41**, 981–991.

Branstator, G. (1983). Horizontal energy propagation in a barotropic atmosphere with meridional and zonal structure. *J. Atmos. Sci.* **40**, 1689–1708.

Charney, J. G. (1947). The dynamics of long waves in a baroclinic westerly current. *J. Meteorol.* **4**, 135–162.

Eady, E. T. (1949). Long waves and cyclone waves. *Tellus* **1**, 35–52.

Edmon, H. J., Jr., Hoskins, B. J., and McIntyre, M. E. (1980). Eliassen–Palm cross sections for the troposphere. *J. Atmos. Sci.* **37**, 2600–2616.

Fjortoft, R. (1951). Stability properties of large-scale disturbances. *In* "Compendium of Meteorology" (T. F. Malone, ed.), pp. 454–463. Am. Meteorol. Soc., Boston, Massachusetts.

Frederiksen, J. S. (1979). The effects of long planetary waves on the regions of cyclogenesis: Linear theory. *J. Atmos. Sci.* **36**, 195–204.

Frederiksen, J. S. (1982). A unified three-dimensional instability theory of the onset of blocking and cyclogenesis. *J. Atmos. Sci.* **39**, 969–982.

Gordon, C. T., and Stern, W. F. (1982). A description of the GFDL global spectral model. *Mon. Weather Rev.* **110**, 625–644.

Holopainen, E. O. (1983). Transient eddies in mid-latitudes: Observations and interpretation. *In* "Large-Scale Dynamical Processes in the Atmosphere" (B. J. Hoskins and R. P. Pearce, eds.), pp. 201–233. Academic Press, New York.

Hoskins, B. J. (1983a). Dynamical processes in the atmosphere and the use of models. *Q. J. R. Meteorol. Soc.* **109**, 1–21.

Hoskins, B. J. (1983b). Modelling of the transient eddies and their feedback on the mean flow. *In* "Large-Scale Dynamical Processes in the Atmosphere" (B. J. Hoskins and R. P. Pearce, eds.), pp. 169–199. Academic Press, New York.

Hoskins, B. J., James, I. N., and White, G. H. (1983). The shape, propagation and mean-flow interaction of large-scale weather systems. *J. Atmos. Sci.* **40**, 1595–1612.

Kuo, H.-L. (1949). Dynamical instability of two-dimensional nondivergent flow in a barotropic atmosphere. *J. Meteorol.* **6**, 105–122.

Lau, N.-C. (1978). On the three-dimensional structure of the observed transient eddy statistics of the Northern Hemisphere wintertime circulation. *J. Atmos. Sci.* **35**, 1900–1923.

Lau, N.-C. (1979). The structure and energetics of transient disturbances in the Northern Hemisphere wintertime circulation. *J. Atmos. Sci.* **36**, 982–995.

Lau, N.-C., and Holopainen, E. O. (1984). Transient eddy forcing of the time-mean flow as identified by quasi-geostrophic tendencies. *J. Atmos. Sci.* **41**, 313–328.

Lau, N.-C., and Oort, A. H. (1981). A comparative study of observed Northern Hemisphere circulation statistics based on GFDL and NMC analyses. Part I. The time mean fields. *Mon. Weather Rev.* **109**, 1380–1403.

Lau, N.-C., Tennekes, H., and Wallace, J. M. (1978). Maintenance of the momentum flux by transient eddies in the upper troposphere. *J. Atmos. Sci.* **35**, 139–147.

Lau, N.-C., White, G. H., and Jenne, R. L. (1981). Circulation statistics for the extra-tropical Northern Hemisphere based on NMC analyses. *NCAR Tech. Note* **NCAR/TN-171**.

Lorenz, E. N. (1955). Available potential energy and the maintenance of the general circulation. *Tellus* **7**, 157–167.

Manabe, S., and Terpstra, T. B. (1974). The effects of mountains on the general circulation of the atmosphere as identified by numerical experiments. *J. Atmos. Sci.* **31**, 3–42.

Onsager, L. (1949). Statistical hydrodynamics. *Nuovo Cimento* **6**, Suppl., 279.

Oort, A. H. (1964). On estimates of the atmospheric energy cycle. *Mon. Weather Rev.* **92**, 482–493.

Oort, A. H. (1983). "Global Atmospheric Circulation Statistics, 1958–1973," NOAA Prof. Pap. No. 14. U.S. Govt. Printing Office, Washington, D.C.

Oort, A. H., and Rasmusson, E. M. (1971). "Atmospheric Circulation Statistics," NOAA Prof. Pap. No. 5. U.S. Govt. Printing Office, Washington, D.C.

Phillips, N. A. (1956). The general circulation of the atmosphere: A numerical experiment. *Q. J. R. Meteorol. Soc.* **82**, 123–164.

Ploshay, J. J., White, R. K., and Miyakoda, K. (1983). FGGE Level III-B Daily global analyses. Parts I–IV. *NOAA Data Rep. ERL* **GFDL-1** to **GFDL-4.**

Saltzman, B. (1963). A generalized solution for the large-scale, time-averaged perturbations in the atmosphere. *J. Atmos. Sci.* **20**, 226–235.

Saltzman, B. (1970). Large-scale atmospheric energetics in the wave-number domain. *Rev. Geophys. Space Phys.* **8**, 289–302.

Simmons, A. J., and Hoskins, B. J. (1978). The life cycles of some nonlinear baroclinic waves. *J. Atmos. Sci.* **35**, 414–432.

Simmons, A. J., Wallace, J. M., and Branstator, G. W. (1983). Barotropic wave propagation and instability, and atmospheric teleconnection patterns. *J. Atmos. Sci.* **40**, 1363–1392.

Smagorinsky, J. (1963). General circulation experiments with the primitive equations. I. The basic experiment. *Mon. Weather Rev.* **91**, 99–164.

Smagorinsky, J. (1972). The general circulation of the atmosphere. *In* "Meteorological Challenges: A History" (D. P. McIntyre, ed.), pp. 3–41. Information Canada, Ottawa.

Wallace, J. M., and Gutzler, D. S. (1981). Teleconnections in the geopotential height field during the Northern Hemisphere winter. *Mon. Weather Rev.* **109,** 785–812.

World Meteorological Organization (1963–1973). "Monthly Climatic Data for the World," Vols. 16–26. U.S. Govt. Printing Office, Washington, D.C.

BALANCE CONDITIONS
IN THE EARTH'S CLIMATE SYSTEM

Abraham H. Oort

Geophysical Fluid Dynamics Laboratory/NOAA
Princeton University
Princeton, New Jersey

1. Introduction

As in many fields of science today, the trend in climate research is toward a holistic approach of the problems encountered. Climatic problems are usually complex since several subsystems of the total climatic system — the atmosphere, oceans, cryosphere, biosphere, and solid earth — tend to be involved, as shown schematically in Fig. 1. The strong interactions and feedbacks between processes (including those due to man's activities) in the different subsystems and within each subsystem itself make it necessary to look at the picture as a whole and not only at its parts. There is a definite need for a unified approach to almost any climate problem using both observational analyses and model calculations. However, in this essay, only the diagnostic or observational approach will be discussed while the relevant interactions among the climatic subsystems are taken into account.

The diagnostic approach to climate problems may be said to have started in the late 1940s when Victor P. Starr and his co-workers at the Massachusetts Institute of Technology (MIT) and Jacob Bjerknes and Yale Mintz at the University of California at Los Angeles (UCLA), among others, started to look at upper-air observations to test the validity of the then prevailing theories of the general circulation. Through painstaking research over several decades largely on the basis of data from the years 1950 and 1957–1958 (the International Geophysical Year), a radically new picture of the atmospheric circulation emerged. In the new scheme, mid-latitude atmospheric

ADVANCES IN GEOPHYSICS, VOLUME 28A

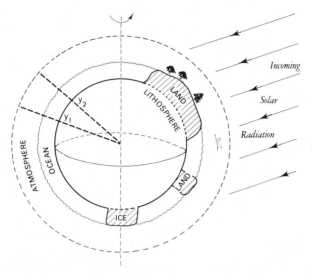

Fig. 1. Schematic diagram of the climatic system consisting of the atmosphere, oceans, cryosphere, lithosphere, and biosphere.

disturbances with time scales between 2 and 10 days were found to play a central role in transporting angular momentum, water vapor, and energy poleward, thereby fulfilling the global balance requirements (Starr and White, 1954). Another important new discovery was what Starr (1953, 1968) coined "negative viscosity" phenomena or a transfer of energy from smaller to larger scales. This phenomenon was found to occur in many different fluid systems, such as the atmospheric and oceanic jet streams, the equatorial jets in the atmospheres of the sun and Jupiter, and various laboratory experiments. The counterintuitive fact of eddies supplying energy to the mean flow seems to be a fundamental property of certain rotating fluid systems.

2. History of Observational Studies at the Geophysical Fluid Dynamics Laboratory

We will now try to sketch how, during the past two decades, the research by members of the Observational Studies Group at the GFDL has contributed to the general trend of climate research and what issues occupy our thoughts at the present time.

2.1. History of GFDL Studies Diagnosing the Atmosphere

Although numerical modeling always has been, and still is, the backbone and main thrust of research at the GFDL [see, e.g., Smagorinsky (1972,

1974 and Peixóto and Oort (1984)], the importance of simultaneously pursuing purely theoretical and observational studies was recognized early in the GFDL's history. In fact, following a joint meeting in November 1963 between representatives of GFDL/ESSA (Environmental Science Services Administration) [including Robert M. White, the administrator of the ESSA, Joseph Smagorinsky, and Syukuro Manabe], members of the Planetary Circulations Project at MIT (including Victor P. Starr, the director of the project, and Abraham H. Oort), and representatives of the data-processing group at Travelers Research Center (TRC) (including Barry Saltzman, G. S. Rao, and Howard Frazier), Joseph Smagorinsky, as director of the GFDL, offered the MIT group substantial amounts of time on the Stretch computer to reduce and analyze the available rawinsonde data for a 5-year period. The switch from operations that were basically hand operations to the use of a computer was essential because the planned project represented a task practically impossible to perform by hand — namely, to collect, check, reduce, and analyze a huge amount of raw observations, on the order of 100 million pieces of information.

The group of researchers at the GFDL working on diagnosing the atmosphere during the 1960s included Ernest C. Kung (now at the University of Missouri) and Eugene M. Rasmusson [now at the Climate Analysis Center of the National Meteorological Center (NMC)]. Their work was at first limited to interpreting portions of the 5-year statistics generated by the MIT group, mainly in terms of the balances of water and kinetic energy over the North American continent [e.g., Kung (1967) and Rasmusson (1968)]. However, in the late 1960s Gene Rasmusson and Abraham H. Oort began to take a more active part in the whole data-processing project. Not unexpectedly, the transition to the new "objective" data reduction and analysis schemes was difficult and required a long period of experimentation. Thus, the final statistics for the 5-year period, May 1958 through April 1963, only became available about 8 years after the MIT–GFDL–TRC project had started [e.g., Oort and Rasmusson (1971)], although some results were reported earlier [e.g., Starr (1968) and Starr et al. (1970)]. During the 1970s the 5-year data set was further extended at the GFDL to a 15-year record covering the period, May 1958 through April 1973, and enlarged from a hemispheric to a global data set. The outcome of this 15-year analysis endeavor has only recently been reported by Oort (1983). Besides a detailed description of month-to-month and regional variability during a typical year, many measures of interannual variability were analyzed and presented, adding a new dimension to the description of the climate in the atmosphere. Among other results, an overall similarity between the processes in the Northern and Southern Hemispheres was found to exist (Oort and Peixóto, 1983a,b). Significant differences, such as the greater intensity of the zonal circulation and the weaker stationary eddies in the Southern Hemisphere, relate to interhemispheric differences in the physiography of the Earth's surface (for the Northern Hemisphere predominently land in the mid-latitudes and ocean in the polar latitudes, whereas for the Southern Hemisphere the situation is reversed).

Until the time that the computer was introduced in data reduction and analysis, the normal procedure had been to compute station statistics by using a simple desk calculator, to plot the computed station values on hemispheric maps, to analyze these maps by hand, and finally to read off values at a regular latitude–longitude grid for further calculations of variances, transports, etc. This procedure had the advantage that, along the way, easy checks could be made by the researchers for reasonableness of the results. However, the process was time-consuming and therefore permitted only the reduction of a limited number of variables for a small number of levels.

Some of the error detection was more difficult in the new system than before, but, overall, the new procedures provided more flexibility and consistency in the analysis. It then became possible to analyze almost any parameter of interest on a monthly basis and to do this for many levels in the vertical and many time periods so that one could obtain a much more detailed picture of the climatic processes occurring in the atmosphere. In our studies at the GFDL we used an objective analysis scheme that fitted a relatively simple two-dimensional surface to the data at each horizontal level in order to interpolate from station data to a regular grid. Our goal was to obtain final fields that would fairly closely approximate the fields analyzed by hand by an experienced meteorologist. The particular interpolation scheme used was introduced by Harris et al. (1966) and is further described by Rosen et al. (1979) and Oort (1983). The field at grid points with no nearby station data was obtained by solving Poisson's equation at the unknown grid points while keeping the station grid-point values as fixed internal boundary values. The forcing term in the Poisson equation was the Laplacian of a first guess field that was initially set to the zonal average of the station data. After smoothing of the analyzed field, the departures at the data points were calculated, and the analysis cycle was repeated for the departures. Addition of the departure field to the initial analysis field then provided a new analysis. It should be added that such an interpolation procedure is only feasible for station statistics that are averaged over a month or, preferably, over a longer period. The reason is that temporal averaging removes the smaller, synoptic-scale variability and leads to larger-scale patterns on the mean maps, which can be defined fairly well by the rawinsonde network, at least over the continents. On the other hand, on daily weather maps the same procedure cannot be used because of the prevalence of small-scale features that get lost over the data-gap regions.

In the case of daily analyses, one probably has to use a mathematical–

physical model of the atmosphere that, in a meteorologically reasonable way, extrapolates by propagating the disturbances through data-gap regions. In those data-gap regions, the 6- or 12-hour forecast values are accepted as being correct, whereas in the data-rich regions, the forecast values are replaced by real observed values. This is an attractive approach because basic, physical relationships, rather than just mathematical fitting, are being used to interpolate or extrapolate. However, a drawback is that there are deficiencies in the forecast models that tend to bias the statistics in a certain direction away from the real world. Since the numerical models and mathematical fitting each have a different bias, both approaches should probably be pursued at the present time [see, e.g., Lau and Oort (1981, 1982) and Rosen *et al.* (1985)].

2.2. History of GFDL Studies Diagnosing the Oceans and the Solid Earth

The fundamental role of the oceans in the Earth's climate was recognized early by Joseph Smagorinsky when he asked Kirk Bryan in 1961 to join the GFDL and to construct one of the first general circulation models of the world ocean. However, besides Sol Hellerman's (1967) widely used wind stress maps based on real wind data over the entire globe, little diagnostic work was done at the GFDL on the oceans until the early 1970s. At that time, Syd Levitus began his systematic analysis of the world ocean. In a joint study with Tom Vonder Haar from Colorado State University (CSU), we used the CSU satellite-radiation data and our observed atmospheric storage and energy flux data to show by indirect means that the oceans transport more heat poleward in low latitudes than was previously believed (Vonder Haar and Oort, 1973). Later, in part on the basis of Levitus's analyses of the ocean temperature structure (Levitus, 1982), we were able to establish the overwhelming importance of the oceans also in the seasonal storage and the seasonal variation of the transport of heat (Oort and Vonder Haar, 1976; Ellis *et al.*, 1978; Carissimo *et al.*, 1985). Although the precise values are still in doubt [see, e.g., Hall and Bryden (1981) and Hastenrath (1982, 1984)], it has become obvious that one cannot discuss the climate in the atmosphere without considering what happens in the oceans. The interconnectedness of the atmosphere and oceans is, we may say, now an observed fact.

The interactions between the atmosphere and the solid earth are perhaps more subtle than those between the atmosphere and the oceans. For example, there is, on a year-to-year and even on a seasonal basis, very little storage of energy and water in the continents. On the other hand, there is no doubt that the solid earth does play a fundamental role in the overall angular momentum balance. Already in the 1950s, seasonal changes in the angular momentum of the Earth (determined from astronomical observations of the length of day) were found to correlate well with changes in the angular momentum of the global atmosphere [Mintz and Munk (1951); for more recent results, see Rosen and Salstein (1983) and Rosen *et al.* (1984)]. Such a (negative) correlation would be expected in view of the conservation of total angular momentum in the Earth–atmosphere–ocean system when the action of external torques as well as the storage of the angular momentum in the oceans can be neglected, which seems to be the case at the period of seasons (Lambeck, 1980).

However, it would be premature to conclude that the oceans are not important in the overall cycle of angular momentum or in the exchange between the atmosphere and the solid earth since, first of all, the oceans cover most of the globe and, furthermore, the strongest surface winds tend to occur over the oceans. In fact, we shall argue in the following section that the oceans play a central role in handing over angular momentum from the atmosphere to the land masses.

3. GLOBAL BALANCE REQUIREMENTS FOR ANGULAR MOMENTUM, WATER, AND ENERGY

A useful way of diagnosing the climatic system is through the analysis of the cycles of angular momentum, water substance, and energy. Through the analysis of the pathways of these three central and very distinct physical quantities, the interrelationships among the various climatic subsystems will become clearer. Without going into the details of the various processes, we shall sketch both the prevailing, well-accepted views and some of our new, more "revolutionary" ideas on how angular momentum, water substance, and energy are cycled through the climatic system.

3.1. Angular Momentum Cycle

As usual, the absolute angular momentum per unit mass about the Earth's axis may be defined by

$$M = \Omega a^2 \cos^2 \phi + u\, a \cos \phi \qquad (3.1)$$

where Ω is the angular velocity of the Earth, a mean radius of the Earth, ϕ latitude, and u the zonal (west-to-east) component of the wind. The first term is often called Ω-angular momentum and the second one relative angular momentum.

Angular momentum balance in the atmosphere per unit volume can be expressed by the equation

$$\rho(dM/dt) = -(\partial p/\partial \lambda) + F_\lambda\, a \cos \phi \qquad (3.2)$$

where ρ is density, t time, p pressure, λ longitude, and F_λ the zonal (eastward) component of the frictional force. Equation (3.2) shows that the rate of change of absolute angular momentum moving with the unit volume is balanced by the sum of the pressure and friction torques acting on the volume. The friction force can be written as the divergence of a stress tensor, in which the vertical component near the Earth's surface is of greatest importance.

When integrated vertically in the atmosphere throughout a unit area column, the pressure and friction terms on the right-hand side of (3.2) reduce to the mountain and friction torques, respectively, which together link the atmosphere with the underlying surface [e.g., Oort and Peixóto (1983a)]. If in addition to the vertical integration we integrate in the zonal direction over a latitudinal belt between y_1 and y_2, Eq. (3.2) becomes

$$\iiint_{\text{belt}} \rho\, \frac{dM}{dt}\, dV = \mathscr{P} + \mathscr{T} \qquad (3.3)$$

where the mountain torque reduces (after carrying out the integration over λ) to   REPLACE WITH $p = 0$

$$\mathscr{P} = \int_0^\infty \int_{y_1}^{y_2} \sum_i (p_E^i - p_W^i)\, a \cos \phi\, dy\, dz \qquad (3.4a)$$

the friction torque to

$$\mathscr{T} = \iint_{\substack{\text{surface} \\ \text{earth}}} \tau_0\, a \cos \phi\, dx\, dy \qquad (3.4b)$$

$p_E^i - p_W^i$ is the pressure difference between the east and west sides of the ith mountain range and τ_0 the surface friction stress in the belt [for a slightly different formulation, see Wahr and Oort (1984)].

After expansion of the total derivative the final balance equation can be written in the form

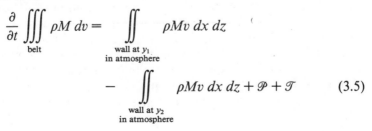

$$\frac{\partial}{\partial t} \iiint_{\text{belt}} \rho M\, dv = \iint_{\substack{\text{wall at } y_1 \\ \text{in atmosphere}}} \rho M v\, dx\, dz$$

$$- \iint_{\substack{\text{wall at } y_2 \\ \text{in atmosphere}}} \rho M v\, dx\, dz + \mathscr{P} + \mathscr{T} \qquad (3.5)$$

where the first two terms on the right-hand side of (3.5) indicate the inflow and outflow of angular momentum through the latitudinal walls, and the last two terms indicate the surface sources and sinks through the mountain and friction torques, respectively. Usually the time rate of change on the left-hand side of (3.5) can be neglected. We may mention that since the net mass flow across latitude circles is negligible, the main contribution to the inflow and outflow of angular momentum has to be in the form of relative angular momentum, i.e., through a correlation between the v (northward) and u (eastward) components of the wind.

The observed cycle of relative angular momentum computed from direct wind observations in the atmosphere (i.e., from $\rho[vu]a \cos \phi$) is shown in Fig. 2 for annual-mean conditions. Westerly angular momentum is extracted from the Earth's surface (mainly from the oceans) in the tropics, transported upward in the tropical Hadley cells, then transported poleward in the upper troposphere, and finally returned down to the Earth's surface in the middle latitudes. In the Northern Hemisphere mid-latitudes, large-scale eddies accomplish the northward transport by a predominant SW – NE tilt of the wave systems, and in the Southern Hemisphere they are responsible for the southward transport through a predominant SE – NW tilt. This scheme, shown in Fig. 3, was presented first by Starr (1948). It leads to the following relations between the u and v components of the wind: $[v^*u^*] > 0$ in the Northern and $[v^*u^*] < 0$ in the Southern Hemisphere, where the brackets indicate a zonal average and the asterisks departures from the zonal average. These conditions are required for the eddies to transfer angular momentum meridionally from the equator to the poles. We may conclude that the atmospheric branch of the cycle of angular momentum as depicted in Fig. 2 is by now reasonably well described and understood. However, almost nothing is known about the terrestrial branch of the cycle. Some speculations will be given in the remainder of this section.

We shall start with the general statement that, for global balance, there has to be an equatorward return flow of angular momentum (see Fig. 4) within either the oceans or the solid earth, or both, from the middle to low latitudes, equal but with opposite sign to the transport in the atmosphere. The first problem is now to determine what the relative roles of the oceans and the solid earth are in this process. To answer this question we will make a rough comparison between the maximum meridional transports to be expected in the oceans and those measured in the atmosphere at middle latitudes. Typical wind velocities in the atmosphere are on the order of 10 m s^{-1} and the directly observed (and therefore reliable) vertical and zonal mean values of the northward flux of momentum in the atmosphere $[vu]$ in the middle latitudes are about 10 m^2 s^{-2}. On the other hand, in the oceans, typical current velocities are much weaker than in the atmosphere, i.e., on the order

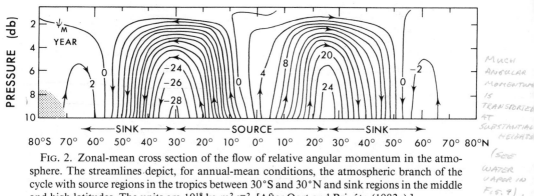

FIG. 2. Zonal-mean cross section of the flow of relative angular momentum in the atmosphere. The streamlines depict, for annual-mean conditions, the atmospheric branch of the cycle with source regions in the tropics between 30°S and 30°N and sink regions in the middle and high latitudes. The units are 10^{18} kg m² s⁻². [After Oort and Peixóto (1983a).]

MUCH ANGULAR MOMENTUM IS TRANSPORTED AT SUBSTANTIAL HEIGHTS (SEE WATER VAPOR IN FIG. 9).

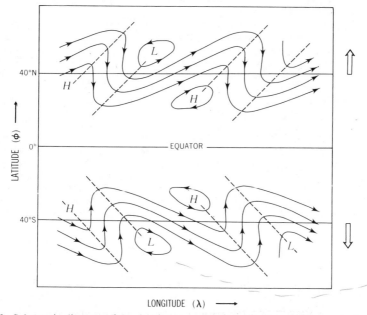

LOW WITHIN RIDGE IN STREAMLINES

EQUATORIAL VIEWPOINT

FIG. 3. Schematic diagram of the dominant mechanism of poleward transport of westerly angular momentum by (quasi-horizontal) eddies in the mid-latitudes. Note the preferred SW–NE tilt of the streamlines in the Northern Hemisphere and the SE–NW tilt in the Southern Hemisphere leading to a poleward transport in both hemispheres through the correlation between the v and u components of the wind.

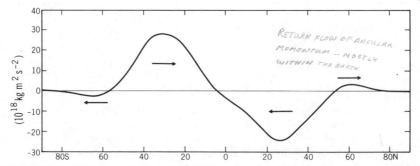

FIG. 4. The annual-mean northward flux of angular momentum in the oceans and/or land (the "terrestrial" branch of the cycle) in units of 10^{18} kg m^2 s^{-2} required to close the angular momentum cycle.

of 0.01 to 0.1 m s^{-1}. Therefore we may expect oceanic $[vu]$ values of about 0.001 m^2 s^{-2} or, in other words, values a factor of 10,000 smaller than in the atmosphere. Taking into account the greater mass of the oceans, i.e., about 1000 m of water in the oceans versus 10 m of equivalent water mass in the atmosphere, we find that the oceanic transports are too weak by about a factor of 100. Thus a different mechanism for the equatorward transport of angular momentum must be found.

What happens, we think, is that the oceans transport the angular momentum only *laterally* within each latitude belt, and not across the latitude circles. In fact, the oceans must transfer the angular momentum to the continents in the same belt, thereby acting as intermediary or hand-over agents between the atmosphere and the continents. This, we speculate, takes place through "continental torques" exerted by the oceans through raised or lowered sea levels along the continental margins in a fashion comparable to the pressure torques across the mountains in the atmosphere. This idea is sketched in Fig. 5a,b. In mathematical terms, the continental torque is given by

$$\mathscr{C} = \int_{-D}^{\eta} \int_{y_1}^{y_2} \sum_i (p_E^i - p_W^i)\, a \cos \phi \, dy \, dz \qquad (3.6)$$

which represents an integral over the entire ocean bottom in the latitude belt between y_1 and y_2. In expression (3.6), $p_E^i - p_W^i$, the difference in bottom pressure between the east and west sides of the ith continent or ith submarine mountain ridge, is a function of z. The integration is carried out with respect to z along the boundaries of all continents and marine ridges in the latitudinal belt between D, the maximum depth of the ocean in the latitude belt, and η, the maximum height of sea level above the geoid. The main contribu-

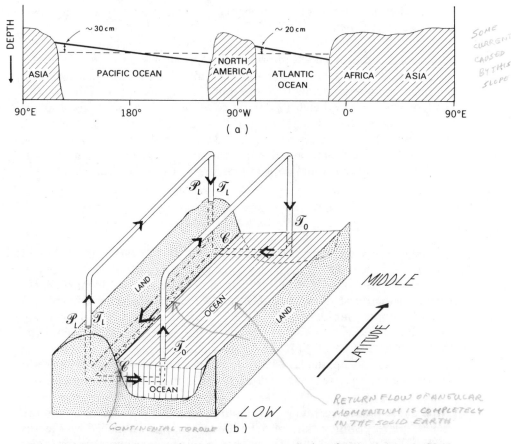

FIG. 5. (a) Schematic diagram of the observed east–west sloping of sea level along the 25°N latitude circle. The resulting pressure differences across the low-latitude continents together with similar differences (but of opposite sign) across the mid-latitude continents are suggested to lead to continental torques needed to satisfy global angular momentum constraints. (b) Schematic diagram of the cycle of angular momentum in the atmosphere–ocean–solid earth system. In the atmosphere, there is a continuous poleward flow of westerly angular momentum with sources in low latitudes through the mountain and friction torques over land $\mathscr{P}_L$ and $\mathscr{T}_L$ and through the friction torque over the oceans $\mathscr{T}_0$. The corresponding sinks of westerly angular momentum are found in the middle and high latitudes. When we consider the atmosphere plus the oceans as the total fluid envelope of the Earth, the low-latitude sources and mid-latitude sinks are given by the three terms $\mathscr{P}_L$, $\mathscr{T}_L$, and the continental torque $\mathscr{C}$. The return equatorward flow of angular momentum must occur entirely in the solid earth (land).

tion to this pressure torque is probably due to the difference in sea level across each continent.

Because the actual height of sea level is not known globally, we have to make some simplifying assumptions. First of all, we only include torque contributions from levels above 1000 m depth. This is equivalent with assuming that $p_E^i = p_W^i$ below 1000 m depth. We then assume that the value of sea level (or dynamic height) η computed at the point at which the 1000-m depth level intersects the continent represents the height of sea level for all points between the intersection point and the nearest coast (taken along the same latitude circle). This is a drastic assumption, but it enables us to compute everywhere the actual bottom pressure p_D from the hydrostatic equation

$$p_D = \rho_0 g \eta + \int_{-D}^{0} \rho_0 g \, dz$$

using the observed density of sea water ρ_0, which may vary with depth and geographical location.

A cursory look at a map of mean sea level as estimated from dynamic height calculations by Levitus and Oort (1977) and reproduced here as Fig. 6 seems to support our ideas. Differences in sea level on the order of 50 cm are found between the west and east coasts of the major continents. Thus the trade winds tend to pile up the water on their east coasts, leading to a westward torque on the low-latitude continents. Similarly an eastward torque would be exerted in the middle latitudes where westerly winds dominate.

For a quantitative estimate of the continental torques we have used more recent but very similar data of dynamic topography published by Levitus (1982). The computed meridional profile of the continental torque $\mathscr{C}$ is presented by the dashed curve in Fig. 7.

The total required surface torque $\mathscr{P}_L + \mathscr{T}_L + \mathscr{T}_0$ as derived with the aid of Eq. (3.5) using atmospheric data only (see Fig. 4) is also presented in Fig. 7 as a solid curve. The agreement between the two curves is remarkable because of (1) the drastic simplifications made in computing the oceanic curve and (2) the neglect of $\mathscr{P}_L$ and $\mathscr{T}_L$ in the comparison. Nevertheless, it gives support to the hypothesis of a dominant lateral exchange of angular momentum between the oceans and the continents as advanced earlier or, in other words, $\mathscr{T}_0 \approx \mathscr{C}$.

Summarizing the previous discussions, we have shown that the oceanic stresses $\mathscr{T}_0$ are almost completely applied on the continents at the same latitudes through the $\mathscr{C}$ term and that, therefore, the total torques on the continents consist of the usual mountain and friction torques at the atmosphere–land interface combined with the newly discovered continen-

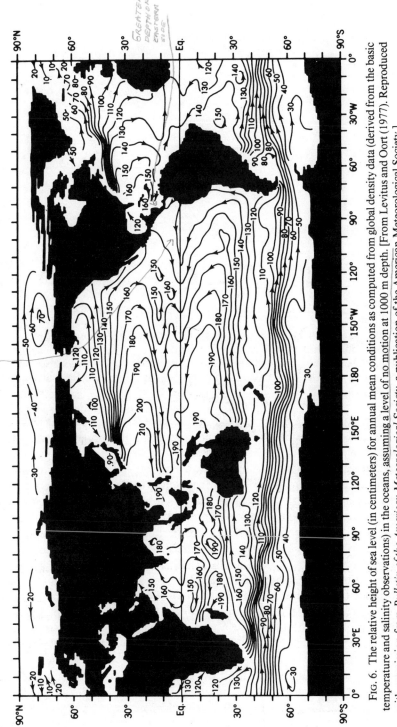

FIG. 6. The relative height of sea level (in centimeters) for annual mean conditions as computed from global density data (derived from the basic temperature and salinity observations) in the oceans, assuming a level of no motion at 1000 m depth. [From Levitus and Oort (1977). Reproduced with permission from *Bulletin of the American Meteorological Society*, a publication of the American Meteorological Society.]

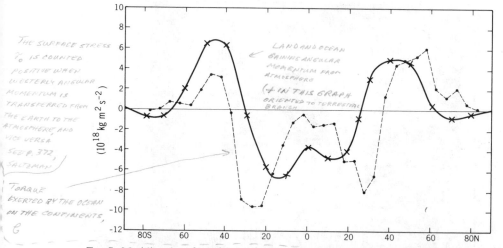

Handwritten margin notes (left side, by figure):
THE SURFACE STRESS τ_0 IS COUNTED POSITIVE WHEN WESTERLY ANGULAR MOMENTUM IS TRANSFERRED FROM THE EARTH TO THE ATMOSPHERE AND VICE VERSA SEE P. 372, SALTZMAN

TORQUE EXERTED BY THE OCEAN ON THE CONTINENTS, $\mathscr{C}$

Handwritten notes within figure:
LAND AND OCEAN GAINING ANGULAR MOMENTUM FROM ATMOSPHERE (+ IN THIS GRAPH ORIENTED TO TERRESTRIAL BRANCH

FIG. 7. Meridional profiles of the surface torque exerted by the atmosphere on the oceans and land (solid line), $\mathscr{P}_L + \mathscr{T}_L + \mathscr{T}_0$, based on the data in Fig. 2, and the torque exerted by the oceans (due to sloping sea level) on the continents (dashed line) $\mathscr{C}$, based on the oceanographic data in Fig. 6 with some further assumptions (see text). If there were no net surface torques over land ($\mathscr{P}_L + \mathscr{T}_L = 0$), and if we disregard observational inaccuracies, the two curves should almost overlap ($\mathscr{C} \approx \mathscr{T}_0$; see text). The values represent integrals over 5° latitude belts in units of 10^{18} kg m² s⁻².

tal pressure torque at the ocean–land interface. However, we have still left unanswered the question of how the required equatorward transports of angular momentum actually take place.

One fact is clear by now, namely, that the required return flow of angular momentum from middle to low latitudes has to occur almost completely *within* the solid earth. A possible mechanism that suggests itself is by a preferred tilting of the motions along faults in the continents, i.e., through relative SE–NW-oriented displacements in the crust in the Northern Hemisphere mid-latitudes and through preferred SW–NE displacements along faults in the Southern Hemisphere mid-latitudes. For example, the observed SE to NW tilt in the displacements along the San Andreas fault and the SW to NE tilt in the New Zealand fault system (see Fig. 8) are in the right sense and would lead to a correlation comparable to that in the atmospheric waves shown earlier in Fig. 3. Of course, the processes in the Earth's crust would be much more localized, extremely slow, and probably of an intermittent nature.

If in the future our speculations are found to be correct, the implications could be important not only in a practical, but also in a philosophical sense. The continental torques would link, in a clear manner, the motions in the atmosphere and oceans with some of the motions in the solid earth's crust.

Handwritten margin notes (left side, lower):
SEE P. 84

EARTH, STRESSED BY THE WIND AND OCEANS CAN RELIEVE SOME OF THIS FORCE WITH A RETURN TRANSPORT.

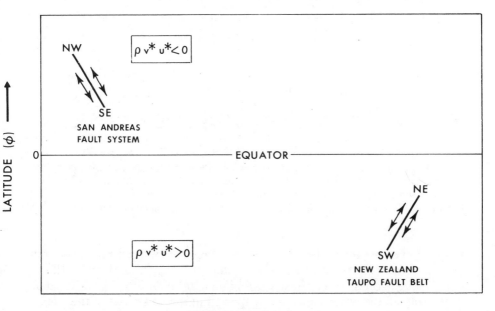

FIG. 8. Two examples of typical fault systems in the continental land masses that could lead to SE–NW mass shifts in the Northern Hemisphere and SW–NE shifts in the Southern Hemisphere required to (occasionally) relieve the angular momentum (atmosphere–ocean) torques imposed on the continents.

Their future study might lead to a better understanding, and perhaps also prediction, of how certain stress patterns may build up in the Earth's crust and how these stresses may eventually be released, perhaps leading to the intermittent occurrence of earthquakes along the fault zones. However, we cannot extend our discussion to very long time scales, because the stresses induced by atmospheric and oceanic torques are many orders of magnitude smaller than those thought to be responsible for most geological phenomena (e.g., those related to continental drift).

3.2. Water Cycle

The climatic element of greatest importance to man is undoubtedly water in its three phases — vapor, liquid, and solid. As before in the case of angular momentum, we can show, on the basis of rawinsonde data of $\rho[vq]$, how in a zonal-mean cross section water is transported meridionally and vertically in the atmosphere. The quantity q indicates here the specific humidity of the air. The so-called atmospheric branch of the hydrological cycle is presented

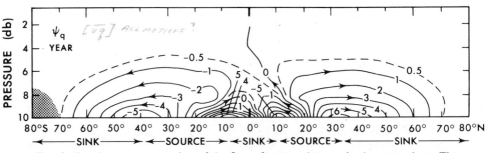

FIG. 9. Zonal-mean cross section of the flow of water substance in the atmosphere. The streamlines depict, for annual-mean conditions, the atmospheric branch of the hydrological cycle with source regions in the subtropics and sink regions in equatorial [intertropical convergence zone (ITCZ)] and middle latitudes. Units are 10^8 kg s^{-1}. [From Peixóto and Oort (1983).]

in Fig. 9. It shows the well-known sources of water in the subtropical oceans of both hemispheres and the sinks in the intertropical and mid-latitude convergence zones. In contrast with angular momentum, we notice that practically all the water vapor is transported in the lower half of the troposphere.

Similarly, as was done before in case of the angular momentum balance in (3.5), the balance of water substance for a latitudinal belt extending throughout the depth of the atmosphere can be written in the form

$$\frac{\partial}{\partial t} \iiint_{\text{belt}} \rho q \, dV = \iint_{\substack{\text{wall at } y_1 \\ \text{in atmosphere}}} \rho q v \, dx \, dz - \iint_{\substack{\text{wall at } y_2 \\ \text{in atmosphere}}} \rho q v \, dx \, dz$$

$$+ \iint_{\text{sfc}} (E - P) \, dx \, dy \qquad (3.7)$$

where E is the rate of evaporation from the Earth's surface and P the rate of precipitation at the surface. Equation (3.7) shows that the time rate of change of water vapor in the belt is balanced by the inflow or outflow of water vapor at the northern and southern boundaries and the evaporation minus precipitation at the surface boundary. Some smaller terms, such as the time rate of change of water in both liquid and solid forms and their horizontal transports, are neglected in (3.7). Usually, the time rate of change of water vapor can also be neglected compared with the three terms on the right-hand side of (3.7).

For an overall balance there should be compensating return flows in the terrestrial branch of the hydrological cycle, where the flows have to be from the equator and mid-latitudes into the subtropics of both hemispheres. The conservation of liquid water for the terrestrial part of the latitudinal belt (neglecting its rate of storage) can be written as

$$\iint\limits_{\substack{\text{surface of} \\ \text{earth}}} (E - P)\, dx\, dy = \iint\limits_{\substack{\text{wall at } y_1 \\ \text{in ocean}}} \rho_0 v\, dx\, dz - \iint\limits_{\substack{\text{wall at } y_2 \\ \text{in ocean}}} \rho_0 v\, dx\, dz$$

+ river and
subterranean
flow into belt   (3.8)

where ρ_0 indicates the density of ocean water. Having computed the evaporation-minus-precipitation term on the left-hand side of (3.8) from the atmospheric flux data using (3.7), we can calculate the required meridional flow of liquid water from (3.8), starting with zero flux at one of the poles. Figure 10 shows the resulting flows that may occur through river and subterranean flows of water in and on the continents and through net north–south transports of water in the oceans. The salinity distribution at the ocean surface results, to a large extent, from the local evaporation–precipitation process and, therefore, reflects largely the distribution of the source and sink regions for atmospheric water vapor. Of course, the actual salinity values are also affected by the oceanic convergence of relatively fresh or saline water and the inflow of fresh river water.

One of the questions we are faced with presently concerns the contribution of the ocean and land areas to the global balance. The problem is illustrated in Fig. 11, taken from Bryan and Oort (1984). Shown are the observed profiles of evaporation minus precipitation $(E - P)$ computed from the total water vapor divergence field integrated separately over ocean (Fig. 11a) and

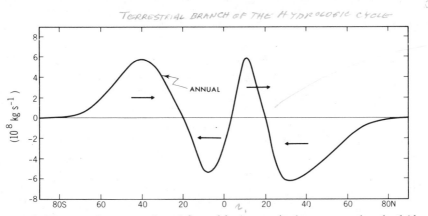

FIG. 10. The annual-mean northward flow of fresh water in the oceans and on land (the terrestrial branch of the hydrological cycle) in units of 10^8 kg s^{-1} required to close the cycle.

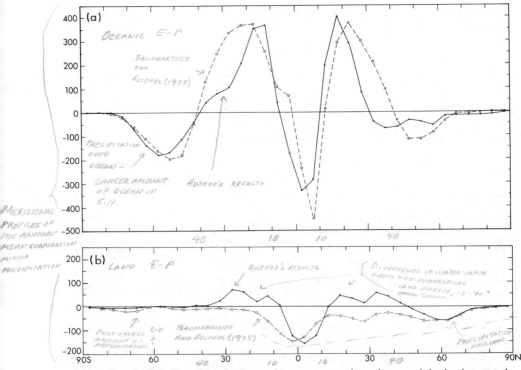

FIG. 11. Meridional profiles of the annual-mean evaporation minus precipitation integrated over (a) the oceanic portions and (b) the land portions for 5° latitude belts in units of 10^3 m^3 s^{-1}. Shown are our results (solid curves) derived from the atmospheric flux data in Fig. 9 and the results of Baumgartner and Reichel (1975) (dashed curves) based on surface observations of precipitation and (tentative) evaporation rates calculated by using a bulk aerodynamic method. [After Bryan and Oort (1984). Reproduced with permission from *JGR, Journal of Geophysical Research* **89** 11,717–11,730, copyright by the American Geophysical Union.]

land areas (Fig. 11b) in each latitude belt. The sum of the two contributions should be equal to the derivative of the required transport curve shown before in Fig. 10. A strange result is the systematic divergence of water vapor from the subtropical land masses between about 10 and 40° latitude in each hemisphere. Since the meridional flow of water in rivers seems negligible [see Hellerman (1974)], our results would suggest some sort of subterranean inflow of water into the subtropics. Conceivably such a transport could take place from the equatorial zone, from mid-latitudes, or through a lateral seepage of ocean water into the continents.

Starr and Peixóto (1958) were the first to point out this issue in their paper on the hydrology of deserts. Even though 25 years have passed since their paper was published, this is still a controversial issue. Estimates of $E - P$ based on conventional surface observations and on certain assumed relationships by Baumgartner and Reichel (1975) are also shown in Fig. 11. These authors do not find a subtropical divergence over the continents. However, the surface balance method they used is unreliable over the continents because, first of all, E could not (and still cannot) be measured directly and also because various adjustments were made to E and P in order to make the results look "reasonable." Of course, our method also has its drawbacks, namely, that the data network is sparse spatially and may be biased by the only once or twice a day sampling. We intend to further investigate these questions in a later study using the improved data sets for 1979, the year of the First GARP (Global Atmosphere Research Programme) Global Experiment (FGGE).

If in future studies the present results were substantiated, the implied strong subsurface transports of water in the continents would be an important new element in the field of hydrology. Therefore this issue warrants further investigation.

3.3. Energy Cycle

The flow of energy in the atmosphere is shown in a zonal-mean cross section in Fig. 12 based on rawinsonde date of $[v(\rho e + p)]$, where e is the total energy (potential + internal + kinetic + latent) and p the atmospheric pressure. The distribution of net incoming or outgoing radiation as measured by satellite from Campbell and Vonder Haar (1980) was specified at the top of the diagram. This radiation forms the ultimate driving force for almost all circulations in the climatic system. The tilting of the streamlines away from the vertical in Fig. 12 is due to the horizontal transports of energy as measured by the rawinsonde network. It is, by now, well established that mean meridional circulations are responsible for the transports at low latitudes and

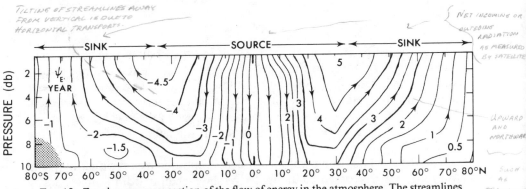

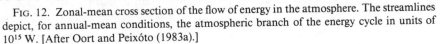

FIG. 12. Zonal-mean cross section of the flow of energy in the atmosphere. The streamlines depict, for annual-mean conditions, the atmospheric branch of the energy cycle in units of 10^{15} W. [After Oort and Peixóto (1983a).]

the large-scale, quasi-horizontal eddies for the transports at high latitudes. To ensure overall balance, the energy that reaches the surface in the tropics has to be transported poleward in the oceans, mainly in the form of sensible heat.

The energy balance in the atmospheric branch of a latitudinal belt extending throughout the depth of the atmosphere can be expressed as

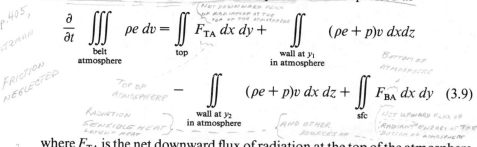

$$\frac{\partial}{\partial t} \iiint_{\substack{\text{belt}\\\text{atmosphere}}} \rho e \, dv = \iint_{\text{top}} F_{\text{TA}} \, dx \, dy + \iint_{\substack{\text{wall at } y_1\\\text{in atmosphere}}} (\rho e + p)v \, dx \, dz$$

$$- \iint_{\substack{\text{wall at } y_2\\\text{in atmosphere}}} (\rho e + p)v \, dx \, dz + \iint_{\text{sfc}} F_{\text{BA}} \, dx \, dy \quad (3.9)$$

where F_{TA} is the net downward flux of radiation at the top of the atmosphere and F_{BA} the net upward flux of energy at the bottom of the atmosphere. Equation (3.9) shows that the rate of change of energy in a belt is balanced by the inflow and outflow of energy through the top boundary, the vertical walls, and the bottom boundary, as well as by pressure work at the boundaries. For annual mean conditions, the term on the left-hand side of (3.9) can be neglected, but usually not for shorter periods.

The energy balance in the terrestrial branch of a latitudinal belt extending throughout the depth of the oceans can be written in the form

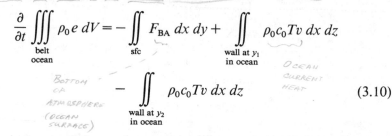

$$\frac{\partial}{\partial t} \iiint_{\substack{\text{belt}\\\text{ocean}}} \rho_0 e \, dV = -\iint_{\text{sfc}} F_{\text{BA}} \, dx \, dy + \iint_{\substack{\text{wall at } y_1\\\text{in ocean}}} \rho_0 c_0 T v \, dx \, dz$$

$$- \iint_{\substack{\text{wall at } y_2\\\text{in ocean}}} \rho_0 c_0 T v \, dx \, dz \quad (3.10)$$

where c_0 is the specific heat of ocean water. In Eq. (3.10) the rate of change of energy is now balanced by the input or output of energy at the ocean surface and by the horizontal inflow and outflow of heat by ocean currents. For annual-mean conditions, the time rate of change term can be neglected. However, for seasonal estimates, the heat storage in the ocean is extremely important; it tends to balance for a large part the net input of energy at the ocean surface.

The required oceanic transport of heat computed as a residual by using (3.9) and (3.10) is presented in Fig. 13. As shown before from similar data by Vonder Haar and Oort (1973) and Trenberth (1979), we find a poleward

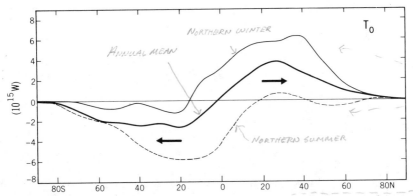

FIG. 13. Meridional profiles of the northward transport of energy in the oceans for annual mean (thick solid line), northern winter (thin solid line) and northern summer (dashed line) conditions in units of 10^{15} W. The transport values were evaluated as a residual using the planetary energy balance requirements. [After Carissimo *et al.* (1985). Reproduced with permission from *Journal of Physical Oceanography*, a publication of the American Meteorological Society.]

transport of heat that is stronger than what many oceanographers believe it should be. Even more controversy arises when we consider the seasonal transport curves for December–February and June–August also shown in Fig. 13. These curves were computed by Carissimo *et al.* (1985) from net radiation data, atmospheric energy storage and transport data, and oceanic heat storage data as a residual in the energy balance equation. It is clear that we need a huge seasonal variation in the oceanic heat transport to satisfy the balance requirements. The discrepancies with the established oceanographic views of a weak seasonal variation are so large that further research is very much needed to find out what causes the discrepancies. In our residual method the oceanic heat storage estimates are most uncertain followed by the radiation data. On the other hand, the arguments by oceanographers for weak heat transports are based largely on very limited data or on theoretical considerations.

4. SUMMARY

In the first part of this review a historical description was given of some of the diagnostic studies conducted at the GFDL during the past two decades. Necessarily this work has led to further questions and issues. The three, in the author's opinion, most pressing remaining issues were discussed in the second part of this review. They deal with the balance requirements imposed on the terrestrial branch of the climate system by the atmospheric branch. This last branch is fairly well known from atmospheric *in situ* data.

(a) In the first issue, we present evidence that the required return flow of angular momentum from the middle latitudes to the tropics is not taking place in the oceans but has to take place in the continents. There seems to be a lateral exchange of angular momentum between the oceans and the continents through changes in sea level, leading to the so-called "continental torque." A possible way for the meridional transfer of angular momentum to occur within the solid earth is through the preferential displacements of mass along fault zones in the NW–SE direction in the Northern Hemisphere and in the NE–SW direction in the Southern Hemisphere. If verified from direct observations, the complete cycle of angular momentum would form another beautiful example of the strong link between the atmosphere, the oceans, and the solid earth.

(b) In the second issue, we confirm the earlier findings by Starr and Peixóto (1958) of a divergence of water vapor from the subtropics both over the oceans and over land. The divergence of water vapor from the subtropical deserts is still controversial and not generally accepted. Nevertheless, a similar pattern shows up in all aerological analyses performed since 1958. The controversy arises because (indirect) *surface* balance studies do not show this divergence over the subtropical land masses. A possibility is that either our samples are biased (e.g., by inadequate sampling of the diurnal cycle) or that the surface balance methods are biased because of the use of unreliable methods to estimate evaporation and *ad hoc* corrections to ensure a balance between evaporation and precipitation over larger regions. If true, the implication of the subtropical divergence of water vapor is that large underground flows of water occur into the desert regions. Some evidence has been found for such effects (Starr and Peixóto, 1958).

(c) In the third issue, we support the earlier suggestions of a strong poleward heat transport in the world oceans and a large annual variation with huge cross-equatorial transports of heat into the winter hemisphere. Our results are in direct conflict with prevailing oceanographic views that seasonal variations tend to be small. These discrepancies require serious consideration in establishing the relative importance of the atmosphere and oceans in maintaining the present climatic conditions, both in the mean and the annual variation and in the year-to-year anomalies.

All three issues are important and unresolved and need to be addressed. Critics may say that the atmospheric data sets are biased and therefore not good enough to derive constraints for the terrestrial branches of the various cycles. This may be true. However, the counterevidence appears to be even more biased, and often based on simplified theories or assumed relationships and not on the basic balance equations and direct data as in our case.

ACKNOWLEDGMENTS

I would like to acknowledge Joe Smagorinsky, the director of the GFDL during the past three decades, for the free, intellectual, and unbiased atmosphere and space he created in the GFDL. Under these conditions it became possible for us at the GFDL to undertake and complete large projects requiring many years of work. For me, the GFDL has been, and still is, a wonderful setting with a remarkable group of people, all free to struggle and to pursue ideas for studying the Earth's climate.

I thank Gabriel Lau, Richard Rosen, David Salstein, and John Wahr for their constructive comments on the manuscript; Joyce Kennedy for typing the manuscript; and the Scientific Illustration Group at the GFDL for drafting the figures.

REFERENCES

Baumgartner, A., and Reichel, E. (1975). "The World Water Balance." Elsevier, Amsterdam.
Bryan, F., and Oort, A. H. (1984). Seasonal variation of the global water balance based on aerological data. *JGR, J. Geophys. Res.* **89**, 11,717–11,730.
Campbell, G. C., and Vonder Haar, T. H. (1980). "Climatology of Radiation Budget Measurements from Satellites," Atmos. Sci. Pap. No. 323. Dep. Atmos. Sci., Colorado State University, Fort Collins.
Carissimo, B., Oort, A. H., and Vonder Haar, T. H. (1985). On estimating the meridional energy transports in the atmosphere and oceans. *J. Phys. Oceanogr.* **15**, 82–91.
Ellis, J. S., Vonder Haar, T. H., Levitus, S., and Oort, A. H. (1978). The annual variation in the global heat balance of the earth. *JGR, J. Geophys. Res.* **83** (C4), 1958–1962.
Hall, M. M., and Bryden, H. L. (1981). Direct estimates and mechanisms of ocean heat transport. *Deep-Sea Res.* **29**, 339–359.
Harris, R. G., Thomasell, A., Jr., and Welsh, J. G. (1966). "Studies of Techniques for the Analysis and Prediction of Temperature in the Ocean. Part III. Automated Analysis and Prediction," Interim Rep. Prepared by Travelers Research Center, Inc. for U.S. Naval Oceanographic Office (Contract No. N62306-1675).
Hastenrath, S. (1982). On meridional heat transports in the World Ocean. *J. Phys. Oceanogr.* **12**, 922–927.
Hastenrath, S. (1984). On the interannual variability of poleward transport and storage of heat in the ocean-atmosphere system. *Arch. Meteorol. Geophys. Bioclimatol., Ser. A* **33**, 1–10.
Hellerman, S. (1967). An updated estimate of the wind stress on the World Ocean. *Mon. Weather Rev.* **95** (9), 607–626; see also corrections: *Ibid.* **96** (1), 63–74.
Hellerman, S. (1974). The net meridional flux of water by the oceans from evaporation and precipitation estimates (unpublished manuscript). Available from GFDL/NOAA, Princeton University, P.O. Box 308, Princeton, New Jersey, 08542.
Kung, E. C. (1967). Diurnal and long-term variations of the kinetic energy generation and dissipation for a five-year period. *Mon. Weather Rev.* **95**, 593–606.
Lambeck, K. (1980). "The Earth's Variable Rotation." Cambridge Univ. Press, London and New York.
Lau, N.-C., and Oort, A. H. (1981). A comparative study of observed Northern Hemisphere circulation statistics based on GFDL and NMC analyses. Part I. The time-mean fields. *Mon. Weather Rev.* **109**, 1380–1403.
Lau, N.-C., and Oort, A. H. (1982). A comparative study of observed Northern Hemisphere circulation statistics based on GFDL and NMC analyses. Part II. Transient eddy statistics and the energy cycle. *Mon. Weather Rev.* **110**, 889–906.

Levitus, S. (1982). "Climatological Atlas of the World Ocean," NOAA Prof. Pap. No. 13. U.S. Govt. Printing Office, Washington, D.C.

Levitus, S., and Oort, A. H. (1977). Global analysis of oceanographic data. *Bull. Am. Meteorol. Soc.* **58,** 1270–1284.

Mintz, Y., and Munk, W. (1951). The effect of winds and tides on the length of the day. *Tellus* **3,** 117–121.

Oort, A. H. (1983). "Global Atmospheric Circulation Statistics, 1958–1973," NOAA Prof. Pap. No. 14. U.S. Govt. Printing Office, Washington, D.C.

Oort, A. H., and Peixóto, J. P. (1983a). Global angular momentum and energy balance requirements from observations. *Adv. Geophys.* **25,** 355–490.

Oort, A. H., and Peixóto, J. P. (1983b). Interhemispheric comparisons based on a 15-year atmospheric data set. *Int. Conf. South. Hemisphere Meteorol., 1st, 1983,* pp. 12–16.

Oort, A. H., and Rasmusson, E. M. (1971). "Atmospheric Circulation Statistics," NOAA Prof. Pap. No. 5. U.S. Govt. Printing Office, Washington, D.C.

Oort, A. H., and Vonder Haar, T. H. (1976). On the observed annual cycle in the ocean-atmosphere heat balance over the Northern Hemisphere. *J. Phys. Oceanogr.* **6** (6), 781–800.

Peixóto, J. P., and Oort, A. H. (1983). The atmospheric branch of the hydrological cycle and climate. *In* "Variations of the Global Water Budget," (A. Street-Perrot, M. Beran, and R. Ratcliffe, ed.) pp. 5–65. Reidel Publ., Dordrecht, Netherlands.

Peixóto, J. P., and Oort, A. H. (1984). Physics of climate. *Rev. Mod. Phys.* **56** (3), 365–430.

Rasmusson, E. M. (1968). Atmospheric water vapor transport in the water balance of North America. II. Large-scale water balance investigations. *Mon. Weather Rev.* **96,** 720–734.

Rosen, R. D., and Salstein, D. A. (1983). Variations in atmospheric angular momentum on global and regional scales, and the length of day. *JGR, J. Geophys. Res.* **88** (C9), 5451–5470.

Rosen, R. D., Salstein, D. A., and Peixóto, J. P. (1979). Variability in the annual fields of large-scale atmospheric water vapor transport. *Mon. Weather Rev.* **107,** 26–37.

Rosen, R. D., Salstein, D. A., Eubanks, T. M., Dickey, J. O., and Steppe, J. A. (1984). An El Niño signal in atmospheric angular momentum and earth rotation. *Science* **225,** 411–414.

Rosen, R. D., Salstein, D. A., Peixóto, J. P., Oort, A. H., and Lau, N.-C. (1985). Circulation statistics derived from level III-b and station-based analyses during FGGE. *Mon. Weather Rev.* **113,** 65–88.

Smagorinsky, J. (1972). The general circulation of the atmosphere. *In* "Meteorological Challenges: A History" (D. P. McIntyre, ed.), pp. 3–41.

Smagorinsky, J. (1974). Global atmospheric modeling and the numerical simulation of climate. *In* "Weather and Climate Modification" (W. N. Hess, ed.), pp. 633–686. Wiley, New York.

Starr, V. P. (1948). An essay on the general circulation of the earth's atmosphere. *J. Meteorol.* **5,** 39–43.

Starr, V. P. (1953). Note concerning the nature of the large-scale eddies in the atmosphere. *Tellus* **5,** 494–598.

Starr, V. P. (1968). "Physics of Negative Viscosity Phenomena." McGraw-Hill, New York.

Starr, V. P., and Peixóto, J. P. (1958). On the global balance of water vapor and the hydrology of deserts. *Tellus* **10,** 189–194.

Starr, V. P., and White, R. M., (1954). Balance requirements of the general circulation. Air Force Cambridge Research Directorate, *Geophys. Res. Pap.* **35.**

Starr, V. P., Peixóto, J. P., and Gaut, N. E. (1970). Momentum and zonal kinetic energy balance of the atmosphere from five years of hemispheric data. *Tellus* **22,** 251–274.

Trenberth, K. E. (1979). Mean annual poleward energy transports by the oceans in the Southern Hemisphere. *Dyn. Atmos. Oceans* **4,** 57–64.

Vonder Haar, T. H., and Oort, A. H. (1973). New estimate of annual poleward energy transport by Northern Hemisphere oceans. *J. Phys. Oceanogr.* **3,** 169–172.

Wahr, J. M., and Oort, A. H. (1984). Friction- and mountain-torque estimates from global atmospheric data. *J. Atmos. Sci.* **41,** 190–204.

CLIMATE SENSITIVITY

ROBERT E. DICKINSON

National Center for Atmospheric Research*
Boulder, Colorado

1. INTRODUCTION

The term "climate sensitivity" refers to possible changes in the climate system resulting from changes in externally prescribed conditions. First, we can ask, Does the external change make a difference? Is the climate system vulnerable to the change? For example, "We need to know what kind and amount of environmental stress derived from man's activities might be tolerated by the climate system before that system would respond significantly" (Schneider and Dickinson, 1974, p. 448). Or in carrying out general circulation model (GCM) climate studies, we want to establish whether the model-simulated climate differs significantly from observed climate or whether changes in model parameterizations significantly affect the model climate [e.g., Chervin (1980, 1981)].

Second, "climate sensitivity" may mean the quantitative change of climate variables that results from some change in external conditions or prescribed model constants or parameterizations. For global average climate models whose only variable is temperature, "sensitivity" necessarily refers to the temperature change that would result from varying some aspect of the model's radiation balance. A standard measure of such a model's performance is the β or ratio of surface temperature change to an incremental change in the prescribed incident solar radiation [e.g., Manabe and Wetherald (1967), Schneider and Mass (1975), Ramanathan and Coakley (1978)].

With more elaborate GCMs, the same question of response of global

---

* The National Center for Atmospheric Research is sponsored by the National Science Foundation.

99

average temperature to solar constant change can be posed [e.g., Wetherald and Manabe (1975), Hansen *et al.* (1984)], with the added bonus of a description of changes in horizontal spatial variations in response to solar constant change.

Studies have been made of such questions as the sensitivity of an early National Center for Atmospheric Research (NCAR) GCM to changes in sea–surface temperatures imposed either globally or in zonal strips (Schneider *et al.,* 1978) or the sensitivity of the Geophysical Fluid Dynamics Laboratory (GFDL) spectral sector model to the method of ocean temperature calculation, whether a simple mixed-layer formulation or a dynamic ocean model (Spelman and Manabe, 1984). Many other such studies have been published, and considerably more have been done by various GCM modeling groups to help optimize and validate the performance of models being developed and to bracket plausible changes.

Again, to summarize, we can ask of a climate model if some change made any significant difference or how much difference it made. The simpler climate models usually respond linearly to small perturbations in model forcing or parameters and the question "How much?" can always be answered by some modest computation. On the other hand, GCM modelers must contend with the problem of model "noise." That is, their simulations include the day-to-day variability of weather events. Because of the instability of the nonlinear hydrodynamic equations, a model integration loses much of its memory of initial conditions after some "predictability" time. Hence, the atmospheric states of two model "January" integrations started from slightly different initial conditions will on the average eventually differ nearly as much from each other as would two days in January taken from different years. Because of the correlation of weather from one day to the next, monthly averages represent only about a half-dozen statistically independent events (Leith, 1973) and so have nearly half the noise level of individual days. With further averaging or additional independent simulations, the noise level is reduced, as in the sampling of statistically independent events, in proportion to the inverse square root of the length of the sampling interval.

The question of whether "any significant climate difference" has occurred for GCMs as well as for the actual climate system must confront the problem of whether a signal is detectable in the presence of meteorological noise. Signal detection has been a key issue in various modern technologies such as communication theory. Little of this theory has found its way down to meteorological and climate studies, perhaps because it is mostly inapplicable. The usual situation in communication theory is that a signal is known to have some time-correlated structure or to exist over some frequency band. Noise is represented by completely random, that is, uncorrelated, pulses superimposed on this signal. The signal is then to be recovered by applying to the measured time series some filter structure that removes as much of the noise as possible while distorting the signal as little as possible [e.g., Lee (1960)]. The question of signal detection simplifies considerably when the signal is regarded as a time average change, as has been done up to now in climate studies. The remaining departures from classical statistical sampling theory then derive from the multivariate time and space correlations of the meteorological noise and the multivariate spatially correlated structure of the signal. (We use the term "multivariate" here to refer to the multiple meteorological variables, e.g., horizontal winds, pressure, temperature.)

The statistical techniques appropriate to determining whether a climate difference has been seen are, with little modification, also applicable to establishing confidence limits (or more generally, a probability distribution) for describing the range of likelihood of a calculated change [e.g., Hayashi (1982)]. The criteria to decide whether a signal has been "detected" are themselves debatable, that is, judgmental, and might benefit from a Bayesian decision theory approach, as discussed later.

Questions of climate sensitivity inevitably must be evaluated by using models of the climate system. The most comprehensive models are the current GCMs. Their development over the past quarter of a century owes much to the enthusiasm and scientific and organizational contributions of Joseph Smagorinsky. The intent of this essay is to comment on some of the important questions related to climate sensitivity, to review some of the current methodologies, and to indicate needs for further development and emphasis.

It is not possible in a brief essay to examine thoroughly important technical aspects of this topic such as, for example, possibly useful efficient mathematical perturbation techniques for studying questions of sensitivity in nonlinear models [e.g., Hall and Cacuci (1983)]. Rather, we will look at some crucial concepts from a physical viewpoint.

2. SENSITIVITY ANALYSES FROM THE VIEWPOINT OF GLOBAL ENERGY BALANCE

One of the earliest areas of speculation regarding climate change was whether the amount of radiation emitted by the sun changes by amounts large enough to affect the climate system. This question still remains unanswered. Precise measurements from space have indicated that variations of solar output over a year's time are small, at most with a range of 0.2% [e.g., Willson et al. (1981)]. Current astrophysical theory indicates increasing solar output on a time scale of eons, about 5% increase per billion years [e.g.,

Newkirk (1983)]. Changes of solar output on all intermediate time scales remain a lively source of debate, although most climate modelers are of the opinion that any such changes are probably small.

However, the more general question of the effect of changes of radiation at the top of the atmosphere on the climate system is now recognized as one of the important unifying concepts of climate theory. For equilibrium conditions neglecting small geophysical energy sources, the sum of the radiative fluxes at all wavelengths must add to zero because of conservation of energy. For example, a change in absorbed solar radiation is eventually balanced by a corresponding change in outgoing long-wave radiation. However, it is useful to distinguish between the changes of radiation due to externally prescribed parameters, such as the solar output, and the changes consequent to the response of the climate system to the external change.

The energy flux at the top of the atmosphere is important to climate modelers because equilibrium global temperatures are usually much more sensitive to externally prescribed changes of energy at the top of the atmosphere than they are to model parameter or boundary condition changes that lead to internal redistributions of energy. Vertical energy redistribution by moist and dry convection processes is rapid compared with the relaxation time for radiation balance within the troposphere. Such radiatively driven convection processes are absent in the stratosphere, which, for a global average, is consequently in near radiative balance at each pressure level (Fels *et al.*, 1980). Where an internal change perturbs radiation balance in the stratosphere as well as the troposphere, e.g., changing concentrations of CO_2 in the atmosphere, it is necessary to look at changes of radiative fluxes at the tropopause rather than at the top of the atmosphere.

A strict condition of equilibrium requires that there be no net fluxes of energy between the atmosphere and the underlying surfaces. However, the oceans, with their large heat capacity, tend to maintain such net fluxes. This energy exchanged by the oceans balances, in part, external changes in radiation acting over relatively short time scales.

To discuss further the sensitivity of the global climate system to external changes, it is useful to consider the very simple global average energy balance climate model

$$C\,[\partial(\Delta T)/\partial t] + \lambda(\Delta T) = \Delta Q \tag{2.1}$$

where ΔT is the global average surface perturbation temperature, ΔQ is an externally prescribed change in net radiation crossing the tropopause, $\lambda(\Delta T)$ is assumed to give the net radiation change at the tropopause resulting from the internal dynamics of the climate system, t is time, and C represents a system heat capacity. Although Eq. (2.1) is an extreme simplification of the actual climate system, it is valuable for interpreting and summarizing the sensitivity of more detailed climate models to changes in global energy balance processes [e.g., Climate Research Board (1979)]. Indeed, it is because the more detailed models can be interpreted using Eq. (2.1) that we have a considerably better understanding of their global average temperature changes than we have of changes in regional climatic patterns.

The parameter ΔQ can represent not only a change in solar constant, but also a change in the absorbed radiation resulting from any other external perturbations in any of the physical processes determining the albedo of the climate system or its trapping of outgoing long-wave radiation. It can, in particular, represent the radiative effect of modifications in atmospheric cloud or aerosol distribution, in the albedo of land surfaces, as well as in the concentrations of radiatively absorbing atmospheric gases. Some radiative perturbations, e.g., those related to cloudiness, water vapor concentrations, or snow cover, are either externally prescribed or calculated as part of λ depending on the physical completeness of the model. We shall here consider such changes as internal where they are not connected to potential human modifications.

Equation (2.1) is useful for interpreting global climate change to the extent that different kinds of radiative perturbations affect climate only through their global average values, and thus λ can be viewed as a system parameter independent of the details of the perturbation for small enough perturbation. For example, a 2% increase of solar constant or a doubling of CO_2 both warm the global average climate system by somewhat over 4 W m^{-2}. General Circulation Model (GCM) simulations with the same model have found strikingly similar climate change for these two hypothetical perturbations (Manabe and Wetherald, 1975; Wetherald and Manabe, 1975). For large departures from present climate conditions, λ would also be expected to change at least somewhat.

Counterexamples suggest the limitations of the global zero-dimensional climate model viewpoint. For example, if a radiative perturbation were confined largely to the tropics, horizontal redistribution to extratropical latitudes would not be complete, so that the largest change would be expected in the tropics. In the tropical troposphere, temperature changes follow closely the moist adiabatic lapse rate and so increase with altitude. A radiative perturbation, e.g., by tropical deforestation (Henderson-Sellers and Gornitz, 1984), is largely balanced by modifications in the outgoing long-wave radiation from the upper troposphere. Hence, surface temperature changes are relatively small. This "negative lapse rate feedback" increases the effective value of λ from what it would have been for a more latitudinally uniform perturbation.

Similarly, perturbations in surface or near-surface heating in high latitudes, e.g., by Arctic aerosol (Cess, 1983), would imply a significantly lower value of λ, both because of the convective decoupling of the surface from the middle and upper troposphere and the large changes in absorbed solar radiation with changed cover of snow and ice. Conversely, upper-tropospheric heating may not couple completely to surface warming. The most drastic example of the failure of "top-of-the-troposphere" energy balance analysis is a nuclear war climate change scenario (Turco *et al.*, 1983) in which a large cloud of smoke particles increases the absorbed solar radiation but becomes convectively decoupled from the surface. The surface consequently cools rather than warms. Linking of radiative perturbations to spatially varying atmospheric dynamic processes can also detract from the usefulness of the global average viewpoint. For example, globally averaged cloudiness and presumably albedo could increase with a positive zonal belt of ocean temperature anomalies in the subtropics but decrease if the anomaly belt were in the region of the upward branch of the Hadley cell [as found in GCM experiments by Schneider *et al.* (1978)].

Having recognized some of the difficulties that can beset the global average energy balance viewpoint of climate, we return to using it for further discussion. The following discussion assumes infinitesimal perturbations so that the magnitude of ΔQ becomes irrelevant. As already mentioned, Eq. (2.1) is used as a framework for comparison of otherwise different radiative

TABLE I. TRACE GAS RADIATIVE EFFECT SCENARIO FOR THE YEAR 2100 (EXCLUDING AEROSOLS)

Species	Current concentrations	Possible concentrations in year 2100	Likely cause of increase	W m^{-2}
CO_2	340 ppm	×2	Fossil fuel, soil, and biomass carbon	4.2
CH_4	1.65 ppm	×2	Changes in OH or sources	0.6
N_2O	0.3 ppm	×2	Changes in nitrification and denitrification, fossil fuel	0.7
O_3 (troposphere)	Profile	×2	Anthropogenic change in tropospheric chemistry	1.2
O_3 (stratosphere)	Profile	5% column loss but 50% loss at 40 km, 5% increase in lower stratosphere	Cl_x, NO_x	0.2
$CFCl_3$	0.20 ppb	2 ppb	Anthropogenic release	0.5
CF_2Cl_2	0.33 ppb	4 ppb	Anthropogenic release	1.1
CCl_4	0.14 ppb	1.0 ppb	Anthropogenic release	0.2
CH_3CCl_3	0.15 ppb	3 ppb	Anthropogenic release	0.1
CH_3Cl	0.6 ppb	1.0 ppb		0.01
All other chlorocarbons	0.1 ppb	1.0 ppb		0.2
				9.0

perturbations of the climate system simply by determination of the global average change in radiative flux at the top of the troposphere. For example, Table I shows plausible future scenarios for changes in carbon dioxide and other trace gases and the implied global heat inputs [based, in part, on World Meteorological Organization (1982)]. As indicated, about half of the global warming expected by the year 2100 is the result of increases in trace gases other than CO_2, though there is such a wide range of probable concentrations of these gases that far into the future that even decreases of some of these trace gases are not entirely improbable. Further clarification of all significant contributions to future ΔQ will continue to be an important objective of climate research.

3. The Global Feedback Parameter

We now turn to the question of interpreting the global temperature response for a given heat input in terms of Eq. (2.1). We refer to the term λ in Eq. (2.1) as the global feedback parameter. It is estimated from any climate model forced by a perturbation ΔQ by dividing ΔQ by the resulting global average temperature change. For a given system heat capacity, positive λ implies stability or negative feedback and determines the "damping" or "relaxation" rate by which a temperature anomaly is restored to equilibrium. The inverse of λ gives the change of global temperature for a given radiative perturbation. If multiplied by the total absorbed radiation, it equals the β term previously mentioned. It can be called the global sensitivity parameter.

It is most convenient to deal directly with λ because of its additive nature. A convenient reference value is

$$\lambda_B = 4\sigma T_e^3 = 3.75 \quad \text{W m}^{-2}\text{ K}^{-1} \tag{3.1}$$

where σ is the Stefan–Boltzmann constant and $T_e \simeq 255$ K is the Earth's effective radiative temperature. The term λ_B is the value of λ that the Earth would have if it were a blackbody with the same albedo as its present value. Hansen et al. (1984) discuss sensitivity in terms of a "gain factor" g that equals $1 - \lambda/\lambda_B$. We prefer use of λ because it is more directly related to temperature change and its definition does not require knowing present albedo or outgoing fluxes as do Schneider's β or Hansen's g factors. The trade-off is a dimensionally more complicated term.

What other processes contribute to λ besides blackbody feedback? We can try to answer this question by referring to observations [e.g., Cess (1976)] or by interpreting more detailed models in terms of Eq. (2.1). In particular, one-dimensional radiative–convective models [reviewed by Ramanathan and Coakley (1978)] have been applied to the question of global temperature change since the study of Manabe and Wetherald (1967). The Manabe–Wetherald paper showed that, for fixed composition, the response of a radiative–convective model to changed heat input in the troposphere is essentially the blackbody response. However, if, more realistically, water vapor is assumed to vary with fixed relative humidity, the temperature response Manabe and Wetherald found is essentially doubled or equivalently,

$$\lambda = \lambda_B + \lambda_W \tag{3.2}$$

where $\lambda_W \simeq -1.7$ W m^{-2} K^{-1} is the water vapor feedback parameter. This term results from largely increased long-wave trapping by the increased water vapor of a warmer climate, but also includes a water vapor albedo feedback term of about -0.2 W m^{-2} K^{-1} (Ramanathan and Coakley, 1978).

More recent radiative–convective model studies have examined the dependence of temperature change on assumptions regarding changes in cloudiness parameters and lapse rate. These studies have suggested that cloud cover, height, and opacity feedbacks, combined with lapse rate feedbacks, could readily change λ by as much as 1 W m^{-2} K^{-1} in either direction [see reviews by Ramanathan and Coakley (1978) and Dickinson (1982)]. However, one-dimensional model sensitivity studies cannot proceed beyond illustrating the nature of the problem in establishing the role of these feedbacks.

Another class of models also more detailed than Eq. (2.1) is the one-dimensional energy balance models (North *et al.*, 1981). These models were introduced by the studies of Budyko (1969) and Sellers (1969), who independently concluded that the temperature dependence of the cover of ice and snow, hence albedo, could greatly increase the temperature change occurring in response to a global radiative perturbation. They also implicitly included long-wave water vapor feedback in their models such that λ could be written

$$\lambda = \lambda_B + \lambda_W + \lambda_I \tag{3.4}$$

where their empirically inferred ice-albedo feedback factor $\lambda_I \simeq -0.8$ W m^{-2} K^{-1} for infinitesimal temperature change according to both models. The Budyko–Sellers ice-albedo feedback suggested an easy route to ice ages and raised the spectre of the climate system falling into a state of complete ice cover from which it could not readily recover.

More recent analyses, based on satellite data [e.g., Lian and Cess (1977)], have suggested that the Budyko–Sellers estimates of ice-albedo feedback were greatly exaggerated and that $\lambda_I \simeq -0.3$ W m^{-2} K^{-1}. However, another recent parameterization, based "on observations of the seasonal cycles of snow cover and sea ice, and the distributions of land surface types over the globe" (Robock, 1983a), finds a relatively high sensitivity $\lambda_I = -0.66$ W m^{-2} K^{-1}, which was found largely to be a result of sea-ice variations. Chou et al. (1982) use a similar ice–snow parameterization and find $\lambda_I = -0.44$ W m^{-2} K^{-1}.

Empirical approaches to climate system parameters [e.g., Cess (1976) and Warren and Schneider (1979)] consider variations in outgoing radiative fluxes with latitude and season, as well as with smaller time and space scales. Even if the observational difficulties could be completely overcome, it is not evident that empirical parameters so derived should be of direct relevance to global average climate change. Thus, it would seem that the question of global climate change should be addressed not only with semiempirical and simplified models, but also with the physically most complete models that can be constructed, subject to the practical limitations of computer resources. This is the rationale for using GCMs that model in detail the dynamics of atmospheric winds and the atmospheric hydrological cycle. In principle, GCMs have the added bonus of being able to evaluate the latitudinal and regional structure of climate change as well as global average values. We shall return later to this question of latitudinal and regional change.

How well can GCMs actually model global climate feedback terms related to the hydrological cycle? In considering this question, it is useful to compare results from different GCM groups and from different models developed by the same group. A danger in accepting GCM results as descriptions of reality is that some aspects, e.g., in the present context of global feedback terms, may depend on poorly modeled processes whose importance for the results obtained is not recognized. In GCM modeling as in all such complex scientific endeavors, there is a "follow-the-leader" tendency to use previously published parameterizations for physical processes without considering the dependence of modeling results on uncertainties in these parameterizations. On the other hand, arbitrary assumptions and parameterizations have at least some possibility of differing randomly between different models, especially those developed at different institutions. Thus, comparison of the results of different models can help uncover serious uncertainties that may not have been demonstrated through sensitivity studies with one particular model.

What can be learned about global feedbacks from surveying GCM results over the last decade or so? General circulation models do seem to give reasonably realistic descriptions of changes in atmospheric water vapor amount as well as in rainfall amounts. However, these changes are largely constrained by the Clausius–Clapyron expression for the dependence of saturation vapor pressure on temperature. Atmospheric water vapor concentrations and evaporation rates, hence global average rainfall, are proportional to saturated mixing ratios at the surface for fixed relative humidities, surface winds, and near-surface lapse rates.

Departures of water vapor change from scaling with saturated vapor pressure may be significant, e.g., by modifying λ by as much as ± 0.5 W m^{-2} K^{-1}. [Hansen *et al.* (1984), e.g., found in their GCM sensitivity studies that λ was decreased by about 1 W m^{-2} K^{-1} by a changed vertical distribution of water but that this positive feedback was largely cancelled by a negative lapse rate feedback.] However, analyses of GCM simulations and observational data may not yet be adequate to establish whether model water vapor feedbacks are realistic in detail or what degree of confidence we should have in the details of water vapor changes.

The question of water vapor radiation feedback is closely linked to the question of effects of cloud changes on global radiation balance. All GCM groups have developed simple cloud parameterizations that simulate model cloudiness using such closely linked parameters as relative humidity, rainfall, and the presence of moist convection.

Some GCM simulations [e.g., Wetherald and Manabe (1980) and Washington and Meehl (1983)] have found minimal changes in global radiation balance with cloud parameter changes accompanying climate change. These results have reinforced the concept articulated by Cess (1976) that cloud albedo and cloud long-wave changes tend to cancel each other. On the other hand, Hansen *et al.* (1984) have found a large positive cloud-radiative feedback with a no-less "state-of-the-art" cloud parameterization scheme. In particular, if we denote the cloud contribution to λ in Eq. (2.1) by λ_C, the Hansen *et al.* results of their Table 1 imply that $\lambda_C \simeq -0.8$ W m^{-2} K^{-1}. Changes in both cloud heights and cloud cover contribute to this positive feedback. While such a result might seem less likely than the conclusion of small cloud feedback, it is apparently not improbable. We also cannot exclude the possibility of a negative cloud feedback of comparable magnitude or for that matter, a cloud feedback that is highly dependent on the spatial distribution of the radiative perturbation [e.g., Schneider *et al.* (1978)]. Clouds, their radiative properties, and their inference from remote sensing have been heavily emphasized in national and international research programs for the past decade because of their recognized importance for climate. Yet it is likely that at least another decade of research effort will be required before cloud-radiation feedback effects can be modeled with confidence in GCMs.

Thus, in summary, an analysis in terms of global feedback emphasizes the need for an improved understanding as to how the distribution of atmospheric water, in vapor and liquid form, will change with climate change.

4. Ice-Albedo Feedbacks

We now turn to the question of the capabilities of GCMs to model the radiative feedbacks of ice and snow for climate change simulations. We refer to the results of several modeling groups who have studied the climate change resulting from CO_2 warming. The following analysis is largely based on reported changes of global albedo with global surface temperature. Where authors simply report the total albedo change with the changed temperature, we remove from this change an increase of absorbed solar radiation with warming due to increased water vapor of -0.2 W m^{-2} K^{-1}. Some studies have indicated relatively small ice-albedo feedback; e.g., Manabe and Stouffer (1980) find $\lambda_I \simeq -0.25$ W m^{-2} K^{-1} (inferred from their Fig. 15), whereas in Washington and Meehl (1983) $\lambda_I \simeq 0$. The model by Hansen *et al.* (1984) gives $\lambda_I = -0.34$ W m^{-2} K^{-1}, according to their Table 1. Wetherald and Manabe (1981), according to their Tables A.1 and A.2, find that $\lambda_I \simeq -0.4$ W m^{-2} K^{-1} for a seasonal insolation and -0.5 W m^{-2} K^{-1} for an annual mean insolation, and Spelman and Manabe (1984) find that $\lambda_I \simeq -0.45$ W m^{-2} K^{-1} for an annual mean insolation and interactive ocean according to their Table 1. Washington and Meehl (1984) have obtained an ice-albedo feedback of -0.6 W m^{-2} K^{-1}, not much smaller than the values inferred from the early studies of Sellers and Budyko. These variations in ice-albedo feedback apparently result in part from large changes in the GCM prescriptions of sea-ice and snow albedo, which appear to have been formulated without sufficient consideration of what would be radiatively realistic but in some models are tuned to compensate for other model deficiencies. They also result from wide variations in the sea-ice cover obtained in control simulations.

It is disconcerting that not only do different GCMs show as wide a range of ice-albedo feedback values as empirical energy balance studies, but that even that same GCM can, under somewhat different modeling assumptions, generate a large range in ice-albedo feedback values. The Washington and Meehl (1983) study assumed annual mean conditions and a "swamp layer ocean," whereas Washington and Meehl (1984) considered a model with a seasonal cycle and a mixed-layer ocean. These two studies also used differing sea-ice parameterizations, and the second study used a somewhat higher value for snow albedo than the first. Otherwise, the two studies used an identical model. The Washington and Meehl (1984) study may overestimate ice-albedo feedback because (1) the simulated current climate had somewhat too large an extent of sea ice, especially in the Southern Hemisphere, and (2) the study used an oversimplified prescription for land-snow albedo that neglects the lowering of albedo of snow-covered terrain in forested areas. The model by Hansen *et al.* (1984) has a more realistic snow-forest albedo, as does the energy balance model study of Robock (1983a). However, the Washington and Meehl (1984) paper finds that changes in planetary albedo with CO_2 warming occur largely over sea-ice margins, especially in the Southern Hemisphere. Changes in the extent of sea ice give greater changes in planetary albedo than do changes in snow cover because of the persistence of sea ice into the spring and summer seasons of greatest solar irradiance (Robock, 1983a). Thus, the details of sea-ice modeling appear to be a crucial issue for determining model sensitivity.

The recent study by Spelman and Manabe (1984) has found a dramatic difference in ice-albedo feedback between a simulation with a swamp ocean versus an ocean with calculated dynamics. Spelman and Manabe interpret their result to be largely a consequence of the differing global average surface temperatures they obtain for their present climate simulations with the different ocean models. Presumably, the modeled global average surface temperature is a good measure of the extent of the modeled sea ice. Thus, obtaining the correct extent of sea ice for current conditions may be as crucial as using realistic albedos for correctly modeling snow–ice albedo feedback. Even if model sea-ice extent is tuned to current conditions, it is not known how accurately its change with climate change can be modeled. Sea-ice change depends in part on horizontal ocean heat transport below the ice and at the ice margins, which is modeled poorly if at all. It also depends on the details of the ice dynamics, that is, the wind- and ocean-driven movement of the sea ice itself [e.g., Hibler (1984), Hibler and Bryan (1984), and Parkinson and Bindschadler (1984)]. This ice movement is neglected in all present GCM simulations of climate change that use purely thermodynamic models of sea-ice cover. Indeed, significant differences can be obtained even with different thermodynamic ice models [e.g., Semtner (1984)].

It would also appear that proper modeling of high-latitude cloud cover and its optical properties is important for obtaining a correct description of ice-albedo feedback in GCM simulations [as also in energy balance models, e.g., Golitsyn and Mokhov (1978)]. Unfortunately, even the climatological cover of high-latitude clouds is poorly known [as reviewed by Barry et al. (1984)], and their modeling in GCMs is totally speculative.

Thus, in summary it appears that the largest sources of uncertainty for the sensitivity of global average temperature to external changes in tropospheric energy balance are the magnitude of the ice-snow albedo feedback processes and the magnitude and sign of cloud-radiation feedback processes. These conclusions have been drawn for over a decade [cf., e.g., Schneider and Dickinson (1974)].

However, what is especially distressing is that recent GCM studies have not contributed to narrowing our uncertainty as to these processes but have suggested that we are rather more ignorant than we previously thought. For example, the Climate Research Board (1979) indicated that λ is likely to lie between 0.9 and 2.5 W m^{-2} K^{-1}. Considering the possibility of large positive feedbacks from both cloud radiation and ice–snow albedo, I would now place my own subjective 95% confidence limits for λ at between 0.8 and 2.8 W m^{-2} K^{-1}. This is equivalent to suggesting that the steady-state global warming for doubled carbon dioxide could be as large as 5 K or as small as 1.5 K.

If all GCMs used to study the question of climate warming use realistic values for sea-ice albedo and develop control simulations with seasonally varying sea ice and polar cloud cover close to that observed, then there may be a much narrower range of calculated ice-albedo feedback. As long as there remains a wide divergence between estimates of future climate change due to CO_2 warming, it might be useful to devote more effort to evaluating the extreme possibilities of climate change than to the expected values and attempting to reduce the range of extreme possibilities. An estimate of the global albedo change from present conditions with total disappearance of sea ice would be useful for limiting the maximum warming possible.

5. THERMAL INERTIA

In attempting to relate modeling results to reality, we must also consider the important role of the thermal inertia of the oceans, as simplistically represented by the term C in Eq. (2.1). The oceans require between a few years and a few thousand years to warm, depending on the depth of ocean that is in thermal contact with the atmosphere. For rapidly varying forcing, i.e., time scales of a few years or less, as given by the seasonal cycle or volcanic dust interruption of incident solar flux [e.g., Robock (1983b)], the thermal inertia of the oceans is determined by the depth of the surface mixed layer. Studies of the transient climate response with mixed-layer oceans of depths about 100 m or less find little difference from steady-state analyses for a gradual increase in CO_2 warming. However, on the time scales of CO_2 warming, water may be mixed to large depths by high-latitude winter convection so that the atmosphere could effectively be in contact with more like 1000 m of ocean (Broecker *et al.*, 1979). On the other hand, the high-latitude ocean may become more stably stratified. For example, the studies of Bryan *et al.* (1982) and Spelman and Manabe (1984) indicate the stabilization of high-latitude oceans by the formation of halocline resulting from large increases in high-latitude precipitation, hence fresh water added to the sea surface. The CO_2-induced climate warming at present may be reduced by as much as half from its steady-state value (Cess and Goldenberg, 1981; Michael *et al.*, 1981; Dickinson, 1981, 1982; Schneider and Thompson, 1981;

Schlesinger, 1983). The transient warming of the oceans is of concern not only because it reduces the magnitude of the global response, but also because it might give a latitudinal variation of the warming significantly different than implied by steady-state calculation [e.g., as discussed by Schneider and Thompson (1981), Bryan et al. (1982), Thompson and Schneider (1982), and North et al. (1984)].

It is not possible to review here the complex oceanic dynamic and thermal processes that ultimately must determine oceanic heat capacity. Rather, we simply point out some obvious conclusions. First, from the present analytic viewpoint, it is evident from Eq. (2.1) that the departure of the expected warming depends on the ratio of the oceanic heat capacity to the climate feedback parameter λ. The time dependence of CO_2 can be approximated by an expression of the form $n(CO_2) = n_0(CO_2) [1 + \epsilon \exp(t/t_c)]$, where t_c is a time scale for increase and ϵ a constant parameter, and the CO_2 heating by $Q \sim \log n(CO_2)$. Thus, for small ϵ

$$Q \sim \exp(t/t_c) \tag{5.1}$$

That is, the warming from CO_2 over the past and next several decades, while the perturbation CO_2 is small compared to background, is roughly exponential. Insertion of Eq. (5.1) in Eq. (2.1) gives

$$T = T_{eq}/[1 + C/(\lambda t_c)] \tag{5.2}$$

where T_{eq} is the equilibrium temperature response. In other words, the departure of the response from equilibrium depends on the ratio of heat capacity to the product of the CO_2 emission growth time and feedback parameter. Fossil fuel use is growing less rapidly than previously so t_c has shifted from about a 25-year (4% per year) growth time to 50-year (2% per year), which implies that the global temperature response to increasing CO_2 will more closely approach its steady-state value over the next several decades than it would with the previous more rapid growth. On the other hand, if λ were much smaller than previously believed, the system would not only have a much larger steady-state response [as argued by Hansen et al. (1984)], but also stay farther from steady state during growth in the rate of warming. Moreover, for very small λ, the solution to Eq. (2.1), i.e., Eq. (5.2), can be approximated by

$$T \simeq t_c Q/C \tag{5.3}$$

That is, the effective climate feedback is given by C/t_c and becomes independent of the parameter λ. In practical terms, if the climate system had very weak feedback, it would probably not be possible to infer this result from only a few decades of observed warming, but the weak feedback might only become apparent after a century or more of climate warming had failed to slow down in the manner expected for a larger feedback. The relative weakness of λ feedback in high latitudes and relatively large C (deep convection) in near polar oceans is the basis for the argument that the transient response to CO_2 warming should have a different latitudinal variation than the steady-state warming. However, as earlier mentioned, there is some suggestion that the deep ocean convection may be weakened during the CO_2 warming. The steady-state response to global warming may still be too poorly understood for much scientific attention to the question of transient effects to yet be warranted.

It is reassuring to keep in mind that if a strong positive ice-albedo feedback were to contribute to a large steady-state warming, this feedback would have to weaken considerably with the large decrease of sea-ice cover accompanying a warmer climate. That is, a large global temperature increase would require a change of external heating considerably larger in magnitude than that required for a temperature decrease of the same magnitude as the increase. Conversely, the question of the stability of the climate system under multicentury cooling processes should also be of some concern. A good focus for this question is in the climate change that occurred during the last ice age and the series of ice ages of the past million years, a topic we turn to next.

6. CLIMATE SENSITIVITY AND PALEOCLIMATES

For large changes from current climate, the feedback parameters discussed in the preceding sections will be rather different than those appropriate to present conditions. A knowledge of the change of the feedback parameter with climate change is important for understanding climate and one of the reasons for studying past climates different from that of today.

Evidence for ice ages over the last million years correlates with the Earth's orbital parameters. This correlation has greatly stimulated studies of millennium time-scale responses of the climate system to external forcing, as well as of the possibility of multiple climatic states and long-period free oscillations of the climate system [cf. the review by Held (1982)].

One criticism of many energy balance climate models able to simulate the growth of continental ice sheets with orbital forcing has been their assumption of apparently excessive ice-albedo feedback. Energy balance climate modelers look at GCMs as a guide for reasonable ice-albedo feedback. However, as already discussed, recent GCM studies themselves have shown a wide variation in the modeled ice-albedo feedbacks and have recently drifted toward larger values.

North et al. (1983) have developed a three-dimensional energy balance climate model with oceans and continents separately distinguished and with relatively low ice-albedo feedback and model sensitivity for present conditions. However, when the solar constant is reduced by more than 1.5%, their solutions drop discontinuously into an ice-age climate. Using orbital parameters appropriate to 115,000 years before present (B.P.) for cool summer forcing, they find solutions suggestive of large ice-sheet growth over northern North America.

The climate of the last ice age (18,000 B.P.) has been modeled in several GCM studies using observed changes in ocean, land, and ice-sheet conditions. The most recent such study by Hansen *et al.* (1984) analyzed the various global average energy balance terms involved.

The Hansen *et al.* model estimates of global radiation balance for 18,000 B.P. indicate an imbalance that would force further temperature decrease. This inferred imbalance suggests possible inaccuracy either in the modeled positive cloud feedbacks or in the assumed concentrations of CO_2 or in other imposed boundary conditions. The Hansen *et al.* calculations include the negative feedback effect of an elevated ice plateau on infrared radiation [as discussed by Bowman (1982)]. However, the positive ice-albedo feedback they find is considerably larger and presumably enhanced by longitudinal asymmetries (Hartmann and Short, 1979). Their analysis suggests that during an ice age the climate system might have a much weaker total feedback parameter λ than at present and would thus have been subject to large oscillations in response to small amounts of global forcing. It is evident that the climate system never dropped into the ice-covered Earth catastrophe, but it is not known how closely it may have approached that condition.

On the time scale of ice ages, the question is raised of the coupling of climate change to the geochemical cycles responsible for maintaining atmospheric carbon dioxide concentrations. Perhaps variation by a factor of two in atmospheric CO_2 concentrations could result from changes in oceanic chemical processes [e.g., as reviewed by Broecker and Takahashi (1984)]. On yet longer time scales, much larger changes in the concentration of atmospheric CO_2 become possible as a result of variations in volcanic sources and geochemical weathering sinks (Berner *et al.,* 1983). Especially interesting is the possible role of increased CO_2 in explaining the warmer temperatures of 100 million B.P. during the Cretaceous period, about 10°C warmer than present. Barron and Washington (1983) have used the annual swamp ocean GCM of Washington and Meehl (1983) to explore the role of continental positions and elevated sea level in promoting this Cretaceous warming. They find that Cretaceous geography by itself can only increase global temperatures by 5°C and conclude that some additional warming mechanism such as increased CO_2 is required. This conclusion might be considered premature since the annual mean swamp ocean model they use [that of Washington and Meehl (1983)] has the largest λ of any GCM published to date, three times stronger than that of the recent seasonal cycle models (Hansen *et al.,* 1984; Washington and Meehl, 1984). However, correlation between paleo-climatic temperatures also supports the hypothesis of large CO_2 variations on geological time scales.

A more serious difficulty in explaining Cretaceous climate is the apparent existence of polar surface temperatures being warmer by about 20°C and equatorial temperatures by no more than 5°C. The annual mean simulation by Barron and Washington showed little sign of such amplification. Possibly, the oceanic transport of heat constrains equatorial temperatures to small variations [as suggested by Hoffert *et al.* (1983)]. Furthermore, the model used by Barron and Washington has little negative lapse rate feedback in high latitudes to promote polar amplification of warming. This lack of high-latitude surface temperature amplification is in contrast to GFDL models, e.g., as discussed by Manabe and Wetherald (1975) and Ramanathan (1977). For example, Spelman and Manabe (1984) find polar surface temperature increases greater than 10°C for doubled CO_2. This high-latitude surface warming couples to ocean deep water at all latitudes which consequently increases in temperature by more than 7°C.

In conclusion, further modeling studies of large departures from the current climate, as suggested by paleoclimatic evidence, will both increase our understanding of the sensitivity of the climate system to external forcing and of model parameterizations important for determining model sensitivity. Seasonal cycles need to be included and more attention should be given to polar inversions and their change with climatic change.

7. LAND-SURFACE PROCESSES AND REGIONAL CLIMATE SENSITIVITY

Much of the practical importance of climate study results from the relationships of the climate system as a whole to processes that occur at the atmosphere–land interface. These include in particular the growth of vegetation for food, fiber, and other amenities and the use of water resources for plant growth, power generation, and industrial and personal applications. Climate processes over land surfaces have been studied in considerable detail because of their importance for these and other human activities and ecological processes. Yet we are still rather ignorant of the sensitivity of the overall climate system to land-surface processes. The global feedback framework, used previously in this paper, may be applied to land-surface changes that perturb the global radiation balance. However, because such changes generally occur on less than a global scale, it is likely that regional processes may modify the global response.

The intent of this section is to simply summarize our current understanding of the connections between questions of climate change and land-surface processes. We need to ask in particular: (1) How does climate change affect land-surface processes? (2) How do land-surface processes and their change affect the climate system? And (3) What model variables, parameterizations, and analyses are most important for answering the first two questions?

Since this essay is especially directed toward the role of future climate change, we can avoid reciting the litany of the total range of influences of climate on surface processes by limiting discussion of (1) to the question of the effect of future warming by CO_2 and other trace gases on land processes. Since the detailed spatial distribution of the additional heat input from these sources is usually considered to be of secondary importance, we can consider, in the abstract, the global climate system uniformly heated to induce a global average warming of several degrees. What then would be the detailed distribution of this warming at the Earth's surface, and what shifts in surface hydrological processes would result?

The most obvious answer is that warmer surfaces evaporate water more rapidly, thus also increase rainfall rates and in other ways speed up the hydrological cycle. Further details beyond this general statement depend on spatial variations of effects and are best examined through study with GCMs. The most relevant such past studies are the previously reviewed model calculations of climate change and scenarios for doubling or quadrupling of CO_2 [e.g., Manabe and Wetherald (1975), Manabe and Stouffer (1980), Wetherald and Manabe (1981), Manabe et al. (1981), Washington and Meehl (1983, 1984)].

Considerable information has also been gained from observational studies of past climate variations. However, we shall not discuss these studies since it is questionable whether past regional patterns of change were a consequence rather than a cause of the accompanying global average changes. We shall further restrict our discussion of GCM results to modeling studies carried out at the GFDL or NCAR [cf. Schlesinger (1983) for review of other modeling studies]. The GCM studies to date can be distinguished according to assumptions as to geography: whether (a) idealized sector or "realistic," (b) annual mean or seasonal heating, and (c) energy balance or dynamic ocean. The more realistic assumptions might be expected to give results of more practical relevance, but the simpler assumptions make it easier to interpret mechanisms and allow greater computational economy.

One of the most commonly quoted features of the GFDL model studies has been a greatest warming in high latitudes. This warming has been interpreted as due to positive lapse rate and snow-albedo feedbacks [e.g., as analyzed by Ramanathan (1977)]. However, the study by Washington and Meehl (1983) found essentially no high-latitude amplification, and Washington and Meehl (1984) obtained essentially no high-latitude amplification over land but only at the sea-ice margins. The relative weakness of the NCAR model high-latitude surface-temperature amplification may be explicable in part by a vertical eddy diffusion coefficient that is unrealistically large in high latitudes. As already discussed, there have been wide intermodel variations in the calculated ice-albedo feedbacks, related to differences in the extent of the modeled sea ice, assumptions as to sea-ice albedo, and possibly cloud cover. All the seasonal models, including that of Hansen *et al.* (1984), find the largest surface warming in early winter over the areas of seasonal sea ice. This is a consequence of the increased high-latitude ocean storage of heat during the summer months and enhanced conduction of heat through the thinner ice in the winter months, as discussed by Manabe and Stouffer (1980).

The second commonly quoted result of GFDL simulations has been a summer reduction of midcontinent soil moisture in the middle latitudes, as analyzed in detail by Manabe *et al.* (1981). This result has showed up most distinctly in the idealized sector seasonal cycle model simulations. It has been interpreted to result from earlier snow melt with a warmer climate and thus a longer summer drying season. A similar but weaker and noisier result has been seen in GFDL simulations with realistic geography (Manabe and Stouffer, 1980). In contrast, Washington and Meehl (1984) have found midcontinental summer soil moisture largely to increase, apparently a consequence of greater spring precipitation. The difference is likely not very dependent on winter precipitation since Manabe *et al.* (1981) report saturated soil in early spring. We see no reason in this instance to prefer the results of the GFDL model studies over those of Washington and Meehl.

The conclusion [e.g., Manabe and Stouffer (1980), and Manabe *et al.* (1981)] that the largest warming over land surfaces at a given latitude will be associated with the largest anomalies in soil moisture is plausible in terms of physical reasoning and observed regional climate anomalies. Both the GFDL and Washington and Meehl models use crude and similar parameterizations for surface energy balance processes, soil moisture, and snow cover, which do not distinguish between vegetated and nonvegetated surfaces. Thus, the only inference that safely can be made regarding warmer Earth soil moisture levels is that they will probably differ from today's; the sign of the change is not obvious.

In arid lands, much of the water used for agriculture comes from irrigation, which is largely supplied from the accumulated snowpack in neighboring mountains. Thus, the question of changes in water availability requires attention to modeling accumulation of snow in mountain areas, a task made extremely difficult by the coarse resolution of current GCM climate models. For example, the mountains of the western United States tend to be aggregated into one big plateau.

Changes in rainfed surface water supplies are also difficult to infer from current model rainfall and runoff parameterizations. A warmer Earth with more precipitation would also be expected to have a greater fraction of its rainfall occurring in intense convective showers. Modeling the consequences of such showers for runoff requires accounting for the spatial distribution and time variability of convective rainfall. Hydrologists have necessarily given considerable attention to such features, but GCM modelers have not yet done so. Insufficient attention has also been given to the question as to whether the internal dynamics of GCMs adequately capture shifts in climate patterns that would modulate surface radiation budgets. For example, how significant are shifts in planetary waves and their internal heat sources [e.g., Trenberth (1983) and Hartmann (1984)]?

To recapitulate, future GCMs could provide considerable valuable information about the climate change of land surfaces. However, much work needs to be done to improve and validate model parameterizations in this area. Large increases in raw computing power would allow more adequate numerical resolution. A wide variety of sensitivity studies will be needed to help clarify priorities in this work.

In the remainder of this section, we briefly summarize what statements can currently be made regarding sensitivity of climate to land-surface processes. The primary thrust of past GCM studies of this question has been to demonstrate that hypothetical large changes in land-surface properties would likely have large climatic effects. For example, comparison of GCM climate simulations with hypothetical completely wet versus completely dry land surfaces shows much less rainfall over land in the dry continent case (Shukla and Mintz, 1982). Removal of model winter snowfall has been found to give drier soil moisture throughout the summer seasons (Yeh *et al.,* 1983). Increases in the surface albedo of sufficiently large magnitude and spatial scale in semiarid lands may imply large decreases in average rainfall (Charney *et al.,* 1977). A study of the effect of large-scale tropical deforestation (Henderson-Sellers and Gornitz, 1984) has indicated that changes in soil moisture capacity could also modulate rainfall rates.

There is also considerable micrometeorological information on the sensitivity of surface energy fluxes and hydrology to values of various important parameters. As examples of explicit sensitivity studies, Saxton (1975) examined the sensitivities of a simple Penman equation for evapotranspiration to various prescribed parameters and found greatest sensitivity to the amount of absorbed solar radiation. Luxmoore *et al.* (1981) considered a more elaborate and realistic soil–plant–atmosphere continuum model and found transpiration to be rather insensitive to absorbed solar radiation, but rather sensitive to prescribed meteorological parameters such as the air temperature and dewpoint depression. They concluded that the inferred relative insensitivity to solar radiation was a consequence of additional model feedbacks involving soil moisture and stomatal resistance. However, it is generally recognized that the Penman–Monteith-like equation that they used for transpiration implies radiative control of evaporation in the limit of small surface (aerodynamic) resistance (i.e., short vegetation) but vapor pressure deficit control in the limit of large surface resistance (i.e., tall vegetation). Their example was for a forest with large surface resistance, so that their primary conclusion might have been inferred without use of a soil water model.

Beven (1979) analyzed a similar model but considered the sensitivity of transpiration to various model parameters. He found, not surprisingly, that for small surface resistance, transpiration was quite sensitive to canopy resistance. Canopy resistance represents the aggregated stomatal resistance of the canopy. Model calculations illustrating sensitivity of interception and transpiration to different vegetative covers have been discussed by Sellers and Lockwood (1981).

One of the frequent themes in the forest-meteorology literature is the strong control of forest evapotranspiration processes by wind ventilation and vapor pressure gradients as determined by foliage temperature, ambient air mixing ratio, and leaf stomatal resistance. If a forest is wet from rainfall or dew, it can evaporate this water much more rapidly than it would have transpired it [e.g., Shuttleworth and Calder (1979)]. Most micrometeorological studies regard the atmosphere at the canopy top as externally prescribed. However, what if the planetary boundary layer is allowed to change in response to surface fluxes? McNaughton (1976), DeBruin (1983), and McNaughton and Jarvis (1983) have studied this question and considered the result of the planetary boundary layer coming into equilibrium with surface fluxes. They find that, after equilibration with the planetary boundary layer, the transpiration is proportional to absorbed solar radiation, as suggested by Priestley and Taylor (1972), and only weakly dependent on canopy resistance.

In summary, large-scale climate changes of considerable practical importance may occur over land surfaces. Land surfaces, through their modulation of radiant, sensible, and latent fluxes, may have important feedbacks on the climate system. However, as discussed previously, feedbacks with the planetary boundary layer may minimize latent and sensible flux changes. Improvement in climate models, especially in their treatment of physical processes at the land surface [e.g., Dickinson (1984)], will allow more realistic examinations of such questions as the impact of CO_2 warming or the effects of large-scale tropical deforestation.

8. QUESTIONS OF STATISTICAL SIGNIFICANCE

One of the complexities of carrying out sensitivity studies with GCMs is that the response to be examined may be obscured by model noise, that is, natural variability. We briefly review the approaches that have been taken to address this question and suggest possible changes in orientation. The usual model sensitivity study consists of one or more control runs to define the unperturbed model climate and one or more model runs with some changed external condition to define the perturbed climate. The apparent signal is the difference between the average of all or some of the control runs and all or some of the perturbation runs.

The simplest approach to examining uncertainties from model noise is to determine some measure of model variability and compare the ratio of apparent model signal to this model "noise"; if the model signal is very large compared with the noise, it is evidently a reproducible result. However, if not, several further questions have to be asked to facilitate interpretation and help economize on the computational burden of model simulation. First, was an appropriate measure of noise used? Hayashi (1982) has pointed out two previously used possible definitions of model noise and suggested a third. He defines a climatic variable X as an average of some meteorological variable over some time interval of interest, e.g., a monthly average, to be sampled N times. He argues that an appropriate measure of noise is the square root of twice the variance of the climatic variable. The factor of two comes from summing the contributions of the estimated variances of the control and perturbed simulations of X, assuming that the same number of samples is available for both. Unfortunately, the Hayashi definition of noise depends on the averaging interval. It would seem that a better definition of noise would be to use an estimate of the variance of the N-sample estimate of the signal, essentially corresponding to the usage of Madden and Ramanathan (1980). We shall use this term for the estimated signal-to-noise ratio. In model studies, it is necessary to include an appropriate numerical factor to allow for the uncertainty in both control and perturbation mean climate estimates (Hayashi, 1982). In any case, it must be remembered that for a small number of samples, the estimated variance itself is of considerable uncertainty, and the variances of the perturbation and control simulations are not necessarily the same.

Second, how large should the signal-to-noise ratio be for a model apparent signal to be accepted as a "real" signal? Chervin and Schneider (1976) first attempted a quantitative approach to this question for GCM studies by introducing classical statistical significance testing. The model control and external change simulations were considered to represent finite samples from hypothetical infinite populations of GCM simulations. They used the

"Student's t," which is the expected statistical distribution of the estimated signal-to-noise ratio, if defined as above. A "null hypothesis" that no change has occurred (that is, both control and external change simulations are from the same population) is introduced and the "probability" that this hypothesis is incorrect is determined from the t distribution. If there is more than some, e.g., a 95%, chance that the hypothesis is incorrect, the null hypothesis is rejected and the signal is accepted as real. Erroneous rejection of the null hypothesis is referred to as a "type I error" and erroneous acceptance of the null hypothesis as a "type II error." The probability of a type II error can only be established in the context of some specific alternative hypothesis. Hayashi (1982) points out that the null hypothesis can apply to any other value of signal besides zero and that it is useful to apply it to the estimated signal and hence develop confidence limits ("error bars") about the apparent signal. Either the confidence limits can be regarded as a random variable with the specified probability of overlapping the true signal or, alternatively, the unknown true signal can be treated as random with the specified probability of falling inside the confidence limits.

To apply the Chervin–Schneider–Hayashi methodology, it is necessary to choose some basic averaging interval, typically 30–100 days, and generate samples of statistically independent GCM simulations over this period. However, with a small number of samples, this procedure loses effectiveness for rejecting null hypotheses because of the uncertainty of the variance estimate, which acts to spread out the wings of the t distribution relative to the corresponding Gaussian. That is, a larger estimated signal-to-noise ratio is required to achieve a given level of statistical confidence.

Katz (1982) points out that the estimated signal-to-noise level required for 95% confidence can be more than a factor of two larger for a low degree of freedom t distribution compared with a Gaussian distribution. He suggests using a time-series analysis for increasing the effective number of independent samples to the point at which a Gaussian distribution can be used, i.e., the limit of the t statistic for a large sample number. His procedure involves fitting an optimum Markov model to the time series, which effectively allows for autocorrelation in time. Thus, it gives the effective number of independent samples achieved by use of daily data. Katz notes that use of a first-order Markov model in the same calculations he carried out gave a somewhat smaller estimate of the effective number of samples. If this were always the case and if the amount of data available to analyze were not already marginal, a first-order Markov fit could be used for a conservative (upper limit) noise estimate. Madden and Ramanathan (1980), on the other hand, argue that a higher-order regression fit is needed to represent adequately the contribution of low-frequency climatic variations.

To obtain simply a variability estimate with adequate degrees of freedom, one might revert to the use of samples over smaller time intervals than conventional, e.g., by using 5-day averages separated by 5-day gaps. The analysis by Madden and Shea (1978) shows that, at least for surface temperature over the United States, the characteristic time in days between effectively independent samples is about 5 days. The number of samples obtained by such a procedure could then be multiplied by some conservative factor, e.g., 0.8, to adjust for the modest autocorrelation occurring between samples. Breaking down a given time interval into a larger number of time samples would not reduce the real signal-to-noise ratio but could help narrow the confidence limits by giving a less uncertain estimate of model noise.

Statistical analyses such as discussed above apply most neatly to analysis of a single scalar signal such as global average surface temperature. However, when applied jointly to a number of variables and a number of model locations, they can lose quantitative usefulness and become only of descriptive value. The most obvious difficulty is illustrated by the fact that if a very large number of independent variables were analyzed with no real signal, 5% of them would lead to a type I error at the 5% significance level. If a smaller number of independent variables were analyzed under the same conditions, then the expected value for type I error would still be 5% of the points. However, there would be a 5% probability of quite a few more type I error points from chance sampling considerations, e.g., 8 points out of 100 points (Henderson-Sellers, 1985).

More seriously, since different model variables are correlated spatially and with each other, patterns of apparent signal may be a consequence of correlated error fluctuations. Thus, a multivariate statistical approach would seem desirable. However, an analysis involving all the grid-point degrees of freedom in a GCM could be computationally prohibitive both from the viewpoint of the size of the data sample required and the statistical computations involved. Hasselman (1979) finds that a single cosine wave signal could be detected at the 95% confidence level in a 100-point white noise system only if 73% of the grid-point response values exceeded their individual 95% confidence limits.

Because of the spatial and variable correlations and the physical processes involved, a GCM climate model may have many fewer real degrees of freedom than apparent degrees of freedom. Various kinds of spatial averaging can be used to reduce the analyzed data to a few degrees of freedom, as illustrated by the example analyzed by Hayashi (1982). Some alternative efficient representation of the model noise such as empirical orthogonal functions may be useful (Hasselman, 1979), although each individual degree of freedom may be statistically unstable, as discussed by North *et al.* (1982). Some variables, in particular rainfall, switch on and off as well as vary in magnitude. Thus, separate statistical models are required for occurrence and intensity (Katz, 1983).

One important practical question in testing the statistical significance of model results is the meaning to be attached to statistical significance. This issue touches on the debates that have raged back and forth between professional statisticians for the past several decades or more. Are there real probability distributions whose properties we are trying to uncover? Or, alternatively, are we trying to improve our own confidence levels as to expected outcomes? If we take the latter Bayesian viewpoint, we should combine whatever *a priori* judgments we have with model results for establishing our real confidence levels in the model outcome. As an extreme example, we might be 95% confident that we would find some effect in a long-enough model run. If we analyzed a simulation of short duration and did not see the effect, wouldn't we still be 95% confident? Alternatively, many of us may be unconvinced by connections between solar variability and climate reported at the 99% confidence level because of our *a priori* conviction as to the improbability of such an effect.

Another serious question is what significance level should be used to accept or reject the hypothesis of no change. The concept of significance testing is most appropriate to such questions as whether or not a change in model parameterization made some obvious change in model performance. Perhaps the safest approach in studies of the model response to external changes of more direct practical interest is to avoid the question of significance testing entirely and simply use the confidence limit approach for reporting results. It certainly should be recognized that such tools as the 5% and 1% probability criteria for rejecting a hypothesis of zero change were developed for questions other than those of climate sensitivity, e.g., quality control in a screw factory, or establishing whether there is a real difference between the length of wings of two species of housefly.

Practically speaking, the appropriate statistical concept in many GCM sensitivity studies is not "significance testing" but rather "decision-making." The question of the appropriate significance level should then be quantified by introducing a "risk" or "cost-benefit" function r; e.g., if there is no cost for correct decisions,

$$r = r_1 p_1 + r_2 p_2$$

where p_1 is the probability of making a type I error and r_1 the cost of making such an error, p_2 the probability of making a type II error, and r_2 the cost of the type II error. The probability criterion should be chosen to minimize such a risk function. In pure (that is, societally irrelevant) research, the primary risks involved are to one's scientific reputation and self-esteem. Since scientists usually suffer more loss of reputation from claiming incorrectly a positive effect than missing a real positive effect (because of lack of enough data), they rightly opt for small probability of type I error. Conversely, if a GCM study were to indicate that action Y might immediately "destroy the world," even a 1% probability that such an event were going to occur (type II error) would prudently suggest avoiding action Y. Of course, if "end of the world" were far enough in the future, we might employ the standard future discounting approach of economists to show that action Y was still sensible.

The problem with using a risk function concept as discussed above is that most scientists dislike subjective choices and would feel unqualified to evaluate any risks beyond their own. However, they may implicitly be evaluating risks but doing so badly by picking some arbitrary probability level for type I error. Perhaps guidelines for acceptable probabilities for type I error for societally important questions of climate change should be established by national committees with sufficient competence to evaluate the relative costs of type I and type II errors. Unfortunately, such committees are sometimes guided more by risks to the funding of their own scientific disciplines than by broader considerations.

Decision making or risk evaluation using climate models may benefit much more from an estimated probability distribution of outcomes than from the simple yes–no framework of classic hypothesis testing just discussed. Furthermore, information as to the nature and probability of the most extreme changes possible may be more important than knowing the most likely outcome, as, e.g., has been the case in the design of nuclear power plants.

In summary, past applications of statistical concepts to GCM studies have suffered from inefficient sampling of model integrations, difficulty in applying univariate techniques to a multivariate system, and inappropriate interpretations of statistical evidence. These problems have also recently been reviewed by Henderson-Sellers (1985). Future studies of climate sensitivity using GCMs will benefit from further efforts to clarify and improve the application of statistical concepts.

9. CONCLUDING REMARKS

By considering the topic of climate sensitivity, this essay has highlighted aspects of climate models especially in need of improvement. The radiative interactions of clouds have long been recognized as possibly very important, but a convincing validated treatment is still far from tractable. The recent Hansen et al. (1984) study has again emphasized the potential of cloud changes to modify greatly the sensitivity of the climate system to external forcing. The storage and redistribution of thermal energy by oceans have also once again been recognized as of major importance though also still intractable in detail.

High-latitude climate feedback processes have also long been recognized to be of considerable importance. However, this essay has pointed out that they may be even more important and more uncertain than generally recognized. In particular, ice-albedo feedbacks generated in GCMs have shown a wide variability in overall magnitude and in detail, and the consensus magnitude of this feedback may have doubled from its accepted value a few years ago. Simulated sea ice appears to be the most important factor in determining model ice-albedo feedback and is of considerable uncertainty because of oversimplified sea-ice models, lack of ocean current interaction, poor knowledge of high-latitude cloudiness and its climatic variation, and questionable treatment of sea-ice albedo.

We have also argued that model treatments of land-surface processes need to be improved in GCMs both from the viewpoint of improved climate simulation and for the study of questions of the impacts of climate change. Modeling studies of paleoclimatic questions help to improve our understanding of climate system and model sensitivities to large perturbations.

Statistical methods have been developed for interpretation of GCM climate sensitivity studies. We have suggested the need for further efficiency and clarification in the use of these procedures to optimize the information they provide and its application. Further clarification of the most extreme possible changes of future climate is needed as well as attempts to narrow the range of possibilities.

ACKNOWLEDGMENTS

I am grateful for helpful comments on the manuscript by E. Barron, R. Chervin, A. Henderson-Sellers, S. Manabe, S. Schneider, S. Thompson, and W. Washington.

REFERENCES

Barron, E. J., and Washington, W. M. (1984). The role of geographic variables in explaining paleoclimates: Results from Cretaceous climate model sensitivity studies. *JGR, J. Geophys. Res.* **89**, 1267–1279.

Barry, R. G., Henderson-Sellers, A., and Shine, K. P. (1984). Climate sensitivity and the marginal cryosphere. *In* "Climate Processes and Climate Sensitivity" (J. E. Hansen and T. Takahashi, eds.), Maurice Ewing Ser. No. 5, pp. 221–237. Am. Geophys. Union, Washington, D.C.

Berner, R. A., Lasaga, A. C., and Garrels, R. M. (1983). The carbonate-silicate geochemical cycle and its effect on atmospheric carbon dioxide over the last 100 million years. *Am. J. Sci.* **283**, 641–683.

Beven, K. (1979). A sensitivity analysis of the Penman-Monteith actual evapotranspiration estimates. *J. Hydrol.* **44**, 169–190.

Bowman, K. P. (1982). Sensitivity of an annual mean diffusive energy balance model with an ice sheet. *JGR, J. Geophys. Res.* **87**, 9667–9674.

Broecker, W. S., and Takahashi, T. (1984). Is there a tie between atmospheric CO_2 content and ocean circulation? *In* "Climate Processes and Climate Sensitivity" (J. E. Hansen and T. Takahashi, eds.), Maurice Ewing Ser. No. 5, pp. 314–326. Am. Geophys. Union, Washington, D.C.

Broecker, W. S., Takahashi, T., Simpson, H. S., and Peng, T.-H. (1979). Fate of fossil fuel carbon dioxide and the global carbon budget. *Science* **206**, 409–422.

Bryan, K., Komro, F. G., Manabe, S., and Spelman, M. J. (1982). Transient climate response to increasing atmospheric carbon dioxide. *Science* **215**, 56–58.

Budyko, M. I. (1969). The effect of solar radiation variations on the climate of the earth. *Tellus* **21**, 611–619.

Cess, R. D. (1976). Climatic change: An appraisal of atmospheric feedback mechanisms employing zonal climatology. *J. Atmos. Sci.* **33**, 1831–1843.

Cess, R. D. (1983). Arctic aerosols: Model estimates of interactive influences upon the surface-atmosphere clear-sky radiation budget. *Atmos. Environ.* **17**, 2555–2564.

Cess, R. D., and Goldenberg, S. D. (1981). The effect of ocean heat capacity upon global warming due to increasing atmospheric carbon dioxide. *JGR, J. Geophys. Res.* **86**, 498–502.

Charney, J., Quirk, W. J., Chow, S.-H., and Kornfield, J. (1977). A comparative study of the effects of albedo change on drought in semiarid regions. *J. Atmos. Sci.* **34**, 1366–1385.

Chervin, R. M. (1980). On the simulation of climate and climate change with general circulation models. *J. Atmos. Sci.* **37**, 1903–1913.

Chervin, R. M. (1981). On the comparison of observed and GCM simulated climate ensembles. *J. Atmos. Sci.* **38**, 885–901.

Chervin, R. M., and Schneider, S. H. (1976). On determining the statistical significance of climate experiments with general circulation models. *J. Atmos. Sci.* **33**, 405–412.

Chou, M.-D., Peng, L., and Arking, A. (1982). Climate studies with a multi-layer energy balance model. Part II. The role of feedback mechanisms in the CO_2 problem. *J. Atmos. Sci.* **39**, 2657–2666.

Climate Research Board (1979). "Carbon Dioxide and Climate: Scientific Assessment." Natl. Acad. Sci., Washington, D.C.

DeBruin, H. A. R. (1983). A model for the Priestley-Taylor parameter α. *J. Clim. Appl. Meteorol.* **22**, 572–578.

Dickinson, R. E. (1981). Convergence rate and stability of ocean-atmosphere coupling schemes with a zero-dimensional climate model. *J. Atmos. Sci.* **38**, 2112–2120.

Dickinson, R. E. (1982). Modeling climate changes due to carbon dioxide increases. *In* "Carbon Dioxide Review 1982" (W. C. Clark, ed.), pp. 101–133. Oxford Univ. Press, London and New York.

Dickinson, R. E. (1984). Modeling evapotranspiration for three-dimensional global climate models. *In* "Climate Processes and Climate Sensitivity" (J. E. Hansen and T. Takahashi, eds.), Maurice Ewing Ser. No. 5, pp. 58–72. Am. Geophys. Union, Washington, D.C.

Fels, S. B., Mahlman, J. D., Schwarzkopf, M. D., and Sinclair, R. W. (1980). Stratospheric sensitivity to perturbations in ozone and carbon dioxide: Radiative and dynamical response. *J. Atmos. Sci.* **37**, 2265–2297.

Golitsyn, G. S., and Mokhov, I. I. (1978). Sensitivity estimates and the role of clouds in simple models of climate. *Izv., Acad. Sci., USSR, Atmos. Oceanic Phys. (Engl. Transl.)* **14**, 569–576.

Hall, M. C. G., and Cacuci, D. G. (1983). Physical interpretation of the adjoint functions for sensitivity analysis of atmospheric models. *J. Atmos. Sci.* **40**, 2537–2546.

Hansen, J., Lacis, A., Rind, D., Russell, G., Stone, P., Fung, I., Ruedy, R., and Lerner, J. (1984). Climate sensitivity: Analysis of feedback mechanisms. *In* "Climate Processes and Climate Sensitivity" (J. E. Hansen and T. Takahashi, eds.), Maurice Ewing Ser. No. 5, pp. 130–163. Am. Geophys. Union, Washington, D.C.

Hartmann, D. L. (1984). On the role of global-scale waves in ice-albedo and vegetation-albedo feedback. *In* "Climate Processes and Climate Sensitivity" (J. E. Hansen and T. Takahashi, eds.), Maurice Ewing Ser. No. 5, pp. 18–28. Am. Geophys. Union, Washington, D.C.

Hartmann, D. L., and Short, D. A. (1979). On the role of zonal asymmetries in climate change. *J. Atmos. Sci.* **36**, 519–528.

Hasselman, K. (1979). On the signal-to-noise problem in atmospheric response studies. *In* "Meteorology over Tropical Oceans," pp. 251–259. R. Meteorol. Soc., London.

Hayashi, Y. (1982). Confidence intervals of a climatic signal. *J. Atmos. Sci.* **39**, 1895–1905.

Held, I. M. (1982). Climate models and the astronomical theory of the ice ages. *Icarus* **50**, 449–461.

Henderson-Sellers, A. (1985). How statistically significant is climate change? (unpublished).

Henderson-Sellers, A., and Gornitz, V. (1984). Possible climatic impacts of land cover transformations, with particular emphasis on tropical deforestation. *Clim. Change* **6**, 231–256.

Hibler, W. D., III (1984). The role of sea ice dynamics in modeling CO_2 increases. *In* "Climate Processes and Climate Sensitivity" (J. E. Hansen and T. Takahashi, eds.), Maurice Ewing Ser. No. 5, pp. 238–253. Am. Geophys. Union, Washington, D.C.

Hibler, W. D., III, and Bryan, K. (1984). Ocean circulation: Its effects on seasonal sea-ice simulations. *Science* **224**, 489–491.

Hoffert, M. I., Flannery, B. P., Callegari, A. J., Hsieh, C. T., and Wiscombe, W. (1983). Evaporation-limited tropical temperatures as a constraint on climate sensitivity. *J. Atmos. Sci.* **40**, 1659–1668.

Katz, R. W. (1982). Statistical evaluation of climate experiments with general circulation models: A parametric time series modeling approach. *J. Atmos. Sci.* **39**, 1446–1455.

Katz, R. W. (1983). Statistical procedures for making inferences about precipitation changes simulated by an atmospheric general circulation model. *J. Atmos. Sci.* **40**, 2193–2201.

Lee, Y. W. (1960). "Statistical Theory of Communication." Wiley, New York.

Leith, C. E. (1973). The standard error of time-averaged estimates of climatic means. *J. Appl. Meteorol.* **12**, 1066–1069.

Lian, M. S., and Cess, R. D. (1977). Energy balance climate models: A reappraisal of ice-albedo feedback. *J. Atmos. Sci.* **34**, 1058–1062.

Luxmoore, R. J., Stolzy, J. L., and Holdeman, J. T. (1981). Sensitivity of a soil-plant-atmosphere model to changes in air temperature, dew point temperature, and solar radiation. *Agric. Meteorol.* **23**, 115–129.

McNaughton, K. G. (1976). Evaporation and advection. I. Evaporation from extensive homogeneous surfaces. *Q. J. R. Meteorol. Soc.* **102**, 181–191.

McNaughton, K. G., and Jarvis, P. G. (1983). Predicting effects of vegetation changes on transpiration and evaporation. *In* "Water Deficits and Plant Growth" (T. T. Kozlowski, ed.), Vol. 7, pp. 1–47. Academic Press, New York.

Madden, R. A., and Ramanathan, V. (1980). Detecting climate change due to increasing carbon dioxide. *Science* **209**, 763–768.

Madden, R. A., and Shea, D. J. (1978). Estimates of the natural variability of time-averaged temperatures over the United States. *Mon. Weather Rev.* **106**, 1695–1703.

Manabe, S., and Stouffer, R. J. (1980). Sensitivity of a global climate model to an increase of CO_2 concentration in the atmosphere. *JGR, J. Geophys. Res.* **85**, 5529–5554.

Manabe, S., and Wetherald, R. T. (1967). Thermal equilibrium of the atmosphere with a given distribution of relative humidity. *J. Atmos. Sci.* **24**, 241–259.

Manabe, S., and Wetherald, R. T. (1975). The effect of doubling the CO_2 concentration on the climate of a general circulation model. *J. Atmos. Sci.* **32**, 3–15.

Manabe, S., Wetherald, R. T., and Stouffer, R. J. (1981). Summer dryness due to an increase of atmospheric CO_2 concentration. *Clim. Change* **3**, 347–386.

Michael, P., Hoffert, M., Tobias, M., and Tichler, J. (1981). Transient climate response to changing carbon dioxide concentration. *Clim. Change* **3**, 137–153.

Newkirk, G., Jr. (1983). Variations in solar luminosity. *Annu. Rev. Astron. Astrophys.* **21**, 429–467.

North, G. R., Cahalan, R. F., and Coakley, J. A. (1981). Energy-balance climate models. *Rev. Geophys. Space Phys.* **19**, 91–122.

North, G. R., Bell, T. L., Cahalan, R. F., and Moeng, F. J. (1982). Sampling errors in the estimation of empirical orthogonal functions. *Mon. Weather Rev.* **110**, 699–706.

North, G. R., Mengel, J. G., and Short, D. A. (1983). Simple energy balance model resolving the seasons and the continents: Application to the astronomical theory of the ice ages. *JGR, J. Geophys. Res.* **88**, 6576–6586.

North, G. R., Mengel, J. G., and Short, D. A. (1984). On the transient response patterns of climate to time-dependent concentrations of atmospheric CO_2. *In* "Climate Processes and Climate Sensitivity" (J. E. Hansen and T. Takahashi, eds.), Maurice Ewing Ser. No. 5, pp. 164–170.

Parkinson, C. L., and Bindschadler, R. A. (1984). Response of Antarctic sea ice to uniform atmospheric temperature increases. *In* "Climate Processes and Climate Sensitivity" (J. E. Hansen and T. Takahashi, eds.), Maurice Ewing Ser. No. 5, pp. 254–264. Am. Geophys. Union, Washington, D.C.

Priestley, C. H. B., and Taylor, R. J. (1972). On the assessment of surface heat flux and evaporation using large-scale parameters. *Mon. Weather Rev.* **100**, 81–92.

Ramanathan, V. (1977). Interactions between ice-albedo, lapse-rate, and cloud-top feedbacks: An analysis of the nonlinear response of a GCM climate model. *J. Atmos. Sci.* **34**, 1885–1897.

Ramanathan, V., and Coakley, J. A., Jr. (1978). Climate modeling through radiative-convective models. *Rev. Geophys. Space Phys.* **16**, 465–489.

Robock, A. (1983a). Ice and snow feedbacks and the latitudinal and seasonal distribution of climate sensitivity. *J. Atmos. Sci.* **40**, 986–997.

Robock, A. (1983b). The dust cloud of the century. *Nature (London)* **301**, 373–374.

Saxton, K. E. (1975). Sensitivity analyses of the combination evapotranspiration equation. *Agric. Meteorol.* **15**, 343–353.

Schlesinger, M. E. (1983). A review of climate models and their simulation of CO_2-induced warming. *Int. J. Environ. Stud.* **20**, 103–114.

Schneider, S. H., and Dickinson, R. E. (1974). Climate modeling. *Rev. Geophys. Space Phys.* **12**, 447–493.

Schneider, S. H., and Mass, C. (1975). Volcanic dust, sunspots, and temperature trends. *Science* **190**, 741–746.

Schneider, S. H., and Thompson, S. L. (1981). Atmospheric CO_2 and climate: Importance of the transient response. *JGR, J. Geophys. Res.* **86**, 3135–3147.

Schneider, S. H., Washington, W. M., and Chervin, R. M. (1978). Cloudiness as a climatic feedback mechanism: Effects on cloud amounts of prescribed global and regional surface temperature changes in the NCAR GCM. *J. Atmos. Sci.* **35**, 2207–2221.

Sellers, P. J., and Lockwood, J. G. (1981). A numerical simulation of the effects of changing vegetation type on surface hydroclimatology. *Clim. Change* **3**, 121–136.

Sellers, W. D. 1969. A global climate model based on the energy balance of the earth-atmosphere system. *J. Appl. Meteorol.* **8**, 392–400.

Semtner, A. J., Jr. (1984). On modelling the seasonal thermodynamic cycle of sea ice in studies of climate change. *Clim. Change* **6**, 27–38.

Shukla, J., and Mintz, Y. (1982). Influence of land-surface evapotranspiration on the earth's climate. *Science* **215**, 1498–1501.

Shuttleworth, W. J., and Calder, I. R. (1979). Has the Priestley-Taylor equation any relevance to forest evaporation? *J. Appl. Meteorol.* **18**, 639–646.

Spelman, M. J., and Manabe, S. (1984). Influence of oceanic heat transport upon the sensitivity of a model climate. *JGR, J. Geophys. Res.* **89**, 571–586.

Thompson, S. L., and Schneider, S. H. (1982). Carbon dioxide and climate: The importance of realistic geography in estimating the transient temperature response. *Science* **217**, 1031–1033.

Trenberth, K. E. (1983). Interactions between orographically and thermally forced planetary waves. *J. Atmos. Sci.* **40**, 1126–1153.

Turco, R. P., Toon, O. B., Ackerman, T., Pollack, J. B., and Sagan, C. (1983). Nuclear winter: Global consequences of multiple nuclear explosions. *Science* **222**, 1283–1292.

Warren, S., and Schneider, S. H. (1979). Seasonal simulations as a test for uncertainties in the parameterizations of a Budyko-Sellers zonal climate model. *J. Atmos. Sci.* **36**, 1377–1391.

Washington, W. M., and Meehl, G. A. (1983). General circulation model experiments on the climatic effects due to a doubling and quadrupling of carbon dioxide concentration. *JGR, J. Geophys. Res.* **88**, 6600–6610.

Washington, W. M., and Meehl, G. A. (1984). Seasonal cycle experiment on the climate sensitivity due to a doubling of CO_2 with an atmospheric general circulation model coupled to a simple mixed layer ocean model. *JGR, J. Geophys. Res.* **59**, 9475–9503.

Wetherald, R. T., and Manabe, S. (1975). The effects of changing the solar constant on the climate of a general circulation model. *J. Atmos. Sci.* **32**, 2044–2059.

Wetherald, R. T., and Manabe, S. (1980). Cloud cover and climate sensitivity. *J. Atmos. Sci.* **37**, 1485–1510.

Wetherald, R. T., and Manabe, S. (1981). Influence of seasonal variation upon the sensitivity of a model climate. *JGR, J. Geophys. Res.* **86**, 1194–1204.

Willson, R. C., Gulkis, S., Janssen, M., Hudson, H. S., and Chapman, G. A. (1981). Observations of solar irradiance variability. *Science* **211**, 700–702.

World Meteorological Organization (1982). "WMO Global Ozone Research and Monitoring Project," Rep. No. 14. Report of the Meeting of Experts on Potential Climatic Effects of Ozone and Other Minor Trace Gases, Boulder, Colorado, 13–17 September 1982. WMO, Geneva.

Yeh, T.-C., Wetherald, R. T., and Manabe, S. (1983). A model study of the short-term climatic and hydrologic effects of sudden snow-cover removal. *Mon. Weather Rev.* **111**, 1013–1024.

CO$_2$ AND HYDROLOGY

SYUKURO MANABE

AND

RICHARD T. WETHERALD

Geophysical Fluid Dynamics Laboratory/NOAA
Princeton University
Princeton, New Jersey

1. INTRODUCTION

In the preceding article, Dickinson (this volume) critically reviews the current status of climate sensitivity research and identifies the issues that require emphasis in future investigations. This article presents, as an example, some of the results from the recent studies of climate sensitivity that have been conducted at the Geophysical Fluid Dynamics Laboratory (GFDL) under the leadership of Joseph Smagorinsky. More specifically, it discusses the hydrologic change of climate due to the future increase of the CO$_2$ concentration in the atmosphere.

It is well known that Smagorinsky (1956) pioneered the development of a numerical weather prediction model of the atmosphere that forecast precipitation. In addition, he and one of the present authors collaborated in the construction of a general circulation model (GCM) of the atmosphere in which the influence of the hydrologic cycle is taken into consideration for the first time (Manabe *et al.*, 1965). Therefore, it appears quite appropriate to discuss the hydrologic aspect of climate sensitivity studies in this volume dedicated to Smagorinsky.

It has been observed that the atmospheric concentration of carbon dioxide has been increasing steadily. According to the latest report of the U.S. National Academy of Sciences (1983), it is most likely that the atmospheric CO$_2$ concentration will exceed 600 ppm (the nominal doubling of the recent level) in the third quarter of the next century due mainly to the future

131

increase in the fossil fuel combustion. Since CO_2 is almost transparent to solar radiation but strongly absorbs the terrestrial radiation around the wave length of 15 μm, it has been suggested that the increase in the concentration of CO_2 raises the atmospheric temperature [e.g., Callender (1938)]. Based on the results from climate models with wide varieties of complexity, a recent report from the U.S. National Academy of Sciences (1982) estimated that a doubling of CO_2 would cause a global surface-air warming of 3.0°C with a probable error of ± 1.5°C. In addition, it suggested that this CO_2-induced warming of surface air is particularly pronounced in high latitudes during winter. The report also noted that the increase of atmospheric CO_2 not only raises the tropospheric temperature but also alters the hydrologic processes that operate in the atmosphere and at the Earth's surface.

Unfortunately, the CO_2-induced changes in hydrology as determined by numerical experiments conducted by various authors differ substantially from one another (Schlesinger, 1983; Dickinson, this volume). Since the temporal variability of hydrology in a general circulation model of climate is very large, it has been very difficult to distinguish the signal (i.e., CO_2-induced change in hydrology) from noise (i.e., natural hydrologic variability in the model). This partly accounts for the difference among the results from various studies mentioned previously.

Nevertheless, general circulation models of the atmosphere, which are currently available, can simulate gross characteristics of the global distribution of hydrologic variables, such as the rates of precipitation and runoff [see, for example, Manabe (1982)]. This encourages one to analyze the results from such a model for the study of hydrologic sensitivity of climate.

This paper represents an attempt to develop a coherent picture of CO_2-induced change in hydrology based on a series of numerical experiments that have been conducted at the Geophysical Fluid Dynamics Laboratory by use of general circulation models of climate with various complexities (Manabe and Wetherald, 1975, 1980; Manabe and Stouffer, 1979, 1980; Wetherald and Manabe, 1981; Manabe et al., 1981). Special emphasis is placed on the identification and evaluation of the physical mechanisms responsible for these hydrologic changes.

2. NUMERICAL EXPERIMENTS

Although a wide variety of climate models have been used for the climate sensitivity studies conducted at the GFDL, the discussion in this article is based mainly on the results from a model in which a general circulation model of the atmosphere is coupled with a static mixed layer model of the ocean. In order to investigate how the increase in atmospheric CO_2 influences climate, two long-term integrations of a climate model are performed with normal and above-normal concentration of carbon dioxide. To facilitate the identification of the CO_2-induced change superposed on natural hydrologic fluctuation, it is assumed that the above-normal concentration has four times the normal value. This is much larger than the CO_2 concentration to be reached during the next century according to the latest projection by the U.S. National Academy of Sciences (1983). The period for the two time integrations is long enough (i.e., about 20 years) so that a model climate attains a quasi-steady state toward the end of these integrations. By comparing two model climates that emerge from these integrations one can evaluate the influence of the CO_2-increase on climate.

The basic structure of the aforementioned atmosphere–mixed layer ocean model is illustrated by the box diagram in Fig. 1. It consists of three basic components. They are (1) a general circulation model of the atmosphere, (2) a heat and water balance model over the continents, and (3) a simple model of the mixed layer ocean. The reader can refer to the paper by Manabe and Stouffer (1980) for the detailed description of the model. Nevertheless, it is worthwhile to briefly describe here the hydrologic and other parts of the model that are relevant to the discussions contained in this article.

In the atmospheric component of the model, the fluxes of solar and terrestrial radiation are computed by incorporating the effects of carbon dioxide, ozone, and water vapor. The mixing ratio of carbon dioxide is assumed to be constant everywhere. Ozone is specified as a function of latitude, height, and season. Cloud cover is prescribed to be zonally uniform and invariant with respect to season. The distribution of water vapor is determined by a prognostic scheme.

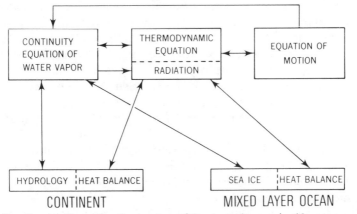

FIG. 1. Box diagram illustrating the structure of the atmosphere–mixed layer ocean model.

Precipitation is predicted wherever supersaturation is indicated by the continuity equation of water vapor. It is identified as snowfall when the air temperature near the surface falls below the freezing point. Otherwise it is identified as rainfall. The moist and dry convection are parameterized by the convective adjustment scheme as formulated by Manabe *et al.* (1965).

The temperature of the continental surface is determined so that the condition of local thermal equilibrium is satisfied among various surface heat balance components. A change in snow depth is computed as a net contribution from snowfall, sublimation, and snowmelt that is determined from the requirement of surface heat balance. High surface albedo is prescribed in snow-covered areas.

The budget of soil moisture is computed by the so-called bucket method. For the sake of simplicity, the field capacity of soil is assumed to be uniform everywhere and is 15 cm. If the soil moisture value exceeds the field capacity, runoff is predicted. A change of soil moisture is computed from the rates of rainfall, evaporation, snowmelt, and runoff. The rate of evaporation from the soil surface is determined as a function of soil moisture and the potential evaporation rate (i.e., hypothetical evaporation rate from a completely wet surface).

The oceanic component of the model is an idealized oceanic mixed layer, i.e., a well-mixed, vertically isothermal layer of sea water. For the sake of simplicity, it is assumed that the mixed layer has a uniform thickness of 68.5 m that is chosen to yield a realistic amplitude for the seasonal variation of sea-surface temperature. The change of the mixed layer temperature is computed from the budget of surface heat fluxes. The effects of horizontal heat transport by ocean currents and that of heat exchange between the mixed layer and the deeper layer of the ocean are neglected. In the presence of sea ice, the mixed layer temperature is fixed at the freezing point of sea water (i.e., $-2°C$) and the heat conduction through ice is balanced by the latent heat of freezing (or melting) at the bottom of the ice layer. This process together with the melting at the ice surface, sublimation, and snowfall determine the change in ice thickness. For the computation of net solar radiation at the oceanic surface, the albedo is prescribed as a function of latitude. Over the regions covered by sea ice, a higher value of albedo is used.

For the discussion in this article, the results from the two versions of the model are presented. The first version was originally used by Manabe and Stouffer (1980) and has a global computational domain with realistic geography. The second version was originally used by Wetherald and Manabe (1981) and has a limited computational domain with idealized geography as illustrated in Fig. 2. These two versions will be referred to as the global and sector models, respectively.

In the atmospheric component of the sector model, cyclic continuity is

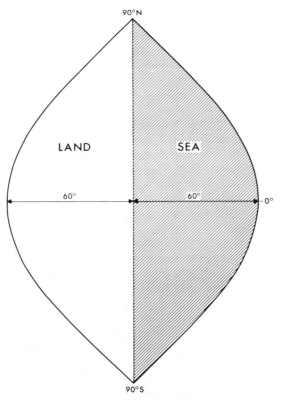

Fig. 2. Computational domain of the sector model.

assumed between the two meridional boundaries. Owing to the simplicity of its geography, this indicates the CO_2-induced climate change with a simple and broad distribution. Therefore, the results from the sector model are often very useful for the interpretation of the results from the global version of the model with more complicated, realistic geography. By seeking the common characteristics in the results from these two versions of the model, it has been possible to distinguish the signal of the CO_2-induced change from the large temporal variability of the model hydrology. Because of these reasons, the discussions in this article are conducted by comparing the results from these two versions of the model. This is essentially what Manabe *et al.* (1981) did in their study of the CO_2-induced hydrologic changes. Since the publication of their paper, it has been noted, however, that some important aspects of their results were not explained or discussed satisfactorily. This article reviews their results together with other studies from the present perspective.

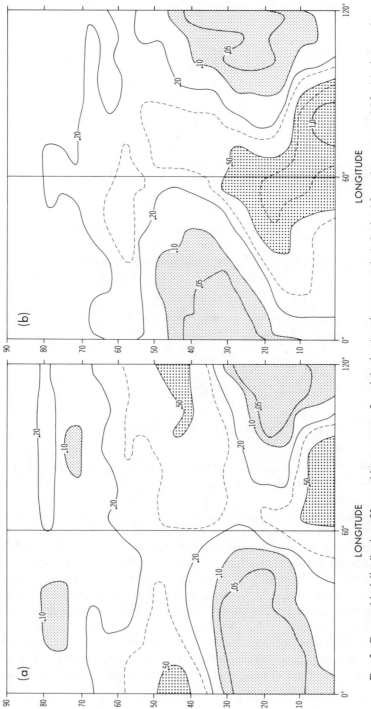

FIG. 3. Geographical distribution of 3-monthly mean rate of precipitation (centimeters per day) obtained from the sector model for (a) winter and (b) summer. The distributions of two hemispheres are averaged after shifting the phase of the seasonal variation of the Southern Hemisphere precipitation by 6 months. In both (a) and (b), the continent occupies the left half of the domain ranging from 0° to 60° longitude. [From Manabe *et al.* (1981).]

Figure 3 illustrates the geographical distributions of precipitation rate as simulated by the sector model for the winter and summer seasons. Despite its idealized geography, the sector model successfully reproduces the broad-scale features of the observed distribution of precipitation rate. For example, one can identify in the winter distribution a portion of the oceanic tropical rainbelt, a subtropical zone of minimum precipitation rate, and the middle-latitude rainbelt centered at about 45° latitude. In addition, one may note a meridional belt of relatively large precipitation rate along the east coast of subtropical part of the idealized model continent.

Turning to the summer distribution, one notes a very extensive region of intense precipitation that extends well into the continent from the western part of the tropical ocean. As compared with the winter distribution, the subtropical zone of minimum precipitation rate extends poleward accompanied by a more northward position of the middle-latitude rainbelt. These characteristics of the distribution of precipitation rate as simulated by the sector model are qualitatively similar to those of the observed precipitation rate.

One can refer to the paper by Manabe and Stouffer (1980) for the distribution of the precipitation rate from the global model with the realistic geography. Although the model distribution contains some unrealistic features, it nevertheless shares many common features with the observed distribution. The similarity between the observed and computed distributions of precipitation rate and other hydrologic variables is one of the important reasons why these models have been used for the climate sensitivity studies discussed in this article.

3. ANNUAL MEAN RESPONSE

As explained earlier, the CO_2-induced changes in hydrology are identified by comparing the two quasi-equilibrium states of a model with normal and above-normal concentrations of atmospheric carbon dioxide. One of the basic changes is the overall intensification of the hydrologic cycle. For example, the area mean rates of both precipitation and evaporation in the global model increase by as much as 7% in response to the quadrupling of atmospheric CO_2. Table I indicates the CO_2-induced percentage increase of the intensity of hydrologic cycle in various models including both the global and sector models described in this article. It clearly shows that the intensification of the hydrologic cycle occurs in a wide variety of models tabulated here.

One of the important factors responsible for the intensification of the hydrologic cycle is the change in surface radiation budget. An increase in atmospheric CO_2 enhances the downward flux of atmospheric radiation

TABLE I. PERCENTAGE INCREASE OF AREA-MEAN RATES OF
PRECIPITATION (OR EVAPORATION) RESULTING FROM DOUBLING (OR
QUADRUPLING) OF CO_2 CONCENTRATION IN A MODEL ATMOSPHERE[a]

Reference	Doubling (%)	Quadrupling (%)
Idealized geography		
Manabe and Wetherald (1975)[b]	7	
Manabe and Wetherald (1980)[b]	7	12
Wetherald and Manabe (1981)[b]		13
Wetherald and Manabe (1981)		10
Realistic geography		
Manabe and Stouffer (1979, 1980)		7
Hansen et al. (1984)[b]	6	
Hansen et al. (1984)	4	

[a] From U.S. Academy of Sciences (1982).
[b] No seasonal variation of insolation.

reaching the Earth's surface. In addition, the increase in the absolute humidity in the troposphere accompanied by the CO_2-induced warming also contributes to the increase in the downward flux of atmospheric radiation. Thus, a larger amount of radiative energy is received by the Earth's surface to be removed as turbulent fluxes of sensible and latent heat. This accounts for the increase in the global mean rate of evaporation.

One can identify another important factor that is responsible for the increase in the global mean evaporation rate. Following the Clausius–Clapeyron relationship, saturation vapor pressure increases almost exponentially with linear increase of temperature. This usually implies that surface-air difference in absolute humidity increases almost exponentially with a linear increase in the surface temperature. Thus, when the surface temperature is high, evaporation becomes a more effective means of ventilating the Earth's surface than the turbulent flux of sensible heat. Accordingly, a larger fraction of radiative energy received by the Earth's surface is removed as latent heat rather than sensible heat. Therefore, the rate of evaporation increases.

In order to balance the quasi-steady state of the model atmosphere, the increase in the area mean rate of evaporation should be matched by a similar increase of precipitation. This explains why the area mean rates of both evaporation and precipitation increase in response to an increase of atmospheric CO_2. For further discussion of the physical mechanisms for the intensification of the hydrologic cycle, see Manabe and Wetherald (1975) and Wetherald and Manabe (1975).

The global intensification of the hydrologic cycle due to an increase in atmospheric CO_2 is evident in Fig. 4, which illustrates the latitudinal distributions of annually averaged, zonal-mean rates of precipitation and evapo-

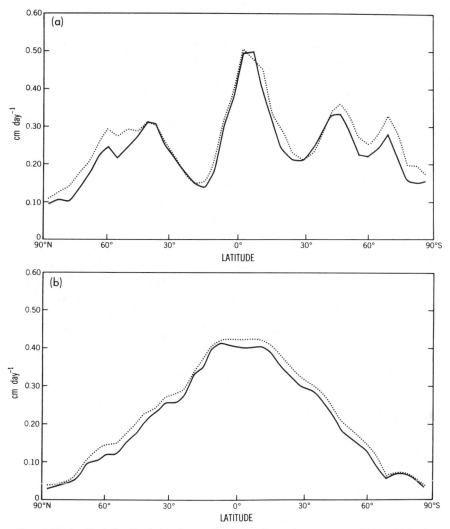

FIG. 4. Latitudinal distributions of annually averaged zonal mean rates of (a) precipitation and (b) evaporation. The results from the $4 \times CO_2$ and $1 \times CO_2$ experiments with the global model are indicated by dotted line and solid line, respectively. [From Manabe and Stouffer (1980). Reproduced with permission from *JGR, Journal of Geophysical Research* **85**(C-10), 5529–5554, copyright by the American Geophysical Union.]

ration from the global model with the normal ($1 \times CO_2$) and four times the normal ($4 \times CO_2$) concentration of the atmospheric CO_2. At high latitudes, the CO_2-induced increase in the precipitation rate is much larger than that of the evaporation rate. This result implies that the poleward moisture transport in the $4 \times CO_2$ atmosphere is larger than the corresponding transport in the $1 \times CO_2$ atmosphere. The increase in the moisture content of air resulting from the CO_2-induced warming of the model troposphere accounts for the increase of the poleward moisture transport as discussed by Manabe and Wetherald (1980).

The CO_2-induced warming is particularly pronounced in the lower tropo-

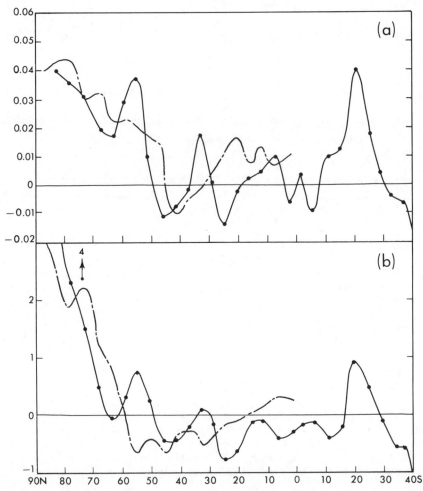

FIG. 5. Latitudinal distributions of the zonally averaged, annual-mean differences in (a) the rates of runoff (centimeters per day) and (b) soil moisture (centimeters) between the $4 \times CO_2$ and $1 \times CO_2$ experiment over the continents of the global model. The solid and dash-dotted lines illustrate the results from the global and sector model, respectively. The zonal averaging is done over the continents only.

sphere in high latitudes. This implies the penetration of warm, moisture-rich air into these latitudes, causing a large increase in precipitation rate. Therefore, both runoff rate and soil moisture also increase markedly in the Arctic and Subarctic regions of the global model. This is indicated in Fig. 5, which shows the latitudinal distributions of annually averaged, zonal-mean differences in the rate of runoff, and soil moisture between the $4 \times CO_2$ and $1 \times CO_2$ experiments. It is estimated that the rate of runoff in the global model, area-averaged over the continental regions poleward of 55°N, increases by as much as 45% in response to the quadrupling of the atmospheric CO_2 concentration. (The continental area chosen for this averaging includes most of the basins of the Siberian and Canadian rivers that flow into the Arctic Ocean.) Similar increases in both soil moisture and the rate of runoff also occur in the high latitudes of the sector model, as illustrated by Fig. 5.

In his recent review article, Schlesinger (1983) compared the distributions of the CO_2-induced changes in precipitation rate obtained from a wide variety of numerical experiments. With the exception of one experiment conducted under the assumption of fixed sea-surface temperature (Gates *et al.*, 1981), all experiments, including those performed by the present authors, indicate a relatively large increase in precipitation rate in high latitudes [see Figures 24 and 28 of Schlesinger (1983)]. Qualitative agreement among the results from these experiments suggests that this aspect of the CO_2-induced hydrologic change is particularly significant.

In Fig. 5, one also notes other CO_2-induced changes in zonally averaged, annual-mean soil moisture. For example, zonal-mean soil moisture reduces slightly in the middle latitudes and the subtropics of both models. In the tropics, zonal-mean soil moisture reduces for the global model, whereas it increases for the sector model. The discrepancy between the global and sector models in the tropics, suggests that the computed changes of soil moisture are not meaningful in this region. This speculation is consistent with the results of statistical significance tests that were conducted in Manabe *et al.* (1981).

4. Seasonal Response

This section evaluates how the CO_2-induced change in hydrology depends on seasons based on the results from both the sector and global models. Figures 6 and 7 contain the latitude–time distributions of the following variables from these two models:

(1) The difference in zonally averaged soil moisture between the $4 \times CO_2$ and $1 \times CO_2$ experiments (i.e., $\Delta[W]$).

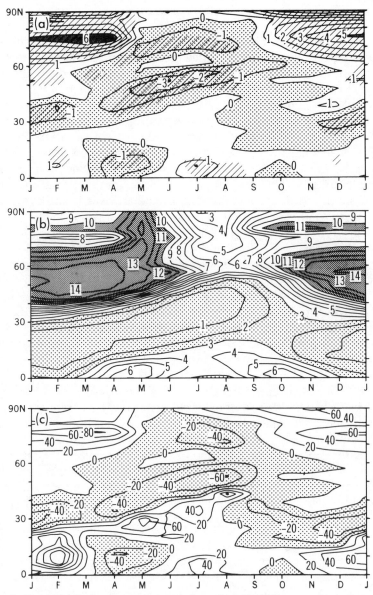

FIG. 6. The latitudinal and seasonal variation of (a) the difference of zonally averaged, monthly mean soil moisture (centimeters) between the $4 \times CO_2$ and the $1 \times CO_2$ experiment, (b) zonally averaged, monthly mean soil moisture from the $1 \times CO_2$ experiment, and (c) percentage change of the zonal-mean soil moisture from the $1 \times CO_2$ to the $4 \times CO_2$ experiment with the sector model. The zonal averaging is made over the continents. In (a) the areas identified by the shading of slant lines indicates the regions in which the soil moisture difference between the two experiments is statistically significant at or above 90% confidence level. [From Manabe *et al.* (1981).]

(2)   The zonally averaged soil moisture from the $1 \times CO_2$ experiment (i.e., $[W]$).

(3)   The fractional difference in zonally averaged soil moisture between the two experiments (i.e., $\Delta[W]/[W]$).

The distributions (2) and (3) are added to the figure for the assessment of the relative magnitude of the CO_2-induced change as compared with the original value of soil moisture. To evaluate the statistical significance of the results, the student t test is conducted. The slant-shaded areas in Figs. 6a and 7a indicate the zones where the CO_2-induced change of zonal-mean soil moisture is statistically significant at or above the 90% confidence level.

Although the idealized geography of the sector model is quite different from the realistic geography of the global model, one can identify several common characteristics in the distribution of the CO_2-induced change of soil moisture obtained from these two models. For example, the difference in soil moisture in high latitudes has a large positive value throughout most of the year with the exception of the summer season. As discussed in the preceding section, this CO_2-induced increase of soil moisture results from penetration of warm, moisture-rich air into the high latitudes of the model. One also notes two zones of reduced soil wetness at the middle and high latitudes during the summer season. In addition, a large fractional reduction of zontal-mean soil moisture is indicated at about 25°N during winter. These changes in soil moisture are statistically significant at or above the 90% confidence level. It is therefore worthwhile to explore the physical mechanisms responsible for these CO_2-induced changes of soil moisture.

To determine the mechanisms responsible for the CO_2-induced summer dryness in the middle and high latitudes described in the preceding, Manabe *et al.* (1981) made an extensive analysis of the seasonal variation of soil moisture budget obtained from the model experiments. Their analysis reveals that, in high latitudes, the CO_2-induced summer dryness results mainly from the change in the timing of the snowmelt season when soil is usually saturated with water. After the disappearance of snow cover, the rate of evaporation becomes very large and the depletion of soil moisture becomes very rapid because of marked reduction in surface albedo and increased surface absorption of insolation. Since the snowmelt season in the $4 \times CO_2$ experiment ends earlier than the corresponding season in the $1 \times CO_2$ experiment, the warm season of rapid soil moisture depletion begins earlier, resulting in less soil moisture in summer in the $4 \times CO_2$ experiment.

With the exception of the summer season, soil moisture in high latitudes increases in response to the increase of CO_2 concentration in the atmosphere. In the $4 \times CO_2$ experiment, a larger fraction of high-latitude precipitation occurs as rainfall during the late fall and early winter because of higher

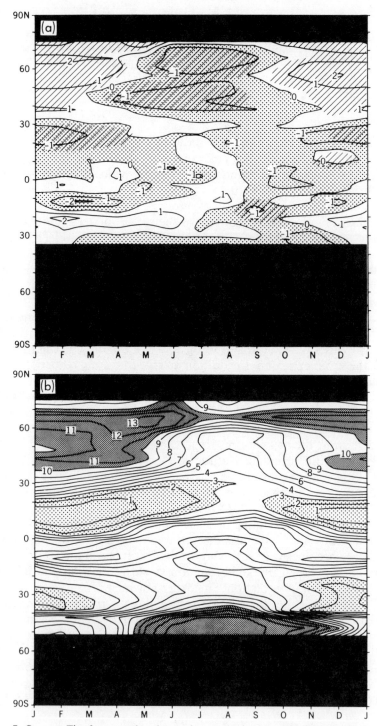

FIG. 7. Same as Fig. 6, except that the results are obtained by use of the global model.

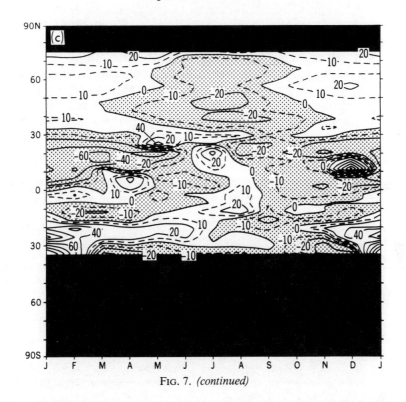

FIG. 7. *(continued)*

surface-air temperatures. This is why the high latitude storage of soil moisture in the 4 × CO₂ experiment is larger than that of the 1 × CO₂ experiment
during the late fall and remains at a high level throughout the winter when
snow cover prevents the evaporative reduction of soil moisture.

In the middle latitudes, the earlier timing of the spring maximum in
snowmelt also contributes to the summer dryness as it does in the high
latitudes. In addition, the CO₂-induced poleward shift of the mid-latitude
rainbelt also helps induce the summer dryness. In the CO₂-rich, warm climate, the mid-latitude rainbelt is located poleward of the corresponding
rainbelt in the normal CO₂ climate because of the penetration of moist and
warm air masses into higher latitudes. For example, this poleward shift is
evident in a later figure (Fig. 9a), which illustrates the latitudinal profile of
winter precipitation from the sector model. In the annual mean profile of
precipitation rate from the global model shown in Fig. 4a, the latitude of
maximum precipitation rate hardly changes in response to the CO₂-increase.
The shift, however, manifests itself as an asymmetric increase in precipitation rate relative to the latitude of maximum precipitation rate (i.e., the
CO₂-induced increase in the zonal belt located poleward of the maximum is

larger than the corresponding increase in the region located equatorward of the maximum). Figure 8 schematically illustrates the impact of this poleward shift on soil wetness. This figure indicates that, at the latitude identified by the thin zonal line, the spring transit of the mid-latitude rainbelt in the $4 \times CO_2$ experiment occurs earlier than the corresponding transit in the $1 \times CO_2$ experiment. Accordingly, the spring to summer reduction in precipitation rate occurs earlier. Since the soil in most regions of the middle latitudes is often saturated with water in spring for both experiments, this implies that the soil is dryer during summer in the $4 \times CO_2$ as compared with the $1 \times CO_2$ experiment.

One can identify another factor that contributes to the summer dryness in the middle latitudes. In the $4 \times CO_2$ experiment, the summer period of weak storminess begins earlier and ends later than the corresponding period in the

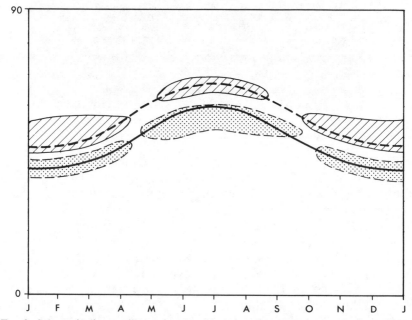

FIG. 8. Schematic diagram illustrating the change in soil wetness that results from the poleward shift of the middle-latitude rainbelt. Solid and dashed lines indicate the positions of the middle-latitude rainbelt in the $1 \times CO_2$ and $4 \times CO_2$ experiment, respectively. Stippled and cross-hatched areas indicate the areas of reduced and increased soil moisture, respectively. In addition to the poleward shift of the latitudinal profile of precipitation rate in the middle latitudes, other changes occur in the distribution of both precipitation and evaporation. The influences of these CO_2-induced changes on soil wetness are not taken into consideration in this schematic diagram.

standard experiment. It is expected that this feature helps reduce soil moisture during the summer season (Manabe *et al.,* 1981).

The possibility of summer reduction of soil moisture in the middle latitudes is also suggested by Mitchell (1983) on the basis of the results from some of his numerical experiments. However, the recent results by Washington and Meehl (1984) fail to indicate a similar CO_2-induced change of soil moisture. A comparative analysis of these results is required in order to determine the cause of the discrepancy.

By reversing the discussion of the relationship between the poleward shift of the middle-latitude rainbelt and the CO_2-induced summer dryness, one can identify the mechanism for the CO_2-induced winter wetness in the middle latitudes that is evident in Figs. 6 and 7. This is illustrated in the schematic diagram of Fig. 8 in which the regions of increased wetness are indicated by slanted shade. For the more rigorous discussion of the CO_2-induced change of soil moisture, refer to the study by Manabe *et al.* (1981) in which both the annual and seasonal components of soil moisture budget are examined.

Another important consequence of the CO_2-induced shift of the mid-latitude rainbelt is the enhanced dryness in the subtropics during winter. This enhanced winter dryness is indicated at about 35° latitude in Fig. 6 (from the sector model) and around 25°N in Fig. 7 (from the global model). It is also illustrated schematically in Fig. 8.

In order to evaluate the mechanism for this CO_2-induced winter dryness, Fig. 9 is constructed. This figure compares the latitudinal distributions of the rates of precipitation P, evaporation E, and $P - E$ during the December–January–February period obtained from both the $4 \times CO_2$ and $1 \times CO_2$ experiments conducted by the use of the sector model. According to this figure, the poleward shift of the mid-latitude rainbelt reduces $P - E$ and runoff equatorward of the latitude of maximum precipitation rate. In winter when the mid-latitude rainbelt is located at its lowest latitude, this $P - E$ reduction occurs in the subtropical latitudes and contributes to the winter dryness of soil, as illustrated in Fig. 8.

The winter dryness in the subtropics is evident in the results of Manabe *et al.* (1981) and was briefly noted in the review paper by Manabe (1983). However, this is the first article in which the physical mechanism responsible for this phenomenon is extensively discussed. A poleward shift of the middle-latitude rainbelt was also found to be responsible for a zonal belt of increased soil dryness in the middle latitudes of a model with the annual-mean insolation [see Figs. 13 and 14 in the paper by Manabe and Wetherald (1980)].

In order to appreciate the practical implication of the CO_2-induced change

148   SYUKURO MANABE AND RICHARD T. WETHERALD

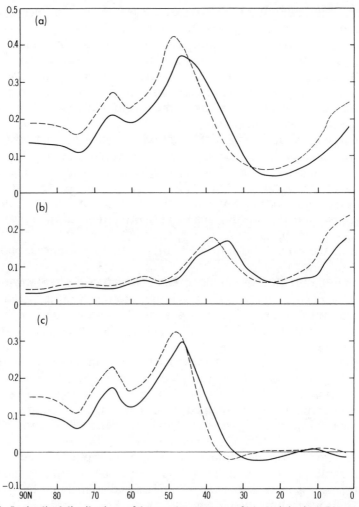

FIG. 9. Latitudinal distributions of the zonal-mean rates of (a) precipitation, (b) evaporation, and (c) precipitation minus evaporation in the continents of the sector model averaged over the three winter months. The zonal averaging is made over the continents. Solid and dashed lines indicate results from the $1 \times CO_2$ and $4 \times CO_2$ experiment, respectively.

of soil moisture described in this section and assess its detectability, one can compare this change with the natural variability of soil moisture by computing the signal-to-noise ratio S/N, defined by

$$S/N = \Delta_c[W]/\sigma_{[W]}$$

where $\Delta_c[W]$ and $\sigma_{[W]}$ are the CO_2-induced change and the standard deviation of zonally averaged soil moisture, respectively.

Manabe and Stouffer (Manabe, 1983) computed the latitudinal and seasonal variation of the signal-to-noise ratio for the CO_2-induced change of zonally averaged soil moisture obtained from the global model. Their results are illustrated in Fig. 10. As expected, the features with relatively high statistical significance also have a high signal-to-noise ratio. These features include the enhanced summer dryness in the middle and high latitudes of the Northern Hemisphere, the enhanced winter dryness around 25°N, and the increased wetness around 60°N during the fall–winter–spring period. The signal-to-noise ratios for these CO_2-induced changes are about two, implying that their magnitude is comparable with the amplitude of natural variability of zonal-mean soil moisture. These ratios may be compared with the signal-to-noise ratio for the CO_2-induced change in zonally averaged surface-air temperature, which ranges from 5 to 20 [see Manabe (1983)]. This result

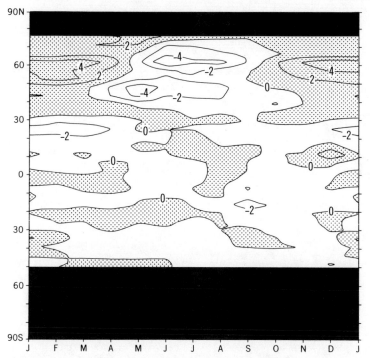

FIG. 10. The latitude–time distribution of the signal-to-noise ratio for the change of zonally averaged, monthly mean soil moisture over continents of the global model in response to the quadrupling of atmospheric CO_2 concentrations. [From Manabe (1983).]

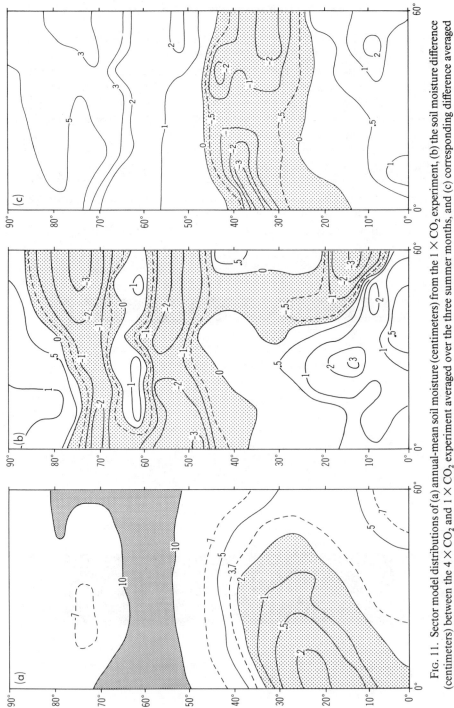

FIG. 11. Sector model distributions of (a) annual-mean soil moisture (centimeters) from the $1 \times CO_2$ experiment, (b) the soil moisture difference (centimeters) between the $4 \times CO_2$ and $1 \times CO_2$ experiment averaged over the three summer months, and (c) corresponding difference averaged over the three winter months. Note that only the distributions over the model continent are illustrated.

suggests that it is much harder to detect the CO_2-induced change of soil moisture than that of surface-air temperature.

So far, only the CO_2-induced changes in zonally averaged distribution of hydrological variables have been discussed. However, it is of particular interest to examine the geographical distributions of the CO_2-induced changes. Unfortunately, the geographical distribution of CO_2-induced hydrologic changes is obscured by the noise due to the natural variability of model hydrology. Therefore, it is often very difficult to distinguish these two from one another. Under these circumstances, the results from the sector model with simple geography are discussed first, followed by the evaluation of the results from the global model with realistic geography.

Figure 11 illustrates the geographical distributions of the CO_2-induced change in soil moisture obtained from the sector model for two seasons of a year. In addition, the geographical distribution of the annual-mean soil moisture itself is added to the same figure for reference. During the winter season, soil moisture reduces along the northern periphery of a subtropical desert (compare Fig. 11c with Fig. 11a). As discussed earlier, the poleward shift of the mid-latitude rainbelt is responsible for this CO_2-induced dryness in the subtropics. In a steppe region located at the poleward periphery of a subtropical desert, significant precipitation occurs only during winter, i.e., the period when the mid-latitude rainbelt is located at its lowest latitude. It is expected that this winter precipitation reduces in response to the CO_2-induced poleward shift of the mid-latitude rainbelt. Therefore, soil moisture reduces substantially during winter in the arid steppe located in the poleward periphery of the subtropical desert.

Figure 11c also indicates that, during winter, soil moisture increases significantly in high latitudes. As discussed already, this partly results from the increase in the fraction of precipitation that occurs as rainfall during the late fall and early winter. Furthermore, precipitation itself increases markedly in high latitudes in response to the increase of atmospheric carbon dioxide because of the penetration of moisture-rich air into the polar regions.

In the summer season, one can identify in Fig. 11b the two belts of reduced soil moisture in the middle and high latitudes. The mechanisms responsible for causing these double belts of reduced dryness were already discussed. The mid-latitude dryness extends the subtropical region of low soil moisture into higher latitudes in summer. This statement may be confirmed by referring to Fig. 6, which illustrates the zonally averaged soil moisture and its CO_2-induced change.

The results from the global model are illustrated in Fig. 12. As was the case in Fig. 11, the distribution of annual-mean soil moisture is added to the top portion of the figure for reference. This figure indicates that the global model successfully reproduces the region of low soil moisture in the Sahara, Gobi,

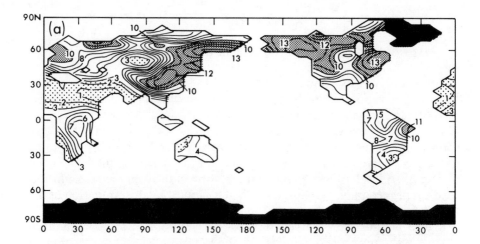

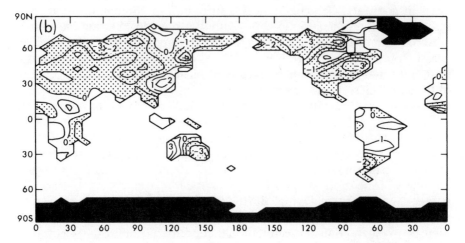

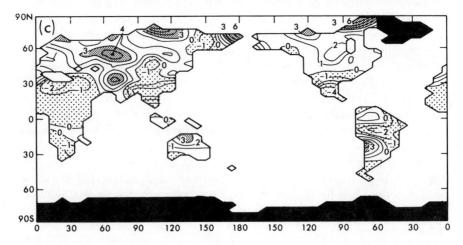

and Kalahari Deserts. However, it appears that soil moisture in Australia and the southwestern part of the United States is overestimated.

In Fig. 12c, which illustrates the geographical distribution of the CO$_2$-induced change of soil moisture during the period of December–January–February, one notes an extensive belt of reduced soil moisture along the northern periphery of the Sahara Desert. This is in qualitative agreement with the results from the sector model described earlier. However, Figs. 12b and 12c indicate that soil moisture does not necessarily reduce in other subtropical deserts with a smaller scale such as those in the Southern hemisphere. As discussed next, these small-scale changes of soil moisture are not statistically significant.

In high latitudes of the global model, i.e., over Siberia and Canada, one can identify extensive regions of increased soil wetness during winter (Fig. 12c) in qualitative agreement with the results from the sector model. Another feature of interest in Fig. 12b is the summer reduction of soil moisture in the middle and high latitudes over the North American and Eurasian continents. It is encouraging that this feature of the soil moisture reduction in the global model also resembles the CO$_2$-induced summer dryness pattern in the sector model described earlier. However, it is desirable to confirm that the mechanism for inducing the summer dryness of the zonally averaged soil moisture also causes the regional summer dryness over both the North American and Eurasian continents.

In the geographical distribution of the CO$_2$-induced change of soil moisture illustrated in Figs. 12b and 12c, one notes many small-scale changes of soil moisture in the tropics and the Southern Hemisphere. However, one should not take these changes too literally in view of (1) the low statistical significance of these details and (2) the failure of the climate model to simulate some of the small-scale changes in the observed geographical distributions of hydrologic variables. Further improvement of the climate model is required before one can determine with confidence the small-scale features of the CO$_2$-induced hydrologic change and investigate how it is related to the zonally averaged change discussed earlier. In addition, it is desirable to extend the period of numerical time integration of a model in a climate sensitivity experiment in order to obtain a result with higher statistical significance.

FIG. 12. Global model distributions of (a) annual-mean soil moisture (centimeters) from the $1 \times CO_2$ experiment, (b) the soil moisture difference (centimeters) between the $4 \times CO_2$ and $1 \times CO_2$ experiment averaged over the three summer months, and (c) corresponding difference averaged over the three winter months.

5. CONCLUDING REMARKS

Based on the results from a series of numerical experiments with climate models, it has been suggested that an increase in atmospheric CO_2 not only alters the atmospheric temperature but also has a profound influence on the global hydrology. The hydrologic changes include (1) an increase in the global-mean rates of both precipitation and evaporation, (2) a particularly large increase in annual-mean rate of runoff in high latitudes, (3) earlier arrival of the snowmelt season, (4) enhanced summer dryness in middle and high latitudes, (5) increased soil moisture in middle and high latitudes during the colder half of the year, and (6) a winter reduction of soil moisture in the poleward periphery of a subtropical desert. The physical mechanisms that cause these hydrologic changes in climate models are discussed.

In the mathematical models of climate that were used in the studies discussed in this article, the distribution of cloud cover is prescribed. If cloud cover is allowed to change, the CO_2-induced hydrologic changes could have been different from those identified here. Nevertheless, it is encouraging that the preliminary results from a GFDL model with predicted cloud cover include the hydrologic changes that are qualitatively similar to these changes. However, a prognostic scheme of cloud cover is at an early stage of development. The difficulty in developing a reliable parameterization of the cloud-radiation feedback process is one of major sources of uncertainty in the current assessment of climate sensitivity. This is why the World Climate Research Program places an increasing emphasis on the improvement of such a parameterization as manifested in the International Satellite Cloud Climatology Project.

Most of the hydrologic changes discussed here are either globally averaged or zonally averaged changes. Unfortunately, it has been very difficult to determine the detailed geographical distribution of the CO_2-induced hydrologic changes for the following reasons. First, the hydrologic states as simulated by a model undergo large temporal fluctuations, particularly in arid regions. Therefore, it is necessary to conduct the numerical time integration of the model with normal and high CO_2 concentrations over a very long period of time in order to distinguish the signals of CO_2-induced changes from the noise of natural hydrologic variability. This requires a very large amount of computer time. The second reason stems from the fact that the current simulations of the geographical distributions of hydrologic variables are far from satisfactory. The geographical details of the CO_2-induced climate change obtained from numerical experiments should be regarded with caution until a further improvement is achieved in the simulation of the observed climate.

One should also note that the atmosphere–mixed layer ocean models discussed in this article do not include oceanic heat transport. The study of Spelman and Manabe (1984) clearly indicates profound effects of oceanic heat transport on climate and hydrology. For the successful simulation of the geographical distribution of climate, it is therefore necessary to use a coupled ocean–atmosphere model in which the effect of oceanic heat transport is taken into consideration. Unfortunately, the currently available coupled models cannot simulate satisfactorily the global distribution of water mass and accordingly the heat exchange between the atmosphere and oceans. At the Geophysical Fluid Dynamics Laboratory of the National Oceanic and Atmospheric Administration (NOAA), continuous effort has been made for the improvement and validation of the ocean circulation model. For example, Sarmiento and Bryan (1982) and Sarmiento (1983) attempted to simulate the temporal and spatial variation of tritium released from nuclear weapon tests. The transient tracer experiment, which monitors various trace materials (including tritium) in the world oceans, will continue to provide ideal data for the validation of an ocean model. In addition, a plan is being developed for an ambitious observational program of the world oceans, i.e., the World Ocean Circulation Experiment. It is expected that the program will yield valuable data for model verification.

In this article, the CO_2-induced change of climate is investigated by comparing two climates of a model with the normal and above-normal concentration of carbon dioxide. In other words, the present article evaluates the total equilibrium response of a model climate to a CO_2 forcing exerted over an infinite length of time. The present authors believe that the physical processes that control this equilibrium response of hydrology also control the transient response of hydrology to a future increase in the atmospheric carbon dioxide. However, it is likely that the geographical details of the equilibrium and the transient response may be quantitatively different from each other because of spatial variation of the effective thermal inertia of the atmosphere–continent–ocean system (Schneider and Thompson, 1981). In order to investigate this issue, it is again necessary to use a coupled ocean–atmosphere model in which the thermal inertia of a full ocean is properly taken into consideration. Although a preliminary study of this kind has been conducted by Bryan et al. (1982) and Spelman and Manabe (1984), it has not investigated the hydrologic aspect of the transient response.

Fortunately, the recent advancement of computer technology has made it possible for the first time to perform a time integration of a coupled ocean–atmosphere model over a sufficiently long period of time. Furthermore, various global observational programs of oceans and atmosphere, which are currently planned by international oceanographic and climate research communities, can yield valuable data for the improvement of a coupled model. Therefore, it is expected that vigorous studies of transient and equilibrium response of climate will begin by use of a model in which a general circulation model of oceans is coupled with that of the atmosphere.

REFERENCES

Bryan, K., Komro, F. G., Manabe, S., and Spelman, M. J. (1982). Transient climate response to increasing atmospheric CO_2. *Science* **215**, 56–58.

Callender, G. S. (1938). The artificial production of carbon dioxide and its influence on temperature. *Q. J. R. Meteorol. Soc.* **64**, 223–240.

Gates, W. L., Cook, K. H., and Schlesinger, M. E. (1981). Preliminary analysis of experiments on the climatic effects of increasing CO_2 with an atmospheric general circulation model and a climatological ocean model. *J. Geophys. Res.* **86**, 6385–6393.

Hansen, J., Lacis, A., Russel, G., Stone, P., Fung, I., Ruedy, R., and Lerner, J. (1984). Climate sensitivity: Analysis of feedback mechanisms. *In "Climate Process and Climate Sensitivity"* (J. E. Hansen and T. Takahashi, eds.), Maurice Ewing Series no. 5, 130–163.

Manabe, S. (1982). Simulation of climate by general circulation models with hydrologic cycle. *In "Land Surface Process in Atmospheric General Circulation Model"* (P. S. Eagleson, eds.), 19–66. Cambridge Univ. Press, London and New York.

Manabe, S. (1983). Carbon dioxide and climatic change in theory of climate. *Adv. Geophys.* **20**, 39–82.

Manabe, S., and Stouffer, R. J. (1979). A CO_2-climate sensitivity study with a mathematical model of the global climate. *Nature (London)* **282**, 491–493.

Manabe, S., and Stouffer, R. J. (1980). Sensitivity of a global model to an increase of CO_2-concentration in the atmosphere. *JGR, J. Geophys. Res.* **85** (C-10), 5529–5554.

Manabe, S. and Wetherald, R. T. (1975). The effect of doubling the CO_2-concentration of the climate of a general circulation model. *J. Atmos. Sci.* **32**, 3–15.

Manabe, S., and Wetherald, R. T. (1980). On the distribution of climate change resulting from an increase in CO_2-content of the atmosphere. *J. Atmos. Sci.* **37**, 99–118.

Manabe, S., Smagorinsky, J., and Strickler, R. F. (1965). Simulated climatology of a general circulation model with a hydrologic cycle. *Mon. Weather Rev.* **93**, 769–798.

Manabe, S., Wetherald, R. T., and Stouffer, R. J. (1981). Summer dryness due to an increase of atmospheric CO_2-concentration. *Clim. Change* **3**, 347–386.

Mitchell, J. F. B. (1983). The seasonal response of a general circulation model to changes in CO_2 and sea temperatures. *Q. J. R. Meteorol.* **109**, 113–152.

Sarmiento, J. L. (1983). A simulation of bomb tritium entry into the Atlantic Ocean. *J. Phys. Oceanogr.* **13**, 1924–1939.

Sarmiento, J. L., and Bryan, K. (1982). An ocean transport model for the North Atlantic. *JGR, J. Geophys. Res.* **87**(C1), 394–408.

Schlesinger, M. E. (1983). Simulating CO_2-induced climate change with mathematical climate models: Capabilities, limitations, and prospects. *In "Proceedings of the Conference on Carbon Dioxide, Climate, and Consensus,"* Vol. III, pp. 3–140. U.S. Dept. of Energy, Washington, D.C.

Schneider, S. H., and Thompson, S. L. (1981). Atmospheric CO_2 and climate: Importance of the transient response. *JGR, J. Geophys. Res.* **86**(C4), 3135–3147.

Smagorinsky, J. (1956). On the inclusion of moist adiabatic process in numerical weather prediction models. *Ber. Dtsch. Wetterdienstes* No. 38, 82–90.

Spelman, M. J., and Manabe, S. (1984). Influence of oceanic heat transport upon the sensitivity of a model climate. *JGR, J. Geophys. Res.* **89**(C1), 571–586.

U.S. National Academy of Sciences (1982). "Carbon Dioxide and Climate: A Second Assessment." Natl. Acad. Press, Washington, D.C.

U.S. National Academy of Sciences (1983). "Changing Climate." Natl. Acad. Press, Washington, D.C.

Washington, W. M., and Meehl, J. (1984). Seasonal cycle experiments on the climate sensitivity due to a doubling of CO$_2$ with an atmospheric general circulation model coupled to a simple mixed layer ocean model. *JGR, J. Geophys. Res.* **89**(D6), 9475–9503.

Wetherald, R. T., and Manabe, S. (1975). The effect of changing solar constant on the climate of a general circulation model. *J. Atmos. Sci.* **32**, 2044–2059.

Wetherald, R. T., and Manabe, S. (1981). Influence of seasonal variation upon the sensitivity of a model climate. *JGR, J. Geophys. Res.* **86**, 1194–1204.

MODELING OF PALEOCLIMATES

IES, Center for Climatic Research
University of Wisconsin — Madison
Madison, Wisconsin

1. INTRODUCTION

The Earth's climate has always been changing and will no doubt continue to change. Climate has a past and a future. The future climate is unknown, although increasing attention is being given to its prediction. Until fairly recently, climates of the past, if not unknown, have at best been perceived in only general and qualitative terms. This situation is now changing. New observational techniques, accurate radiometric dating methods, and comprehensive sampling strategies have evolved. As a result, detailed knowledge of the early evolution of atmosphere and ocean, of shifts of continents, and of the wax and wane of ice sheets, forests, lakes, and deserts has increased dramatically. This knowledge has in turn stimulated the development of both qualitative and quantitative models of paleoclimates.

This paper will focus on studies of the climate of the past that have used quantitative mathematical/physical models of climate — especially the general circulation models that Professor Smagorinsky has done so much to develop over the past several decades.

Section 2 presents selected examples of observational and modeling studies of the eighteenth, nineteenth, and early twentieth centuries. These examples provide a perspective for viewing the current work. Section 3 reviews

ADVANCES IN GEOPHYSICS, VOLUME 28A

some of the new observations of paleoclimates that have stimulated the formulation of new models, as well as the application of existing models. The main focus of Section 4 is on modeling studies. Summary comments and a brief survey of future prospects are in Section 5.

2. SETTING THE STAGE

2.1. Eighteenth and Nineteenth Centuries

Sir Edmund Halley is well known to many meteorologists for his early ideas on the atmosphere's general circulation and for his role in encouraging and financing Sir Isaac Newton's publication of the *Principia*. In addition to his work on the atmosphere's general circulation, Halley studied other aspects of the Earth's climate in a quantitative manner—such as the latitudinal and seasonal distribution of solar radiation and the salt budget of the ocean. His studies did not constitute climate models in the sense of incorporating *all* climate-related processes. Rather, he examined components of climate, or components of the "climate system" to use a modern term.

Halley began a paper of 1693 by referring to previous discussion concerning "that part of heat of weather" that is "simply produced by the action of the sun." Halley then proceeded to clarify the role of solar radiation in producing the latitudinal differences of temperature between the equator and the poles. He estimated from trigonometric considerations the latitudinal profile of diurnal-average insolation for summer and winter solstices and for the equinox. These calculations, which took into account both sun angle and length of day, were summarized in tables. He concluded:

> From the Table and these corollaries may a general *idea* be conceived of the sum of all actions of the sun in the whole year, and that part of heat that arises simply from the preference of the sun be brought to a geometrical certainty.

Halley's consideration of hydrological and chemical budgets (Halley, 1715) anticipated the multidisciplinary problems that are associated with the study of climate and climatic history. He proposed that estimates of the saltiness of the oceans and of the rate of change of saltiness might provide an estimate for the age of the Earth—an age that some had reckoned to be as little as 6000 years. Because precipitation, evaporation, runoff, and weathering are all involved in the salt budget, it is closely related to the climate. Offering both a lament concerning the lack of observations and a plan for an experiment, he stated,

> . . . it were to be wished that the ancient *Greek* and *Latin* Authors had delivered down to us the degree of Saltiness of the Sea, as it was about

2000 years ago: for then it cannot be doubted but that the Difference between what is now found and what then was, would become very sensible. I recommend it therefore to the *Society,* [i.e., the Royal Society of London] as opportunity shall offer, to procure the Experiments to be made of the present degree of saltiness of the Ocean. . . .

Moving ahead an entire century, the work of the famous scholar and world traveler Alexander von Humboldt provided a global perspective on the Earth's climate. He plotted temperature observations from selected observing stations on a global chart and then drew lines of equal temperature based on the station data (von Humboldt, 1817). From the resulting map of isotherms, von Humboldt was able to illustrate the fundamental importance of land–sea distribution for explaining large-scale climatic patterns.

Whereas Halley's and von Humboldt's early studies of the Earth's climate were based on reasoning that appears modern to us, in fact most eighteenth- and early-nineteenth-century geologists relied on catastrophic events to explain climates of the past, rather than the application of physical principles derived from their observations. Even so, changes were under way. As noted by Princeton historian of science, Charles Gillispie (1960, p. 299), "By laying hold on fossils, geology had come into control of its materials by the 1830s." The case for the physical uniformity of nature was made skillfully by Sir Charles Lyell in his famous book "Principles of Geology," first edition published in 1830, a book that Gillispie describes as "perhaps the most famous and certainly the most influential book in the history of the science."

In this book, Lyell laid a framework for a rational approach to the study of past climates. Quoting from the first American edition of 1837 (p. 113),

But if, instead of forming vague conjecture as to what might have been the state of the planet at the era of its creation, we fix our thoughts on the connexion at present existing between climate and the distribution of land and sea; and then consider what influence former fluctuations in the physical geography of the earth must have had on theory. If doubts and obscurities still remain, they should be ascribed to our limited acquaintance with the laws of Nature, not to revolutions in her economy; — they should stimulate us to further research, not tempt us to indulge our fancies in framing imaginary systems for the government of infant worlds.

Thus, Lyell stressed the thermal properties and geographic distribution of land and ocean as the source of explanation for the varied climates of both the present and the past. He also mentioned the dynamical processes that influence climate, including the vast currents of both the atmosphere and the ocean that exchange heat between the equator and the poles. Lyell summarized evidence for former climates, particularly the warmer climates as de-

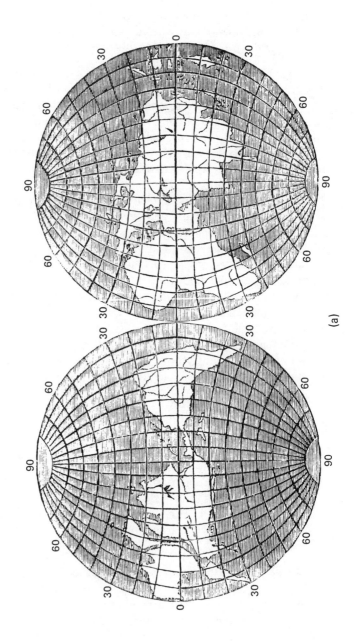

(a)

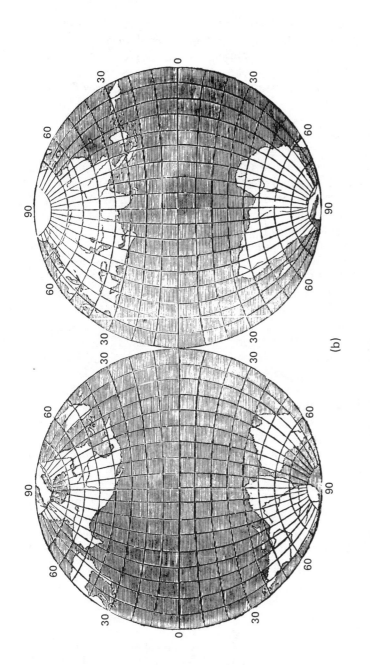

(b)

FIG. 1. Maps showing the position of land and sea which might produce the extremes of heat and cold in the Climates of the Globe. *Observations:* These maps are intended to show that Continents and Islands having the same shape and relative dimensions as those now existing might be placed so as to occupy either the equatorial or polar regions. In (a), scarcely any of the land extends from the Equator towards the Poles beyond the 30th parallel of Latitude; and in (b), a very small proportion of it extends from the Poles towards the Equator beyond the 40th parallel of Latitude. [Caption and figure from Lyell (1837)].

163

duced from the fossil plants of the carboniferous strata, and postulated distributions of land and sea that might produce extremes of heat and cold in global climates (Fig. 1). Lyell referred briefly to ideas of Herschel and Humboldt on the possible importance of astronomical factors, such as eccentricity of the Earth's orbit and precession of the equinoxes, as a cause of climatic change.

After the middle of the century, William Thomson, later Lord Kelvin, applied Fourier's mathematical theory of heat conduction to the problem of the long-period thermal history of the Earth (Thomson, 1862). His purpose was to estimate the age of the Earth, but in the process he described the long-term cooling of the Earth from an assumed molten state to its present temperature. Thomson estimated that the age of the Earth was between 20 million and 400 million years, depending on assumptions. Today, even the longer of the two age estimates is known to be too short by an order of magnitude; the 20 million year age, which Thomson came to favor as he refined his calculations, was thought to be far too short by many geologists, and it especially troubled Darwin and his followers, who required a long time for the operation of evolution by natural selection. By the turn of the century, it was recognized that Thomson's results were wrong because his assumptions were wrong (Ekholm, 1901). Nevertheless, by using a quantitative model of heat conduction to study the geologic history of the planet, Thomson was setting an example for the application of the laws of physics to the study of geologic and climatic history.

At about the same time as Thomson's work, James Croll (1864) reported his initial investigations of the causes of climatic change. Croll mentioned briefly the work of Thomson on early Earth history and also the ideas of Lyell on shifting continents and described in detail his own ideas on the role of changes in Earth's orbital parameters (obliquity, precession, eccentricity) in producing glacial epochs. Croll's ideas stemmed both from the geologic evidence of large-scale glaciations, which became recognized and accepted only gradually between 1840 and 1870, and from the work of mathematician–astronomers, such as Laplace and Leverrier, who developed the equations for orbital variations. For his pioneering work, Croll is often mentioned with Milankovitch (Section 2.2) as cofounder of the orbital theory of ice ages [see Imbrie and Imbrie (1979)].

2.2. Early Twentieth Century

The quantitative treatment of climate and climatic change advanced significantly in the late 1800s. Ferrell (1884) and Zenker (1888), among others, refined the relationship between the latitudinal distribution of solar radiation and surface temperature. Of course, this work remained partly empirical until the radiation laws governing the exact dependence between temperature and radiation were formulated (the results of Stefan and Boltzmann date from 1879 and 1884, respectively). By the turn of the century, quantitative concepts of global energy budgets were developing (von Bezold, 1892). Concepts of the climatic response to hypothetical changes of external conditions also emerged; as part of their study of solar variability as a possible cause of climatic change, Abbot and Fowle (1908) formulated a quantitative expression for the change of global temperature as a function of the change of solar radiation.

Milankovitch, in work begun in 1911 and published in 1920, developed a mathematical model of the zonal-average climate. Milankovitch's model was based on the laws of radiation, both solar and terrestrial, and was applicable for a "calm atmosphere." While mathematical models had been used previously to describe components of the climate (for example, the distribution of solar radiation), Milankovitch used, more fully than his predecessors, the explanatory power of the laws of physics for the study of climate. In that sense, he "invented" the climate model as a tool for the study of present and past climate. Using a modern term, Milankovitch's model was an energy balance model of the same form as those developed in the 1960s by Budyko and Sellers, but with the restrictive assumption of local radiative equilibrium, i.e., no latitudinal redistribution of heat. Because of the simplifying assumption that there was no latitudinal heat exchange, Milankovitch's climate model predicted annual-average equatorial temperatures that were too high and polar temperatures that were too low (Fig. 2). Nevertheless, with this powerful new tool, he began to explore quantitatively the climatic implications of shifting continents and changing Earth orbits.

2.3. Development of General Circulation Models

Only in recent years have numerical and theoretical capabilities made it possible to investigate paleoclimates both efficiently and quantitatively while including the atmospheric (and oceanic) transports that Milankovitch had found necessary to ignore. Smagorinsky (1983), writing about the beginning of numerical weather prediction and general circulation modeling, noted that a new era opened with the work of Phillips, who completed the first general circulation experiment in 1955. Smagorinsky recalls that von Neumann recognized the great significance of Phillips's paper and called for a conference on the application of numerical integration technologies to the problem of the general circulation. Von Neumann's opening remarks at the

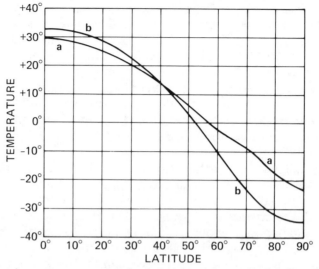

FIG. 2. Zonal-average temperatures simulated with a zonal-average energy budget climate model for a static atmosphere and for annual-average insolation (line b–b) and observed temperatures (line a–a), adjusted to estimate the temperature that would correspond to a 28% land, 72% ocean distribution at each latitude — as assumed in the model calculations. [From Milankovitch (1920).]

1955 conference included the following reference to the modeling of climate (von Neumann, 1960, p. 11. Reprinted with permission from von Neumann, Copyright 1960, Pergamon Press):

> . . . it seems quite clear that the problem of forecasting long-term fluctuations of the general circulation will involve a great deal of mathematical analysis and a great deal of calculation. It will not be possible to arrive at the answers by dialectic methods. To illustrate this point further, I should like to make a very commonplace observation:
>
> Ten thousand years ago extensive glaciation took place over the world. The average temperature of the atmosphere at that time was a little less than 10°C lower than it is now. One popular explanation of this situation is that the radiative intensity of the sun was different from what it is now. It is true that this is not the only possibility, but practically everyone who considers the problem thinks first of this possibility. The one important question that no one has been able to answer so far by dialectic methods is whether the ice age was due to the fact that the sun became hotter, or that the sun became cooler! One can argue either view for some time, but the refutation of neither has thus far been possible. Now, if such simple questions of science cannot be decided by

verbal methods, then it is fairly clear that one has to view the general circulation as a difficult hydrodynamical problem, and that qualitative arguments, which might be useful in the preliminary stages where calculations often go astray, will obviously not be adequate to provide even simple qualitative answers.

Although von Neumann's specific remarks on the time and possible cause of the last glaciation are wrong in detail, his fundamental points about the complexity of the climate system and the necessity for quantitative analysis remain central to the study of climatic change.

The focal point of the 1955 conference was numerical weather prediction, but various papers and the summarized discussion dealt frequently with topics of climate. At the conference, Smagorinsky (1960) reviewed work, including his own, on the role of topography and land – ocean heating contrasts for explaining the observed quasi-stationary wave patterns of the middle latitudes — wave patterns that in turn help to shape the surface climate of the present or of the past.

The development of general circulation and climate models offered the promise of quantitative and comprehensive treatment of climate, both present and past. That a new era had begun was underscored a few years later by J. Murray Mitchell, Jr., who prepared a comprehensive statement on theoretical paleoclimatology for the International Union of Quaternary Research (INQUA) meeting in Boulder, Colorado (Mitchell, 1965). He stated that [p. 899 (in H. W. Wright, Jr., and David G. Frey (eds.), "The Quaternary of the United States." Copyright © 1965 by Princeton University Press)]:

> Speculation and hypothesis, over which this discussion has freely ranged in places, will — in due course — be upheld or be discarded according as it is revealed as substance or shadow by our ever-increasing depth of insight into atmospheric (and oceanic) behavior. Already, today, the atmospheric scientist is finding it possible to construct remarkably realistic mathematical models of the atmosphere (e.g., Smagorinsky, 1963), by which he can explore the nature and extent of various subtle forms of dynamical unrest that underlie the perpetual evolution of climate and circulation from one pattern to another. Indeed, he is now standing at the threshold of a new era in which, for the first time, he will be able to derive *quantitative* evaluations of a number of hypotheses of climatic change by means of suitable controlled experiments with these mathematical stand-ins for the real atmosphere.

The 1963 paper of Smagorinsky, referenced by Mitchell, described the first comprehensive general circulation experiments with a model that was based on the complete equations of motion, i.e., a dynamical model that was much like those in use today.

3. Observations of Paleoclimates

A combination of greatly expanded observations (in both space and time) and theoretical deductions based on these observations is leading to a rapid increase of knowledge about the geologic record of climate. Two excellent multiauthored reviews covering aspects of observations and models are available: National Research Council (NRC) Panel on Climatic Variation (1975) and NRC Panel on Pre-Pleistocene Climates (1982). In addition, review articles by Crowley (1983) and Lloyd (1983) provide comprehensive and up-to-date information on the geologic record of climate. This section highlights a few examples of recent discoveries about paleoclimates that lead rather directly to potential modeling applications. For brevity, the list of examples omits references to publications [for references, see Crowley (1983) and Lloyd (1983)].

3.1. *Precambrian* (4.7 to 0.6 billion years ago)

(1)   The solar constant may have increased 20–30% over the past 4.7 billion years. The reduced solar luminosity of Precambrian time is posing new questions for explaining the generally ice-free nature of earliest climates.

(2)   During the early evolution of the atmosphere, an enhanced "greenhouse effect" may have compensated for the reduced solar intensity.

(3)   The rotation rate of the Earth may have been considerably faster in early Precambrian time — with attendant changes in the Hadley and middle-latitude circulation regimes.

3.2. *Paleozoic* (600 to 225 million years ago)

(1)   It has become possible to chart the movement of the continental blocks of Gondwana and Laurasia, and their consolidation into one "supercontinent," Pangaea, near the end of the Paleozoic. With the land–ocean distribution being specified, it is possible to begin to describe the climate of this era.

(2)   By the middle of this era, as atmospheric oxygen concentration rose, ozone levels may have become sufficiently high to shield most of the UV radiation from the Earth's surface. Vegetation began to develop and flourish

on the continents, causing changes of surface properties (albedo, soil moisture, etc.).

3.3. *Mesozoic* (275 million to 65 million years ago)

(1)   During this era, the general size, shape, and location of the continents
is reasonably well known, as is the timing of the breakup of Pangaea, the
opening of the North Atlantic Ocean basin, and the movement of the continents toward their present locations.

(2)   Sea-floor spreading was accompanied by thermal expansion of sea-
floor ridges, producing high sea levels; shallow seas covered perhaps 20% of
today's land surface.

(3)   Detailed analyses of land and ocean sediment records have provided
quantitative estimates of climate. For example, in the late Cretaceous (about
100 million years ago) the equator-to-pole temperature gradient may have
been only half of what it is today, and global-average temperature may have
been 5–15 K higher.

(4)   Oceanic bottom water temperature may have been 15°C rather than
5°C (present). If the source of this warm bottom water was high-salinity
water of the Tethys Sea, then the deep-water circulation was vastly different
from what it is today.

(5)   Some sedimentary records show cyclic features that suggest climatic
changes at the periods of orbital cycles — about 100,000, 40,000, and 20,000
years.

(6)   At the end of the Cretaceous, widespread faunal extinctions occurred; these extinctions were perhaps the result of an asteroid impact that
may have filled the Earth's atmosphere with dust and caused land surface
temperature to plummet below freezing.

3.4. *Tertiary* (65 million to about 3–2 million years ago)

(1)   Paleogeographic information and estimates of both ocean-surface
and ocean-bottom temperatures are relatively detailed. Questions concern
the time of development of the Antarctic ice sheet (as early as 40 or as late as
15 million years ago) and the timing of that event relative to when Antarctica
became a polar continent. The formation of the Antarctic ice sheet marked
the beginning of the climatic "ice age" that has continued to the present.

(2)   Major uplift of the Rockies, the Alps, and the Himalayas occurred
during this period, providing opportunities for the study of the influence of
orography on climate.

3.5. Quaternary (the past 3 – 2 million years)

(1)   The onset of Northern Hemisphere continental glaciations, starting in Greenland, was around 3 million years ago. Causes for the timing of the initiation of glaciation are uncertain. Perhaps some threshold was crossed in connection with a general climatic trend, or perhaps some specific event triggered the onset. For example, the isthmus of Panama may have developed at about this time, and this land barrier may have changed the ocean circulation.

(2)   The CLIMAP and SPECMAP projects have obtained high-resolution and accurately dated oxygen-isotope chronologies from ocean sediment cores; these chronologies have served as indices of the fluctuating volume of ice on the continents—the glacials and interglacials. The importance of having accurately dated chronologies for testing ideas on climatic mechanisms cannot be overemphasized. Time series analysis of the isotope chronologies has shown concentrations of variance at the same periods as the orbital variations: eccentricity, about 100,000 years; obliquity, about 40,000 years; and precession of the equinox, about 20,000 years. Phase locking between the orbital variations and the isotope variations is further strong evidence that orbital changes are "pacemakers" of the glacial – interglacial fluctuations of the Quaternary.

(3)   Ice cores from both Greenland and Antarctica and ocean sediment cores contain evidence of striking changes in concentration of atmospheric carbon dioxide over the past 150,000 years—low CO_2 levels at the last glacial maximum (around 200 ppm compared to the modern value of around 330 ppm) and high levels during the previous interglacial at about 125,000 yr B.P. This evidence, along with chronologies of orbital parameters, ice volume, and ocean temperatures, permits modeling of possible couplings between these components of the climate system.

(4)   The last glacial maximum (i.e., a maximum in the volume of land ice) occurred about 18,000 years ago. Because this event represents a climatic extreme and because it occurred so recently (geologically speaking) that its traces are easily recognized, it has become a focal point for detailed study of climatic patterns and processes. The location, height, and possible flow dynamics of the most recent continental ice sheets and ice shelves have been studied in detail, and ideas for dynamics of deglaciation are being tested. From planktonic and pollen records in ocean and lake sediments, the CLIMAP project has estimated the ocean temperature, sea-ice extent, and land albedo for 18,000 yr B.P. for a 2° by 2° latitude – longitude grid. This information served as boundary conditions for a series of experiments with general circulation models for full glacial climates (Section 4).

(5)   The COHMAP project is estimating ocean temperature and land

conditions for 3000-year intervals from glacial maximum (18,000 yr B.P.) to present — encompassing the period of deglaciation and a major climatic change in the tropics exemplified by stronger monsoons and increased rainfall between 12,000 and 5000 years ago (Section 4).

(6) Pollen data record the human-induced deforestation of much of Europe over the past 5000 years and of east-central North America over the past 300 years. The potential climatic effects of these changes are yet to be studied.

(7) Historical and instrumental records, tree-ring records, and records from annually layered ice cores, or lake or ocean sediment cores (some of which are annually laminated), provide detailed chronologies of recent climatic fluctuations on time scales of years to centuries. Records of solar activity and volcanic eruptions are also being developed and refined. There is strong evidence that volcanic activity produces climatic changes at these time scales.

4. Modeling of Paleoclimates

The problems of climate and paleoclimates have been studied by using a hierarchy of models, and a number of excellent review articles describe this work: Schneider and Dickinson (1974), Smagorinsky (1974), Saltzman (1978), Ghil (1981), Imbrie (1981, 1982), and Gates (1975, 1981, 1982). Climate models are frequently divided into two very broad categories: (1) explicit dynamical models, which include general circulation models, and (2) statistical–dynamical models, which include thermodynamic, or energy balance, models. In the first category, the day-to-day synoptic-scale weather systems and their associated patterns of precipitation are treated explicitly — requiring time steps of the order of minutes to hours for the atmospheric portion of the climate model; in the second set of models, the equations are often formulated in terms of averages for days, months, years, or still longer intervals.

Both statistical–dynamical models and explicit dynamical models have been used for the modeling of paleoclimates. Statistical–dynamical models have been coupled to slow-responding portions of the climate system (e.g., deep oceans and ice sheets) and have been used for investigating the temporal evolution of climate on all time scales; examples of recent work are summarized in Section 4.1. Explicit dynamical (general circulation) models have been used for simulating geographic features of paleoclimates and for including, in the most explicit form, processes such as precipitation that depend on details of the atmospheric flow. However, because of the large computational costs that are involved, general circulation models have only been used to provide "snapshot" views of the climate at specific times in Earth's history. Examples of the application of these models are in Section 4.2.

Another important rationale for using two different modeling approaches in paleoclimatology has been that the climatic records have generally fallen into two categories. Ice- and ocean-core records that describe the long-period fluctuations of climate are available at only a few locations; however, in some cases they reflect conditions over large areas. It is therefore often natural to investigate the long-period evolution of climate with simplified land–ocean, zonal, or even global-average statistical–dynamical models. On the other hand, the relatively few periods for which global networks of data exist with accurate time control lend themselves to detailed studies with general circulation models.

4.1. Statistical–Dynamical Models

4.1.1. Early Earth History. Models of the early evolution of Earth's climate are taking into account that the Sun's luminosity has been increasing. According to some models of solar evolution, the increase has been roughly linear with time, starting (about 4 billion years ago) at perhaps 75% of the present value. If one assumes present levels of atmospheric CO_2, then energy budget climate models predict that the Earth should have been ice-covered at that time and, because of its high albedo, should have remained so. Yet, geologic evidence suggests the early presence of life and oceans. Pollack (1982) summarizes models of early atmospheric composition that might have produced a sufficiently large greenhouse effect to compensate for the "faint sun" and give surface temperatures that are compatible with the geologic record. Such models of atmospheric evolution involve processes of outgassing and chemical and biological activity.

Owen *et al.* (1979) combined an atmospheric evolution model that predicts CO_2 abundance with a radiative–convective global-average climate model. The model simulated the history of Earth's surface temperature from 4.5 billion yr B.P. to present at half-billion-year intervals; it gave temperatures mostly higher than present (Fig. 3). The simulated surface temperature was at most 4 K lower than at present; this minimum occurred about 1 billion yr B.P. when the model-generated CO_2 surface pressure was approaching modern values but the estimated solar luminosity was still more than 5% below present.

Large uncertainties are associated with the model assumptions for these early climates, as was also the case for the models put forward during the nineteenth century; however, there is a striking contrast between earlier and

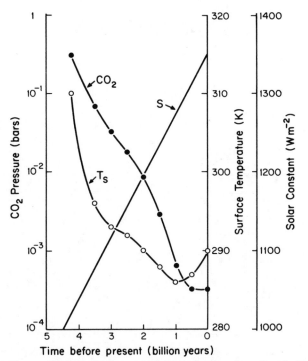

FIG. 3. Time history of the partial pressure of atmospheric carbon dioxide (CO_2), the solar constant S, and global-average surface temperature T_s, as simulated by a radiative–convective climate model for the prescribed values of CO_2 and S. Data points refer to prescribed inputs and equilibrium model solutions at half-billion-year intervals. [Based on results of Table 1 from Owen *et al.* (1979).]

current models in terms of the growing number of variables that are incorporated and the increasing complexity of the physical–chemical–biological processes that are simulated.

4.1.2. Paleozoic–Mesozoic. Building on the much earlier ideas of Lyell, Wegener, and others, Donn and Shaw (1977) used a statistical–dynamical climate model to estimate the sensitivity of the climate to the changing position of the continents over the past 200 million years (Fig. 4). "Snapshot" estimates of the equilibrium climate were produced at roughly 50-million-year intervals. This work provided quantitative support to the notion that both the relative warmth of the Mesozoic (compared to present) and the decline of temperature since the Cretaceous can be linked to the poleward shift of land in the Northern Hemisphere. According to their model, temperatures at polar latitudes (60 – 70°N) fell below freezing about 15 million years ago.

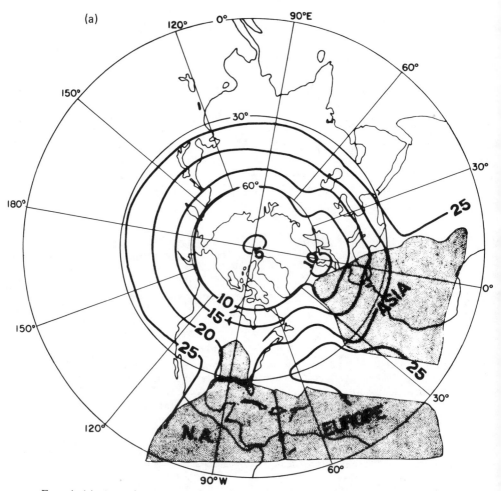

Fig. 4. (a) Annual-average surface temperature (degrees Celsius) simulated with a statistical–dynamical climate model for early Triassic time, about 200 million yr B.P. Shaded regions are the Triassic positions of the continents used in the simulation. Outlines of modern continents are shown for comparison.

Barron *et al.* (1981) used a zonal-average energy budget model to investigate additional aspects of the Cretaceous climate of around 100 million yr B.P. They were able to confirm the earlier findings of Donn and Shaw concerning the importance of continent location. In response to the decreased land fraction at high latitudes at 100 million yr B.P., compared to present, the global-average temperature was 1.6 K higher and the polar temperature was about 5 K higher than for the modern control experiment.

(b)

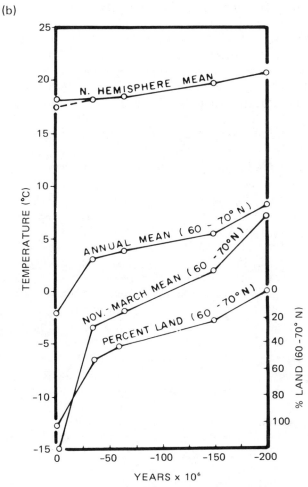

FIG. 4. (b) Annual-mean surface temperature for the Northern Hemisphere, annual-mean and November–March surface temperature for 60–70°N, and percentage land for 60–70°N for selected times for the past 200 million years. Temperatures (degrees Celsius) are simulated with a statistical–dynamical climate model. [From Donn and Shaw (1977). Reproduced with permission from *Geological Society of America Bulletin* **88**, 390–396, a publication of The Geological Society of America.]

However, the simulated temperature at high latitudes remained below freezing. They speculated that factors not included in the model, such as a hypothesized higher atmospheric CO_2 concentration, would be necessary to simulate a Cretaceous climate that would agree with the geologic evidence for a global warming of at least 6 K, compared to present, and for ice-free conditions at the poles.

At the Cretaceous/Tertiary boundary, about 65 million years ago, widespread extinctions occurred, including the final extinction of dinosaurs. Recent work has focused on the possibility that an asteroid struck the Earth and ejected dust-size material into the stratosphere (Alvarez *et al.*, 1980). The stratospheric dust veil could have reduced the amount of solar radiation reaching the surface and, according to the results of a one-dimensional radiative–convective climate model, caused the land-surface temperature to fall below the freezing point for several months (Pollack *et al.*, 1983). This possible scenario illustrated that even short-term climatic changes could have had profound and long-term consequences for life on the Earth.

4.1.3. Quaternary. The development and interpretation of new paleoclimatic records (Section 3.5) has led to renewed interest in models of glacial and interglacial climates that build on the pioneering modeling work of Milankovitch (1920, 1941). Hays *et al.* (1976) identified two key features of glacial/interglacial fluctuations that were recorded in ocean sediment cores. They found a concentration of climatic variance at periods of about 100,000 years, 40,000 years, and 20,000 years, i.e., the periods of known variations in the Earth's orbital parameters. Moreover, they showed that the ice-volume fluctuations and orbital variations were phase locked (Section 3.5); these results led them to conclude that changes in the Earth's orbital geometry were the fundamental cause of the succession of Quaternary glaciations. Subsequent work has shown that changes in tropical monsoonal circulations are also linked to orbital variations (Prell, 1984).

Assuming that the cause or "pacemaker" of glacial cycles is now known, much work remains to explore and understand the mechanism or mechanisms by which the orbital variations influence climate. Imbrie and Imbrie (1980) emphasized the need to explain the relative amplitude and phase relationships between orbital forcing and climatic response and other characteristic features of glacial cycles such as the slow growth and rapid decay of ice sheets.

An energy balance model was used by Suarez and Held (1976, 1979) to simulate Northern Hemisphere surface temperature and associated changes in snow and sea-ice limits. These experiments represented a major advance in the level of physical modeling of the climate system — as compared to the model of Milankovitch. Their model was forced by the seasonally varying insolation as predicted by orbital theory. It had two atmospheric levels and a surface level, it allowed for the meridional transport of energy by diffusion, and it contained separate surface energy balance equations for land and for a static mixed-layer ocean and snow and sea ice feedback mechanisms. Solutions were obtained at 5000-year intervals for the past 150,000 years. The time series of hemisphere-average surface temperature that was simulated with the model agreed qualitatively with an ocean sediment core record of abundance of temperature-sensitive planktonic foraminifera; the model's temperature extremes tended to precede the foraminifer abundance extremes by several thousand years—possibly due to the absence of slow-responding components of climate such as ice sheets or a deep ocean.

Glacial–interglacial fluctuations are now being studied with the aid of statistical–dynamical models that incorporate additional climate subsystems such as ice sheets, deeper oceans, carbon dioxide, and properties of the land surface (Saltzman, 1978). Both the forced response, associated with either orbital forcing [for which the radiation changes are being calculated with increasing accuracy and for longer periods (Berger, 1978)] or stochastic forcing (Hasselman, 1981), and the free response of such models are being considered. At least three climate subsystems are receiving attention: (1) ice sheet feedback systems—often involving crustal dynamics; (2) sea-ice, ocean, CO_2 feedback systems; and (3) important details of land–ocean distribution. All of these features, and perhaps more, may be needed in a truly comprehensive model.

Ghil (1981) has reviewed treatments of ice sheet dynamics and the geodynamics of the lithosphere (crust) and the asthenosphere (upper mantle) for climate modeling [see also Budd and Smith (1979), Birchfield et al. (1981), Ghil and LeTreut (1981), and Pollard (1982) for examples of recent work]. For simulating glacial–interglacial fluctuations, Pollard (1982) coupled an ice sheet model to a one-level energy-balance climate model containing land–ocean contrasts and both north–south and east–west heat exchange. The ice sheet model had provisions for bedrock response and for rapid melting at the southern tip of the ice sheet due to proglacial lakes and/or marine incursions. The ice sheet model had a basic 100-year time step; the climate model equations were solved to determine an equilibrium seasonal cycle every 2000 years. Solutions were obtained by using the solar radiation variations associated with orbital forcing for the past 700,000 years (Fig. 5a); the cumulative addition of bedrock lag and ice calving improved the fit to the oxygen isotope record of ice-volume fluctuations.

Saltzman and Sutera (1984) described a climate model representing a continental ice sheet, adjoining marine ice, and ocean. Their model was not forced by the insolation changes caused by orbital variations; rather, the simulated "glacial–interglacial" fluctuations (Fig. 5b) resulted from the free, unforced behavior of the coupled system of equations with linear and nonlinear feedbacks. The ice sheet fluctuated in size at about a 100,000-year period, even though no individual component of the climate model had a time constant longer than 10,000 years; the ice sheet also exhibited slow

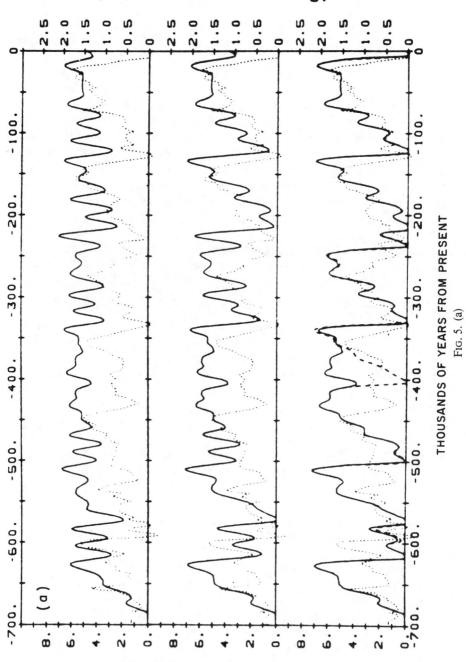

DELTA O18 MINUS PRESENT VALUE (PER MIL)

ICE SHEET CROSS-SECTIONAL AREA (10^9 M2)

THOUSANDS OF YEARS FROM PRESENT

Fig. 5. (a)

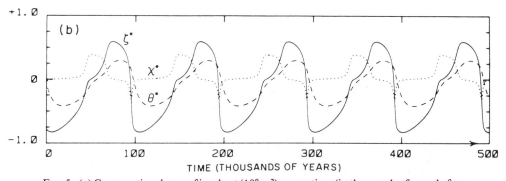

FIG. 5. (a) Cross-sectional area of ice sheet (10^9 m^2) versus time (in thousands of years before present) from various simulations with an ice sheet model coupled to a statistical–dynamical climate model with orbital forcing. The dotted curve in each panel is an oxygen-isotope deep-sea core record, plotted relative to its present value. Equilibrium bedrock (top), bedrock lag (middle), and ice calving added (bottom). [From Pollard (1982). A coupled climate-ice sheet model applied to the Quaternary Ice Ages. Climate Research Institute, Report No. 37, Oregon State University, Corvallis, Oregon.] (b) Relative continental ice sheet mass ζ^* adjoining marine ice mass χ^* and mean ocean temperature θ^* versus time (in thousands of years, time increasing to the right) from a simulation with a three-component statistical–dynamical climate model with no deterministic or stochastic forcing. [From Saltzman and Sutera (1984). Reproduced with permission from *Journal of the Atmospheric Sciences,* a publication of the American Meteorological Society.]

growth and rapid decay. The phasing of marine ice and mean ocean temperature, with respect to each other and the continental ice, are in a sense "predictions" because the geologic record is not yet detailed enough to verify such features.

Another avenue of fruitful investigation has focused on how land–sea distribution has influenced the development of ice sheets (North *et al.,* 1983). With cool summers favoring the persistence of snow cover, the northeastern North American–Greenland–Scandinavian sector is particularly susceptible to ice sheet development. The relatively small land/water fraction in this sector leads to cool summers today; moreover, a small decrease in solar radiation, or in summertime solar insolation (due to orbital changes), causes the summer temperature to fall below 0°C. For the same decrease of radiation, central Asia, because of its size and distance from the ocean, remains too warm in summer to maintain perennial snow cover.

The observational evidence for climatic changes on the scale of years to centuries is detailed and voluminous. Statistical–dynamical models have been used to study these short-term climatic changes, but this literature will not be reviewed here. As one example, Schneider and Mass (1975) used a global-average climate model to illustrate the possible climatic response to volcanic eruptions and changes of solar radiation over the past several centuries.

4.2. General Circulation Models

4.2.1. Precambrian Climates. Precambrian climates differed so drastically from those of today that the formulation of comprehensive experiments with general circulation models is largely a task for the future. For most current purposes, radiative–convective models (Section 4.1.1) have the appropriate level of detail. One general circulation model experiment has shown interesting climatic implications of a postulated faster rotation of the Earth for the Precambrian. For a fivefold increase of rotation rate, i.e., 4.8-hr "days," but with other model parameterizations based on present conditions, Hunt (1979) obtained the following results: reduced scale size of motion fields; reduced poleward transport of heat by large-scale eddies — causing colder poles and warmer tropics; reduced latitudinal extent of the Hadley cell and a related equatorward shift of the latitude of maximum upper-level westerlies from 20° latitude (24-hr rotation rate) to 10° latitude (4.8-hr rotation rate). The arid region of the tropics (under the descending branch of the Hadley cell) narrowed in latitudinal extent and moved toward the equator, and most regions poleward of 45° also became semiarid as the increased coldness of the troposphere caused a general decline in evaporation and precipitation. Some of the results, such as the contracted latitudinal extent of the Hadley cell, could have been anticipated on theoretical grounds. However, the general circulation model provided details of the possible changes in the hydrological budget. Hunt emphasized the need to include in the model many more features of the Precambrian world in order to produce a more realistic simulation (see Section 4.1). Walker (1982) argued that a fivefold increase of rotation rate would have been restricted at most to very early Earth history and that perhaps a twofold increase would be more representative of most of Precambrian time.

4.2.2. Cretaceous Climates. General circulation models are now being used to model the Cretaceous climate (Barron and Washington, 1982, 1984). The warm, equable Cretaceous is, in the words of Barron and Washington (1984), "the largest well-documented climatic contrast from the present day." No evidence of permanent land ice has been found for this time and estimates are that the global average temperature was at least 6 K higher than present (Section 3.4).

Because so many factors may have influenced the climate, Barron and Washington (1984) conducted a series of single-variable sensitivity experiments to study the role of such factors as geography, sea level, and topography. The influences of higher sea level and reduced topographic relief proved to be relatively minor. The major importance of continental positions, indicated previously by simulations with statistical–dynamical models, was underscored. The simulated global average surface temperature was 4.8 K higher for the Cretaceous, when, especially in the Northern Hemisphere, there was decreased land (compared to present) at high latitudes (Fig. 6).

The model studies of Barron and Washington produced two additional results of interest here: First, the sensitivity (to the Cretaceous geographic change) of their zonal-average energy budget model and their general circulation model differed by a factor of about 3 (a 1.5 K versus a 4.8 K warming, respectively). They noted that the general circulation models' explicit treatment of land – sea distribution and topography, and its more explicit heat transport formulation (compared to the north – south diffusive heat transport of the zonal-average energy budget model), may have contributed to its large sensitivity to changes of high-latitude land area. Second, the simulated Cretaceous climate, although significantly warmer than the control, was still cooler than the *minimal* geologic estimates of Cretaceous warmth. Especially at high latitude, the simulated temperatures, although above 0°C, appeared to be too low. The authors concluded that unless the geologic record could be reinterpreted to narrow the gap between observation and simulation, either model deficiencies were responsible for the difference — such as an inadequate treatment of atmospheric or oceanic poleward energy fluxes — or one or more additional factors must have been acting — such as increased atmospheric CO_2 content.

General circulation model experiments with doubled or quadrupled atmospheric CO_2 concentration (Manabe and Wetherald, 1980) have also contributed to the study of paleoclimates, although they were undertaken primarily for the purpose of studying possible future climates. Manabe and Wetherald speculated, on the basis of the results of their CO_2 experiments, that in a generally warmer climate, such as the late Mesozoic, there would be an accompanying increase in atmospheric moisture content and in poleward transport of latent heat; as a result, total poleward heat transport (dry static plus latent) could be maintained at relatively constant levels with warm polar climates and reduced equator/pole temperature gradients.

4.2.3. Last Glacial Maximum. The first simulations of glacial climates with general circulation models were made by Alyea (1972) and Williams *et al.* (1974). When more detailed boundary conditions for August 18,000 yr B.P. became available (CLIMAP Project Members, 1976), simulation experiments were performed by Gates (1976a,b) and Manabe and Hahn (1977). Since then, both August and February boundary conditions have been summarized (CLIMAP Project Members, 1981). These sets are forming the basis for additional experimentation (Manabe and Broccoli, 1984; Hansen *et al.,* 1984; Kutzbach and Guetter, 1984a).

In order to contrast our knowledge of glacial maximum boundary condi-

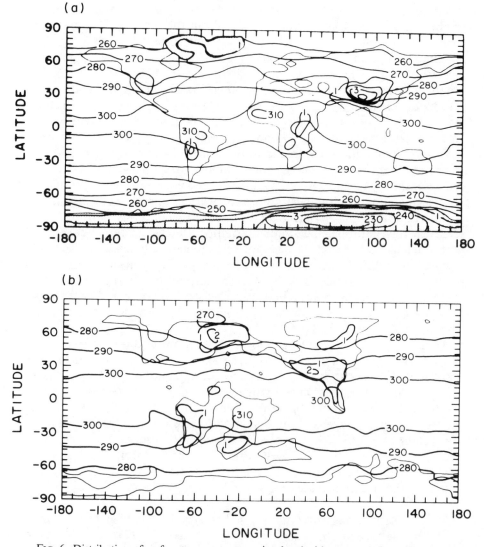

FIG. 6. Distribution of surface temperatures as simulated with a general circulation model for (a) present-day control and (b) the Cretaceous, given in degrees Kelvin, for an average of simulation days 300–400. Continental elevations are indicated by contours (kilometers); areas of high-latitude continent with prescribed permanent ice cover in the present day are stippled. Antarctica was specified to have no permanent ice cover in the Cretaceous. [From Barron and Washington (1984). Reproduced with permission from *JGR, Journal of Geophysical Research* **89**, 1267–1279, published by the American Geophysical Union.]

tions with the relatively vague information currently available for specifying, say, Cretaceous boundary conditions, it is useful to review briefly the detailed estimates of surface conditions at the last glacial maximum that are now available; quoting from the CLIMAP Project Members (1976) [*Science* **191**, 1131–1137; copyright 1976 by the AAAS] summary:

> In the Northern Hemisphere the 18,000 BP world differed strikingly from the present in the huge land-based ice sheets, reaching approximately 3 km in thickness, and in a dramatic increase in the extent of pack ice and marine-based ice sheets. In the Southern Hemisphere the most striking contrast was the greater extent of sea ice. On land, grasslands, steppes, and deserts spread at the expense of forests. This change in vegetation, together with extensive areas of permanent ice and sandy outwash plains, caused an increase in global surface albedo over modern values. Sea level was lower by at least 85 m.

> The 18,000 BP oceans were characterized by: (i) marked steepening of thermal gradients along polar frontal systems, particularly in the North Atlantic and Antarctic; (ii) an equatorward displacement of polar frontal systems; (iii) general cooling of most surface waters, with a global average of $-2.3°C$; (iv) increased cooling and upwelling along equatorial divergences in the Pacific and Atlantic; (v) low temperatures extending equatorward along the western coast of Africa, Australia, and South America, indicating increased upwelling and advection of cool waters; and (vi) nearly stable positions and temperatures of the central gyres in the subtropical Atlantic, Pacific, and Indian oceans.

The ice-age simulations of Gates (1976a,b) and Manabe and Hahn (1977) indicated that global-average surface air temperature was $4-5°C$ below present for August 18,000 yr B.P. Consistent with the generally lower temperature, an approximate 15% reduction in the intensity of the hydrologic cycle was simulated by both models, i.e., less precipitation and less evaporation. For both models, the simulated decrease in temperature over land exceeded the prescribed decrease of ocean temperature. Moreover, the larger cooling of the land relative to the ocean tended, from hydrostatic considerations, to weaken the Northern Hemisphere summer monsoon circulations and, more generally, to produce a tendency for anticyclonic outflow from the continents (Fig. 7). Consistent with these changes in the pressure field, Manabe and Hahn (1977) reported that the global-average reduction in precipitation resulted primarily from reduced rainfall over land; a pronounced increase in tropical aridity agreed with the paleoclimatic evidence. Through sensitivity experiments involving selected elements of CLIMAP's boundary conditions, Manabe and Hahn found that the increase of land albedo was primarily responsible for the weakened Indian monsoon of 18,000 yr B.P.

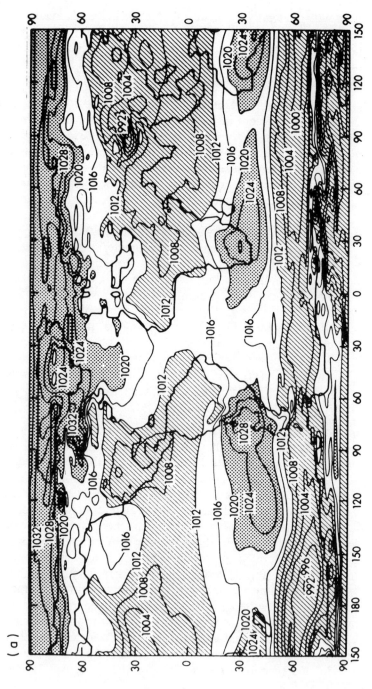

(a)

184

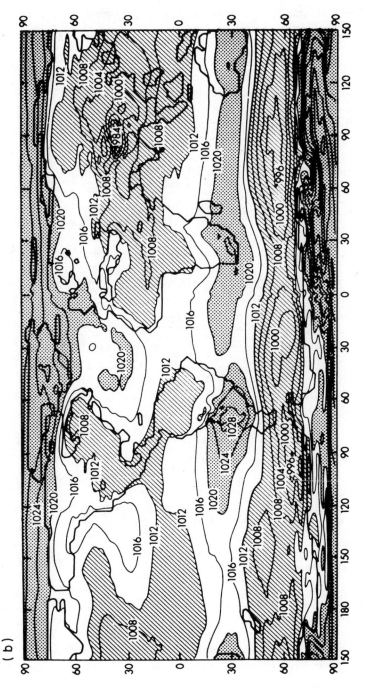

FIG. 7. Distribution of August sea level pressure (millibars) as simulated (a) for glacial maximum conditions around 18,000 yr B.P. (Ice Age) and (b) for modern conditions. [From Manabe and Hahn (1977). Reproduced with permission from *JGR, Journal of Geophysical Research* **82**, 3889–3911, copyright by the American Geophysical Union.]

By using models that incorporate more of the climate system, such as atmosphere–ocean models, the number of prescribed boundary conditions can be reduced and, simultaneously, the paleoclimatic information can be used for verification rather than prescription. For example, Manabe and Broccoli (1984) used a general circulation model of the atmosphere coupled with a static mixed-layer ocean model to study the influence of the 18,000 yr B.P. ice sheet on the simulated atmosphere–ocean climate—i.e., the model's ocean surface temperature was free to adjust to the presence of the ice sheet and the altered atmospheric circulation. They found that in the Northern Hemisphere the simulated temperature distribution of the mixed-layer ocean resembled that estimated by CLIMAP from geologic records. However, the influence of the ice sheet on the Southern Hemisphere oceans was small; they concluded that other changes in the heat budget, besides those directly caused by changes in ice sheet distribution, might be needed to explain the glacial climate; they suggested that changes in atmospheric CO_2 concentration and interhemispheric oceanic heat transport were two possible candidates.

Another area of current research with general circulation models involves increasingly detailed comparisons between the simulations and the geologic record. For example, in a study with prescribed ocean-surface temperature, Hansen *et al.* (1984) identified features of the simulated glacial maximum climate that appeared to be incompatible with geologic evidence. Specifically, the model simulated a decrease of surface air temperature over the tropical and subtropical oceans of about 1 °C, but geologic evidence showed descent of snowlines on tropical mountains of about 1 km, which, assuming that glacial-age lapse rates were similar to present ones and using a typical lapse rate of about 6 K per kilometer, would imply that surface temperature might have been about 6 °C colder than present. Climatic interpretation of inferred tree line lowering from pollen data also indicated substantial cooling of the order of 5 °C in certain areas. Because the simulated temperature of the surface and lower tropospheric air, even over land, would be strongly influenced by the prescribed temperature of the ocean, they suggested that the low-latitude ocean temperature might have been set too high.

4.2.4. Changes of Climate Since the Last Glacial Maximum. COHMAP Project Members (1985) are obtaining and comparing global-scale maps of geologic conditions with the climatic conditions simulated by a general circulation model; their study covers the past 18,000 years at 3000-year intervals. This focus was chosen because (1) the climatic changes of this period were large, having ranged from full glacial to full interglacial, (2) the times of climatic change are known accurately from radiocarbon dating, (3) near-global coverage of information about the past environments is possible, and (4) the known changes in the latitudinal and seasonal distribution of the solar radiation (associated with orbital parameter changes) were large and have been shown, from studies with statistical–dynamical models (Section 4.1.3), to be a likely factor in explaining the temporal evolution of climate over this period.

The starting point for COHMAP studies is the time of the most recent glacial maximum around 18,000 yr B.P. Beginning around 16,000 yr B.P., the climate system experienced major change during which the ice sheets retreated, ocean fronts shifted poleward, and the areas covered by sea ice contracted (Ruddiman and McIntyre, 1981). In the mid-latitudes, vegetation zones shifted poleward and after 14,000 yr B.P. lake levels (for example, in the southwestern United States) fell. About 10,000 to 12,000 years ago, lake levels rose throughout much of Africa and the Middle East (Street and Grove, 1979) and the Indian monsoon strengthened (Prell, 1984). By 5000 to 6000 years ago, the global ice volume was at a minimum, certain types of vegetation extended farther poleward than they are today (Webb et al., 1983), and lake levels in central Africa indicate that the Sahara desert, as we know it, did not exist. Shortly thereafter, the southern boundary of spruce forests in eastern North America moved southward, and the water levels in tropical lakes decreased rapidly.

The Earth's orbit about the sun changed during the same period, allowing the response of a general circulation model to this large and accurately known change in external forcing to be evaluated (Mason, 1976). Whereas the effects of changing orbital parameters have been studied extensively with global- or zonal-average climate models, the COHMAP project has used these radiation changes in general circulation models in order to demonstrate their influence on the spatial patterns of seasonal (monsoonal) climate in various parts of the globe. Since about 20,000 yr B.P., the time of perihelion shifted from January to July (about 10,000 yr B.P.) and back to January (modern). This change, along with changes in the tilt of the rotational axis, led after 18,000 yr B.P. to increasing solstitial extremes of solar radiation in the Northern Hemisphere that reached a maximum around 10,000 yr B.P., followed by decreasing extremes from 10,000 yr B.P. to present. Compared to modern conditions, at 10,000 yr B.P., solar radiation at the top of the atmosphere was increased by about 8% (30 W m^{-2}) in June–July–August and was decreased by about 8% (20 W m^{-2}) in December–January–February over the Northern Hemisphere.

When the amplified seasonal cycle of solar radiation for 9000 yr B.P. was used as the external forcing in a low-resolution general circulation model, Northern Hemisphere continental interiors warmed in summer and cooled in winter, and the summer monsoon circulation of Africa and southern Asia was intensified (Kutzbach, 1981; Kutzbach and Otto-Bliesner, 1982). Ex-

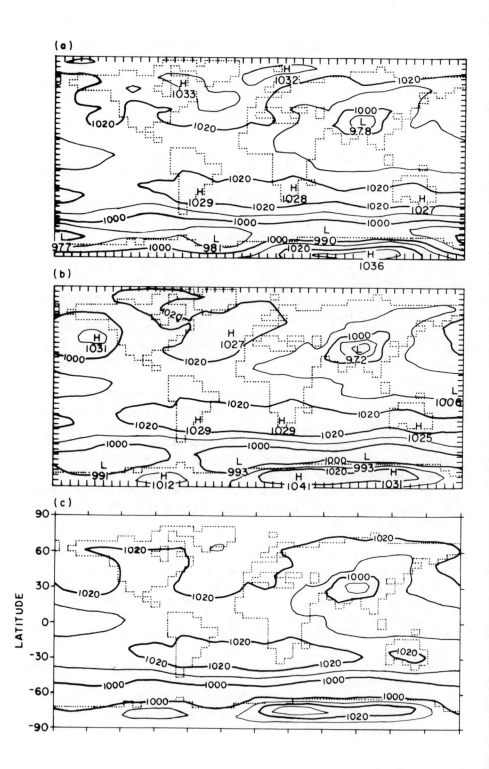

periments with the National Center for Atmospheric Research (NCAR) high-resolution general circulation model have confirmed these earlier results for 9000 yr B.P. (Kutzbach and Guetter, 1984b).

Changes in solar radiation are only one of several modifications that must be made in atmospheric general circulation models in order to simulate paleoclimates of the past 18,000 years. Even at 9000 yr B.P., but especially for preceding periods, there were differences (compared to present) in internal portions of the climate system that are not explicitly modeled by the general circulation model. Certain changes must therefore be prescribed as boundary conditions for each snapshot experiment: for example, the ice sheet configuration, sea-ice extent, and ocean temperature specified by CLIMAP Project Members (1981) for 18,000 yr B.P. were adjusted for conditions at 15,000 yr B.P. and 12,000 yr B.P. based on geologic evidence. By 9000 yr B.P., only a small ice sheet remained over North America, and sea-ice and ocean temperature were assumed to be the same as present. Changes (from present levels) in atmospheric carbon dioxide content and aerosol loading need to be considered in future experiments.

Combining the changes in solar radiation due to orbital forcing with the changes in prescribed boundary conditions, paleoclimate "snapshots" were obtained from 18,000 yr B.P. to present at 3000-year intervals for both January and July conditions (Kutzbach and Guetter, 1984a). Examples of the July simulations for 18,000, 9000, and 0 yr B.P. are shown in Fig. 8. At the glacial maximum conditions of 18,000 yr B.P., a band of high pressure extended across the North American ice sheet, the sea-ice-covered North Atlantic, and the European ice sheet; farther to the south, the North African–South Asian monsoon system was somewhat weaker than at present. By 9000 yr B.P. the pressure distribution at high northern latitudes had become similar to present, but the central pressure of the South Asian monsoon was lowered and the region of low pressure enclosed by the 1010 mb isobar had extended westward across North Africa, indicative of stronger North African–South Asian monsoon circulations.

The temporal evolution of climate (Fig. 9), as summarized from the "snapshot" simulations with the general circulation model, indicated cold conditions in both July and January at 18,000 and 15,000 yr B.P. By 12,000 yr B.P. the surface air temperature was rising, especially in summer over the Northern Hemisphere continents, in response to the changing solar radiation regime. At 9000 and 6000 yr B.P. the Northern Hemisphere continents experienced warmer summers and colder winters, i.e., increased seasonality.

FIG. 8. Distribution of July sea level pressure (millibars) as simulated (a) for glacial maximum conditions around 18,000 yr B.P., (b) in early Holocene time around 9000 yr B.P., and (c) for modern conditions. [From Kutzbach and Guetter (1985).]

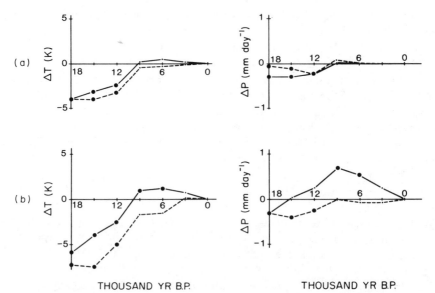

Fig. 9. Change of temperature (degrees Kelvin) and precipitation (millimeters per day) for the period 18,000 yr B.P. to present, as simulated by a general circulation model at 3000-year intervals and expressed as the difference between the past climate and the present control. July (solid lines) and January (dashed lines) conditions are indicated. Large solid circles indicate that the difference between past and control exceeds the 5% significance level: (a) global-average temperature and precipitation, land and ocean; (b) Northern Hemisphere average temperature and precipitation, land. [From Kutzbach and Guetter (1985).]

Simulated changes in global-average precipitation were small. However, the large increase of precipitation at 9000 and 6000 yr B.P. over Northern Hemisphere land, associated primarily with the strengthened summer monsoon over North Africa and South Asia, was a direct consequence of the increased heating of the continents that occurred when perihelion was in northern summer. Only small climatic differences were simulated at 3000 yr B.P., consistent with the correspondingly small differences of orbital parameters between 3000 yr B.P. and the present.

5. Summary and Prospects for the Future

Major advances in the theory of climate are under way (Hecht, 1985). Key ingredients to this progress include the large variety of paleoclimatic indicators (geochemical, botanical, biological), the increasing accuracy of dating, the expanding geographic coverage of measurements, and the application of statistical techniques for extracting the climatic signal from the other signals

— and noise — contained in geologic records. Simultaneously, a hierarchy of climate models of increasing accuracy, dimensionality, and versatility are being developed and applied.

It should be clear, from this review of recent work, that new observations continue to play a key role in stimulating the development and testing of new theories of climatic change. Likewise, the climate model has proved to be an invaluable tool for the quantitative testing of theories and for predicting or suggesting phenomena that can subsequently be studied with observations.

The level of accuracy and completeness of the paleoclimatic observations place constraints on verifying the climatic simulations. For example, the paleoclimate of early Earth history is not well known. As a result, climate models with a variety of external forcing mechanisms, internal feedbacks, and prescribed boundary conditions can, in principle, produce climate simulations that are within the range of observational uncertainty. By way of contrast, the climate since the last glacial maximum is now known in considerable detail so that good agreement between model and observations is to be expected only if the model includes, in appropriate form, the correct external forcing, internal feedbacks, and prescribed boundary conditions.

This review has mentioned examples of comparisons between observed paleoclimates and simulated climates but has perhaps not emphasized the scientific effort that is required to make detailed and meaningful comparisons possible. The interpretation of either pollen, plankton, or isotopic abundances or lake levels, dunes, or moraines in terms of standard climatic variables represents a major scientific challenge. Alternatively, transforming the standard output of climate models (temperature, precipitation) into biological, geochemical, or geomorphic indices is equally challenging. Moreover, the spatial and temporal sampling strategy for observations and simulations should be compatible. This task of comparing observations and model simulations will require considerable attention.

Looking toward the future in another area, computers with larger memory banks and greater computational speed will facilitate efforts to construct climate models that include additional detail about the role of the ocean and other climate subsystems such as the biosphere. Increased computer resources will have the additional benefit of permitting more and/or longer simulation studies. The improvement of models will continue to depend crucially on the development of more detailed knowledge of present-day climate dynamics from modern observational and theoretical work.

One important goal of current climate modeling efforts is to estimate the climate of the future, for example, the climate that might result from increased levels of carbon dioxide. Paleoclimate modeling contributes to these goals in at least three ways. First, the paleoclimatic record contains information of specific interest, such as past levels of carbon dioxide concentration.

This fact permits observational and model studies of the interaction between the carbon cycle and climate. Second, improvements in our general knowledge of the processes of large-scale climatic change (for example, spatial modes, time scales, feedbacks, nonlinearities), even if not specifically related to past changes of CO_2 concentration, provide a foundation of climate theory that may help in the study of possible CO_2 effects on climate. Third, if climate models can accurately simulate past climates and past climatic changes, then this type of "verification" of the models can provide at least one basis for estimating the probable reliability of estimates of future climates that might differ substantially from the current climate.

Many of the hopes for advances in climate research expressed by von Neumann and initiated by his colleagues—Charney, Phillips, and Smagorinsky—through the development of general circulation models are becoming realities; and many of the ideas about climate and climatic change put forward by early students of climate, such as Halley, Humboldt, Lyell, and Milankovitch, are being put to quantitative test. Mathematical models of climate have become powerful tools for testing and developing theories of paleoclimate.

Acknowledgements

Research grants to the University of Wisconsin–Madison from the National Science Foundation's Climate Dynamics Program (NSF Grants ATM-8219079 and ATM81-11455) supported this work. The author thanks Peter Guetter for performing the general circulation model experiments reported in Section 4.2.4, Melanie Woodworth and Maria Kohanowski for preparing the manuscript, and Thompson Webb III for a critical reading and improvement of the text. The computations reported in Section 4.2.4 were made at the National Center for Atmospheric Research, Boulder, Colorado, which is sponsored by the National Science Foundation, with a computing grant (35381017) from the NCAR Computing Facility.

References

Abbott, C. G., and Fowle, F. E., Jr. (1908). Variations of solar radiation and their effects on the temperature of the earth. *In* "Annals of the Astrophysical Observatory of the Smithsonian Institution," Vol. 2, Chapter 5. Smithson. Inst. Washington, D.C.

Alvarez, L. W., Alvarez, W., Asaro, F., and Michel, H. V. (1980). Extraterrestrial cause for the Cretaceous-Tertiary extinction. *Science* **208**, 1095–1108.

Alyea, F. N. (1972). "Numerical Simulation of an Ice Age Paleoclimate," Atmos. Sci. Pap. No. 193. Colorado State University, Fort Collins.

Barron, E. J., and Washington, W. M. (1982). Cretaceous climate: A comparison of atmospheric simulations with the geologic record. *Paleogeogr., Paleoclimatol., Paleoecol.* **40**, 103–133.

Barron, E. J., and Washington, W. M. (1984). The role of geographic variables in explaining paleoclimates: Results from Cretaceous climate model sensitivity studies. *JGR, J. Geophys. Res.* **89**, 1267–1279.

Barron, E. J., Thompson, S. L., and Schneider, S. H. (1981). An ice-free Cretaceous? Results from climate model simulations. *Science* **212**, 501–508.

Berger, A. (1978). Long-term variations of caloric solar radiation resulting from the earth's orbital elements. *Quat. Res. (N.Y.)* **9**, 139–167.

Birchfield, G. E., Weertman, J., and Lunde, A. T. (1981). A paleoclimate model of northern hemisphere ice sheets. *Quat. Res. (N.Y.)* **15**, 126–142.

Budd, W. F., and Smith, I. N. (1979). The growth and retreat of ice sheets in response to orbital radiation changes. *IAHS-AISH* **131**.

CLIMAP Project Members (1976). The surface of the Ice-Age Earth. *Science* **191**, 1131–1136.

CLIMAP Project Members (1981). Seasonal reconstructions of the earth's surface at the last glacial maximum. *Geol. Soc. Am. Map Chart Ser.* **MC-36**.

COHMAP Project Members (1985). Reconstructions of climate, and comparison with general circulation model simulations, for 18,000 yr BP to present at 3000 year intervals. (In preparation.)

Croll, J. (1864). On the physical cause of the change of climate during geological epochs. *Philos. Mag.* [4] **28**, 121–137.

Crowley, T. J. (1983). The geological record of climatic change. *Rev. Geophys. Space Phys.* **21**, 828–877.

Donn, W. L., and Shaw, D. M. (1977). Model of climate evolution based on continental drift and polar wandering. *Geol. Soc. Am. Bull.* **88**, 390–396.

Ekholm, N. (1901). On the variations of the climate of the geological and historical past and their causes. *Q. J. R. Meteorol. Soc.* **27**, 1–62.

Ferrell, W. (1884). "Temperature of the Atmosphere and Earth's Surface." Prof. Pap. Signal Serv. No. 13. U.S. Govt. Printing Office, Washington, D.C.

Gates, W. L. (1975). Numerical modelling of climatic change: A review of problems and prospects. *In* "Long-Term Climatic Fluctuations," WMO No. 421, pp. 343–353. World Meteorol. Organ., Geneva.

Gates, W. L. (1976a). Modeling the Ice Age climate. *Science* **191**, 1138–1144.

Gates, W. L. (1976b). The numerical simulation of Ice-Age climate with a global general circulation model. *J. Atmos. Sci.* **33**, 1844–1873.

Gates, W. L. (1981). The climate system and its portrayal by climate models: A review of basic principles. II. Modeling of climate and climatic change. *In* "Climatic Variations and Variability: Facts and Theories" (A. Berger, ed.), pp. 435–460. Reidel, Dordrecht, Netherlands.

Gates, W. L. (1982). Paleoclimatic modeling—a review with reference to problems and prospects for the pre-Pleistocene. *In* "Climate in Earth History" (NRC Panel on Pre-Pleistocene Climates), pp. 26–42. Natl. Acad. Sci., Washington, D.C.

Ghil, M. (1981). Internal climatic mechanisms participating in glaciation cycles. *In* "Climatic Variations and Variability: Facts and Theories" (A. Berger, ed.), pp. 539–558. Reidel, Dordrecht, Netherlands.

Ghil, M., and LeTreut, H. (1981). A climate model with cryodynamics and geodynamics. *JGR, J. Geophys. Res.* **86**, 5262–5270.

Gillispie, C. C. (1960). "The Edge of Objectivity." Princeton Univ. Press, Princeton, New Jersey.

Halley, E. (1693). A discourse concerning the proportional heat of the sun in all latitudes, with the method of collecting the same. *Philos. Trans. R. Soc. London* **17**, 878–885.

Halley, E. (1715). On the causes of the saltiness of the ocean, and of the several lakes that emit no rivers. *Philos. Trans. R. Soc. London* **29**, 296–300.

Hansen, J., Lacis, A., Rind, D., Russell, G., Stone, P., Fung, I., Ruedy, R., and Lerner, J. (1984). Climate sensitivity: Analysis of feedback mechanisms. *In* "Climate Processes and Climate Sensitivity" (J. E. Hansen and T. Takahashi, eds.), Maurice Ewing Ser. No. 5, pp. 130–163. Am. Geophys. Union, Washington, D.C.

Hasselman, K. (1981). Construction and verification of stochastic climate models. *In* "Climatic Variations and Variability: Facts and Theories" (A. Berger, ed.), pp. 481–500. Reidel, Dordrecht, Netherlands.

Hays, J. E., Imbrie, J., and Shackleton, N. J. (1976). Variations in the earth's orbit: Pacemaker of the ice ages. *Science* **194**, 1121–1132.

Hecht, A. (1985). Paleoclimatology. A retrospective of the past 20 years. *In* "Paleoclimate Analysis and Modeling" (A. Hecht, ed.), pp. 1–26. Wiley, New York.

Hunt, B. G. (1979). The effects of past variations of the earth's rotation rate on climate. *Nature (London)* **281**, 188–191.

Imbrie, J. (1981). Time dependent models of the climatic response to orbital variations. *In* "Climatic Variations and Variability: Facts and Theories" (A. Berger, ed.), pp. 527–538. Reidel, Dordrecht, Netherlands.

Imbrie, J. (1982). Astronomical theory of the Pleistocene Ice Ages: a brief historical review. *Icarus* **50**, 408–422.

Imbrie, J., and Imbrie, J. Z. (1979). "Ice Ages: Solving the Mystery." Enslow Publishers, Short Hills, New Jersey.

Imbrie, J., and Imbrie, K. P. (1980). Modeling the climatic response to orbital variations. *Science* **207**, 943–953.

Kutzbach, J. E. (1981). Monsoon climate of the early Holocene: Climatic experiment using the Earth's orbital parameters for 9000 years ago. *Science* **214**, 59–61.

Kutzbach, J. E., and Guetter, P. J. (1984a). Sensitivity of late-glacial and Holocene climates to the combined effects of orbital parameter changes and lower boundary condition changes: "Snapshot" simulations with a general circulation model for 18, 9, and 6 ka BP. *Ann. Glaciol.* **5**, 85–87.

Kutzbach, J. E., and Guetter, P. J. (1984b). The sensitivity of monsoon climates to orbital parameter changes for 9000 years BP: Experiments with the NCAR general circulation model. *In* "Milankovitch and Climate" (A. Berger, J. Imbrie, J. Hays, G. Kukla, and B. Saltzman, eds.), Part 2, pp. 801–820. Reidel Publ., Dordrecht, Netherlands.

Kutzbach, J. E., and Guetter, P. J. (1985). The influence of changing orbital parameters and surface boundary conditions on the simulated climate of the past 18,000 years. (In preparation).

Kutzbach, J. E., and Otto-Bliesner, B. L. (1982). The sensitivity of the African-Asian monsoonal climate to orbital parameter changes for 9000 years BP in a low-resolution general circulation model. *J. Atmos. Sci.* **39**, 1177–1188.

Lloyd, C. R. (1983). "Pre-pleistocene Paleoclimates: A Summary of the Geological and Paleontological Evidence," Climate Res. Inst. Rep. No. 44. Oregon State University, Corvallis.

Lyell, C. (1837). "Principles of Geology," Vol. 1. James Kay, Jr. & Brother, Philadelphia, Pennsylvania.

Manabe, S., and Broccoli, A. J. (1984). Influence of the CLIMAP ice sheet on the climate of a general circulation model: Implications for the Milankovitch theory. *In* "Milankovitch and Climate" (A. Berger, J. Imbrie, J. Hays, G. Kukla and B. Saltzman, eds.), Part 2, pp. 789–800. Reidel Publ., Dordrecht, Netherlands.

Manabe, S., and Hahn, D. G. (1977). Simulation of the tropical climate of an Ice Age. *JGR, J. Geophys. Res.* **82**, 3889–3911.

Manabe, S., and Wetherald, R. T. (1980). On the distribution of climatic change resulting from an increase in CO_2 content of the atmosphere. *J. Atmos. Sci.* **37**, 99–118.

Mason, B. J. (1976). Towards the understanding and prediction of climatic variations; and addendum by A. Gilchrist. *Q. J. R. Meteorol. Soc.* **102**, 473–498.

Milankovitch, M. (1920). "Théorie mathématique des phénomènes thermiques produits par la radiation solaire." Gauthier-Villars, Paris.

Milankovitch, M. (1941). Kanon der Erdbestrahlung und seine Anwendung auf das Eiszeiten-problem. *R. Serb. Acad. Spec. Publ. (Belgrade)* **133**, 1–633. (English translation published by Israel Program for Scientific Translations, Jerusalem, 1969. Available from U.S. Dept. of Commerce, Washington, D.C.)

Mitchell, J. M., Jr. (1965). Theoretical paleoclimatology. *In* "The Quaternary of the United States" (H. E. Wright, Jr. and D. G. Frey, eds.), pp. 881–901. Princeton Univ. Press, Princeton, New Jersey.

North, G. R., Mengel, J. G., and Short, D. A. (1983). A simple energy balance model resolving the seasons and the continents: Application to the astronomical theory of the Ice Ages. *JGR, J. Geophys. Res.* **88**, 6576–6586.

NRC Panel on Climatic Variation, U.S. Committee for GARP (1975). "Understanding Climatic change: A Program for Action." Natl. Acad. Sci., Washington, D.C.

NRC Panel on Pre-Pleistocene Climates (1982). "Climate in Earth History." Natl. Acad. Sci., Washington, D.C.

Owen, T., Cess, R. D., and Ramanathan, V. (1979). Enhanced CO_2 greenhouse to compensate for reduced solar luminosity on early Earth. *Nature (London)* **277**, 640–642.

Pollack, J. B. (1982). Solar, astronomical, and atmospheric effects on climate. *In* "Climate in Earth History" (NRC Panel on Pre-Pleistocene Climates), pp. 68–76. Natl. Acad. Sci., Washington, D.C.

Pollack, J. B., Toon, O. B., Ackerman, T., and McKay, C. P. (1983). Environmental effects of an impact-generated dust cloud: Implications for the Cretaceous-Tertiary extinctions. *Science* **219**, 287–289.

Pollard, D. (1982). "A Coupled Climate-Ice Sheet Model Applied to the Quaternary Ice Ages," Clim. Res. Inst. Rep. No. 37. Oregon State University, Corvallis.

Prell, W. L. (1984). Monsoonal climate of the Arabian Sea during the Late Quaternary: A response to changing solar radiation. *In* "Milankovitch and Climate" (A. Berger, J. Imbrie, J. Hays, G. Kukla, and B. Saltzman, eds.), Part 1, pp. 349–366. Reidel Publ., Dordrecht, Netherlands.

Ruddiman, W. F., and McIntyre, A. (1981). Oceanic mechanisms for amplification of the 23,000-year ice-volume cycle. *Science* **212**, 617–627.

Saltzman, B. (1978). A survey of statistical-dynamic models of the terrestrial climate. *Adv. Geophys.* **20**, 184–304.

Saltzman, B., and Sutera, A. (1984). A model of the internal feedback system involved in Late Quaternary climatic variations. *J. Atmos. Sci.* **41**, 736–745.

Schneider, S. H., and Dickinson, R. E. (1974). Climate modeling. *Rev. Geophys. Space Phys.* **12**, 447–493.

Schneider, S. H., and Mass, C. (1975). Volcanic dust, sunspots, and temperature trends. *Science* **190**, 741–746.

Smagorinsky, J. (1960). A synopsis of research on quasi-stationary perturbations of the mean zonal circulation caused by topography and heating. *In* "Dynamics of Climate" (R. L. Pfeffer, ed.), pp. 44–49. Pergamon, Oxford.

Smagorinsky, J. (1963). General circulation experiments with the primitive equations. I. The basic experiment. *Mon. Weather Rev.* **91**, 99–165.

Smagorinsky, B. (1974). Global atmospheric modeling and the numerical simulation of climate. *In* "Weather and Climate Modification" (W. N. Hess, ed.), pp. 633–686. Wiley, New York.

Smagorinsky, J. (1983). The beginnings of numerical weather prediction and general circulation modeling: Early reflections. *Adv. Geophys.* **20**, 3–37.

Street, F. A., and Grove, A. T. (1979). Global maps of lake-level fluctuations since 30,000 yr B.P. *Quat. Res. (N.Y.)* **12**, 83–118.

Suarez, M. J., and Held, I. M. (1976). Modeling climatic response to orbital parameter variations. *Nature (London)* **263**, 46–47.

Suarez, M. J., and Held, I. M. (1979). The sensitivity of an energy balance climate model to variations in the orbital parameters. *JGR, J. Geophys. Res.* **84**, 4825–4836.

Thomson, W. (1862). On the secular cooling of the earth. *Trans. R. Soc. Edinburgh* **23**, 157–169.

von Bezold, W. (1892). Der Wärmeaustausch an der Erdoberfläche und in der Atmosphäre. *Sitzungsber. K. Preuss. Akad. Wiss.,* pp. 1139–1178.

von Humboldt, A. (1817). Résearches sur les causes des inflexion de lignes isotherms. *Memoirs de Physique d.l. Soc. d'Arcueil* (Paris) **3**.

von Neumann, J. (1960). Some remarks on the problem of forecasting climatic fluctuations. *In* "Dynamics of Climate" (R. L. Pfeffer, ed.), pp. 9–11. Pergamon, Oxford.

Walker, J. C. G. (1982). Climatic factors on the Archean Earth. *Paleogeogr., Paleoclimatol., Paleoecol.* **40**, 1–11.

Webb, T., III, Cushing, E. J., and Wright, H. E., Jr. (1983). Holocene changes in the vegetation of the Midwest. *In* "Late-Quaternary Environments of the United States" (H. E. Wright, Jr., ed.), Vol. 2, pp. 142–165. Univ. of Minnesota Press, Minneapolis.

Williams, J., Barry, R. G., and Washington, W. M. (1974). Simulation of the atmospheric circulation using the NCAR global circulation model with Ice Age boundary conditions. *J. Appl. Meteorol.* **13**, 305–317.

Zenker, W. (1888). "Die Vertheilung der Wärme auf der Erdoberfläche." Springer-Verlag, Berlin and New York.

THE SOUTHERN OSCILLATION AND EL NIÑO

S. George Philander

Geophysical Fluid Dynamics Laboratory/NOAA
Princeton University
Princeton, New Jersey

AND

Eugene M. Rasmusson

Climate Analysis Center
National Meteorological Center
National Weather Service/NOAA
Washington, D.C.

1. Introduction

"When pressure is high in the Pacific Ocean, it tends to be low in the Indian Ocean from Africa to Australia." That is how Walker described the large-scale climate fluctuations that he named the Southern Oscillation (SO) (Walker and Bliss, 1932). Studies during the past half-century have revealed that the SO involves far more than a seesaw in the surface pressure between the Southeast Pacific subtropical high-pressure cell and the North Australian–Indonesian low-pressure trough. It has emerged as the dominant interannual climate signal on a global scale. Over the tropical Pacific Ocean, the SO is associated with large year-to-year variations in the intensity of the trade winds and in rainfall patterns (Fig. 1). The SO also has a signature that extends into the middle latitudes of each hemisphere during its winter season (Horel and Wallace, 1981; van Loon and Madden, 1981).

Early investigators were unable to identify the physical processes responsi-

197

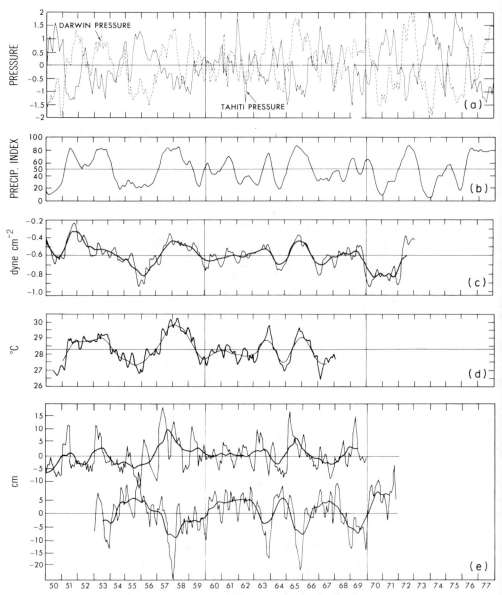

FIG. 1. Interannual fluctuations: (a) sea-level pressure anomalies (3-month running means) for Darwin (72°S, 131°E) and Tahiti (17°S, 150°W); (b) precipitation index (6-month running mean) for Ocean and Naura Islands (7°S, 167°E); (c) zonal component of the monthly mean wind stress over the region 4°N to 4°S, 140°W to 180°W (after Wyrtki, 1973); (d) monthly mean sea-surface temperature at Canton Island (3°S, 171°W) (after Wyrtki, 1973); (e) monthly mean sea level at Talara (4°S, 81°W) and Truk Atoll (7°N, 151°E) (after Hickey, 1975). The smooth lines are 12-month running means.

ble for the long-term memory of the atmosphere implied by the persistence, over several seasons, of anomalous conditions associated with the SO. Only in the late 1960s did Bjerknes (1966, 1969) and others show that the SO is closely linked with interannual sea-surface temperature variations in the eastern and central Pacific Ocean. Bjerknes proposed that the ocean, whose relatively large heat content provides it with a memory much longer than that of the atmosphere, is of central importance in the SO.

Interannual sea-surface temperature variations in the tropical Pacific Ocean are primarily associated with a phenomenon known as El Niño. This term originally referred to a warm current that flows southward along the coasts of Ecuador and Peru in January, February, and March. The current marks the end of the local fishing season during which sea-surface temperatures are low and the southeast trade winds are intense. [The trades drive the surface waters of the eastern Pacific westward (offshore) and hence induce the upwelling of cold, nutrient-rich water near the coast.] In certain years, temperatures are exceptionally high during the warm season and continue to be so during the normally cold upwelling season. At present, the term El Niño is reserved for those interannual events when anomalously warm surface waters cover not only the coastal zone of South America, but also most of the tropical Pacific Ocean as far west as the dateline. The ecological and climatic disruptions associated with these events have disastrous consequences not only for the economies of Ecuador and Peru (Barber and Chavez, 1983), but for many other regions of the tropics and higher latitudes as well (Rasmusson and Wallace, 1983).

Rapid progress in our understanding of the El Niño – Southern Oscillation (ENSO) phenomenon during the past few years leaves little doubt that interactions between the ocean and atmosphere are at the heart of the problem. This paper briefly reviews these recent developments.

2. SEASONAL VARIABILITY

On time scales of weeks or longer, the large-scale atmospheric circulation of the tropics exhibits a pattern of direct thermal circulations. The upward branches are over the continents and over the tropical zones of highest sea-surface temperatures (SST), where convection is intense and rainfall is heavy. Figure 2 shows these regions. In the tropical Pacific sector they are over Central and South America, the western Pacific – Indonesian "Maritime Continent" region, and northern Australia, and along the Intertropical Convergence Zone (ITCZ) north of the equator and along the South Pacific Convergence Zone (SPCZ) in the southwestern Pacific Ocean. An important descending branch of the atmospheric circulation is over the cold waters of

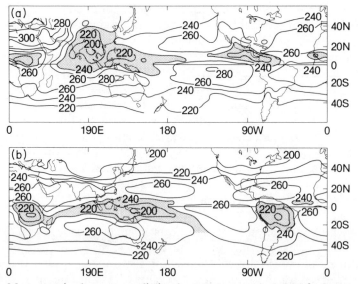

FIG. 2. Mean outgoing long-wave radiation (watts per square meter) (a) for June to August and (b) for December to February as measured by polar orbiting satellites. Tropical regions with values less than 240 W m⁻² (shaded) are regions of strong convection and heavy rainfall.

the southeastern tropical Pacific Ocean. The southeast trade winds that blow from there to the convective region over the western Pacific complete the zonal Walker circulation (Bjerknes, 1969). The other important descending branches of the circulation, in the subtropics, complete the meridional over-turning known as the Hadley cell.

The convective regions and the trade-wind belts move meridionally with the seasons (Fig. 2) so that the seasonal cross-equatorial surface flow (relative to the annual mean) is directed into the summer hemisphere. For example, the southeast trade winds penetrate well into the Northern Hemisphere and are most intense in August and September when the ITCZ is at its northern-most latitude near 12°N. In February and March, when the ITCZ is close to the equator, the southeast trades are weak but the northeast trades are in-tense (Horel, 1982).

The seasonal migrations of the atmospheric convective zones are asso-ciated with seasonal changes in the sea-surface temperature. The isoline of 240-W m⁻² outgoing long-wave radiation, which delineates the region of most intense convection, is usually enclosed by the 27.5°C isotherm throughout the year. These warm surface waters are predominantly in the western tropical Pacific and off the coast of Central America. The southeast-ern tropical Pacific, on the other hand, has the lowest average sea-surface temperatures (Fig. 3). These horizontal SST gradients also reflect the distri-

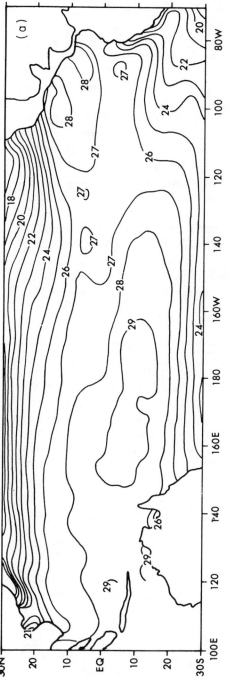
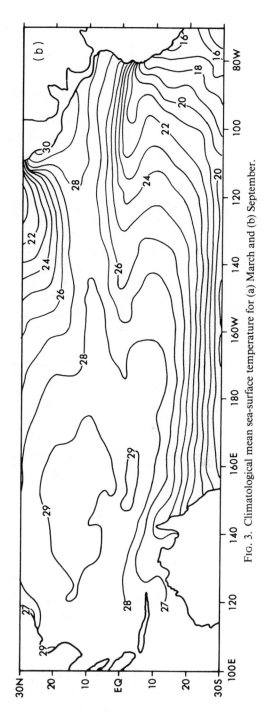

Fig. 3. Climatological mean sea-surface temperature for (a) March and (b) September.

bution of oceanic heat content. The thermocline — the highly stratified layer that separates the warm surface waters from the cold water at depth — slopes downward toward the west so that the surface mixed layer is more than 150 m deep in the west but essentially disappears along the South American coast. The westward component of the trade winds drives westward currents along the equator and maintains the buildup of excess warm water on the western side. The northward component of the southeast trades causes upwelling along the coast of South America (but downwelling along the coast in the Northern Hemisphere) and contributes to the low sea-surface temperatures in the southeast. Rossby waves, which disperse the coastal upwelling westward, travel more rapidly the lower the latitude, so that the cold surface waters extend farthest westward near the equator, where the zonal winds induce upwelling and cause a further reduction in the SST. Sea-surface temperatures in the southeastern tropical Pacific are at a minimum in September when the southeast trades are most intense and the ITCZ is in its northernmost position and are at a maximum in March when the southeast trades are weak and the ITCZ is close to the equator.

3. Interannual Variability

Figure 1 shows that the oceanic and atmospheric fluctuations associated with the Southern Oscillation are highly correlated. The coherence of the meteorological variables is attributable to anomalous movements of the major convective zones. For example, during periods of unusually high SST in the central and eastern tropical Pacific, the convective zone over the western tropical Pacific moves eastward as the pressure over Indonesia and northern Australia rises and the pressure over the southeastern tropical Pacific falls. This relaxation of the equatorial pressure gradient is accompanied by weakening of the easterly winds in the central equatorial Pacific Ocean and an equatorward displacement of the ITCZ (Ramage and Hori, 1981; Pazan and Meyers, 1982). This warm phase of the Southern Oscillation is followed by one during which complementary conditions prevail: SST in the central and eastern equatorial Pacific is exceptionally low, the convective zones move westward and poleward, and the surface pressure gradient across the tropical Pacific Ocean increases as does the intensity of the trade winds.

The oceanic variations associated with the SO reflect the adjustment of the ocean to the changing surface winds. For example, when the trade winds are weak, the zonal slope of the thermocline decreases so that the depth of the thermocline, and sea level, increase in the eastern tropical Pacific but decrease in the western tropical Pacific. The associated eastward transfer of warm water causes the SST in the central and eastern Pacific to rise. This transfer is effected by an intensification of the eastward current between approximately 3°N and 10°N (the North Equatorial Countercurrent) and by a weakening of the westward South Equatorial Current to the south of the Countercurrent (Wyrtki, 1975, 1977; Enfield, 1981). During the complementary phase of the SO when the trade winds are intense, the zonal slope of the thermocline increases and the SST is low.

Since World War II, the average period of the Southern Oscillation has been approximately 3–4 years, but, as is evident from Figs. 1 and 4, the SO is very aperiodic. Though the period between successive warm events varies considerably, most of these warm events nonetheless evolve in remarkably similar ways (Fig. 4). Rasmusson and Wallace (1983) suggest that this evolution normally involves two stages. The first stage starts toward the end of the calendar year in the eastern tropical Pacific Ocean and amounts to an amplification and extension of the warm phase of the local seasonal cycle. Hence, unusually warm surface waters appear off the coast of Peru and Ecuador at a time when the local SST approaches its seasonal maximum. The appearance of this warm water is preceded by a weakening of the Southeast Pacific Anticyclone for which the surface pressure at Tahiti serves as an index. The unusually warm surface waters off Peru persist during the subsequent months so that El Niño is a failure of the cold season in the southeastern tropical Pacific to develop fully (Fig. 5).

The second stage in the evolution of a warm event involves the central and western Pacific and starts towards the middle of the year — approximately 6 months after the appearance of unusual conditions in the east. (Figure 4 shows the phase difference between developments in the eastern and western tropical Pacific.) This second stage is associated with an eastward displacement of the convective zone that is normally over the western Pacific Ocean, an increase in the sea-level pressure at Darwin, a massive collapse of the equatorial easterlies in the central Pacific, and a rapid increase in central equatorial rainfall anomalies. These conditions reach a peak near the end of the year, at which time the entire eastern and central tropical Pacific is anomalously warm. Early in the new year, normal conditions are restored to the west of the dateline. During the subsequent months, anomalous conditions attenuate over the rest of the tropical Pacific.

The development of these surface anomalies is accompanied by the development of pronounced circulation anomalies in the upper-tropical troposphere. The upper-level divergence from the region of heavy precipitation generates anticyclonic upper-troposphere vorticity in the central equatorial Pacific. This is associated with the development of an anomalous anticyclonic circulation cell centered south of the equator during the austral winter. Six months later, the single cell has evolved into an anticyclonic

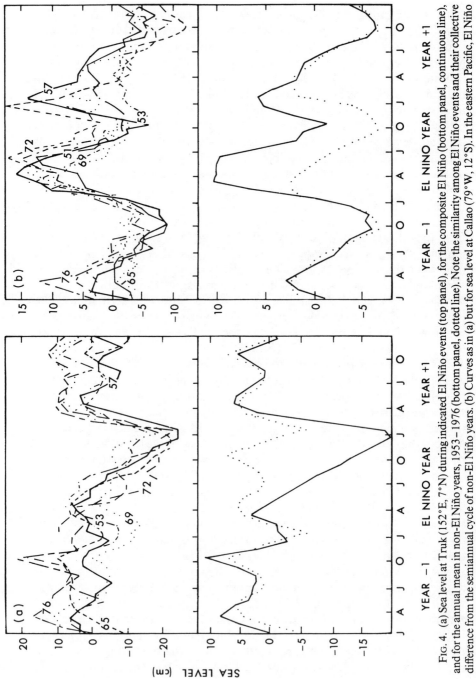

FIG. 4. (a) Sea level at Truk (152°E, 7°N) during indicated El Niño events (top panel, continuous line), for the composite El Niño (bottom panel, continuous line), and for the annual mean in non-El Niño years, 1953–1976 (bottom panel, dotted line). Note the similarity among El Niño events and their collective difference from the semiannual cycle of non-El Niño years. (b) Curves as in (a) but for sea level at Callao (79°W, 12°S). In the eastern Pacific, El Niño events typically appear as an enhancement of the annual cycle.

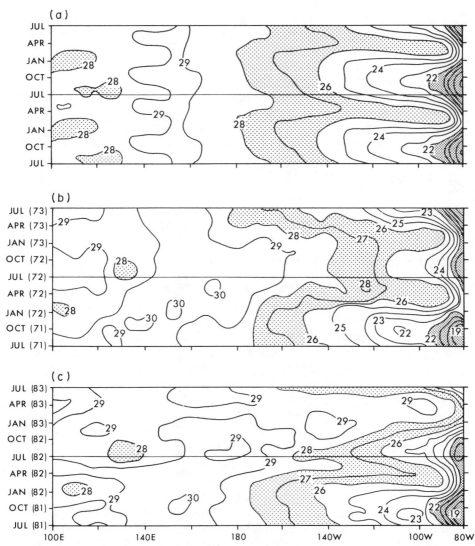

FIG. 5. Sea-surface temperature variations along the equator between 100°E and 100°W and along a line from 0°N 100°W to the South American coast at 8°S. (a) Equatorial climatological SST, (b) 1972 event, and (c) 1982 event.

couplet that straddles the equator. The anomaly pattern reflects an eastward extension of the upper-troposphere monsoon highs normally located over the western Pacific in this season. This pattern is associated with anomalous easterlies over the equatorial region of enhanced convection and with anomalous westerlies on the poleward flanks of the cells so that there is an enhancement of the subtropical jet streams in the central and eastern Pacific.

The major changes associated with a warm episode are usually preceded by modest anomalies that appear in the western tropical Pacific toward the end of the year preceding the onset of El Niño in the east. These anomalies include a rise in SST and a relaxation of the time-averaged trade winds to the west of the dateline. This weakening of the winds apparently results from an increase in the frequency of disturbances [synoptic scale cyclone pairs (Keen, 1982)] that are associated with westerly wind anomalies (Luther *et al.*, 1983). These early time-averaged anomalies are far smaller in amplitude than those that occur later and are sometimes observed when no El Niño is imminent (in 1979, for example).

4. THE 1982–1983 EPISODE

A typical ENSO episode, as pointed out in Section 3, evolves in two stages: one stage involves principally the eastern tropical Pacific, the other involves the central and western Pacific, too. The differences between individual ENSO events reflect the relative strengths, and on rare occasions the order of occurrence, of the two stages. The 1982–1983 episode was distinctive in that it apparently bypassed the typical first stage. The phase of the event was normal in the central and western equatorial Pacific but abnormal in the east. In the central equatorial Pacific the SST rose above normal during April and May 1982, and pronounced equatorial westerly wind anomalies appeared west of the dateline in June. These anomalies next amplified and expanded eastward (Fig. 6). By September the eastern tropical Pacific was affected. Temperatures there increased sharply between September and the end of 1982. Thereafter, the SST increased gradually to a plateau near 29°C. The termination of the event did not start until June 1983 when cold surface waters appeared on the equator near 140°W. Shortly afterward the SST in the east, at the Galapagos Islands, for example, started to fall precipitously.

Sea-surface-temperature anomalies attained an exceptional amplitude in 1982 and 1983. During the previous El Niño events since 1950, the 29°C isotherm never migrated east of 140°W at the equator; but in 1982 it reached the coast of South America, resulting in an insignificant SST gradient along the equator in February 1983 (Gill and Rasmusson, 1983). The equatorial westerly wind anomalies were so intense that the thermocline along the equator was horizontal toward the end of 1982 (Cane, 1983) and the normally intense Equatorial Undercurrent disappeared completely for a while, first at 159°W in September 1982 (Firing *et al.*, 1983) and a few months later at 110°W (Halpern *et al.*, 1983). The extreme eastward displacement of the warm water contributed to a huge increase in the number of hurricanes and

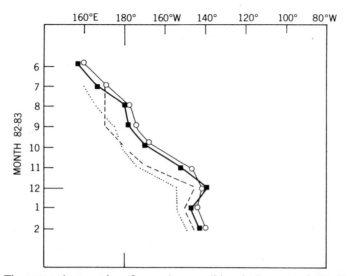

FIG. 6. The eastward progression of anomalous conditions in the equatorial Pacific (5°N to 5°S) during 1982 and 1983. The axes of the anomalous cloudiness and winds are shown. (○———○, center of gravity of surface waters warmer than 29°C; ■———■, infrared anomaly; ------, easterly wind anomaly at 200 mb; · · ·, westerly wind anomaly at 850 mb.)

tropical storms in the central Pacific, a region in which such phenomena are relatively rare (De Angelis, 1983).

The eastward displacement in the tropical Pacific of the warm surface waters and the atmospheric convection affected the atmospheric circulation globally. Particularly striking was the intensification of the westerly wind anomalies in the upper troposphere of the tropical Atlantic Ocean. This was associated with a cyclone dipole pattern over the Americas in the tropics.

5. TELECONNECTIONS

The anomalous heating of the tropical Pacific atmosphere during ENSO episodes affects the global atmospheric circulation. Bjerknes (1969) was the first to examine the tropical–extratropical links in a dynamical context, although the existence of such relationships was implied by Walker's SO correlation patterns (Walker and Bliss, 1932). Bjerknes proposed that the observed intensification of the Aleutian Low during an ENSO winter results from an enhanced regional Hadley Circulation, which increases the north-ward transport of angular momentum in the upper troposphere, leading to stronger westerlies and an enhanced meridional pressure gradient. The downstream circulation anomalies over western and eastern North America

were viewed as a response to the North Pacific anomaly. Within this conceptual framework, Arkin (1983) demonstrated that the enhanced upper-tropospheric westerlies during an ENSO episode are associated with increased
poleward ageostrophic flow, primarily into the winter hemisphere. This flow
emanates from the region of divergence in the neighborhood of the enhanced
equatorial convection.

The triplet of North Pacific–North American circulation anomalies described by Bjerknes is referred to as the Pacific–North American (PNA)
teleconnection (Wallace and Gutzler, 1981). During an "average" ENSO
winter, these "centers of action," together with the anticyclonic anomaly
center near the equator, trace out an apparent wave train with the polarity
shown in Fig. 7. Horel and Wallace (1981) suggest that this pattern might
reflect a Rossby-wave train that propagates along a great circle path into
higher latitudes from the equatorial region of anomalous forcing (Hoskins
and Karoly, 1981). More recent results from simple dynamic models (Simmons et al., 1983) indicate that in the Northern Hemisphere during wintertime, when the stationary waves are very strong, the response to tropical
forcing may take the form of a geographically fixed normal mode, which
resembles the PNA pattern. Under these circumstances, an eastward or
westward movement of the region of enhanced rainfall and associated
upper-troposphere anticyclonic couplet will result in the same PNA pattern
of response, although the amplitude and perhaps even the polarity might
change. This normal mode behavior is associated with barotropic instability
of the mean flow pattern and may be excited in many different ways; forcing
by equatorial precipitation is just one way.

In 1982–1983 the anomalous convection in the tropical Pacific moved
much farther east than during earlier ENSO episodes. A characteristic PNA
pattern was nonetheless identifiable in the December-to-February-averaged
200-mb circulation anomalies. The PNA pattern showed little or no systematic eastward displacement from its normal position. Blackmon et al. (1983)
have recently performed an experiment using the National Center for Atmospheric Research (NCAR) spectral general circulation model in which the
equatorial SST anomaly was moved progressively farther east of its typical
position. In the model, the PNA response remained geographically locked in
position, but its amplitude decreased the farther east the SST anomaly was
placed. These results seem to support the hypothesis that the PNA pattern is
an unstable mode of the mid-latitude troposphere (Simmons et al., 1983).

Teleconnection patterns in the Southern Hemisphere have been less extensively documented and studied. The data now appear adequate to clarify
their relationship with ENSO. Further analysis of teleconnections in both
hemispheres may clarify a number of unresolved issues, including the role of
low-latitude intraseasonal fluctuations (Sardeshmukh and Hoskins, 1984),

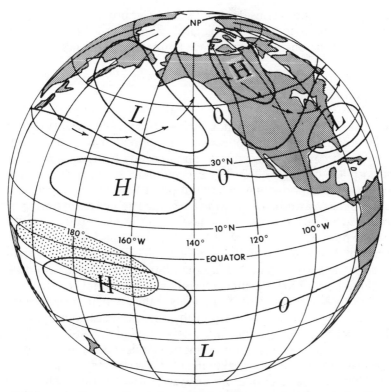

FIG. 7. Schematic diagram of upper-tropospheric height anomaly pattern during the mature phase (Northern Hemisphere winter) of ENSO. (After Horel and Wallace, 1981.)

cross-equatorial propagation (Webster and Holton, 1982), and the effect of the highly anomalous basic state of the westerlies on propagation character-istics during ENSO.

A number of Southern Hemisphere extratropical relationships have re-cently been documented by van Loon and Madden (1981), Quinn (1979), Trenberth (1976), and others. Van Loon (1984) shows that the annual cycle of the trough in the South Pacific westerlies is enhanced during El Niño episodes but is attenuated during the year preceding ENSO.

6. AIR–SEA INTERACTIONS

During ENSO episodes, anomalous conditions develop simultaneously in the ocean and atmosphere (Fig. 6). This strongly suggests that interactions between the ocean and atmosphere are of central importance. To understand these interactions consider first two simpler problems: the response of the ocean to the observed meteorological changes and the response of the atmosphere to the observed sea-surface temperature changes.

6.1. Response of the Ocean

The weakening of the trade winds during ENSO could reduce evaporation from the ocean, but this cannot explain the anomalously warm sea-surface temperature because the ocean loses an unusually large amount of heat to the atmosphere during ENSO. The exceptionally warm surface waters are caused by a rapid horizontal redistribution of heat in the upper ocean in response to the relaxation of the winds over the Pacific Ocean during ENSO (Wyrtki, 1975). In the tropical Pacific Ocean the sea-surface temperature has a minimum along the coast of South America and increases in both a westward and northward direction (Fig. 3). These temperature gradients exist below the surface, too, and are maintained by the trade winds. If the winds should stop blowing altogether, then a horizontal redistribution of heat will cause horizontal density gradients in the ocean to weaken considerably. Several mechanisms are responsible for the redistribution, but their relative importance changes during the development of ENSO and also from episode to episode. The most important mechanism is the zonal redistribution of heat induced by the weakening of the westward component of the trades. These winds maintain an eastward pressure force, which can be inferred from the zonal temperature gradients in the upper ocean. When the winds weaken, the pressure force is unbalanced and accelerates the warm surface equatorial waters in the west toward the east (McCreary, 1976; Hurlburt et al., 1976). The convergent eastward current, which can be observed seasonally during the boreal spring when the trades are weak (Halpern et al., 1983), is augmented during a typical ENSO. The weakening of westward winds over a confined region will result in a warming not only of that region but, because of eastward propagating equatorial Kelvin waves, also of the region to the east (Cane and Sarachik, 1977). This warming in the east depends on the zonal extent of the region over which the winds weaken, the magnitude of the change in wind stress, and the length of time for which the winds relax (Philander, 1981). The amplitude of the changes in the western Pacific in mid-1982 were apparently sufficient to induce the appearance of exceptionally warm surface waters in the central Pacific Ocean. The subsequent increase in the area of westerly wind anomalies was sufficient to cause unusually warm surface waters across the entire tropical Pacific Ocean.

Changes in the curl of the wind stress also contribute to the redistribution of heat in the tropical Pacific Ocean during ENSO (Wyrtki, 1973, 1975). The curl drives the warm eastward surface current between 3°N and 10°N and the cold westward current south of 3°N. During most ENSO episodes, the wind changes in such a manner that the eastward current intensifies while the westward current weakens.

The success (Busalacchi and O'Brien, 1981) with which adiabatic models, forced with the observed winds, simulate thermocline displacements observed during ENSO confirms the thesis that the oceanic changes during ENSO are caused primarily by the weakening of the trade winds. This, however, is not an explanation for ENSO because the weakening of the trades is part of the atmospheric response to the anomalously high sea-surface temperatures.

6.2. The Atmospheric Response

The tropical atmosphere responds to anomalous heat sources with changes in the configuration of the direct thermal circulations. A heating anomaly near the equator that is associated with rising air will drive convergent surface winds (Matsuno, 1966; Webster, 1972, 1981; Gill, 1980). It is for this reason that westerly wind anomalies appear over the western and central equatorial Pacific when the heated region of rising air is over the eastern equatorial Pacific Ocean.

The relation between heating anomalies in the atmosphere and SST anomalies in the ocean is a very complex one. The effectiveness of an SST anomaly to influence the atmosphere depends on the actual value of the SST (as opposed to the magnitude of the SST anomaly) and on the large-scale atmospheric conditions in the neighborhood of the anomaly. For example, exceptionally warm surface waters in a region of low-level atmospheric convergence can readily enhance the upward motion and convection in that region, thus amplifying the low-level moisture convergence. In a region of low-level divergence, on the other hand, the latent heat released from a warm SST anomaly may be insufficient to reverse the downward motion and may fail to induce local heating. Since the major upward branches of the tropical circulation are over the warmest water, the regions of highest SST are also the dynamically favored regions for initiating a significant change in the thermal circulations of the tropics.

6.3. Air–Sea Interactions

The arguments advanced above to explain the response of the ocean to anomalous winds and the response of the atmosphere to unusually high sea-surface temperatures suggest that unstable interactions between the ocean and atmosphere are possible (Philander, 1983). Suppose, for example, that unusually warm surface waters on the equator in the eastern Pacific lead to anomalous convection there. The westerly wind anomaly created by the convection will drive an anomalous oceanic current downwind. Given that sea-surface temperatures increase to the west in the Pacific, this implies an eastward transport of warm water that will enhance the convection in the east. This, in turn, will cause even more intense westerly wind anomalies, and so on. Consider next the appearance of anomalous convection on the equator near the dateline. To the west of this region, positive feedback will again cause the amplitude of westerly wind anomalies and eastward oceanic currents to grow. To the east of the anomalous convection the situation is more complex because two factors affect the SST in that region: the local easterly winds, induced by the convection, cause equatorial upwelling that reduces the SST; but oceanic Kelvin waves, excited by the westerly winds in the west, deepen the thermocline in the east and cause the SST to increase. The results from a model of these air–sea interactions (Philander *et al.*, 1984) indicate that the effect of the Kelvin waves is dominant so that the SST in the east increases. The convective region therefore moves eastward. This happened in 1982 (Fig. 6).

The close relation between El Niño events and the seasonal cycle suggests that the phase of the initial perturbations that trigger instabilities cannot be random. From Fig. 4 it is evident that, off South America, the initial perturbation must appear as an amplification of the warm phase of the seasonal cycle. The reasons were given in Section 6.2. For an SST anomaly to influence the atmosphere significantly, the cooperation of the large-scale atmospheric fields is required. For example, if the warm anomaly is situated in a region of large-scale descending motion — the southeastern tropical Pacific in September, for example — then no instability is possible because the water vapor released there will condense where the air rises, over the western Pacific probably. The most favorable time for a warm anomaly in the eastern equatorial Pacific to amplify is early in the calendar year, when the seasonal migration of the ITCZ takes it to its lowest latitude. In the western Pacific, instabilities are most likely when the convergence zone moves from the Southern to the Northern Hemisphere, in April and May (Fig. 4). The seasonal movements of the atmospheric convergence zones clearly determine where and when instabilities can be initiated. El Niño events can therefore be viewed as unstable air–sea interactions modulated by the seasonal cycle. An event could be triggered by an irregularity in the seasonal cycle. Since the seasonal cycle depends on many factors, of which the sea-surface temperature is only one, it is possible that El Niño is initiated by factors outside the tropical Pacific Ocean. Identification of the other factors is necessary for the prediction of ENSO events.

7. Discussion

The global seasonal cycle appears to be a dominant factor in the phasing and evolution of ENSO. Indeed, the Southern Oscillation can be viewed as an amplitude modulation of the annual cycle of various climate features in the tropics. Many aspects of the seasonal cycle are poorly understood. There are practically no measurements that describe the seasonal changes of the currents in the western equatorial Pacific Ocean. It is not known whether the westward phase propagation that characterizes the seasonal variations of SST in the eastern tropical Pacific (Horel, 1982) is also a property of subsurface fields. The extent to which air–sea interactions affect the seasonal migrations of the ITCZ, and the seasonal migrations of the region of high SST and intense convection in the western tropical Pacific, is unknown. To understand the Southern Oscillation better, further studies of the seasonal cycle are required.

The principal area of air–sea interaction during ENSO is the tropical Pacific, but warm episodes typically involve much of the globe, especially the rest of the tropics. For example, during ENSO there are significant rainfall anomalies in the Amazon Basin and in the Indian Ocean. It is unclear whether these anomalies are merely passive reflections of the interactions in the tropical Pacific or whether they are active elements that influence the evolution of ENSO. This question and others related to the initiation and predictability of an episode will be difficult to answer without numerical experiments that use coupled ocean–atmosphere–land models.

References

Arkin, F. (1983). An examination of the Southern Oscillation in the upper tropospheric tropical and subtropical wind-field. Ph.D. Thesis, University of Maryland, College Park.

Barber, R. T. and Chavez, F. P. (1983). Biological consequences of El Niño. *Science* **222,** 1203–1210.

Bjerknes, J. (1966). A possible response of the atmospheric Hadley circulation to equatorial anomalies of ocean temperature. *Tellus* **18,** 820–829.

Bjerknes, J. (1969). Atmospheric teleconnections from the equatorial Pacific. *Mon. Weather Rev.* **97,** 163–172.

Blackmon, M. L., Geisler, J. E., and Pitcher, E. J. (1983). A general circulation model study of January climate anomaly patterns associated with interannual variation of equatorial Pacific sea surface temperature. *J. Atmos. Sci.* **40,** 1410–1425.

Busalacchi, A. J., and O'Brien, J. J. (1981). Interannual variability of the equatorial Pacific in the 1960's. *JGR, J. Geophys. Res.* **86,** 10901–10907.

Cane, M. A. (1983). Oceanographic events during El Niño. *Science* **222,** 1189–1195.

Cane, M. A., and Sarachik, E. S. (1977). Forced baroclinic ocean motions. II. *J. Mar. Res.* **35**(2), 395–432.

De Angelis, D. (1983). Hurricane alley. *Mon. Weather Log* **27,** 106–109.

Enfield, D. B. (1981). El Niño — Pacific eastern boundary response to interannual forcing. *In* "Resource Management and Environmental Uncertainty" (M. H. Glantz and J. D. Thompson, eds.), pp. 213–254. Wiley, New York.

Firing, E., Lukas, R., Sades, J., and Wyrtki, K. (1983). Equatorial undercurrent disappears during 1982–1983 El Niño. *Science* **222**, 1121–1123.

Gill, A. E. (1980). Some simple solutions for heat-induced tropical circulation. *Q. J. R. Meteorol. Soc.* **106**, 447–462.

Gill, A. E., and Rasmusson, E. M. (1983). The 1982–1983 climate anomoly in the equatorial Pacific. *Nature* **306**, 229–234.

Halpern, D., Hayes, S., Leetmaa, A., Hansen, D., and Philander, G. (1983). Oceanographic observations of the 1982 warming of the tropical Pacific. *Science* **221**, 1173–1175.

Hickey, B. (1975). The relationship between fluctuations in sea level, wind-stress and sea surface temperature in the Equatorial Pacific. *J. Phys. Oceanogr.* **5**, 460–475.

Horel, J. D. (1982). The annual cycle in the tropical Pacific atmosphere and ocean. *Mon. Weather Rev.* **110**, 1863–1878.

Horel, J. D., and Wallace, J. M. (1981). Planetary scale atmospheric phenomena associated with the Southern Oscillation. *Mon. Weather Rev.* **109**, 813–829.

Hoskins, B. J., and Karoly, D. J. (1981). The steady linear response of a spherical atmosphere in thermal and orographic forcing. *J. Atmos. Sci.* **38**, 1179–1196.

Hurlburt, H. E., Kindle, J. C., and O'Brien, J. J. (1976). A numerical simulation of the onset of El Niño. *J. Phys. Oceanogr.* **6**, 621–631.

Keen, R. A. (1982). The role of cross-equatorial cyclone pairs in the Southern Oscillation. *Mon. Weather Rev.* **110**, 1405–1416.

Luther, D. S., Harrison, D. E., and Knox, R. A. (1983). Zonal winds in the central equatorial Pacific and El Niño. *Science* **222**, 327–330.

McCreary, J. (1976). Eastern tropical ocean response to changing wind systems with application to El Niño. *J. Phys. Oceanogr.* **6**, 632–645.

Matsuno, T. (1966). Quasi-geostrophic motions in equatorial areas. *J. Meteorol. Soc. Japan* **2**, 25–43.

Pazan, S., and Meyers, G. (1982). Pacific trade wind fluctuations and the Southern Oscillation index. *Mon. Weather Rev.* **110**, 587–600.

Philander, S. G. H. (1981). The response of equatorial oceans to a relaxation of the trade winds. *J. Phys. Oceanogr.* **11**, 176–189.

Philander, S. G. H. (1983). El Niño Southern Oscillation phenomena. *Nature (London)* **302**, 295–301.

Philander, S. G. H., Yamagata, T., and Pacanowski, R. C. (1984). Unstable air-sea interactions in the tropics. *J. Atmos. Sci.* **41**, 604–613.

Quinn, W. H. (1979). Monitoring and predicting short-term climate changes in the South Pacific ocean. *Proc. Int. Conf. Mar. Sci. Technol., 1979*, Part 1, pp. 26–30.

Ramage, C. S., and Hori, A. M. (1981). Meteorological aspects of El Niño. *Mon. Weather Rev.* **109**, 1827–1835.

Rasmusson, E. M., and Carpenter, T. H. (1982). Variations in tropical sea surface temperature and surface wind fields associated with the Southern Oscillation/El Niño. *Mon. Weather Rev.* **110**, 354–384.

Rasmusson, E. M., and Wallace, J. M. (1983). Meteorological aspects of the El Niño/Southern Oscillation. *Science* **222**, 1195–1202.

Sardeshmukh, P. D., and Hoskins, B. J. (1984). Vorticity balances in the tropics during the 1982–83 El Niño/South Oscillation event. *Mon. Weather Rev.* (in press).

Simmons, A. J., Wallace, J. M., and Branstater, G. W. (1983). Barotropic wave propagation and instability, and atmospheric teleconnection patterns. *J. Atmos. Sci.* **40**, 1363–1392.

Trenberth, K. E. (1976). Spatial and temporal variations in the Southern Oscillation. *Q. J. R. Meteorol. Soc.* **102,** 639–653.

van Loon, H. (1984). The Southern Oscillation. Part III. Associated with the trades and with the trough in the westerlies of the South Pacific Ocean. *Mon. Weather Rev.* **112,** (in press).

van Loon, H., and Madden, R. A. (1981). The Southern Oscillation. Part I. *Mon. Weather Rev.* **109,** 1150–1162.

Walker, G. T., and Bliss, E. W. (1932). World weather. V. *Mem. R. Meteorol. Soc.* **4,** 53–84.

Wallace, J. M., and Gutzler, D. S. (1981). Teleconnections in the geopotential height field during the Northern Hemisphere winter. *Mon. Weather Rev.* **109,** 784–812.

Webster, P. S. (1972). Response of the tropical atmosphere to local steady forcing. *Mon. Weather Rev.* **100,** 518–541.

Webster, P. S. (1981). Mechanisms determining the atmospheric response to sea surface temperature anomalies. *J. Atmos. Sci.* **38,** 554–571.

Webster, P. S., and Holton, J. R. (1982). Cross-equatorial response to middle latitude forcing in a zonally varying basic state. *J. Atmos. Sci.* **39,** 722–733.

Wyrtki, K. (1973). Teleconnections in the Equatorial Pacific ocean. *Science* **180,** 66–68.

Wyrtki, K. (1975). El Niño — The dynamic response of the Equatorial Pacific Ocean to atmospheric forcing. *J. Phys. Oceanogr.* **5,** 572–584.

Wyrtki, K. (1977). Sea level during the 1972 El Niño. *J. Phys. Oceanogr.* **7,** 779–787.

Part II

THE MIDDLE ATMOSPHERE

SOME ASPECTS
OF STRATOSPHERIC DYNAMICS

DENNIS L. HARTMANN

Department of Atmospheric Sciences
University of Washington
Seattle, Washington

1. INTRODUCTION

The stratosphere has a consistent history of providing scientists with sur-prises and challenging problems. This history begins around 1900, at which time the decrease of temperature with altitude in the atmosphere was widely known. It was argued on theoretical grounds that this decrease should con-tinue and merge smoothly with the absolute coldness of space. On 28 April 1902, the surprising observations of Léon Phillipe Teisserenc de Bort were presented to the Academy of Sciences in Paris. He presented convincing evidence that the temperature above France did not decrease monotonically with altitude, but that above about 11 km the temperature became constant or even increased slightly with elevation. Teisserenc de Bort obtained these observations with unmanned balloons, a measurement technique that he helped to develop and that is still in use today.

It is interesting to look for parallels between the career of Teisserenc de Bort and that of Joseph Smagorinsky, on the occasion of whose retirement this article is being written. An obvious parallel is that they were both influ-ential pioneers during the formative stages in the development of their chosen subjects. In addition, it can be noted that both worked for the central meteorological bureaus in the capital cities of their respective countries and that both retired from government service while still at the peak of their

ADVANCES IN GEOPHYSICS, VOLUME 28A

powers. In 1896 Teisserenc de Bort retired to his private observatory at Trappes near Versailles and began the experiments with high-flying balloons for which he is most famous. It is clear that Teisserenc de Bort had achieved the technical capability to make his discovery as early as the summer of 1898 (Teisserenc de Bort, 1898), but his conclusions about the existence of the tropopause and the stratosphere (names he later suggested) were not formally presented until four years later (Teisserenc de Bort, 1902). At that time his data base included the measurements from no less than 236 balloon ascents that passed the 11-km level. Of these, 74 returned data from as high as 14 km. His data were well distributed with season, and he had earlier reported on the seasonal variation of temperature up to the 10-km level (Teisserenc de Bort, 1900). In his 1902 paper, Teisserenc de Bort was able to speculate correctly on the systematic variation of tropopause height with synoptic situation, surface pressure, and tropospheric temperature, but he reserved a final judgment on these matters until after further study and, no doubt, more balloon flights.

The care and thoroughness shown by Teisserenc de Bort is also a mark of the work of Joseph Smagorinsky. A specific example can be found in the pioneering work of Smagorinsky (1963) on the long-term numerical integration of the primitive equations of atmospheric motion. As in the case of the discovery of the stratosphere, there was a long period between the achievement of the basic scientific objective and the publication of the results. The success of the General Circulation Research Laboratory effort was known in 1958, but it was not until four years later, in October of 1962, that the results were submitted for publication. This was a few months in excess of 60 years after Teisserenc de Bort went to press with his discovery. As Smagorinsky (1983) recalls in his memoir of the early days of general circulation modeling, publication was delayed until a thorough analysis of the nongeostrophic modes and the energetics could be completed.

Several weaknesses in the analogy drawn here should be pointed out. Although both publications were carefully researched and written, Teisserenc de Bort's (1902) paper scarcely exceeded two pages and contained a single table, whereas Smagorinsky's (1963) article spanned a very full 66 pages that constituted a complete issue of the *Monthly Weather Review.* Also, during one particularly elaborate and unfortunate experiment involving the use of kites, Teisserenc de Bort succeeded in trailing miles of wire across his capital city, interrupting some transportation within it and cutting off telegraph communication between Paris and Rennes on the day when the results of the famous Dreyfus court-martial trial were expected. There is no record of Joe Smagorinsky accomplishing a comparable feat in Washington, D.C., but it can certainly be said that there were wires in the IBM 701 used in "The Basic Experiment."

The importance of his discovery of the stratosphere was apparent to Teisserenc de Bort. After stating the basic fact of his discovery that the decrease of
temperature with altitude stopped abruptly at about 11 km and that the
temperature was constant above that level for as far as he had observations,
Teisserenc de Bort (1902) quickly pointed out, "C'est la un fait ignoré
jusqu'ici et qui mérite d'être pris en très sérieuse considération dans l'étude
de la circulation générale." The belief in the importance of the stratosphere
in a comprehensive theoretical understanding of the general circulation
expressed by Teisserenc de Bort has survived succeeding generations of
scientists and has been augmented by very practical concerns stimulated by
the role of the stratosphere as a repository for gases and particles of biological
and climatological importance.

The significance of the stratosphere for numerical weather prediction also
remains a topic of concern. This role for the stratosphere was foreseen in an
early work by Smagorinsky (1953) who, with reference to the steady linear
model he was discussing, stated that "in order to obtain an undistorted
estimate of the magnitude of the disturbances in the upper third of the
troposphere, it appears that the influence of the stratosphere must be taken
into account." The extent to which an accurate forecast of weather in the
troposphere depends on an accurate simulation of the stratosphere remains a
problem of current interest.

In what follows, a survey of progress and current problems with the dynamical interpretation of observations of the stratosphere is presented. This
is not a comprehensive review, however, but rather an essay about those
problems that have particularly interested the author. While a historical
perspective will be taken in many instances, no attempt has been made to
mention every important discovery or provide a complete list of references.

2. The Concept of a Stratosphere Driven from Below

2.1. Stratospheric Behavior Contrasted with the Troposphere

Many aspects of the observed behavior of the stratosphere seem particularly intriguing when contrasted with the troposphere. Historically, new
observations of the stratosphere have been set in the context of prior experience with tropospheric data. It is useful to enumerate some observed features
of the stratospheric general circulation that seemed most surprising when
they were discovered. In this way it can be appreciated how the stratosphere
has stimulated the interest of scientists, challenged the easy answers to some
questions about the general circulation, and led to the development of better
ideas.

That the temperature in the stratosphere does not decrease with height as it does in the troposphere is readily explained by the radiative balance of the stratosphere and the contrasting radiative–convective balance of the troposphere (see Fels, this volume). There is no simple radiative explanation, however, for the observation that temperatures in the mid-latitude lower stratosphere (below 25 km) increase with latitude rather than decrease as they do in the troposphere. To explain this behavior requires the consideration of radiative processes, convective processes, and large-scale dynamics. The basic mechanisms are set forth in the discussion of the first results of the Geophysical Fluid Dynamics Laboratory (GFDL) nine-level model, which successfully simulated many observed features of the lower stratosphere (Smagorinsky et al., 1965; Manabe et al., 1965). Manabe and Hunt (1968) investigated the general circulation of the lower stratosphere in more detail by considering a model with 18 levels between the surface and 4 mb (37.5 km). Their study further clarified the role of the upward branch of the Hadley Cell in maintaining the coldness and sharpness of the equatorial tropopause and of large-scale subsidence in maintaining the warmth of the mid-latitude lower stratosphere against radiative cooling. Their model was the first to produce two distinct and separated jet streams at the subtropical tropopause and in the polar upper stratosphere, as observed.

While the meridional gradient of zonal-mean temperature reverses at the tropopause in the Northern Hemisphere, the eddy heat transport continues to be poleward, making it an up-gradient heat transport in the lower stratosphere (White, 1954). Dines (1925) and others showed that not only does the mean lapse rate change abruptly at the tropopause, but the temporal correlation between temperature and pressure reverses sign. This change in correlation at the tropopause is a natural concomitant of the initiation of rapid decay with height of the amplitude of synoptic-scale waves [e.g., Hartmann (1974)].

At higher levels in the stratosphere the meridional temperature gradient reverses with season, being poleward in summer and equatorward in winter. This regular seasonal variation is often interrupted during winter in the Northern Hemisphere by a sudden warming. During sudden warmings polar upper-stratospheric temperatures increase by more than 40 K at 30 km in only a few weeks. Accompanying these temperature increases are reversals of the zonal-mean wind from strong westerly to weak easterly. In the upper stratosphere of the Southern Hemisphere there are also rapid, large-amplitude changes in zonal-mean wind and temperature during winter. They do not result in a reversal of the zonal-mean wind at 10 mb, however, and so are not classified as major warmings. Such dramatic changes in zonal-mean quantities are never observed in the troposphere.

The variations of zonal-mean wind and temperature in the troposphere are dominated by the annual cycle and its higher harmonics. In the equatorial stratosphere near 25 km, however, the variability of the zonal-mean wind is dominated by variations with an irregular periodicity between 2 and 2.5 years, the quasi-biennial oscillation (Reed *et al.*, 1961; Wallace, 1973). The quasi-biennial oscillation has a constant amplitude of about 20 m s^{-1} between 22 and 30 km and is centered directly over the equator. The initiation of the westerly phase of the quasi-biennial oscillation is associated with the downward propagation of a region of strong westerly shear. Six months to a year may elapse between the time the winds reverse at 30 km and when they change at 20 km. The westerly phase of the oscillation is particularly interesting, since the angular velocity of westerly winds on the equator is greater than that of the Earth itself. Above 30 km the zonal-mean wind variations are dominated by a semiannual oscillation with easterlies in the solstitial seasons (Reed, 1966).

The observed peculiarities of the stratosphere mentioned above have kept dynamical meteorologists interested for decades. In the remainder of this section the evolution of our current concept of the general circulation of the stratosphere and its basis in observation will be discussed.

2.2. Diagnostic Studies of the Lower Stratosphere

The nearly hemispheric data on winds and temperatures from the balloon network that became available during the International Geophysical Year (1957–1958) made possible the construction of synoptic charts up to the 10-mb level. With gridded winds and temperatures it became possible to estimate heat transport and to diagnose approximately how the atmosphere in general and the stratosphere in particular satisfy the constraints placed on them by the laws of conservation of heat, mass, momentum, and energy. In doing this it became traditional to divide the flow field into a zonal-mean component and a remainder or eddy component and to diagnose the exchanges between them. The philosophy and formulation of this type of study are stated elegantly in Lorenz (1967).

The first synoptic charts produced for the stratosphere revealed that the amplitudes of the synoptic-scale waves decrease above the tropopause while the amplitudes of the planetary-scale waves increase with altitude. Consequently, at the 10-mb level the geopotential field is almost solely composed of the zonal-mean plus the contributions from zonal wave numbers 1 and 2. It was also apparent that in the Northern Hemisphere the planetary waves are quasi-stationary and could be traced downward and linked with quasi-stationary features in the troposphere [e.g., Muench (1965)]. Theories for why waves with only the longest horizontal scales propagate into the upper stratosphere were quickly offered (Charney and Drazin, 1961; Charney and Pedlosky, 1963). These theories have been improved on by reducing the number of assumptions made [e.g., Dickinson (1968), Matsuno (1970), and Holton (1974)] and provide the basic explanation for why synoptic-scale baroclinically unstable waves are trapped in the troposphere and only the planetary-scale waves propagate into the stratosphere.

In applying the Lorenz (1955) energy cycle formulation to the stratosphere, early investigators were immediately aware of the potential for large boundary flux terms at the bottom, top, and equatorward boundaries of the domain in which they chose to compute the energy amounts and conversions. The question of fundamental interest, which was posed by Starr (1960), was whether the kinetic energy of the stratosphere is imported vertically from other regions or is generated internally in a manner typical of the troposphere. Several early studies of the energetics of the stratosphere focused on the stratospheric warming phenomenon and searched specifically for evidence that the phenomenon might be interpreted as a manifestation of the classical baroclinic or barotropic instabilities [e.g., Reed et al. (1963), Miyakoda (1963), Julian and Labitzke (1965), Perry (1967), Mahlman (1969), and Miller et al. (1972)]. Calculations of the energy cycle of the lower stratosphere in the Northern Hemisphere using a full year of data were performed by Oort (1964) and Dopplick (1971). Their studies showed that on an annual basis there was no internal source of wave energy in the lower stratosphere. Only during the winter was there a conversion from zonal-mean available energy to eddy kinetic energy. Later it was noted that even these energy conversions could be thought of as a necessary concomitant of the upward propagation of planetary waves in a westerly wind shear, but not necessarily as a sign of *in situ* instability (Hartmann, 1976b). The results of these energy budget studies and the failure of theoretical studies to produce an instability that bore any resemblance to a stratospheric warming led to the conclusion that wave activity in the stratosphere, both climatologically and during a sudden warming, was a result of transport from the troposphere.

2.3. *Climatology of the Northern and Southern Hemispheres*

Since the successful launch of the selective chopper radiometer (SCR) on the Nimbus 4 satellite in April of 1970, global information on the temperature of the stratosphere up to the stratopause level has been available (Abel *et al.*, 1970; Barnett, 1974). Previous to the SCR, satellite measurements had been restricted to the lower stratosphere. Rocket soundings available at that time provided *in situ* measurements with much better vertical resolution than the SCR could provide, but they were expensive and could only be launched from a few areas. Although rocket observations still provide an essential data base for comparison and calibration of satellite temperatures, they cannot provide the kind of economical global coverage available from satellites. Improvements and generalizations of the SCR instrument were incorporated in later experimental satellites (Curtis *et al.,* 1974) and on operational NOAA satellites (Smith *et al.,* 1979) that continue to return global information on temperature up to the stratopause level.

In addition to temperature on constant pressure surfaces, geopotential height can be obtained by integrating the hydrostatic equation if a suitable boundary condition is supplied. Approximate winds can then be obtained from the height field by using the geostrophic or balance equations. These satellite-derived data have provided nearly continuous measurements of the global stratosphere. A data base is accumulating that will make possible studies of the climatology and interannual variability of the stratosphere. The interannual variability in the stratosphere is large and its study requires long, homogeneous records of temperature and geopotential [e.g., Labitzke (1977), Hamilton (1982), Smith (1983), and Geller *et al.* (1983, 1984)].

It is interesting to use the relatively homogeneous global coverage available from satellites to compare the circulations in the Northern and Southern Hemispheres. Figure 1 is a latitude–time section of the zonal-mean

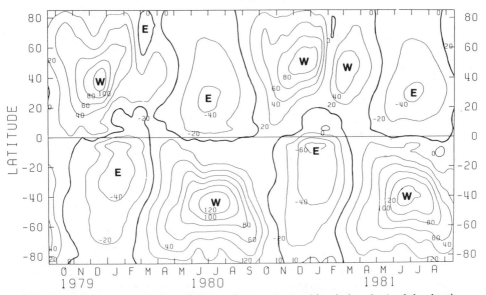

FIG. 1. Latitude–time section of the zonal-mean geostrophic wind at the 1-mb level estimated from the 20-day average height field inferred from Tiros-N SSU data. Units are meters per second. [From Hirota *et al.* (1983).]

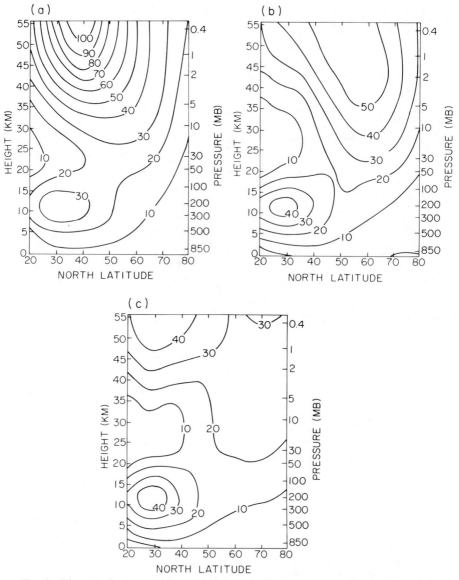

FIG. 2. Climatological geostrophic zonal-mean wind in the Northern Hemisphere: (a) December, (b) January, and (c) February. [After Geller, Wu, and Gelman (1983). Reproduced with permission from *Journal of the Atmospheric Sciences,* a publication of the American Meteorological Society.]. Climatological geostrophic zonal-mean wind in the Southern Hemisphere: (d) June, (e) July, and (f) August. (From C. R. Mechoso, private communication.) Units are meters per second.

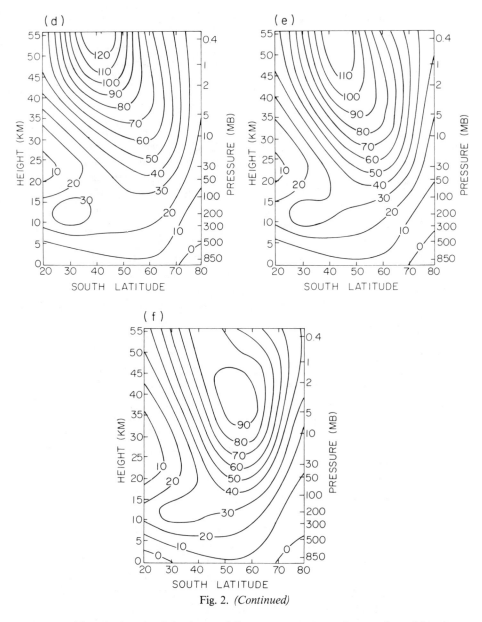

Fig. 2. *(Continued)*

geostrophic wind at 1 mb estimated from temperature data gathered by the stratospheric sounding unit (SSU) aboard the TIROS N satellite. In both hemispheres, the annual variation between an intense westerly jet in winter and a weaker summertime easterly jet centered closer to the equator is apparent. Some rather important differences between the hemispheres are also visible in Fig. 1. The wintertime westerly jets in the Northern Hemisphere are weaker in intensity than those in the Southern Hemisphere. The Northern Hemisphere wintertime westerlies are often interrupted by an abrupt reduction associated with a stratospheric warming in mid to late winter. Such reductions are evident in both Northern Hemisphere winters shown in Fig. 1, but most clearly in February of 1981.

The differences in the wintertime zonal wind climatology are illustrated in more detail in Fig. 2, which shows latitude–height sections of the average monthly mean winds during winter. On the top in Fig. 2 are the monthly mean zonal winds in the Northern Hemisphere for the months of December, January, and February. These are adapted from Geller *et al.* (1983) and are four-year averages of the 1978–1979 through 1981–1982 winters. On the bottom are shown the monthly mean zonal winds in the Southern Hemisphere for the months of June, July, and August. These are an average of the three winters 1980 through 1982 (C. R. Mechoso, private communication, 1984). All of the zonal-mean winds in Fig. 2 were derived geostrophically from operational height analyses prepared by the National Meteorological Center (NMC), with modifications as described in Geller *et al.* (1983).

During the solstitial months of December and June, the zonal winds are more similar than they are later in the winter. Nonetheless, there are large differences between the two hemispheres at the winter solstice. The most important, perhaps, is in the lower and middle stratosphere, where the zonal-mean winds are about twice as intense in the Southern Hemisphere. The zonal-mean winds in the Northern Hemisphere during January are much weaker than those in the Southern Hemisphere during July. This is due primarily to the much stronger wave–mean-flow interaction in the Northern Hemisphere. The individual monthly means for the four years of Northern Hemisphere data used in Fig. 2 are shown in Geller *et al.* (1984). A major stratospheric warming occurred only once, in February of 1979, out of the 12 months in the sample. This is less than the climatological average of one major warming every other year (Schoeberl, 1978).

There is one interesting similarity between the zonal-mean winds during Northern Hemisphere January and Southern Hemisphere July. That is that the zonal-mean westerlies in the lower stratosphere have intensified from those of the preceding month. In the Southern Hemisphere the poleward and downward movement of the wintertime stratospheric jet stream continues during July and August. The position of the stratospheric jet moves from 40°S and somewhere above 55 km during June to about 55°S and 40 km during August. In the Northern Hemisphere during February, only a remnant of the stratospheric jet is evident. The very different climatologies of the two hemispheres illustrated in Figs. 1 and 2 provide a good test for our understanding of stratospheric dynamics that has not yet been fully exploited.

Hartmann (1976c) compared the energetics of the 100–10-mb layer in the Southern Hemisphere during July and August 1973 with those during December and January 1964 computed by Dopplick (1971). As expected, the Southern Hemisphere is characterized by larger zonal-mean energies and smaller eddy energies in this layer. The generation of zonal-mean available energy by radiative heating is large and positive in the Southern Hemisphere but negligible in the Northern Hemisphere. Rather surprisingly, however, the flux of eddy energy upward through the 100-mb surface and the energy conversions within the lower stratosphere are about the same in the two cases. The role of eddies in the general circulation of the Southern Hemisphere stratosphere should not be underestimated.

3. PLANETARY WAVE PROPAGATION AND WAVE–MEAN-FLOW INTERACTION

Early studies of the stratosphere strongly suggested that the large-scale wave motions there are primarily a result of upward propagation of planetary waves from a source region in the troposphere. It is not surprising then that considerable research has been devoted to understanding the sources of planetary waves in the troposphere, their propagation into the stratosphere, and their interaction with the mean flow.

3.1. Forced Extratropical Waves

The principal mechanisms for forcing planetary-scale quasi-stationary waves involve orography and zonal variations in atmospheric heating. Smagorinsky (1953) compared these two methods of forcing linear planetary waves in a beta-plane model and concluded that the relative importance of orographic forcing increases with altitude so that the stationary planetary waves observed in the stratosphere are largely a result of mountains. Subsequent studies have come to the same general conclusion [e.g., Lin (1982)] and the observed stationary waves in the stratosphere appear to be consistent with this idea. General circulation model experiments in which the mountains are removed show very weak stationary waves in the Northern Hemisphere stratosphere compared to experiments with mountains included (Manabe and Terpstra, 1974). In the less mountainous Southern Hemisphere the observed stationary waves are much weaker and traveling waves play an important role in the circulation [e.g., van Loon and Jenne (1972), Leovy and Webster (1976), and Hartmann (1976a, 1977)].

In the mountain–no mountain experiments of Manabe and Terpstra
(1974), the addition of mountains decreased the transient waves in the
troposphere but increased them by 50% in the stratosphere. This result is
consistent with the idea that mountains serve as a significant source of
transient planetary-scale wave activity. In the troposphere the stationary
waves generated by mountains compete with synoptic-scale baroclinically
unstable eddies for a limited supply of available potential energy. It is the
reduction of these synoptic-scale traveling waves that results in a decrease in
the transient wave activity in the troposphere. A direct simulation of the
contrast between the hemispheres including seasonal variations has been
described by Manabe and Mahlman (1976). They found that rather significant asymmetries between the hemispheres in the stratosphere could be
traced to the more substantial orography in the Northern Hemisphere that
produced a dramatic contrast in the stationary planetary wave amplitudes in
the two hemispheres. Interestingly, the transient wave activity in the stratosphere was about the same in the two hemispheres. Hayashi and Golder
(1983a,b) have shown that removing the mountains in a general circulation
model (GCM) simulation increases the eastward-propagating planetary
waves and decreases the westward-propagating waves. They also showed that
the primary source of energy for the eastward-moving waves is conversion
from zonal-mean potential energy, whereas westward-moving planetary
waves in the simulation are forced by wave–wave interactions.

Observational studies of the propagation of planetary waves and their
interaction with the zonal-mean wind have been greatly aided by the transformed Eulerian mean formulation of the governing equations (Andrews
and McIntyre, 1976; Boyd, 1976; Edmon et al., 1980). For quasi-geostrophic
scaling the transformed Eulerian mean formulation of the zonal-mean momentum and heat equations can be written as

$$\frac{\partial \bar{u}}{\partial t} - f\bar{v}^* = \frac{\nabla \cdot \mathbf{F}}{\rho_s a \cos \phi} \tag{3.1}$$

$$\frac{\partial \bar{\theta}}{\partial t} + \bar{\theta}_p \bar{\omega}^* = \bar{Q} \tag{3.2}$$

where the residual mean circulation is defined by

$$\bar{v}^* = \bar{v} - \frac{\partial}{\partial p}\left(\frac{\overline{v'\theta'}}{\bar{\theta}_p}\right) \tag{3.3}$$

$$\bar{\omega}^* = \bar{\omega} + \frac{1}{a \cos \phi}\frac{\partial}{\partial \phi}\left(\frac{\overline{v'\theta'}\cos \phi}{\bar{\theta}_p}\right) \tag{3.4}$$

and the components of the Eliassen–Palm (EP) flux vector are given by

$$\mathbf{F} = (F_{(\phi)}, F_{(p)}) = \rho_s a \cos \phi \left(-\overline{u'v'}, f \frac{\overline{u'\theta'}}{\bar{\theta}_p} \right) \tag{3.5}$$

These equations have the virtue that the effect of the eddies on the mean flow is collected into a single term in the zonal-mean momentum equation. For quasi-geostrophic conservative waves on a slowly varying mean state, the EP flux vector is parallel to the group velocity, so that the EP flux vector should be a good measure of wave propagation (Edmon *et al.*, 1980; Palmer, 1982). According to the "nonacceleration"theorems (e.g., Andrews, this volume), when waves are steady and dissipationless they do not affect the mean flow and the divergence of their EP flux is zero. The divergence of the EP flux is thus a measure of the departure from nonacceleration conditions.

The transformed equations have been very useful for characterizing the observed planetary wave propagation and interaction with the mean flow. An example is provided in Fig. 3, which shows the EP cross sections for the Southern Hemisphere winter of 1979. The stationary or time-averaged

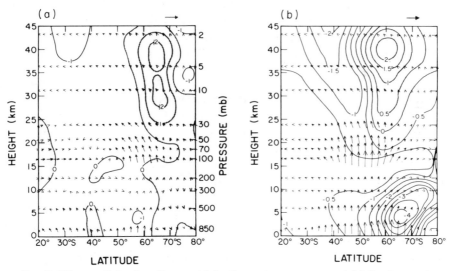

FIG. 3. Eliassen–Palm flux diagram (a) for the stationary waves and (b) for the transient components of zonal wave numbers 1 through 3 for the period 14 May–13 September 1979 in the Southern Hemisphere. The contours are labeled in meters per second per day, positive contours are shaded, and the scaling factor for the vectors is 2×10^{15} kg m s^{-1}. The scaling factor for the vectors decreases by a factor of 10 at 100 mb and above. [From Hartmann, Mechoso, and Yamazaki (1984). Reproduced with permission from *Journal of the Atmospheric Sciences,* a publication of the American Meteorological Society.]

waves propagate upward across the 100-mb surface at about 60°S, as indicated by the long upward-pointing vectors centered near that latitude. Farther up in the stratosphere, the vectors turn more equatorward. This equatorward turning is predicted by the linear theory for the refraction of quasi-geostrophic Rossby waves (Matsuno, 1970; Palmer, 1982). The transient planetary waves enter the stratosphere slightly more toward the equator at about 50–55°S but show the same tendency to turn equatorward with height.

An interesting feature of Fig. 3 is that the vertical component of the EP flux vector at 100 mb associated with the transient waves is larger than that associated with stationary waves. This is consistent with the observation that traveling waves are very important in the Southern Hemisphere in comparison to their role in the Northern Hemisphere, where quasi-stationary waves and the transients associated with them dominate the flow field. Also shown in Fig. 3 are the contours of the eddy driving of the mean flow. In the upper stratosphere both stationary and transient eddies are acting to accelerate the mean westerlies in high latitudes and decelerate them in low latitudes. The dipole pattern of wave driving in Fig. 3 is interesting, since it is more complex than the common conception of wave–mean-flow interaction in which planetary waves propagate upward and uniformly decelerate the westerlies as they are dissipated [e.g., Andrews et al. (1984)]. This dipole pattern is believed to be real, since it is associated with a corresponding dipole pattern in the zonal-mean wind acceleration (Hartmann et al., 1984). For linear waves on a slowly varying mean flow, a divergent EP flux like that seen in high latitudes in Fig. 3 implies a source region for the waves. A discussion of possible sources of wave activity in this region is presented in Section 4.1, but a general theoretical explanation for this dipole structure is not available at this writing.

Eliassen–Palm cross sections have been very helpful in diagnosing observed and simulated stratospheric warmings (Holton, 1980; McIntyre, 1982). The conceptual model of Matsuno (1971) emphasized the role of the meridional eddy heat flux associated with an upward-propagating Rossby wave and its behavior near a critical line. O'Neill and Taylor (1979) pointed out that the momentum flux is apparently very important in determining the evolution of observed warmings. This is reflected in the EP flux vectors as a turning from upward and equatorward to upward and poleward during a warming (Palmer, 1981; Kanzawa, 1982). This poleward focusing of the waves is associated with a large convergence of the EP flux and a strong deceleration of the westerly flow. The poleward turning of the waves seems to be consistent with the changing refractive properties of the zonal-mean flow (Butchart et al., 1982; O'Neill and Youngblut, 1982). The warming process can thus be viewed as a feedback between the upward propagating planetary waves and the zonal flow in the stratosphere. Upward-propagating waves, through transience and dissipation, modify the mean flow. The distribution of the refractive index for planetary waves evolves with the mean flow and alters the propagation of waves within the stratosphere. If an upward flux of wave activity is occurring when the stratospheric mean flow becomes conditioned to focus the waves into the pole, then a major warming can result. This conceptual model does not require a critical line in the early stages of the warming.

Shiotani and Hirota (1985) have compared the wintertime wave – mean-flow interaction in the Northern and Southern Hemispheres during June 1981 – May 1982 by using Eliassen – Palm flux diagnostics. They found instances in both hemispheres when the stratospheric westerly jet was shifted into high latitudes. The EP flux vectors became focused into high latitudes during these periods in agreement with linear theory. As a result of this focusing, rapid deceleration of the westerly winds occurred in high latitudes. In the Northern Hemisphere this led to the major stratospheric warming of late January 1982. In the Southern Hemisphere a significant easterly acceleration also was observed, but it was not sufficient to bring about a major warming. Thus the direction of the EP flux vectors seems to be related to the wind distribution in the manner expected from WKB theory, but the evolution of the mean flow toward warming conditions depends sensitively on the intensity of the westerly winds (greater in the Southern Hemisphere) and the intensity and duration of the wave driving (probably less in the Southern Hemisphere).

3.2. Tropical Waves

For studies of the tropical stratosphere, satellite data have generally been less useful than they are in the extratropics for two reasons. First, because of the small Coriolis parameter and the consequent frailty of the geostrophic approximation, near the equator large velocity variations can be associated with rather small temperature changes. Therefore much greater precision in the measurement of the temperature field is required to obtain the same level of accuracy in the inferred wind field. Second, the vertical resolution of nadir-viewing sounding systems has not been adequate to resolve the vertical structure of equatorial Kelvin waves in the stratosphere. Kelvin waves provide the westerly zonal wind accelerations for the quasi-biennial and semiannual oscillations.

Data from the Nimbus-7 LIMS (limb infrared monitor of the stratosphere) have provided an unprecedented view of the tropical stratosphere. The limb infrared monitor of the stratosphere measured the radiation emit-

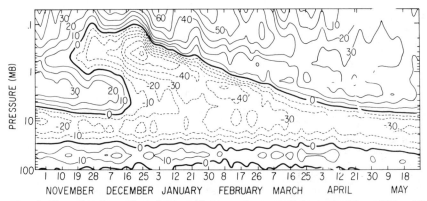

FIG. 4. Time–height section of the gradient zonal-mean wind averaged from 8°S to 8°N inferred from LIMS temperatures data and NMC geopotential at 100 mb. Easterly winds are dashed. Units are meters per second.

ted along a tangent path to the atmosphere by using cryogenically cooled detectors (Gille and Russell, 1984) and from these measurements it is possible to deduce temperature accurately with a vertical resolution of 2 to 3 km. This is much better than nadir-viewing instruments that have effective resolutions of 15 to 20 km. The LIMS instrument produced data from 25 October 1978 until 28 May 1979 when the coolant was exhausted. Figure 4 shows the zonal-mean gradient wind averaged over the latitude belt 8°N–8°S during the LIMS operational period. The major features of this diagram have been confirmed with *in situ* wind measurements from rockets by Leovy *et al.* (1984a). The descent of the upper easterly jet and the region of intense westerly shear above it are associated with the semiannual oscillation. The downward-propagating westerly shear zone is maintained by upward-propagating Kelvin waves.

Salby *et al.* (1984) performed a space–time spectral analysis of the LIMS temperature data in the equatorial area. They found two well-defined peaks in the frequency domain for wave numbers 1 and 2. During this period, wave number 1 had eastward-moving components with periods of 6.7 to 8.6 days (phase speeds of 54 to 69 m s^{-1}) and 3.5 to 4.0 days (115 to 135 m s^{-1}). Wave number 2 also had slow and fast eastward moving components with periods of 6.0 to 7.5 days (31 to 39 m s^{-1}) and 3.8 to 4.3 days (55 to 62 m s^{-1}). The faster waves appeared primarily in the upper stratosphere. The vertical structure of the waves was as predicted by linear theory with the faster waves having longer vertical wavelengths. The longer vertical wavelengths of the fast-moving waves reduce the effect of radiative damping, and the fast eastward phase speeds allow the waves to propagate easily through the easterly jet. These fast-moving Kelvin waves undoubtedly are important in providing the westerly accelerations required for the semiannual oscillation. The existence of fast Kelvin waves and their role in the semiannual oscillation was strongly suggested in rocket data analyzed by Hirota (1978). Hirota (1979) also found evidence of wave-number-1 Kelvin waves with periods of 4 to 9 days in SCR data. Analysis of the equatorial waves present in the GFDL SKYHI model by Hayashi *et al.* (1984) showed essentially the same Kelvin wave signatures in the stratosphere as are present in the observations. In addition, they found that gravity waves with periods of a few days and less play an important role in the momentum budget of the model equatorial mesosphere.

The Kelvin waves appear to be forced sporadically, presumably by tropical convection, although attempts to identify specific events in the troposphere with the initiation of an upward-propagating group of Kelvin waves have met with little success. An example of a Kelvin-wave pulse propagating upward is shown in Fig. 5, which is a height–time cross section of the cosine component of the wave-number-1 zonal Fourier expansion of the temperature field averaged between 8°N and 8°S. The cosine component is equivalent to the value of the temperature field of wave number 1 at the Greenwich meridian. Similar figures for other periods have been shown by Coy and Hitchman (1984). The time interval included in Fig. 5 is the 6 April–28 May period when the zero wind line and associated westerly shear zone in Fig. 4 have reached about the 5-mb level. We can clearly see downward propagation of phase and suggestions of upward propagation of amplitude with time that are expected to occur in association. The wave pattern appears to have a vertical wavelength of about 15 km and a period of about 10 days, which are consistent with the values expected for a Kelvin wave. The increase in

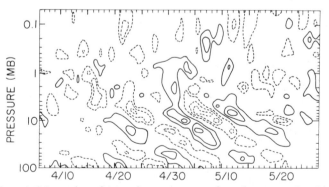

FIG. 5. Time–height section of the cosine component of zonal wave number 1 in ths LIMS temperatures along the equator. The contour interval is 1 K, and the zero contour has not been plotted.

amplitude with height ceases abruptly in the vicinity of the reversal to westerly zonal-mean winds around 5 mb.

It is notable that little evidence of westward-propagating equatorial waves in the middle and upper stratosphere exists. In their analysis of the LIMS data, Salby *et al.* (1984) found spectral peaks only for eastward moving waves and very little variance that was asymmetric about the equator. It is possible that the observing techniques need to be improved still further before these waves can be detected, if indeed they are present in the upper stratosphere.

4. INSTABILITY IN THE STRATOSPHERE

Observational and theoretical studies discussed thus far have emphasized the importance of the upward propagation of quasi-stationary planetary waves from the troposphere and their interaction with the mean flow as the primary dynamical mechanism of interest in the extratropical stratosphere. There are several observational aspects of the stratosphere that cannot be readily explained by this mechanism. One of these is the existence of steadily eastward-propagating waves in the stratosphere, which are evident in the Southern Hemisphere. There exist slowly eastward-propagating waves with periods of a few weeks with broad meridional scales like that of the polar night jet stream (Harwood, 1975; Hartmann, 1976a; Leovy and Webster, 1976). Rapidly eastward-propagating waves with periods of 2 to 4 days and narrow meridional scales that are trapped poleward of the polar night jet are also observed (Venne and Stanford, 1982; Prata, 1984). One would expect the geographically fixed tropospheric forcing due to mountains to produce a response that was dominated by its geographically fixed component. The existence of steadily eastward-propagating modes suggests the possibility of an instability. The unexplained region of divergent EP flux shown in Fig. 3 also suggests a source region for planetary waves in the stratosphere.

4.1. Instability within the Stratosphere

To investigate the stability of the zonal-mean state in the stratosphere we should consider the meridional gradient of zonal-mean quasi-geostrophic potential vorticity. The gradient of quasi-geostrophic potential vorticity can be defined in the following way [e.g., Matsuno (1970), Hartmann (1979)]:

$$\frac{\partial \bar{q}}{\partial \phi} = 2\Omega \cos \phi - \frac{1}{a} \frac{\partial}{\partial \phi} \left[\frac{1}{\cos \phi} \frac{\partial}{\partial \phi} (\cos \phi \bar{u}) \right]$$

$$- (2\Omega)^2 a \sin^2 \phi \frac{1}{\rho_s} \left(\frac{\rho_s}{N^2} \frac{\partial \bar{u}}{\partial z} \right) \qquad (4.1)$$

The theory for the stability of baroclinic jets in a rotating atmosphere states that a necessary condition for the flow to be unstable to small wave perturbations is that a temperature gradient at the lower boundary or a reversal of the meridional gradient of potential vorticity within the atmosphere must exist (Charney and Stern, 1962).

   The distribution of zonal-mean wind and the meridional gradient of potential vorticity for the month of August 1979 in the Southern Hemisphere are shown in Fig. 6. There are two regions where the potential vorticity gradient is weak or negative and that might therefore satisfy the necessary condition for instability. One region is on the equatorward flank of the jet at about 40°S and the other region is on the poleward flank near 70°S and 40-km altitude. These weak potential vorticity gradients result from very strong positive meridional curvature of the zonal-mean wind, represented by the second term on the right-hand side of (4.1). Although the intense stratospheric jet during winter in the Southern Hemisphere results primarily from thermal driving, the potential instabilities result not from the vertical shear per se, but from the fact that the vertical shear is forced over such a deep layer and over a narrow range of latitudes. The resulting instabilities can thus be expected to be primarily barotropic in nature.

   The linear unstable waves that grow on a mean state like that shown in Fig. 6 have been investigated by Hartmann (1983). A region of strong meridional

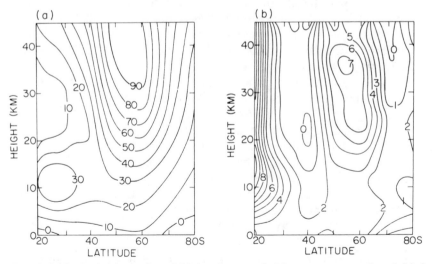

FIG. 6. Latitude–height section of (a) zonal-mean wind (meters per second) and (b) the smoothed gradient of potential vorticity (divided by $\Omega = 7.292 \times 10^{-5} \, s^{-1}$) for the month of August 1979 in the Southern Hemisphere. [From Hartmann (1983). Reproduced with permission from *Journal of the Atmospheric Sciences*, a publication of the American Meteorological Society.]

curvature of the zonal-mean wind on the poleward flank of the stratospheric jet gives rise to barotropic instability of zonal wave numbers 1 and 2. Strong meridional curvature of the zonal-mean wind can be maintained by radiative forcing. For conditions near the altitude of the stratospheric jet during winter, wave number 1 moves eastward with a period of 3 to 4 days and wave number 2 moves eastward with a period of 1.5 to 2 days. The phase speeds of the unstable modes are set by the requirement that they have a critical line near the latitude at which the potential vorticity gradient reverses sign. Because the angular velocity of the zonal-mean wind increases equatorward of the source region, these modes are trapped poleward of the stratospheric jet and they have their maximum amplitude near 70° latitude.

Waves with these properties have been observed by Venne and Stanford (1982) and Prata (1984). The phases of the waves are observed to be constant with height, confirming that they are approximately barotropic, at least at the altitudes at which their amplitudes are large. The observed meridional phase shift is consistent with barotropic instability in the majority of cases shown by Venne and Stanford (1982) and Prata (1984), but it seems to be variable. Prata (1984) showed a series of synoptic maps that indicated that the wave-number-1 4-day wave and the wave-number-2 2-day wave tend to remain phase locked over extended periods, giving the resulting anomalies a "bloblike" behavior. He suggested that nonlinearity is important in encouraging this behavior. The instability of basic states with longitudinal variations has been investigated by Matsuno and Hirota (1966), Hirota (1967), and Frederiksen (1982). These studies showed that a mean state composed of a zonal-mean flow and a wave can be unstable even when the zonal-mean flow by itself is not. This is an area in which more research could be fruitful.

Hartmann (1983) showed that the region of reversed potential vorticity gradient on the equatorward flank of the jet can result in unstable modes that bear many similarities to the observed slowly eastward-propagating planetary waves in the Southern Hemisphere. For wind profiles near marginal stability the most unstable modes are of planetary scale. These modes propagate eastward, have periods on the order of weeks, and have latitudinal amplitude structure like that of the mean flow itself. The fatal shortcoming of these unstable modes as a possible source of the slowly eastward-propagating variance in the Southern Hemispheric stratosphere is the predominantly equatorward momentum flux associated with them. The observed momentum flux is overwhelmingly poleward and marks a predominance of equatorward wave flux.

The Eliassen–Palm cross sections in Fig. 3 indicate that the equatorward flank of the stratospheric jet is a region in which the EP flux converges. This convergence drives easterly accelerations and tends to enhance the positive meridional curvature of the zonal wind. It seems, therefore, that the waves act to *maintain* the weak potential vorticity gradient on the equatorward flank of the stratospheric jet. To see this in another way we can consider the equation for the zonal-mean quasi-geostrophic potential vorticity:

$$\partial \bar{q}/\partial t = -(\partial/\partial y)(\overline{v'q'}) + \bar{S} \tag{4.2}$$

$$\partial \bar{q}/\partial t = -(\partial/\partial y)(\nabla \cdot \mathbf{F}) + \bar{S} \tag{4.3}$$

where (4.3) was obtained by noting that the meridional transport of potential vorticity by the eddies is equal to the divergence of the EP flux for quasi-geostrophic scaling and $\bar{S}$ represents the source of zonal-mean potential vorticity due to radiative driving and zonal-mean circulations. According to (4.3) a localized region of convergent EP flux will produce a dipole pattern in the potential vorticity tendency with potential vorticity increasing with time equatorward of the convergence center and potential vorticity decreasing with time poleward of it. This pattern of wave driving of mean potential vorticity will tend to reduce the poleward gradient of potential vorticity in the vicinity of the maximum convergence of the EP flux. Planetary waves propagating into the tropics will therefore tend to reduce the poleward gradient of potential vorticity where they exhibit a convergent EP flux.

A physical picture of how planetary waves mix potential vorticity on the equatorward flank of the stratospheric wintertime jet has been presented by McIntyre and Palmer (1984). McIntyre and Palmer characterize the mixing process as one of the planetary waves "breaking," wrapping up fluid elements, and producing mixing. This behavior has been shown even more clearly in ozone data by Leovy *et al.* (1985b). Ozone is a quasi-conservative tracer in the lower stratosphere and is correlated with potential vorticity, a quasi-conservative property of the flow field. The potential vorticity and ozone fields show that as the tropics are approached from the mid-latitudes, the perturbations take on an increasingly pronounced westward and equatorward tilt until finally the perturbations vanish in a well-mixed region in or near the tropics.

Radiative forcing will also tend to produce regions of strong positive meridional curvature of the zonal-mean wind and a corresponding weak or reversed potential vorticity gradient on the equatorward flank of the wintertime stratospheric jet. It is not yet certain what relative contributions radiative driving and wave driving make to the maintenance of the zone or weak potential vorticity gradients on the equatorward flank of the jet.

4.2. Upward-Propagating Baroclinic Instability

One possible mechanism for producing steadily eastward-propagating planetary waves in the stratosphere is through the upward propagation of baroclinically unstable planetary waves from the troposphere. True propagation with its attendant growth of amplitude with height is possible for baroclinically unstable modes with low zonal wave numbers and broad meridional scales (Geisler and Garcia, 1977). Baroclinically unstable modes of low zonal wave number and narrow meridional scale may exist in the high latitudes (Hartmann, 1979), but the amplitude of these modes does not increase with height in the stratosphere.

Mechoso and Hartmann (1982) attempted to trace the structure of the traveling waves in the Southern Hemisphere stratosphere down into the troposphere. Westward-propagating waves in the stratosphere were found to be coherent with westward-propagating waves in the troposphere. There was very little phase variation with height, so that these were judged to be barotropic modes. The eastward-moving planetary waves show a consistent westward tilt with height, suggesting a more baroclinic character [see also Pratt and Wallace (1976) and Hayashi and Golder (1977)]. For eastward-moving components of zonal wave numbers 1 and 2, there was so little coherence between the troposphere and the stratosphere, that it was concluded that the dominant eastward-moving waves in the stratosphere are linearly independent of those in the troposphere with the same zonal wave number and frequency. The independence of the waves in the two regions could be explained by nonlinearity or by the waves in the two regions being linear but independent. Linear independent waves could be produced by a separate source of instability in the stratosphere and the troposphere or from two linearly independent modes originating in the troposphere.

Two linearly independent modes, one of which would dominate the variance in the troposphere and the other that in the stratosphere, are expected to result from baroclinic instability associated with temperature gradients at the lower boundary. These are the Charney and Green modes of classic baroclinic instability theory. For a general baroclinic mean flow on a sphere, both of these modes can exist for zonal wave numbers 1 and 2. The Charney mode for zonal wave number 2 is confined in the high latitudes and has a relatively narrow meridional scale (Hartmann, 1979). It does not propagate well, so that its amplitude does not increase with altitude in the stratosphere. The Green mode has a broad meridional scale with its largest amplitude in the mid-latitudes (Strauss, 1981). Since its energy is more nearly constant with height, its amplitude increases dramatically from the troposphere to the stratosphere. The maximum upward flux of transient wave activity at 100 mb shown in Fig. 3 occurs near 50°S and extends over the latitude range from 35 to 65°S. This is roughly the latitude band over which Green modes are expected to have their largest amplitudes.

The results presented by Mechoso and Hartmann (1982) are consistent with the hypothesis that the tropospheric variance for eastward-moving zonal wave numbers 1 and 2 is dominated by a tropospherically trapped

Charney mode and that the stratospheric variance is associated with an upward-propagating Green mode. They showed a coherent structure within the troposphere with a narrow meridional scale confined to the high latitudes. There are two amplitude and coherence maxima at about 50°S and 70°S with a rapid phase change of 180° with latitude between them. This structure is similar to that expected for baroclinically unstable planetary waves confined to the high latitudes (Hartmann, 1979).

5. CONCLUSION

The basic large-scale behavior of the extratropical atmosphere below 55 km is now reasonably well measured with balloons, rockets, and satellite-borne instruments. Nonetheless, as techniques of observation and analysis improve, new phenomena in the stratosphere continue to be discovered. Recent examples include the identification in stratospheric data of an increasing number of the eigenmodes of an unbounded isothermal atmosphere in uniform rotation [see, e.g., review by Salby (1985)]. These have the vertical structure of a Lamb wave and the horizontal structure of Hough functions. The polar modes and the equatorial Kelvin waves discussed in the body of this paper also have been discovered only recently. Past experience suggests that any significant increase in observational capability will lead to the discovery of new phenomena in the stratosphere and better understanding of phenomena that are already known. The potential for new insights seems particularly great in the equatorial stratosphere. The Upper Atmosphere Research Satellite, to be launched later in this decade, will provide high vertical resolution measurements of temperature and constituents and, for the first time, direct wind measurements from space.

While the fundamental mechanisms that make possible the seasonal variations, the sudden stratospheric warming, the quasi-biennial oscillation, and other features of the stratospheric circulation have been sketched out, a host of more refined questions remains. For example, we have observed the seasonal variation of the zonal-mean wind in the two hemispheres and we know that both wave driving and radiative heating play important roles in determining this evolution and its contrast in the two hemispheres. We do not understand in detail, however, why the zonal-mean wind follows a particular pattern of seasonal evolution in the two hemispheres and what factors control that evolution. This question is important since a satisfactory answer to it is a prerequisite for a complete understanding of downward and poleward ozone transport in the stratosphere (see Mahlman, this volume). Closely related questions include the following: What are the precise conditions required for a stratospheric warming? What are the root causes of interannual variability in the stratosphere? What role do *in situ* instabilities play in the general circulation of the stratosphere?

Many of these and other questions can be addressed with the long sequence of maps of stratospheric temperature and geopotential height that is being built upon each year with operational satellite sounding systems and conventional measurement techniques. Others will require special observations or the development of new observational techniques.

A great deal of understanding can be gained from experimentation with mathematical models of the stratosphere. General circulation models are now being developed that include the entire stratosphere and mesosphere [e.g., Fels *et al.* (1980) and Mahlman and Umscheid (1983)]. The extension of state-of-the-art GCMs to 80 km will bring to the upper stratosphere and mesosphere the full synergy between modeling, theory, and observation that has proved to be so productive of understanding.

Model simulations suggest very strongly the need for a powerful sink of zonal momentum in the mesosphere [e.g., Holton and Wehrbein (1980)]. Lindzen (1981) and Weinstock (1982) have described a mechanism whereby breaking gravity waves could provide the necessary damping of the zonal-mean momentum and also provide a significant source of turbulent mixing. New data from surface radar facilities are becoming available and will aid in the study of gravity waves, turbulence, and short vertical wavelength equatorial waves [e.g., Balsley and Gage (1980)].

Observations of the stratosphere collected and analyzed over the past 30 years continue to provide challenges to dynamical meteorologists. In this paper some of the areas in which progress is being made have been mentioned. Improved observing techniques, better hypotheses to be tested, and more precise model simulations will continue to make observational studies of the stratosphere an interesting and productive endeavor.

ACKNOWLEDGMENTS

The author's research on this subject is supported by the National Aeronautics and Space Administration under Grant NAGW-471. M. A. Geller, J. R. Holton, C. B. Leovy, J. D. Mahlman, A. H. Oort, and M. L. Salby provided constructive criticisms of an earlier version of this paper. The presentation of the figures would not have been possible without the kind cooperation of M. A. Geller, I. Hirota, M. H. Hitchman, C. B. Leovy, C. R. Mechoso, and G. B. Raga.

REFERENCES

Abel, P. G., Ellis, P. J., Houghton, J. T., Peckham, G., Rodgers, C. D., Smith, S. D., and Williamson, E. J. (1970). Remote sounding of atmospheric temperatures from satellites II. The selective chopper radiometer for Nimbus D. *Proc. R. Soc. London, Ser. A* **320**, 35–55.

Andrews, D. G., and McIntyre, M. E. (1976). Planetary waves in horizontal and vertical shear: The generalized Eliassen-Palm relation and the mean zonal acceleration. *J. Atmos. Sci.* **33**, 233–2048.

Andrews, D. G., Mahlman, J. D., and Sinclair, R. W. (1984). Eliassen-Palm diagnostics of wave-mean flow interaction in the GFDL "SKYHI" general circulation model. *J. Atmos. Sci.* **40**, 2768–2784.

Balsley, B. B., and Gage, K. S. (1980). The MST radar technique: Potential for middle atmospheric studies. *Pure Appl. Geophys.* **118**, 452–493.

Barnett, J. J. (1974). The mean meridional temperature behavior of the stratosphere from November, 1970 to November 1971 derived from measurements by the Selective Chopper Radiometer on Nimbus IV. *Q. J. R. Meteorol. Soc.* **100**, 505–530.

Boyd, J. P. (1976). The noninteraction of waves with the zonally-averaged flow on a spherical earth and the interrelationships of eddy fluxes of energy, heat and momentum. *J. Atmos. Sci.* **33**, 2285–2292.

Butchart, N., Clough, S. A., Palmer, T. N., and Trevelyan, P. J. (1982). Simulations of an observed stratospheric warming with quasigeostrophic refractive index as a model diagnostic. *Q. J. R. Meteorol. Soc.* **108**, 475–502.

Charney, J. G., and Drazin, P. G. (1961). Propagation of planetary-scale disturbances from the lower into the upper atmosphere. *J. Geophys. Res.* **66**, 83–109.

Charney, J. G., and Pedlosky, J., Jr. (1963). On the trapping of unstable planetary waves in the atmosphere. *J. Geophys. Res.* **68**, 6441–6442.

Charney, J. G., and Stern, M. E. (1962). On the stability of internal baroclinic jets in a rotating atmosphere. *J. Atmos. Sci.* **19**, 159–172.

Coy, L., and Hitchman, M. (1984). Kelvin wave packets and flow acceleration: A comparison of modeling and observations. *J. Atmos. Sci.* **41**, 1875–1880.

Curtis, P. D., Houghton, J. T., Peskett, G. D., and Rodgers, C. D. (1974). Remote sounding of atmospheric temperature from satellites. V. The pressure modulator radiometer for Nimbus F. *Proc. R. Soc. London, Ser. A* **337**, 135–150.

Dickinson, R. E. (1968). Planetary Rossby waves propagating vertically through weak westerly wind wave guides. *J. Atmos. Sci.* **25**, 984–1002.

Dines, W. H. (1925). The correlation between pressure and temperature in the upper air with a suggested explanation. *Q. J. R. Meteorol. Soc.* **51**, 31–38.

Dopplick, T. G. (1971). The energetics of the lower stratosphere including radiative effects. *Q. J. R. Meteorol. Soc.* **97**, 209–237.

Edmon, H. J., Jr., Hoskins, B. J., and McIntyre, M. E. (1980). Eliassen-Palm cross-sections for the troposphere. *J. Atmos. Sci.* **37**, 2600–2616; corrigendum: **38**, 1115 (1981).

Fels, S. B., Mahlman, J. D., Schwarzkopf, M. D., and Sinclair, R. W. (1980). Stratospheric sensitivity to perturbations in ozone and carbon dioxide: Radiative and dynamical response. *J. Atmos. Sci.* **37**, 2265–2297.

Frederiksen, J. S. (1982). Instability of the three-dimensional distorted polar vortex at the onset of the sudden warming. *J. Atmos. Sci.* **39**, 2313–2329.

Geisler, J. E., and Garcia, R. R. (1977). Baroclinic instability at long wavelengths on a β-plane. *J. Atmos. Sci.* **34**, 311–321.

Geller, M. A., Wu, M.-F., and Gelman, M. E. (1983). Troposphere-stratosphere (surface-55 km) monthly winter general circulation statistics for the Northern Hemisphere — four year averages. *J. Atmos. Sci.* **40**, 1334–1352.

Geller, M. A., Wu, M.-F., and Gelman, M. E. (1984). Troposphere-stratosphere (surface-55 km) monthly winter general circulation statistics for the Northern Hemisphere — Interannual variations. *J. Atmos. Sci.* **42**, 1726–1744.

Gille, J. C., and Russell, J. M., III (1984). The limb infrared monitor of the stratosphere (LIMS); an overview of the experiment and its results. *JGR, J. Geophys. Res.* **89**, 5125–5140.

Hamilton, K. 1982. Some features of the climatology of the Northern Hemisphere stratosphere revealed by NMC upper atmosphere analyses. *J. Atmos. Sci.* **39**, 2737–2749.

Hartmann, D. L. (1974). Time spectral analysis of mid-latitude disturbances. *Mon. Weather Rev.* **102**, 348–362.

Hartmann, D. L. (1976a). The structure of the stratosphere in the Southern Hemisphere during late winter 1973 as observed by satellite. *J. Atmos. Sci.* **33**, 1141–1154.

Hartmann, D. L. (1976b). The dynamical climatology of the stratosphere in the Southern Hemisphere during late winter 1973. *J. Atmos. Sci.* **33**, 1789–1802.

Hartmann, D. L. (1976c). Dynamic studies of the Southern Hemisphere stratosphere. *Space Res.* **19**, 167–174.

Hartmann, D. L. (1977). Stationary planetary waves in the Southern Hemisphere. *JGR, J. Geophys. Res.* **82**, 4930–4934.

Hartmann, D. L. (1979). Baroclinic instability of realistic zonal mean states to planetary waves. *J. Atmos. Sci.* **36**, 2336–2349.

Hartmann, D. L. (1983). Barotropic instability of the polar night jet stream. *J. Atmos. Sci.* **40**, 817–835.

Hartmann, D. L., Mechoso, C. R., and Yamazaki, K. (1984). Observations of wave mean-flow interaction in the Southern Hemisphere. *J. Atmos. Sci.* **41**, 351–362.

Harwood, R. S. (1975). The temperature structure of the Southern Hemisphere stratosphere, August-October, 1971. *Q. J. R. Meteorol. Soc.* **101**, 75–92.

Hayashi, Y., and Golder, D. G. (1977). Space-time spectral analysis of mid-latitude disturbances appearing in a GFDL general circulation model. *J. Atmos. Sci.* **34**, 237–262.

Hayashi, Y., and Golder, D. G. (1983a). Transient planetary waves simulated by GFDL spectral general circulation models. Part I. Effects of mountains. *J. Atmos. Sci.* **40**, 941–950.

Hayashi, Y., and Golder, D. G. (1983b). Transient planetary waves simulated by GFDL spectral general circulation models. Part II. Effects of nonlinear energy transfer. *J. Atmos. Sci.* **40**, 951–957.

Hayashi, Y., Golder, D. G., and Mahlman, J. P. (1984). Stratospheric and mesospheric Kelvin waves simulated by the GFDL SKYHI general circulation model. *J. Atmos. Sci.* **41**, 1971–1984.

Hirota, I. (1967). Dynamic instability of the stratospheric polar vortex. *J. Meteorol. Soc. Jpn.* **45**, 409–421.

Hirota, I. (1978). Equatorial waves in the upper stratosphere and mesosphere in relation to the semiannual oscillation of the zonal wind. *J. Atmos. Sci.* **35**, 714–722.

Hirota, I. (1979). Kelvin waves in the equatorial middle atmosphere observed by the Nimbus 5 SCR. *J. Atmos. Sci.* **36**, 217–222.

Hirota, I., Hirooka, T., and Shiotani, M. (1983). Upper stratospheric circulations in the two hemispheres observed by satellites. *Q. J. R. Meteorol. Soc.* **109**, 443–454.

Holton, J. R. (1974). On the trapping of unstable baroclinic waves. *J. Atmos. Sci.* **31**, 2220–2222.

Holton, J. R. (1980). The dynamics of sudden stratospheric warmings. *Annu. Rev. Earth Planet. Sci.* **8**, 169–190.

Holton, J. R., and Wehrbein, W. M. (1980). A numerical model of the zonal mean circulation in the middle atmosphere. *Pure Appl. Geophys.* **118**, 284–306.

Julian, P. R., and Labitzke, K. B. (1965). A study of atmospheric energetics during the January–February 1963 stratospheric warming. *J. Atmos. Sci.* **22**, 597–610.

Kanzawa, H. (1982). Eliassen-Palm flux diagnostics and the effect of the mean wind on planetary wave propagation for an observed sudden stratospheric warming. *J. Meteorol. Soc. Jpn.* **60**, 1063–1073.

Labitzke, K. (1977). Interannual variability of the winter stratosphere in the Northern Hemisphere. *Mon. Weather Rev.* **105**, 762–770.

Leovy, C. B., and Webster, P. J. (1976). Stratospheric long waves: Comparison of thermal structure in the Northern and Southern Hemispheres. *J. Atmos. Sci.* **33**, 1524–1638.

Leovy, C. B., Hitchman, M. H., Smith, A. K., Gille, J. C., Bailey, P. L., and Remsberg, E. E. (1985a). Properties of quasi-global fields of temperature, geopotential and wind derived from the Nimbus-7 LIMS experiment. *JGR, J. Geophys. Res.* **90**, (in press).

Leovy, C. B., Sun, C. R., Hitchman, M. H., Remsberg, E. E., Russell, J. M., III, Gordley, L. L., Gille, J. C., and Lyjak, L. V. (1985b). Transport of ozone in the middle stratosphere: Evidence for planetary wave breaking. *J. Atmos. Sci.* **42**, 230–244.

Lin, B.-D. (1982). The behavior of winter stationary planetary waves forced by topography and diabatic heating. *J. Atmos. Sci.* **39**, 1206–1226.

Lindzen, R. S. (1981). Turbulence and stress due to gravity wave and tidal breakdown. *JGR, J. Geophys. Res.* **86**, 9707–9714.

Lorenz, E. N. (1955). Available potential energy and the maintenance of the general circulation. *Tellus* **7**, 157–167.

Lorenz, E. N. (1967). "The Nature and Theory of the General Circulation of the Atmosphere," Monogr. No. 218. World Meteorol. Organ., Geneva.

McIntyre, M. E. (1982). How well do we understand the dynamics of stratospheric warmings? *J. Meteorol. Soc. Jpn.* **60**, 37–65.

McIntyre, M. E., and Palmer, T. N. (1984). Breaking planetary waves in the stratosphere. *Nature (London)* **305**, 593–600.

Mahlman, J. D. (1969). Energetics of a "minor breakdown" of the polar night vortex. *J. Atmos. Sci.* **26**, 1306–1317.

Mahlman, J. D., and Umscheid, L. J. (1983). Dynamics of the middle atmosphere: Successes and problems of the GFDL "SKYHI" general circulation model. *In* "Dynamics of the Middle Atmosphere" (J. R. Holton and T. Matsuno, eds.), pp. 501–526, Terra Scientific Publishing Co., Tokyo.

Manabe, S., and Hunt, B. G. (1968). Experiments with a stratospheric general circulation model. *Mon. Weather Rev.* **96**, 477–539.

Manabe, S., and Mahlman, J. D. (1976). Simulation of seasonal and interhemispheric variations in the stratospheric circulation. *J. Atmos. Sci.* **33**, 2185–2217.

Manabe, S., and Terpstra, T. B. (1974). The effects of mountains on the general circulation of the atmosphere as identified by numerical experiments. *J. Atmos. Sci.* **31**, 3–42.

Manabe, S., Smagorinsky, J., and Strickler, R. F. (1965). Simulated climatology of a general circulation model with a hydrologic cycle. *Mon. Weather Rev.* **93**, 769–798.

Matsuno, T. (1970). Vertical propagation of stationary planetary waves in the winter Northern Hemisphere. *J. Atmos. Sci.* **27**, 871–883.

Matsuno, T. (1971). A dynamical model of the stratospheric sudden warming. *J. Atmos. Sci.* **28**, 1479–1494.

Matsuno, T., and Hirota, I. (1966). On the dynamic stability of the polar vortex in wintertime. *J. Meteorol. Soc. Jpn.* **44**, 122–128.

Mechoso, C. R., and Hartmann, D. L. (1982). An observational study of traveling planetary waves in the Southern Hemisphere. *J. Atmos. Sci.* **39**, 1921–1935.

Miller, A. J., Brown, J. A., and Campana, K. A. (1972). A study of the energetics of an upper stratospheric warming (1969–70). *Q. J. R. Meteorol. Soc.* **98**, 730–744.

Miyakoda, K. (1963). "Some Characteristic Features of Winter Circulation in the Troposphere and Lower Stratosphere," Tech. Rep. No. 14. Dyn. Predict. Group., Dep. Geophys. Sci., University of Chicago, Chicago, Illinois.

Muench, H. S. (1965). On the dynamics of the wintertime stratospheric circulation. *J. Atmos. Sci.* **22**, 349–360.

O'Neill, A., and Taylor, B. F. (1979). A study of the major stratospheric warming of 1976/77. *Q. J. R. Meteorol. Soc.* **105**, 71–92.

O'Neill, A., and Youngblut, C. E. (1982). Stratospheric warmings diagnosed using the transformed Eulerian-mean equations and the effect of the mean state on wave propagation. *J. Atmos. Sci.* **39,** 1370–1386.

Oort, A. H. (1964). On the energetics of the mean and eddy circulations in the lower stratosphere. *Tellus* **16,** 309–327.

Palmer, T. N. (1981). Diagnostic study of a wavenumber 2 stratospheric sudden warming in a transformed Eulerian mean formalism. *J. Atmos. Sci.* **39,** 844–855.

Palmer, T. N. (1982). Properties of the Eliassen-Palm flux for planetary scale motions. *J. Atmos. Sci.* **39,** 992–997.

Perry, J. S. (1967). Long-wave energy processes in the 1963 sudden stratospheric warming. *J. Atmos. Sci.* **24,** 539–550.

Prata, A. J. (1984). The 4-day wave. *J. Atmos. Sci.* **41,** 150–155.

Pratt, R. W., and Wallace, J. M. (1976). Zonal propagation characteristics of large-scale fluctuations in the mid-latitude troposphere. *J. Atmos. Sci.* **33,** 1184–1194.

Reed, R. J. (1966). Zonal wind behavior in the equatorial stratosphere and lower mesosphere. *J. Geophys. Res.* **71,** 4223–4233.

Reed, R. J., Campbell, W. J., Rasmusson, L. A., and Rogers, D. G. (1961). Evidence of the downward-propagating annual wind reversal in the equatorial stratosphere. *J. Geophys. Res.* **66,** 813–818.

Reed, R. J., Wolfe, J. L., and Nishimoto, H. (1963). A spectral analysis of the energetics of the stratospheric sudden warming of early 1957. *J. Atmos. Sci.* **20,** 256–275.

Salby, M. L. (1985). Survey of planetary-scale traveling waves: The state of theory and observations. *Rev. Geophys. Space Phys.* (in press).

Salby, M. L., Hartmann, D. L., Bailey, P. L., and Gille, J. C. (1984). Evidence for equatorial Kelvin modes in NIMBUS 7 LIMS. *J. Atmos. Sci.* **41,** 220–235.

Schoeberl, M. R. (1978). Stratospheric warmings: Observation and theory. *Rev. Geophys. Space Phys.* **16,** 521–538.

Shiotani, M. and Hirota, I. (1985). Planetary wave–mean-flow interaction in the stratosphere: A comparison between the Northern and Southern Hemispheres. *Q.J.R. Meteorol. Soc.* (in press).

Smagorinsky, J. (1953). The dynamical influence of large-scale heat sources and sinks on the quasi-stationary mean motions of the atmosphere. *Q. J. R. Meteorol. Soc.* **79,** 342–366.

Smagorinsky, J. (1963). General circulation experiments with the primitive equations. 1. The basic experiment. *Mon. Weather Rev.* **91,** 99–164.

Smagorinsky, J. (1983). The beginnings of numerical weather prediction and general circulation modeling: Early recollections. *Adv. Geophys.* **25,** 3–37.

Smagorinsky, J., Manabe, S., and Holloway, J. L. (1965). Numerical results from a nine-level general circulation model of the atmosphere. *Mon. Weather Rev.* **93,** 727–768.

Smith, A. K. (1983). Stationary waves in the winter stratosphere: Seasonal and interannual variability. *J. Atmos. Sci.* **40,** 245–261.

Smith, W. L., Woolf, H. M., Hayden, C. M., Wark, D. Q., and McMillan, L. M. (1979). TIROS-N operational vertical sounder. *Bull. Am. Meteorol. Soc.* **60,** 1177–1197.

Starr, V. P. (1960). Questions concerning the energy of stratospheric motions. *Arch. Meteorol., Geophys. Bioklimatol. Ser. A* **12,** 25–31.

Strauss, D. M. (1981). Long-wave baroclinic instability in the troposphere and stratosphere with sperical geometry. *J. Atmos. Sci.* **38,** 409–426.

Teisserenc de Bort, L. P. (1898). Résultats des ascensions des trois ballons-sondes lancés à trappes, le 8 juin. *C. R. Hebd. Seances Acad. Sci.* **129,** 135–138.

Teisserenc de Bort, L. P. (1900). Variation saisonniere de la température diverses hauteurs dans l'atmosphère libre. *C. R. Hebd. Seances Acad. Sci.* **131,** 920–922.

Teisserenc de Bort, L. P. (1902). Variations de la température de l'air libre dans la zone comprise entre 8 km et 13 km d'altitude. *C. R. Hebd. Seances Acad. Sci.* **134,** 987–989.

Van Loon, H., and Jenne, R. L. (1972). Zonal harmonic standing waves in the Southern Hemisphere. *J. Geophys. Res.* **77,** 992–1003.

Venne, D. E., and Stanford, J. L. (1982). An observational study of high-latitude stratospheric planetary waves in winter. *J. Atmos. Sci.* **39,** 1026–1034.

Wallace, J. M. (1973). General circulation of the tropical lower stratosphere. *Rev. Geophys. Space Phys.* **11,** 191–222.

Weinstock, J. (1982). Nonlinear theory of gravity waves: Momentum deposition, generalized Rayleigh friction and diffusion. *J. Atmos. Sci.* **39,** 1698–1710.

White, R. M. (1954). The counter-gradient flux of sensible heat in the lower stratosphere. *Tellus* **6,** 177–179.

WAVE–MEAN-FLOW INTERACTION IN THE MIDDLE ATMOSPHERE

David G. Andrews

Department of Atmospheric Physics
Clarendon Laboratory, Oxford University
Oxford, United Kingdom

1. Introduction

Faced with the complexity of global-scale atmospheric flows, meteorologists have for many years attempted to compress the volume of information to be handled, and improve its statistical reliability, by averaging the observational data in various ways. For example, a standard approach has been to take the zonal averages of wind, temperature, and other atmospheric fields; meridional cross sections of such quantities are to be found in almost every meteorology textbook. Zonal averaging is not appropriate for all applications, however, and another popular procedure is to perform time averages over various periods, from days to years in the case of large-scale phenomena. Modern facilities for data collection and handling have led to several variations on these two basic types of average.

Straightforward averages over a set of points fixed in space–time (or its analog in which pressure or log pressure is used as a vertical coordinate) are known as *Eulerian* averages and are comparatively easy to perform with standard atmospheric data. Of some theoretical interest, however, are *Lagrangian* averages, which are taken over an appropriately chosen set of moving fluid particles. Unfortunately, since detailed information on the time history of the motion of individual fluid particles is more difficult to obtain than that of the motion at fixed points in space, such averages have so far had little direct application to atmospheric phenomena (but see Sections 2 and 6).

249

Given any particular average, one can define the deviation or departure of each atmospheric variable from its mean value. These deviations are often known as "wave" or "eddy" quantities, in recognition of the fact that in simple idealized models, such as linearized disturbances to otherwise homogeneous states, these deviations can have an obvious "wavelike" character — for example, a propagating, sinusoidal form. However, it should be borne in mind that the mathematical procedure of subtracting the Eulerian or Lagrangian mean value from an atmospheric field may not produce the physically most satisfactory definition of a "wave." This is particularly true when the departure from the mean is of large amplitude in some sense. We shall, nevertheless, use the word "wave" in this article, in accordance with common practice.

Owing to the inherent nonlinearity of the equations of motion, there is in general a coupling between the waves and the mean state. Thus the configuration of the mean flow may influence the propagation of the waves, leading, for example, to refraction of the "ray paths"; conversely, nonlinear rectified effects associated with the waves may induce mean-flow changes. We shall discuss later some dramatic atmospheric examples of both of these aspects of wave–mean-flow interaction. However, it should be emphasized that one's picture of such a two-way interaction process is an artifact of the way in which "mean flow" and "wave" are defined: if an inappropriate averaging procedure is used, the picture may become unnecessarily complicated. Indeed, there are atmospheric phenomena that are undoubtedly of a "wavy" nature for which *any* conventional average may well confuse our view of the dynamics (see the ends of Sections 3 and 6). Nonetheless, the "wave–mean-flow" approach has successfully elucidated a number of atmospheric phenomena, and the purpose of this paper is to outline the theoretical background of the subject and to describe some of its applications to dynamical processes in the stratosphere and mesosphere.

2. THEORETICAL BACKGROUND

An important accompaniment to any form of separation of atmospheric quantities into "mean-flow" and "wave" parts is the development of a suitable theoretical framework for the diagnosis and interpretation of data that are thus separated. One requires quantitative information on both aspects of the wave–mean-flow interaction, namely, the influence of the mean flow on the propagation of the waves and the rectified back effect of the waves on the mean flow. Ideally, the theoretical formalism should also be capable of providing qualitative physical insights into the two-way process.

A theoretical framework of this kind has most satisfactorily been constructed for the case when the mean is a zonal mean; other types of average, such as the time average, present additional complications. For the most part, therefore, we shall discuss the interaction of waves with the zonal-mean flow, although other kinds of wave–mean-flow interaction will be mentioned briefly in Section 6. Furthermore, we shall generally restrict attention to Eulerian means since, as mentioned earlier, this class of average has been used in most atmospheric studies despite the theoretical advantages of Lagrangian means (Andrews and McIntyre, 1978b,c).

We start with the primitive equations in log-pressure coordinates on the sphere [see, e.g., Holton (1975)]:

$$(Du/Dt) - (f + ua^{-1} \tan \varphi)v + (a \cos \varphi)^{-1}\Phi_\lambda = X \qquad (2.1a)$$

$$(Dv/Dt) + (f + ua^{-1} \tan \varphi)u + a^{-1}\Phi_\varphi = Y \qquad (2.1b)$$

$$D\theta/Dt = Q \qquad (2.1c)$$

$$(a \cos \varphi)^{-1}[u_\lambda + (v \cos \varphi)_\varphi] + \rho_0^{-1}(\rho_0 w)_z = 0 \qquad (2.1d)$$

$$\Phi_z - H^{-1}R\theta e^{-\kappa z/H} = 0 \qquad (2.1e)$$

Here λ is longitude, φ is latitude, and $z \equiv -H \ln(p/p_s)$, where p is pressure, p_s a standard pressure, and H a standard scale height; the corresponding velocities are (u, v, w), θ denotes the potential temperature, and Φ the geopotential. Also, a denotes the radius of the Earth, R is the gas constant for dry air, and κ ($\doteq \frac{2}{7}$) equals R divided by the specific heat at constant pressure; X and Y represent unspecified zonal and meridional forcing terms, respectively, and Q represents diabatic effects. Finally, $\rho_0(z) \equiv \rho_s e^{-z/H}$ is a reference density profile, proportional to p (where ρ_s is a constant); $f = 2\Omega \sin \varphi$ (where Ω is the Earth's rotation rate); $D/Dt \equiv \partial/\partial t + u(a \cos \varphi)^{-1} \partial/\partial\lambda + va^{-1} \partial/\partial\varphi + w \partial/\partial z$ is the material derivative; and suffixes λ, φ, z, t denote partial derivatives.

We next introduce the (Eulerian) zonal average of any quantity $\psi(\lambda, \varphi, z, t)$, denoted by an overbar:

$$\overline{\psi}(\varphi, z, t) \equiv (2\pi)^{-1} \int_0^{2\pi} \psi(\lambda, \varphi, z, t) \, d\lambda \qquad (2.2a)$$

and the departure from that average, denoted by a prime:

$$\psi'(\lambda, \varphi, z, t) \equiv \psi - \overline{\psi} \qquad (2.2b)$$

Primed variables will be referred to as "wave" or "eddy" quantities. Standard manipulations lead to the following equations, in which "wave-forcing" terms are written on the right:

$$\bar{u}_t + \bar{v}[(a\cos\varphi)^{-1}(\bar{u}\cos\varphi)_\varphi - f] + \bar{w}\bar{u}_z - \bar{X}$$

$$= -(a\cos^2\varphi)^{-1}(\overline{u'v'}\cos^2\varphi)_\varphi - \rho_0^{-1}(\rho_0\overline{u'w'})_z \tag{2.3a}$$

$$\bar{v}_t + a^{-1}\bar{v}\bar{v}_\varphi + \bar{w}\bar{v}_z + \bar{u}(f + \bar{u}a^{-1}\tan\varphi) + a^{-1}\bar{\Phi}_\varphi - \bar{Y}$$

$$= -(a\cos\varphi)^{-1}(\overline{v'^2}\cos\varphi)_\varphi - \rho_0^{-1}(\rho_0\overline{v'w'})_z - \overline{u'^2}a^{-1}\tan\varphi \tag{2.3b}$$

$$\bar{\theta}_t + a^{-1}\bar{v}\bar{\theta}_\varphi + \bar{w}\bar{\theta}_z - \bar{Q} = -(a\cos\varphi)^{-1}(\overline{\theta'v'}\cos\varphi)_\varphi - \rho_0^{-1}(\rho_0\overline{\theta'w'})_z \tag{2.3c}$$

$$(a\cos\varphi)^{-1}(\bar{v}\cos\varphi)_\varphi + \rho_0^{-1}(\rho_0\bar{w})_z = 0 \tag{2.3d}$$

$$\bar{\Phi}_z - H^{-1}R\bar{\theta}e^{-\kappa z/H} = 0 \tag{2.3e}$$

The wave-forcing terms include the convergences of the eddy momentum and heat fluxes.

A somewhat more revealing set of mean-flow equations was pointed out by Andrews and McIntyre (1976a, 1978a) and Boyd (1976). One can define a "residual" mean meridional circulation $(0, \bar{v}^*, \bar{w}^*)$ by

$$\bar{v}^* = \bar{v} - \rho_0^{-1}(\rho_0\overline{v'\theta'}/\bar{\theta}_z)_z, \qquad \bar{w}^* = \bar{w} + (a\cos\varphi)^{-1}(\cos\varphi\,\overline{v'\theta'}/\bar{\theta}_z)_\varphi \tag{2.4}$$

[note that other definitions of the residual circulation are sometimes preferable; see Andrews and McIntyre (1978a) and Holton (1981)]. On substituting Eqs. (2.4) into Eqs. (2.3) and rearranging, one obtains the following "transformed Eulerian mean" (TEM) set:

$$\bar{u}_t + \bar{v}^*[(a\cos\varphi)^{-1}(\bar{u}\cos\varphi)_\varphi - f] + \bar{w}^*\bar{u}_z - \bar{X} = (\rho_0 a\cos\varphi)^{-1}\nabla\cdot\mathbf{F} \tag{2.5a}$$

$$\bar{u}(f + \bar{u}a^{-1}\tan\varphi) + a^{-1}\bar{\Phi}_\varphi = G \tag{2.5b}$$

$$\bar{\theta}_t + a^{-1}\bar{v}^*\bar{\theta}_\varphi + \bar{w}^*\bar{\theta}_z - \bar{Q} = -\rho_0^{-1}[\rho_0(\overline{v'\theta'}\,\bar{\theta}_\varphi/a\bar{\theta}_z + \overline{w'\theta'})]_z \tag{2.5c}$$

$$(a\cos\varphi)^{-1}(\bar{v}^*\cos\varphi)_\varphi + \rho_0^{-1}(\rho_0\bar{w}^*)_z = 0 \tag{2.5d}$$

$$\bar{\Phi}_z - H^{-1}R\bar{\theta}e^{-\kappa z/H} = 0 \tag{2.5e}$$

where $\mathbf{F} = (0, F_{(\varphi)}, F_{(z)})$, with

$$F_{(\varphi)} = \rho_0 a\cos\varphi[\bar{u}_z\overline{v'\theta'}/\bar{\theta}_z - \overline{u'v'}] \tag{2.6a}$$

$$F_{(z)} = \rho_0 a\cos\varphi[\{f - (a\cos\varphi)^{-1}(\bar{u}\cos\varphi)_\varphi\}\overline{v'\theta'}/\bar{\theta}_z - \overline{u'w'}] \tag{2.6b}$$

In Eq. (2.5b), G represents all the terms that lead to departures from gradient-wind balance between $\bar{u}$ and $\bar{\Phi}$ and can readily be calculated from Eqs. (2.3b) and (2.4).

At first sight, the transformation leading to Eqs. (2.5) appears to be no more than a mathematical device. However, it turns out to have the advantage that the wave-forcing terms on the right of Eqs. (2.5a,c), unlike those on the right of Eqs. (2.3a,c), can be shown to depend directly on certain simple physical properties of the waves. In particular, if the flow is conservative (that is, $X = Y = Q = 0$) and the waves are steady and linear, then

$$\nabla \cdot \mathbf{F} = 0 \qquad (2.7)$$

and the right-hand side of Eq. (2.5c) vanishes, also. Equation (2.7) was first derived, under the given hypotheses, by Eliassen and Palm (1961), and the vector $\mathbf{F}$ is now known as the Eliassen–Palm (EP) flux. Andrews and McIntyre (1976a, 1978a) have shown how Eq. (2.7) extends to cases in which the waves are transient and nonconservative. They derived a "generalized Eliassen–Palm theorem" in the form

$$\partial A/\partial t + \nabla \cdot \mathbf{F} = D + O(\text{amplitude}^3) \qquad (2.8)$$

where A and D are mean quadratic functions of "wave" quantities; their explicit forms generally involve particle displacements and will not be given here. The expression $\partial A/\partial t$ represents wave-transience effects, vanishing when the waves are steady, while D contains nonconservative terms (i.e., X', Y', and Q') and thus vanishes when the waves are conservative; the $O(\text{amplitude}^3)$ term represents nonlinear wave effects and vanishes when the waves are purely linear. [Note incidentally that $\overline{X}$, $\overline{Y}$, and $\overline{Q}$ are here assumed to be $O(\text{amplitude}^2)$, thus excluding, for example, an $O(1)$ mean meridional circulation associated with the diabatic heating $\overline{Q}$.]

Equation (2.8) makes explicit the dependence of $\nabla \cdot \mathbf{F}$ on the physical processes of wave transience, nonconservativeness, and nonlinearity; more fundamentally, when the terms on the right-hand side are zero, it takes the form of a "conservation law" for wave properties. The "density" A appearing in this law has been named the "wave-activity density" by Edmon et al. (1980), and the EP flux is then the flux of wave activity. The form of Eq. (2.8) is simpler than that of the wave-energy equation, which, in the presence of a basic shear flow, includes terms representing exchange of energy between the waves and the mean flow. For this reason, Eq. (2.8) has certain advantages as a diagnostic of wave propagation in complicated mean flows, especially when A is one signed. Moreover, in the limit of "slowly varying" waves, it can be shown that $\mathbf{F}/A$ equals the group velocity $\mathbf{c}_g$ (which is only defined in that limit); thus $\mathbf{F}$ can be regarded as a generalization of the group velocity concept to cases in which the waves are not slowly varying. Examples of the use of $\mathbf{F}$ and Eq. (2.8) as diagnostics of wave propagation in the middle atmosphere will be described in Section 3.

We can now return to the TEM equations (2.5) and, using Eq. (2.8), replace $\nabla \cdot \mathbf{F}$ in Eq. (2.5a) to show that the wave forcing on the right of that equation vanishes if the waves are steady and linear and the flow is conservative. A similar statement holds for the term on the right side of Eq. (2.5c), and it can further be shown that under such hypotheses, and with appropriate boundary conditions, a possible mean flow is given by

$$\bar{u}_t = \bar{\theta}_t = \bar{v}^* = \bar{w}^* = 0$$

(Andrews and McIntyre, 1976a, 1978a; Boyd, 1976). This is an example of a "nonacceleration" or "Charney–Drazin" theorem [cf. Charney and Drazin (1961)] and shows how the waves induce no mean-flow changes under the stated conditions. [Note that zonally symmetric oscillations, involving a significant contribution $-\partial\bar{v}^*/\partial t$ to the term G in Eq. (2.5b), are possible in principle, but that these are not forced by the waves. In most meteorological applications, however, G is small and only produces slight deviations from the thermal wind balance of the mean flow, as can be seen from the equation

$$\bar{u}_z(f + 2\bar{u}a^{-1}\tan\varphi) + (Ha)^{-1}R\bar{\theta}_\varphi e^{-\kappa z/H} = G_z \qquad (2.9)$$

which follows by elimination of $\bar{\Phi}$ from Eqs. (2.5b,e).]

As a result of the development of the body of theory associated with the TEM set [Eqs. (2.5)] and the generalized EP theorem [Eq. (2.8)], particular attention has been paid to the physical processes that violate the nonacceleration theorem [e.g., Dunkerton (1980)]. There has also been an emphasis in several observational and modeling studies [e.g., Edmon et al. (1980) and Andrews et al. (1983)] on the use of $\nabla \cdot \mathbf{F}$, rather than the separate eddy momentum and heat flux convergences, as a measure of the forcing of the mean flow by the waves. The latter approach is especially appropriate when quasi-geostrophic scaling holds, since the forcing on the right of Eqs. (2.5b,c) is then formally negligible, leaving $(\rho_0 a \cos\varphi)^{-1} \nabla \cdot \mathbf{F}$ as the only wave-forcing term in Eqs. (2.5). Examples of the use of $\nabla \cdot \mathbf{F}$ in the interpretation of this aspect of the wave–mean-flow interaction process will be described later.

The appearance of the $O(\text{amplitude}^3)$ error in Eq. (2.8) means that the terms in the generalized EP theorem [but not the TEM set, Eqs. (2.5)] are given explicitly only for small-amplitude waves. Finite-amplitude results analogous to Eq. (2.8) can be obtained but require either a "generalized Lagrangian mean" (GLM) formulation (Andrews and McIntyre, 1978b,c) or a restriction to "nonacceleration conditions" (Edmon et al., 1980, p. 2603; Andrews, 1983b). The GLM formalism in principle provides a finite-amplitude conservation law, which generalizes the "wave-action" law of Bretherton and Garrett (1968), and a set of mean-flow equations that lead to a finite-amplitude nonacceleration theorem. However, direct application of GLM theory to atmospheric data, and even to numerical models of the atmosphere, encounters serious difficulties [see, e.g., McIntyre (1980a)]. A somewhat analogous approach, based on the use of potential temperature and Ertel's potential vorticity as tracers of particle motion, is perhaps more promising (see Section 6).

The final item to be discussed in this section is the "refractive index squared" [cf. Matsuno (1970)], defined as

$$n_k^2(\varphi, z) \equiv (\bar{u} - ac \cos \varphi)^{-1}a\bar{q}_\varphi - k^2 \sec^2 \varphi - a^2 f^2 (4N^2 H^2)^{-1} \quad (2.10a)$$

where

$$\bar{q}_\varphi \equiv 2\Omega \cos \varphi - [(a \cos \varphi)^{-1}(\bar{u} \cos \varphi)_\varphi]_\varphi + f \rho_0^{-1}(\rho_0 \bar{\theta}_\varphi / \theta_{0z})_z \quad (2.10b)$$

is the northward quasi-geostrophic potential vorticity gradient, $\theta_0(z)$ is a reference potential temperature and $N^2 = H^{-1}R\theta_{0z}e^{-\kappa z/H}$. For quasi-geostrophic wave disturbances of zonal wave number k and angular phase speed c, superimposed on a basic zonal shear flow $\bar{u}(\varphi, z)$, n_k^2 controls the refraction in the meridional plane. Thus waves tend to propagate into regions in which $n_k^2 > 0$ and avoid regions in which $n_k^2 < 0$. When meridional wavelengths are much less than typical meridional scales of $\bar{u}$ and n_k^2, so that a "slowly varying wave" or "WKBJ" approach can be used, one can define the group velocity $\mathbf{c_g}$ and "rays," which are everywhere parallel to the local $\mathbf{c_g}$ and thus to the EP flux $\mathbf{F}$. In this limit, "ray-tracing" [e.g., Lighthill (1978)] is a powerful and revealing technique: the rays (and $\mathbf{c_g}$ and $\mathbf{F}$ vectors) tend to favor regions of large positive n_k^2 and avoid those of small or negative n_k^2. Even if the waves are not strictly slowly varying, the EP flux $\mathbf{F}$ is frequently found to behave much as would be predicted by ray theory [cf. McIntyre (1982)].

3. Sudden Warmings in the Polar Stratosphere

The stratospheric sudden warming is perhaps the most dramatic large-scale dynamical event to occur in the middle atmosphere. It takes place in the Northern Hemisphere winter, a "major" warming happening roughly every other year, and is manifested by a breakdown and (often) reversal of the basic zonal-mean polar westerly vortex, accompanied by a rapid rise in temperature in the stratospheric polar cap. A number of review articles have been devoted to the phenomenon, examples including those by Labitzke (1982) (dealing mostly with observations) and McIntyre (1982) (dealing mostly with theory). The object of the present section is not to attempt to summarize the material covered by these reviews, but to indicate how the theory outlined in Section 2 may help to elucidate the dynamics of sudden warmings.

There is now little doubt that sudden warmings are intimately linked with the propagation from the troposphere into the stratosphere of some form of large-amplitude "wave disturbance." This kind of dynamical mechanism was originally proposed by Matsuno (1971), although some of the details of his hypothesis have since required modification. In recent years, data from satellite-borne radiometers have provided a wealth of information on the development of sudden warmings and their various forms. At the same time, a hierarchy of numerical models, from the simplest "mechanistic" models of the type used by Matsuno to the highly complex numerical forecast models [e.g., Simmons and Strüfing (1983)], have simulated sudden warmings with differing degrees of fidelity and have also allowed the testing of hypotheses concerning the nature of the phenomenon. The interpretation of atmospheric and model behavior requires diagnostics with a sound dynamical basis, and the theoretical developments mentioned in Section 2 have played a valuable role in increasing our understanding of sudden warmings.

Ray-tracing calculations [e.g., Karoly and Hoskins (1982)] have indicated that the ultralong stationary planetary waves that are generated in the mid-latitude troposphere and that can penetrate into the winter stratosphere normally tend to propagate equatorward, owing to the spherical geometry of the Earth. This can be verified from observations by plotting suitably scaled arrows representing the EP flux $\mathbf{F}$ for such waves at various points in the meridional plane, following Edmon *et al.* (1980). Typical observed winter climatological patterns for these arrows are of the form shown in Fig. 1; cf. Fig. 9 of Hamilton (1982a).

For certain winter conditions, however, this equatorward flux of wave activity may be partially blocked by the appearance of a patch of negative squared refractive index n_k^2 [see Eqs. (2.10) with $c = 0$] in the mid-latitude stratosphere. This may happen, for example, if the polar night jet is farther

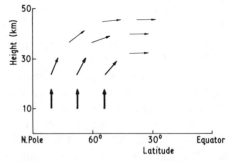

FIG. 1. Schematic meridional cross section showing EP flux vectors under typical winter conditions. The direction of each arrow gives the local direction of $\mathbf{F}$, and (following a suggestion by M. E. McIntyre, private communication, 1983) the thickness of each arrow is a measure of the logarithm of $|\mathbf{F}|$.

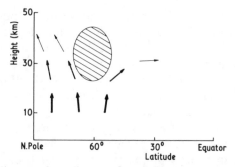

FIG. 2. Schematic diagram of the effect on the EP flux vectors of a patch of negative n_k^2 in the mid-latitude stratosphere (hatched), showing some focusing into the polar cap.

poleward than usual, leading to a large "curvature" contribution $-\bar{u}_{\varphi\varphi}$ to $\bar{q}_{\varphi}$. The rays or **F** arrows will tend to avoid this patch, and some of them may be focused into the polar cap in the upper stratosphere, as indicated in Fig. 2.

The effect of this focusing on the mean flow can readily be investigated with the TEM equations. In the quasi-geostrophic approximation, Eq. (2.5a) reduces to

$$\bar{u}_t - f\bar{v}^* = (\rho_0 a \cos \varphi)^{-1}\nabla \cdot \mathbf{F} \tag{3.1}$$

if $\bar{X}$ is negligible. Values of $\nabla \cdot \mathbf{F}$ in the polar stratosphere at the time of a sudden warming are found to be large and negative [e.g., Palmer (1981a)]. A physical reason for this is suggested by Eq. (2.8): as wave amplitudes grow when waves are first focused into the polar cap, $\partial A/\partial t$ is positive, giving a negative contribution to $\nabla \cdot \mathbf{F}$. [For an explicit expression for A in the quasi-geostrophic case, see, e.g., Edmon et al. (1980).] In practice, nonlinear wave effects and dissipation are also likely to contribute to $\nabla \cdot \mathbf{F}$.

As for the forcing of mean-flow changes by the waves, Eq. (3.1) shows that the effect of a large negative $\nabla \cdot \mathbf{F}$ is enhanced in the high-altitude polar cap, where ρ_0 and $\cos \varphi$ are both small. It is, in fact, found that the large negative force on the right side of Eq. (3.1) is mitigated to some extent by a northward (positive) $\bar{v}^*$, but a rapid mean deceleration still results in the neighborhood of the region of negative $\nabla \cdot \mathbf{F}$. This is most easily seen by eliminating $\bar{v}^*$ and $\bar{w}^*$ from Eq. (3.1) and the quasi-geostrophic version of (2.5c), namely,

$$\bar{\theta}_t + \theta_{0z} \bar{w}^* = \bar{Q} \tag{3.2}$$

where $\theta_0(z)$ is a reference potential temperature. Thermal wind balance then allows one to obtain an elliptic equation for $\bar{u}_t$ [see, e.g., Andrews et al. (1983), Eq. (B.8)]; contributions from $\bar{Q}$ are negligible for these sudden warming events. A rapid rise in temperature in the polar stratosphere is associated by thermal wind balance with the rapid deceleration, and by Eq. (3.2) a residual mean descent $\bar{w}^* < 0$ occurs; on the other hand, the Eulerian mean $\bar{w}$ can be positive during warmings. It is also observed that air parcels tend, on average, to descend during these events (Mahlman, 1969; Dunkerton et al., 1981); note, however, that $\bar{w}^*$ is not in general equal to the Lagrangian-mean vertical velocity.

This description of sudden warmings leaves a number of questions to be answered. In the first place it is necessary to explain why the polar night jet moves poleward in some winters, giving the patch of negative n_k^2. Such "preconditioning" appears, in at least some cases (such as the 1979 warming), to be due to an earlier wave event. One must also explain why wave amplitudes grow; one possibility, suggested by Plumb (1981), is that there is a near resonance between a stationary wave and a traveling wave that slows down. McIntyre (1982) addresses both of these questions.

The preceding discussion, although far from complete, should give the reader a flavor of the ways in which the theoretical studies described in Section 2 can provide diagnostics for analyzing and interpreting observations and models of sudden warmings. Papers that have used these diagnostics include those by Dunkerton et al. (1981), Palmer (1981a,b), Butchart et al. (1982), O'Neill and Youngblut (1982), and Simmons and Strüfing (1983).

More recent studies, however, suggest that for some planetary wave events, especially those of large amplitude, the separation into zonal mean and eddy parts may be an unnecessarily complicated way of viewing the dynamics. In particular, McIntyre and Palmer (1983) present maps of Ertel's potential vorticity on an isentropic surface in the middle stratosphere, which demonstrate that Rossby waves can attain large amplitudes and "break" as they penetrate to regions of low basic density ρ_0, rather as ocean waves can break on a shelving beach. This leads to irreversible mixing of potential vorticity and important consequences for the stratosphere as a whole. Potential vorticity maps of this kind may eventually provide the simplest method for analyzing sudden warmings and related phenomena, especially those that involve large departures from a zonal-mean state. However, a body of theory, comparable to that outlined in Section 2 and capable of showing how to interpret such maps in a quantitative way, has yet to be developed. Even without "breaking" of Rossby waves, the cross-polar propagation of localized disturbances (A. O'Neill, private communication, 1983) may be an important aspect of the dynamics of sudden warmings, and once again the zonal mean is not a satisfactory form of average for describing such behavior. Attempts to handle the interaction of zonally asymmetric basic states with disturbances to such states are discussed in Section 6.

4. THE QUASI-BIENNIAL OSCILLATION OF THE EQUATORIAL LOWER STRATOSPHERE

For more than twenty years meteorologists have known of the existence of the quasi-biennial oscillation (QBO) of the equatorial lower stratosphere. The form of this oscillation is illustrated by a time–height section of the monthly-mean zonal wind at a tropical station, shown in Fig. 3. Easterly and westerly regimes follow one another in a fairly regular fashion, each new regime appearing at about 30 km altitude and progressing downward to the tropopause: a complete cycle takes about 28 months. The oscillation has a latitudinal width of about 12°, and although Fig. 3 only shows conditions at one longitude, the oscillation is in fact highly zonally symmetric. Reviews of observations and theories of the QBO are given by Wallace (1973), Holton (1975, 1983a), and Plumb (1984), for example.

The paper by Holton and Lindzen (1972) (hereafter called HL) proposed a dynamical mechanism that has formed the basis of nearly all the later models of the QBO. They suggested a wave–mean-flow interaction process, in which the alternating bands of westerly and easterly acceleration that occur in the oscillation are driven by nonlinear rectified effects associated with two types of observed equatorially trapped, planetary-scale waves: the Kelvin waves (of eastward phase speed, period approximately 15 days, zonal wave number 1 or 2, and vertical wavelength 6–10 km) and the Rossby-gravity waves (of westward phase speed, period 4–5 days, zonal wave number about 4, and vertical wavelength 4–8 km). These waves are thought to be generated in the equatorial troposphere (the precise generation mechanism is still uncertain), whence they propagate upward into the stratosphere.

Holton and Lindzen's dynamical mechanism is based on theoretical studies that indicate that Kelvin waves have a larger vertical group velocity in the easterlies than in the westerlies and *vice versa* for Rossby-gravity waves. As the vertical group velocity decreases, each wave becomes more susceptible to dissipation: it can further be shown that dissipating Kelvin waves tend to induce westerly accelerations, while dissipating Rossby-gravity waves tend (in the latitudinal average) to induce easterlies.

Consider then a period in which mean easterlies in the lower equatorial stratosphere are overlaid by mean westerlies in the middle stratosphere. Kelvin waves propagate readily through the lower easterlies, but less so as they approach the upper westerlies, where their upward group velocity starts to decrease and they become increasingly liable to dissipation. As this happens, they induce westerly acceleration near the level of zero mean wind, thus moving that level downward. In this way, Kelvin waves can cause the westerly shear zone (westerlies above, easterlies below) to descend; conversely, Rossby-gravity waves can cause an easterly shear zone to descend.

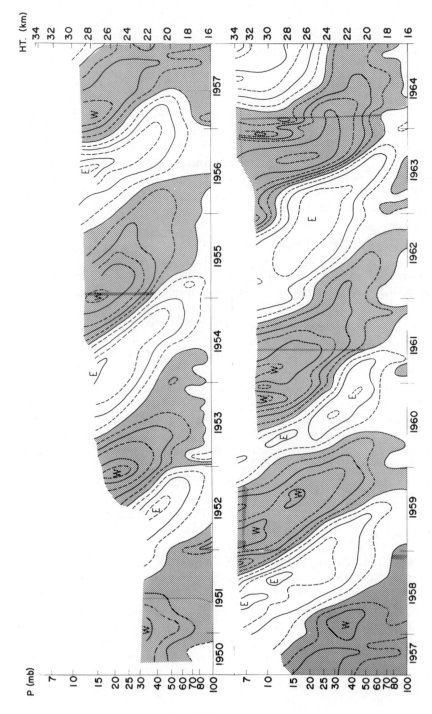

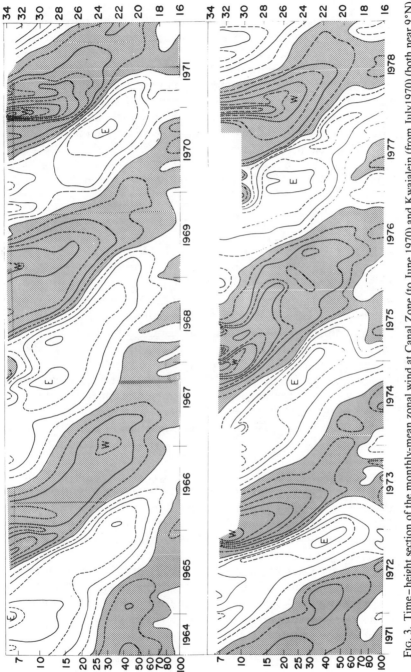

FIG. 3. Time–height section of the monthly-mean zonal wind at Canal Zone (to June 1970) and Kwajalein (from July1970) (both near 9°N). Annual and semiannual cycles have been removed; shaded areas indicate westerlies. [From Coy (1979, 1980). Reproduced with permission from *Journal of the Atmospheric Sciences*, a publication of the American Meteorological Society.]

The viability of this semiqualitative hypothesis must, of course, be tested in more detailed theoretical models, and these will be described in this section. Before doing so, it is worth noting that an analogous phenomenon has been demonstrated by Plumb and McEwan (1978) in a laboratory experiment involving two sets of internal gravity waves of opposite phase speeds, rather than equatorial waves, interacting with the mean azimuthal flow in a nonrotating annulus of stratified fluid. Alternate descending bands of "easterly" and "westerly" flow were observed when the internal gravity waves were of sufficiently large amplitude.

Theoretical studies of the QBO have mostly used the equatorial beta-plane approximation, in which the TEM equations can be written

$$\bar{u}_t + \bar{v}^*(\bar{u}_y - \beta y) + \bar{w}^*\bar{u}_z = \bar{X} + (\rho_0 a)^{-1}\nabla \cdot \mathbf{F} \tag{4.1a}$$

$$(\partial/\partial t)(\beta y\bar{u}_z + H^{-1}Re^{-\kappa z H}\bar{\theta}_y) = 0 \tag{4.1b}$$

$$\bar{\theta}_t + \bar{v}^*\bar{\theta}_y + \bar{w}^*\bar{\theta}_z = \bar{Q} + \mathcal{H} \tag{4.1c}$$

$$\bar{v}_y^* + \rho_0^{-1}(\rho_0\bar{w}^*)_z = 0 \tag{4.1d}$$

Here we have taken $f = \beta y$, $y = a\varphi$ in Eqs. (2.5), set $\cos \varphi = 1$ in various places, and replaced Eqs. (2.5b,e) by the approximate equation (4.1b), expressing a time-differentiated thermal wind balance, which is reasonable for quasi-steady waves under equatorial scaling [see also Eq. (2.9)]. Also, $\mathcal{H}$ denotes the term on the right side of Eq. (2.5c).

It was shown by Andrews and McIntyre (1976a) that if the mean flow is "tall," in the sense that the mean-flow Richardson number $N^2\bar{u}_z^{-2}$ is large and the vertical wavelengths of equatorial waves are much less than the vertical scale of the mean flow, then Eq. (4.1a) can be approximated by

$$\bar{u}_t = (\rho_0 a)^{-1}\nabla \cdot \mathbf{F} + \bar{X} \tag{4.2}$$

if $\bar{Y} = \bar{Q} = 0$. (Andrews and McIntyre also took $\bar{X} = 0$, but this is not necessary here.) In other words, the contribution of advection by the residual circulation $(\bar{v}^*, \bar{w}^*)$ to the zonal-mean zonal momentum balance is negligible under the stated conditions. Given sufficient information about the waves to determine $\nabla \cdot \mathbf{F}$, one can then calculate $\bar{u}_t$ under this approximation ($\bar{X}$ is assumed to be small for most purposes here).

To determine the wave structure it is necessary to solve the equations for disturbances to the zonal-mean flow $\bar{u}(y, z, t)$. In general, these equations are very complicated, even when linearized; however, if $\bar{u}$ can be considered uniform in space and constant in time, linearized analytical equatorial wave solutions of steady amplitude can be sought in the form

$$u' = \rho_0^{-1/2} \text{Re}[\hat{u}(y)e^{i(kx+mz-\omega t)}] \tag{4.3}$$

etc., where x is eastward distance. Matsuno (1966) showed that when $\bar{u} = 0$

and dissipation is absent, an infinite set of such solutions exists for any given k and m, each with its own dispersion relation $\omega = \omega_n(k, m)$ and latitudinal structure $\hat{u}_n(y)$; the latter functions tend rapidly to zero away from the equator. Similar solutions occur for constant nonzero $\bar{u}$. The two gravest solutions correspond closely to the observed Kelvin and Rossby-gravity waves.

Now it was noted in Section 2 that $\nabla \cdot \mathbf{F}$ vanishes identically for steady, conservative, linear waves; this applies in particular to the solutions presented by Matsuno. Such waves cannot induce mean-flow changes, and in order to break this nonacceleration constraint one must include dissipation, transience, or nonlinearity in the waves. The first two of these can be treated by a WKBJ method that allows for weak dissipation and slow transience; at the same time weak latitudinal and vertical shear can be included. This technique was introduced in the present context by Lindzen (1971, 1972) and extended by Andrews and McIntyre (1976a,b), who used it to compute the mean-flow tendency $\bar{u}_t$ in various cases, from Eq. (4.2) with $\overline{X} = 0$. These calculations generally confirmed the heuristic mechanism put forward earlier by HL, although they showed that the latitudinal profile of $\bar{u}_t$ could be quite sensitive to the relative magnitudes of thermal and mechanical wave dissipation. [Incidentally, they found that, owing to the nature of Matsuno's lowest-order solutions, $\nabla \cdot \mathbf{F}$ is most readily computed using the generalized EP theorem Eq. (2.8), rather than directly from Eq. (2.6); indeed, the full form of Eq. (2.8) was first developed during the investigation of this problem.]

A more comprehensive theoretical test of the HL mechanism must go beyond the computation of $\bar{u}_t$ at a single time and must recalculate wave structures at successive times as the mean flow develops under the influence of wave forcing. A simple approach is to assume that the waves and $\bar{u}_t$ both have a meridional scale $O(L)$ and define

$$\bar{u}_0(z, t) = L^{-1} \int_{-\infty}^{\infty} \bar{u}(y, z, t) \, dy \qquad (4.4)$$

which is supposed to vary slowly in z and t. By Eq. (4.2) we have

$$\frac{\partial \bar{u}_0}{\partial t} = (\rho_0 a L)^{-1} \frac{\partial}{\partial z} \int_{-\infty}^{\infty} F_{(z)} \, dy + L^{-1} \int_{-\infty}^{\infty} \overline{X} \, dy \qquad (4.5)$$

$\partial F_{(\varphi)}/\partial y$ integrates out, since $F_{(\varphi)} \to 0$ as $|y| \to \infty$. One now calculates quasi-steady wave structures at each time in the y-independent but slowly varying flow $\bar{u}_0(z, t)$: this can be done analytically, given simple forms of the wave dissipation. Then $(\rho_0 a L)^{-1} \partial/\partial z \int_{-\infty}^{\infty} F_{(z)} \, dy$ is calculated for each relevant wave mode n, giving some functional $\mathscr{F}_n(\bar{u}_0)$, which also depends on the wave amplitudes at the lower boundary (taken as close to the tropopause). The resulting mean-flow equation is essentially that used by HL (although they did not derive it in quite the way given here). They also parameterized the last term in Eq. (4.5) as a vertical diffusion $K \, \partial^2 \bar{u}_0 / \partial z^2$, and then integrated

$$\frac{\partial \bar{u}_0}{\partial t} = \sum_n \mathcal{F}_n(\bar{u}_0) + K \frac{\partial^2 \bar{u}_0}{\partial z^2} \tag{4.6}$$

forward in time, where the sum Σ_n is taken over the Kelvin and Rossby-gravity waves. The resulting form of $\bar{u}_0(z, t)$ showed a remarkable similarity to the observed structure in Fig. 3 when suitable wave amplitudes and dissipation magnitudes were chosen. An important finding is that the 28-month period depends on parameters such as these, and not on any externally imposed periodicities.

Further refinements of this one-dimensional model have been made by several authors, including Plumb (1977), Dunkerton (1981, 1982a, 1983), and Hamilton (1981b), incorporating various physical effects ignored by HL. For example, Dunkerton (1981) re-examined the validity of the quasi-steady assumption in the calculation of the wave structures and suggested that wave transience is not in fact negligible, while Hamilton used more realistic forms of thermal dissipation of the waves to improve the simulation of the vertical structure of the QBO. Dunkerton (1983) also attempted to assess the importance of easterly forcing by latitudinally propagating planetary Rossby waves.

A next stage beyond the HL model might be to use Eq. (4.2) without taking latitudinal integrals and to compute the wave structures at each time in a mean flow $\bar{u}(y, z, t)$ as was done by Boyd (1978), who used WKBJ methods in the vertical and numerical methods in the horizontal. So far, however, the only attempt to use this kind of procedure in a QBO simulation appears to be the preliminary calculation mentioned by Hamilton (1981a).

The most sophisticated model of the QBO to date is that of Plumb and Bell (1982a,b), who do not make the "tall" scaling assumption, but work with a set of equations essentially equivalent to Eqs. (4.1). They solve for the meridional and vertical wave structure at each time step by fully numerical methods and represent $\bar{Q}$ by Newtonian cooling; a quite realistic-looking QBO results, with qualitatively reasonable latitudinal structure. They find that, away from the equator, advection by $\bar{v}^*$ and $\bar{w}^*$ is not negligible in Eq. (4.1a). They also make the important point that a small vertical grid length (~ 0.5 km) is necessary to resolve the wave structure adequately; this is presumably one reason why even the most sophisticated general circulation models of the middle atmosphere have as yet failed to produce anything like a QBO [cf. Mahlman and Umscheid (1984)].

It seems fair to conclude that HL's wave–mean-flow interaction mechanism for the QBO is broadly correct. However, further studies, especially of the two-dimensional form of the mean-flow development, will be needed before we can claim to have a comprehensive understanding of all the major features of the phenomenon.

5. Other Wave–Mean-Flow Interaction Phenomena

In this section we give brief descriptions of a selection of other examples of wave–mean-flow interaction in the middle atmosphere. This list is not exhaustive, but it is intended to give the reader a feel for some of the topics of current meteorological interest that are being investigated with the aid of the kind of theory discussed in Section 2.

5.1. Breaking Gravity Waves

It has been known for many years [see, e.g., Murgatroyd (1969)] that the upper mesosphere is far from radiative equilibrium, with the summer mesopause much colder than the winter mesopause. Thus net radiative heating and cooling occurs in this region. At the level of quasi-geostrophic theory, and if time derivatives are neglected, Eqs. (2.5a,c) reduce to

$$-f\bar{v}^* = \bar{X} + (\rho_0 a \cos \varphi)^{-1} \nabla \cdot \mathbf{F} \qquad (5.1a)$$

$$\theta_{0z}\bar{w}^* = \bar{Q} \qquad (5.1b)$$

[cf. also Eq. (3.1), in which $\bar{X}$ was omitted, and Eq. (3.2)]; hence by continuity [Eq. (2.5d)] we have

$$(2\Omega a \cos \varphi)^{-1}\{[\bar{X} + (\rho_0 a \cos \varphi)^{-1} \nabla \cdot \mathbf{F}] \cot \varphi\}_\varphi = \rho_0^{-1}(\rho_0 \bar{Q}/\theta_{0z})_z \qquad (5.2)$$

Thus, to the extent that Eqs. (5.1a,b) are valid, $\bar{Q}$ must generally be balanced by a divergence of the EP flux $\nabla \cdot \mathbf{F}$ or the friction term $\bar{X}$. [Note that in many cases one can regard $\bar{X}$ and $\nabla \cdot \mathbf{F}$ as *causing* the net diabatic heating $\bar{Q}$ and the residual circulation ($\bar{v}^*$, $\bar{w}^*$); cf. Kurzeja (1981) and Plumb (1982). This contrasts with the commonly held notion that $\bar{Q}$ *drives* a "diabatic circulation."] Scaling arguments suggest that for phenomena whose time scales are much longer than typical radiative relaxation times, the steady-state arguments leading to Eq. (5.2) are in fact a reasonable first approximation. Thus, to explain the departures of the upper mesosphere from radiative equilibrium, one should look for processes that provide the requisite $\bar{X}$ or $\nabla \cdot \mathbf{F}$.

The question then arises as to what physical mechanisms contribute to the friction term $\overline{X}$. When the quasi-geostrophic equations are used, it is natural to let $\nabla \cdot \mathbf{F}$ represent the divergence of the EP flux associated with the planetary-scale waves described by quasi-geostrophic theory and to let $\overline{X}$ represent contributions to the mean zonal momentum balance from all smaller-scale phenomena, such as rectified effects associated with gravity waves, the turbulent Reynolds stress convergence, and molecular viscosity. The relative importance of $\overline{X}$ and $(\rho_0 a \cos \varphi)^{-1}\nabla \cdot \mathbf{F}$ will depend on the part of the atmosphere under consideration. For example, the well-known departures of the stratospheric polar night from a cold radiative equilibrium are probably mostly attributable to planetary-wave activity there.

Planetary waves are, however, essentially absent in the summer mesosphere, and in that region another mechanism is required to explain the departures from radiative equilibrium. Developing some earlier ideas of Hodges (1969), several recent studies have suggested that internal gravity waves may make a sufficient contribution to $\overline{X}$ to account for the required $\overline{Q}$. Gravity waves (with periods of a few minutes, horizontal wavelengths of some tens of kilometers, vertical wavelengths of 5 to 15 km, and horizontal phase speeds up to about 50 m s^{-1}) have indeed been detected in the upper mesosphere by VHF radars [e.g., Balsley and Gage (1980)]. As these gravity waves propagate upward, their temperature amplitudes will be expected to increase with height roughly as $\rho_0^{-1/2} \propto e^{z/2H}$ (the usual "density effect" for a compressible atmosphere). Such growth will lead to "breaking," that is, local steepening and then overturning of the isentropes. Localized patches of turbulence are likely to occur, with enhanced dissipation, and the $\rho_0^{-1/2}$ growth with height is presumably arrested or at least limited.

A strongly nonlinear process of this kind is clearly difficult to study theoretically. However, Lindzen (1981) has developed a nonrigorous but plausible approach, which essentially assumes that above the breaking altitude dissipative effects are such as to keep the waves "saturated," that is, on the verge of breaking. The resulting $\overline{X}$ has two parts: first, a contribution $-\rho_0^{-1}(\rho_0 \overline{u'w'})_z$ due to the gravity waves (the leading contribution to the EP flux divergence associated with these waves) and, second, a *mean* diffusive term whose diffusion coefficient is supposed to equal that required to keep the *waves* saturated. Numerical estimates of $\overline{X}$ can be several tens of meters per second per day, and even with some scaling down to allow for the probable intermittency of breaking events, these calculations suggest that gravity-wave breaking can account for much of the departure of the upper mesosphere from radiative equilibrium.

Further investigations and applications of this type of theory have been performed by Holton (1982, 1983b), Matsuno (1982), Dunkerton (1982b,c), and Weinstock (1982), among others. Nevertheless, much needs to be done to elucidate the nonlinear dynamics of breaking gravity waves, to assess their impact on the middle atmosphere, and to compare model predictions with observational data.

5.2. The Equatorial Semiannual Oscillation

In addition to the QBO and a weak annual cycle (Wallace, 1973), the equatorial middle atmosphere also exhibits a long-period oscillation with a 6-month time scale. This "semiannual oscillation" (SAO) is most prominent near the tropical stratopause and mesopause; the oscillations at these two levels appear to be in antiphase with one another. Observational details are given for example by Hirota (1978) and Hamilton (1982b).

The general consensus appears to favor the idea that the westerly accelerations observed in the SAO are due to rectified effects associated with upward-propagating equatorial Kelvin waves, as in the Holton–Lindzen QBO mechanism. However, the relevant Kelvin waves have higher zonal phase speeds than those that are observed in the lower equatorial stratosphere and that are believed to force the QBO westerlies; they have been found in satellite data by Hirota (1979) and Salby et al. (1984) and in a general circulation model by Hayashi et al. (1984). The forcing mechanism for the easterlies in the SAO seems less certain at present. It is likely that the cross-equatorial advection of zonal-mean easterlies by the mean meridional circulation may contribute (Holton and Wehrbein 1980; Mahlman and Sinclair, 1980), as may horizontally propagating planetary waves from the winter hemisphere (Hopkins, 1975). Indeed, Mahlman and Umscheid (1984) argue that both of these mechanisms are important in forcing the observed easterlies, the former on the "summer" side of the equator and the latter on the "winter" side. Dunkerton (1982d) suggests that the breaking of upward-propagating gravity waves may help to force the mesopause SAO; he also points out that significant time-mean zonal flows appear in these regions, as well as the oscillating components, and these are likely to influence wave propagation there.

5.3. Wave–Mean-Flow Interaction in Some General Circulation Models of the Middle Atmosphere

In this article honoring Joseph Smagorinsky, it is appropriate to include a discussion of wave–mean-flow interaction processes in atmospheric general circulation models (GCMs). Rather than undertaking a comprehensive review of this topic, we shall present here a brief retrospective view of particular features simulated by selected models, as interpreted in the light of current theory. Moreover, we shall mostly restrict attention to those models developed at GFDL under Dr. Smagorinsky's leadership.

The first comprehensive GCM to include a portion of the stratosphere was the pioneering model of Smagorinsky et al. (1965). This was a hemispheric nine-level model, forced by annual-mean insolation, and although it only included two or three levels in the stratosphere, it obtained some indication of a mid-latitude temperature maximum there, in accordance with observation. The authors noted a fact that was frequently to be found by later modelers and observationalists, namely, the near cancellation in the heat balance [Eq. (2.3c)] between the advection by the Eulerian-mean meridional circulation and the eddy heat flux convergence.

A next step, taken by Manabe and Hunt (1968), was to increase the vertical resolution to 18 levels, including about 10 in the stratosphere. Not surprisingly, the model simulated observed conditions more closely than did the earlier one, although the lower polar stratosphere was still some 10 K colder than annual-mean observations.

Full global coverage and seasonally varying insolation were incorporated in the 11-level GCM (including 5 stratospheric levels) used by Manabe and Mahlman (1976). This model successfully simulated a number of aspects of the observed seasonal variation of the stratosphere, including the reversal of zonal-mean zonal winds from winter westerlies to summer easterlies. It also simulated quasi-stationary planetary waves in the winter (but not the summer) stratosphere, in qualitative agreement with observations and the simple linear theories of Charney and Drazin (1961) and Matsuno (1970). However, the polar night stratosphere was too cold, and the associated westerly polar night vortex was too strong.

A considerable increase in vertical resolution was introduced by Fels et al. (1980), whose 40-level SKYHI model extended from the ground to about 80 km. Their main aim was to study the stratospheric effects of perturbed ozone and carbon dioxide amounts, but their simulations also contain many interesting dynamical features. Among other things, they investigated the role of the "dynamical heating" term $D\theta/Dt$, which by (2.1c) balances the diabatic term Q; in the middle atmosphere, the latter depends only on the net *radiative* heating. Fels et al. showed that in experiments involving perturbed chemical constitution it is frequently a good approximation to take the long-term zonal average of $D\theta/Dt$ as given (the "fixed dynamical heating" approximation); the response to the perturbation can then be determined by a purely radiative calculation using the average $D\theta/Dt$ from a "control" run of the GCM.

The study by Andrews et al. (1983) applied "Eliassen–Palm diagnostics" to the SKYHI model, employing the EP flux **F** to describe planetary-wave propagation in an annual-mean insolation run and the TEM equations (2.5) to discuss the forcing of the mean flow by the waves. It also examined the reasons for the near cancellation between eddies and mean flow mentioned earlier. This cancellation or compensation can occur in both the mean momentum equation and the mean thermodynamic equation; close to the "nonacceleration limit" it will be more prominent in the standard Eulerian-mean equations (2.3a,c) than in the TEM equations (2.5a,c). However, when the zonal-mean diabatic heating $\bar{Q}$ is significant, as it frequently is in atmospheric applications, and if mean-flow time scales are much longer than typical radiative relaxation times (or if long time averages are performed), then Eqs. (5.1) and (5.2) may be reasonable first approximations for quasigeostrophic flows, and compensation will occur in the TEM equations as well.

Mahlman and Umscheid (1984) have used insights from the two previous studies to examine the behavior of the SKYHI model under seasonally varying insolation. In particular, they conclude that the over-strong polar night vortex, present in this and earlier models, can be attributed to the (negative) zonal force per unit mass $(\rho_0 a \cos \varphi)^{-1} \nabla \cdot \mathbf{F} + \bar{X}$ [cf. Eq. (2.5a)] being too weak in the model stratosphere, probably because of insufficient wave activity there. Equivalently, the winter polar stratospheric temperature is too near to a cold radiative quasi-equilibrium because the diabatic heating $\bar{Q}$ associated with that force [cf. Eq. (5.2)] is too small. The cold winter polar stratosphere in other models, such as the U.K. Meteorological Office model (O'Neill *et al.*, 1982), probably occurs for the same reason.

Other problems still remain with the simulation of wave–mean-flow interaction phenomena in GCMs like these. For example, zonal-mean easterly winds are too strong and temperatures too warm in the summer upper mesosphere compared with observation (Mahlman and Umscheid, 1984), presumably because of deficiencies in the parameterization of frictional effects associated with breaking gravity waves (see Section 5.1). Moreover, a quasi-biennial oscillation is not found in the model (see Section 4). On the other hand, a "minor" warming was reported by Mahlman and Umscheid (1984), and a "major" warming has occurred in a version of the model incorporating higher horizontal resolution (J. D. Mahlman, personal communication, 1983). Comparison of the dynamics of these warmings (and other events taking place during long runs of the GCMs) with similar phenomena in the real middle atmosphere should continue to be aided by some of the ideas stemming from wave–mean-flow interaction theory. It is also likely that the theory will continue to help in the diagnosis, and perhaps cure, of shortcomings in the models.

6. Conclusions and Future Outlook

This paper has described some of the most significant examples of the interaction of waves with the zonal-mean flow in the stratosphere and mesosphere, and the ways in which recent theoretical studies have provided a framework for the diagnosis and interpretation of the dynamics of these phenomena.

It was mentioned in Section 1 that other types of average, such as the time average, have also been used in many atmospheric studies. The theory of the interaction of transient disturbances with the time-mean state is more complicated and less well developed than that for disturbances to the zonal mean. In the first place, although a conservation law for wave propagation, analogous to Eq. (2.8), can be derived under quasi-geostrophic scaling (Andrews, 1983a), it involves highly differentiated quantities that may be difficult to evaluate from observations. Further approximations involving a separation of scales between the eddy statistics and the mean flow may be needed if practically useful wave conservation laws are to be derived (Plumb, 1985). The feedback of the disturbances onto the mean flow also presents difficulties. Although a generalization to three dimensions of the "residual circulation" concept can reduce the eddy forcing of the time-mean flow to a zonal body force and an inhomogeneous lower boundary condition under suitable scaling (Hoskins *et al.,* 1983), the calculation of the three-dimensional response to such forcing may still be quite complicated. At a more fundamental level, the notion of the eddies "maintaining" the time-mean state may be difficult to formulate very precisely, if only because the removal of the time dependence by the averaging process blurs ideas about causality. This problem is compounded by the fact that the transient eddy structures, and therefore the eddy-forcing terms, are likely to depend on the mean-flow configuration (particularly its zonal asymmetries) even more than in the zonal-mean case. Thus eddies and mean flow are very tightly coupled, and a clear separation of their interaction into the *propagation* of the eddies in the time-mean state and their *feedback* onto the mean state may be difficult to accomplish. As yet, most of the studies of this type have had tropospheric applications in mind (such as the maintenance of "storm tracks" over the oceans), although similar techniques may be required to deal with the propagation of Rossby waves in zonally asymmetric stratospheric flows (see the end of Section 3).

It was also mentioned in Section 3 that a recent observational study by McIntyre and Palmer (1983) of a breaking planetary wave in the stratosphere presented maps of an approximation to Ertel's potential vorticity ($P = \rho^{-1}\omega \cdot \nabla\theta$, where ω is the absolute vorticity and ρ is density) on an isentropic surface. They demonstrated that it is just feasible to derive this quantity from current satellite measurements and indicated its usefulness as a dynamical diagnostic. Their study did not attempt any kind of "wave–mean-flow" separation, and indeed the dynamical interpretation of the event would have been much more complicated if a standard "wave–zonal-mean" separation had been used, even in the economical TEM formalism. This diagnostic technique may well prove fruitful in other areas, provided that P can be calculated with sufficient accuracy from data. However, although such potential vorticity maps give qualitative hints on the dynamical processes that are operating (such as wave propagation and irreversible mixing), a theoretical framework for quantitative diagnosis is desirable. One possible approach might be to use the quasi-Lagrangian intersections of P surfaces and θ surfaces as reference lines [cf. McIntyre (1980a,b) and Katz and Lynden-Bell (1982)]. This approach has affinities with the GLM technique of Andrews and McIntyre (1978b); for example, the Kelvin–Bjerknes circulation theorem applied to such a "$P\theta$ line" is analogous to Theorem I of that paper.

Ideas about atmospheric wave–mean-flow interaction may perhaps be at the beginning of a new period of transition. It has been shown in this paper how recent developments in the theory of the interaction of waves with zonal-mean flows have provided new tools for the analysis and understanding of phenomena like the stratospheric sudden warming and the QBO. One can argue that such tools are more physically based and potentially less misleading than some of those used hitherto [see, e.g., Edmon et al. (1980), Dunkerton et al. (1981), Plumb (1983), and Andrews et al. (1983)]. However, new observational studies are bringing to light atmospheric phenomena that cannot satisfactorily be handled with these tools. We have seen that the development of theoretical techniques for treating such phenomena is attended by formidable problems, but that there are several avenues that offer the possibility of deeper physical insights into these processes.

If such techniques are successfully introduced, we must still keep in mind the danger that the routine calculation of diagnostic quantities—so easily generated by computer nowadays—may lull us into a false sense of security about our understanding of the phenomena under consideration. Continual close collaboration among theoreticians, modelers, and observationalists will be needed to avoid pitfalls of this kind.

Acknowledgments

I acknowledge the support of a Royal Society Meteorological Office Research Fellowship during the writing of this paper. Many individuals, too numerous to list here, have contributed to my understanding of wave–mean-flow interaction. I experienced a particularly valuable exposure to the dynamics of the middle atmosphere during an enjoyable year at GFDL, and

I am most grateful to Dr. Joseph Smagorinsky for inviting me there and for providing such a stimulating environment in which to work.

I am indebted to Dr. L. Coy for a copy of Fig. 3, and to Dr. J. D. Mahlman for helpful comments on a first draft of this paper.

REFERENCES

Andrews, D. G. (1983a). A conservation law for small-amplitude quasi-geostrophic disturbances on a zonally-asymmetric basic flow. *J. Atmos. Sci.* **40**, 85–90.

Andrews, D. G. (1983b). A finite-amplitude Eliassen–Palm theorem in isentropic coordinates. *J. Atmos. Sci.* **40**, 1877–1883.

Andrews, D. G., and McIntyre, M. E. (1976a). Planetary waves in horizontal and vertical shear: The generalized Eliassen-Palm relation and the mean zonal acceleration. *J. Atmos. Sci.* **33**, 2031–2048.

Andrews, D. G., and McIntyre, M. E. (1976b). Planetary waves in horizontal and vertical shear: Asymptotic theory for equatorial waves in weak shear. *J. Atmos. Sci.* **33**, 2049–2053.

Andrews, D. G., and McIntyre, M. E. (1978a). Generalized Eliassen-Palm and Charney-Drazin theorems for waves on axisymmetric mean flows in compressible atmospheres. *J. Atmos. Sci.* **35**, 175–185.

Andrews, D. G., and McIntyre, M. E. (1978b). An exact theory for nonlinear waves on a Lagrangian-mean flow. *J. Fluid Mech.* **89**, 609–646.

Andrews, D. G., and McIntyre, M. E. (1978c). On wave-action and its relatives. *J. Fluid Mech.* **89**, 647–664.

Andrews, D. G., Mahlman, J. D., and Sinclair, R. W. (1983). Eliassen-Palm diagnostics of wave, mean-flow interaction in the GFDL "SKYHI" general circulation model. *J. Atmos. Sci.* **40**, 2768–2784.

Balsley, B. B., and Gage, K. S. (1980). The MST radar technique: Potential for middle atmosphere studies. *Pure Appl. Geophys.* **118**, 452–493.

Boyd, J. P. (1976). The noninteraction of waves with the zonally averaged flow on a spherical earth and the interrelationships of eddy fluxes of energy, heat and momentum. *J. Atmos. Sci.* **33**, 2285–2291.

Boyd, J. P. (1978). The effects of latitudinal shear on equatorial waves. Part I. Theory and methods. *J. Atmos. Sci.* **35**, 2236–2258.

Bretherton, F. P., and Garrett, C. J. R. (1968). Wavetrains in inhomogeneous moving media. *Proc. R. Soc. London, Ser. A* **302**, 529–554.

Butchart, N., Clough, S. A., Palmer, T. N., and Trevelyan, P. J. (1982). Simulations of an observed stratospheric warming with quasigeostrophic refractive index as a model diagnostic. *Q. J. R. Meteorol. Soc.* **108**, 475–502.

Charney, J. G., and Drazin, P. G. (1961). Propagation of planetary-scale disturbances from the lower into the upper atmosphere. *J. Geophys. Res.* **66**, 83–109.

Coy, L. (1979). An unusually large westerly amplitude of the quasi-biennial oscillation. *J. Atmos. Sci.* **36**, 174–176; corrigendum: **37**, 912–913 (1980).

Dunkerton, T. J. (1980). A Lagrangian mean theory of wave, mean-flow interaction with applications to nonacceleration and its breakdown. *Rev. Geophys. Space Phys.* **18**, 387–400.

Dunkerton, T. J. (1981). Wave transience in a compressible atmosphere. Part II. Transient equatorial waves in the quasi-biennial oscillation. *J. Atmos. Sci.* **38**, 298–307.

Dunkerton, T. J. (1982a). Shear zone asymmetry in the observed and simulated quasi-biennial oscillation. *J. Atmos. Sci.* **39**, 461–469.

Dunkerton, T. J. (1982b). Wave transience in a compressible atmosphere. Part III. The saturation of internal gravity waves in the mesosphere. *J. Atmos. Sci.* **39**, 1042–1051.

Dunkerton, T. J. (1982c). Stochastic parameterization of gravity wave stresses. *J. Atmos. Sci.* **39**, 1711–1725.

Dunkerton, T. J. (1982d). Theory of the mesopause semiannual oscillation. *J. Atmos. Sci.* **39**, 2681–2690.

Dunkerton, T. J. (1983). Laterally-propagating Rossby waves in the easterly acceleration phase of the quasi-biennial oscillation. *Atmos.-Ocean* **21**, 55–68.

Dunkerton, T. J., Hsu, C.-P. F., and McIntyre, M. E. (1981). Some Eulerian and Lagrangian diagnostics for a model stratospheric warming. *J. Atmos. Sci.* **38**, 819–843.

Edmon, H. J., Hoskins, B. J., and McIntyre, M. E. (1980). Eliassen-Palm cross sections for the troposphere. *J. Atmos. Sci.* **37**, 2600–2616.

Eliassen, A., and Palm, E. (1961). On the transfer of energy in stationary mountain waves. *Geophys. Norv.* **22**, No. 3, 1–23.

Fels, S. B., Mahlman, J. D., Schwarzkopf, M. D., and Sinclair, R. W. (1980). Stratospheric sensitivity to perturbations in ozone and carbon dioxide: radiative and dynamical response. *J. Atmos. Sci.* **37**, 2265–2297.

Hamilton, K. (1981a). Numerical studies of wave-mean flow interaction in the stratosphere, mesosphere and lower thermosphere. Ph.D. Thesis, Princeton University, Princeton, New Jersey.

Hamilton, K. (1981b). The vertical structure of the quasi-biennial oscillation: Observations and theory. *Atmos.-Ocean* **19**, 236–250.

Hamilton, K. (1982a). Some features of the climatology of the northern hemisphere stratosphere revealed by NMC upper atmosphere analyses. *J. Atmos. Sci.* **39**, 2737–2749.

Hamilton, K. (1982b). Rocketsonde observations of the mesospheric semiannual oscillation at Kwajalein. *Atmos.-Ocean* **20**, 281–286.

Hayashi, Y., Golder, D. G., and Mahlman, J. D. (1984). Stratospheric and mesospheric Kelvin waves simulated by the GFDL "SKYHI" general circulation model. *J. Atmos. Sci.* **41**, 1971–1984.

Hirota, I. (1978). Equatorial waves in the upper stratosphere and mesosphere in relation to the semiannual oscillation of the zonal wind. *J. Atmos. Sci.* **35**, 714–722.

Hirota, I. (1979). Kelvin waves in the equatorial middle atmosphere observed by the Nimbus 5 SCR. *J. Atmos. Sci.* **36**, 217–222.

Hodges, R. R. (1969). Eddy diffusion coefficients due to instabilities in internal gravity waves. *J. Geophys. Res.* **74**, 4087–4090.

Holton, J. R. (1975). "The Dynamic Meteorology of the Stratosphere and Mesosphere," Meteorol. Monogr. No. 37. Am. Meteorol. Soc., Boston, Massachusetts.

Holton, J. R. (1981). An advective model for two-dimensional transport of stratospheric trace species. *JGR, J. Geophys. Res.* **86**, 11989–11994.

Holton, J. R. (1982). The role of gravity wave induced drag and diffusion in the momentum budget of the mesosphere. *J. Atmos. Sci.* **39**, 791–799.

Holton, J. R. (1983a). The stratosphere and its links to the troposphere. *In* "Large-Scale Dynamical Processes in the Atmosphere" (B. J. Hoskins and R. P. Pearce, eds.), pp. 277–303. Academic Press, New York.

Holton, J. R. (1983b). The influence of gravity wave breaking on the general circulation of the middle atmosphere. *J. Atmos. Sci.* **40**, 2497–2507.

Holton, J. R., and Lindzen, R. S. (1972). An updated theory for the quasi-biennial cycle of the tropical stratosphere. *J. Atmos. Sci.* **29**, 1076–1080.

Holton, J. R., and Wehrbein, W. M. (1980). A numerical model of the zonal mean circulation of the middle atmosphere. *Pure Appl. Geophys.* **118**, 284–306.

Hopkins, R. H. (1975). Evidence of polar-tropical coupling in upper stratospheric zonal wind anomalies. *J. Atmos. Sci.* **32**, 712–719.

Hoskins, B. J., James, I. N., and White, G. H. (1983). The shape, propagation and mean-flow interaction of large-scale weather systems. *J. Atmos. Sci.* **40**, 1595–1612.

Karoly, D. J., and Hoskins, B. J. (1982). Three dimensional propagation of planetary waves. *J. Meteorol. Soc. Jpn.* **60**, 109–123.

Katz, J., and Lynden-Bell, D. (1982). A Lagrangian for Eulerian fluid mechanics. *Proc. R. Soc. London, Ser. A* **381**, 263–274.

Kurzeja, R. (1981). The transport of trace chemicals by planetary waves in the stratosphere. Part I. Steady waves. *J. Atmos. Sci.* **38**, 2779–2788.

Labitzke, K. (1982). On the interannual variability of the middle stratosphere during the northern winters. *J. Meteorol. Soc. Jpn.* **60**, 124–139.

Lighthill, J. (1978). "Waves in Fluids." Cambridge Univ. Press, London and New York.

Lindzen, R. S. (1971). Equatorial planetary waves in shear. Part I. *J. Atmos. Sci.* **28**, 609–622.

Lindzen, R. S. (1972). Equatorial planetary waves in shear. Part II. *J. Atmos. Sci.* **29**, 1452–1463.

Lindzen, R. S. (1981). Turbulence and stress owing to gravity waves and tidal breakdown. *JGR, J. Geophys. Res.* **86**, 9707–9714.

McIntyre, M. E. (1980a). Towards a Lagrangian-mean description of stratospheric circulations and chemical transports. *Philos. Trans. R. Soc. London, Ser. A* **296**, 129–148.

McIntyre, M. E. (1980b). An introduction to the generalized Lagrangian-mean description of wave, mean-flow interaction. *Pure Appl. Geophys.* **118**, 152–176.

McIntyre, M. E. (1982). How well do we understand the dynamics of sudden warmings? *J. Meteorol. Soc. Jpn.* **60**, 37–65.

McIntyre, M. E., and Palmer, T. N. (1983). Breaking planetary waves in the stratosphere. *Nature (London)* **305**, 593–600.

Mahlman, J. D. (1969). Heat balance and mean meridional circulations in the polar stratosphere during the sudden warming of January 1958. *Mon. Weather Rev.* **97**, 534–540.

Mahlman, J. D., and Sinclair, R. W. (1980). Recent results from the GFDL troposphere-stratosphere-mesosphere general circulation model. *In* "Collection of Extended Abstracts Presented at ICMUA Sessions and IUGG Symposium 18, pp. 11–18. XVII IUGG General Assembly, Canberra, Australia.

Mahlman, J. D., and Umscheid, L. J. (1984). Dynamics of the middle atmosphere: Successes and problems of the GFDL "SKYHI" general circulation model. *In* "Dynamics of the Middle Atmosphere" (J. R. Holton and T. Matsuno, eds.), pp. 501–525, Terra Scientific Publishing Co., Tokyo.

Manabe, S., and Hunt, B. G. (1968). Experiments with a stratospheric general circulation model. I. Radiative and dynamical aspects. *Mon. Weather Rev.* **96**, 477–539.

Manabe, S., and Mahlman, J. D. (1976). Simulation of seasonal and interhemispheric variations in the stratospheric circulation. *J. Atmos. Sci.* **33**, 2185–2217.

Matsuno, T. (1966). Quasi-geostrophic motions in the equatorial area. *J. Meteorol. Soc. Jpn.* **44**, 25–43.

Matsuno, T. (1970). Vertical propagation of stationary planetary waves in the winter northern hemisphere. *J. Atmos. Sci.* **27**, 871–883.

Matsuno, T. (1971). A dynamical model of the stratospheric sudden warming. *J. Atmos. Sci.* **28**, 1479–1494.

Matsuno, T. (1982). A quasi one-dimensional model of the middle atmosphere circulation interacting with internal gravity waves. *J. Meteorol. Soc. Jpn.* **60**, 215–226.

Murgatroyd, R. J. (1969). The structure and dynamics of the stratosphere. *In* "The Global Circulation of the Atmosphere" (G. A. Corby, ed.), pp. 159–195. R. Meteorol. Soc., London.

O'Neill, A., and Youngblut, C. E. (1982). Stratospheric warmings diagnosed using the transformed Eulerian-mean equations and the effect of the mean state on wave propagation. *J. Atmos. Sci.* **39,** 1370–1386.

O'Neill, A., Newson, R. L., and Murgatroyd, R. J. (1982). An analysis of the large-scale features of the upper troposphere and the stratosphere in a global three-dimensional general circulation model. *Q. J. R. Meteorol. Soc.* **108,** 25–53.

Palmer, T. N. (1981a). Diagnostic study of a wavenumber-2 stratospheric sudden warming in a transformed Eulerian-mean formalism. *J. Atmos. Sci.* **38,** 844–855.

Palmer, T. N. (1981b). Aspects of stratospheric sudden warmings studied from a transformed Eulerian-mean viewpoint. *JGR, J. Geophys. Res.* **86,** 9679–9687.

Plumb, R. A. (1977). The interaction of two internal waves with the mean flow: implications for the theory of the quasi-biennial oscillation. *J. Atmos. Sci.* **34,** 1847–1858.

Plumb, R. A. (1981). Instability of the distorted polar night vortex: a theory of stratospheric warmings. *J. Atmos. Sci.* **38,** 2514–2531.

Plumb, R. A. (1982). The circulation of the middle atmosphere. *Aust. Meteorol. Mag.* **30,** 107–121.

Plumb, R. A. (1983). A new look at the energy cycle. *J. Atmos. Sci.* **40,** 1669–1688.

Plumb, R. A. (1984). The quasi-biennial oscillation. *In* "Dynamics of the Middle Atmosphere" (J. R. Holton and T. Matsuno, eds.), pp. 217–251, Terra Scientific Publishing Co., Tokyo.

Plumb, R. A. (1985). Three-dimensional propagation of transient quasigeostrophic eddies and its relationship with the eddy forcing of the time-mean flow. *J. Atmos. Sci.* (submitted for publication).

Plumb, R. A., and Bell, R. C. (1982a). Equatorial waves in steady zonal shear flow. *Q. J. R. Meteorol. Soc.* **108,** 313–334.

Plumb, R. A., and Bell, R. C. (1982b). A model of the quasi-biennial oscillation on an equatorial beta-plane. *Q. J. R. Meteorol. Soc.* **108,** 335–352.

Plumb, R. A., and McEwan, A. D. (1978). The instability of a forced standing wave in a viscous stratified fluid: A laboratory analogue of the quasi-biennial oscillation. *J. Atmos. Sci.* **35,** 1827–1839.

Salby, M. L., Hartmann, D. L., Bailey, P. L., and Gille, J. C. (1984). Evidence for equatorial Kelvin waves in Nimbus-7 LIMS. *J. Atmos. Sci.* **41,** 220–235.

Simmons, A. J., and Strüfing, R. (1983). Numerical forecasts of stratospheric warming events using a model with a hybrid vertical coordinate. *Q. J. R. Meteorol. Soc.* **109,** 81–111.

Smagorinsky, J., Manabe, S., and Holloway, J. L. (1965). Numerical results from a nine-level general circulation model of the atmosphere. *Mon. Weather Rev.* **93,** 727–768.

Wallace, J. M. (1973). General circulation of the tropical lower stratosphere. *Revs. Geophys. Space Phys.* **11,** 191–222.

Weinstock, J. (1982). Nonlinear theory of gravity waves: Momentum deposition, generalized Rayleigh friction and diffusion. *J. Atmos. Sci.* **39,** 1698–1710.

RADIATIVE – DYNAMICAL INTERACTIONS IN THE MIDDLE ATMOSPHERE

STEPHEN B. FELS

Geophysical Fluid Dynamics Laboratory/NOAA
Princeton University
Princeton, New Jersey

1. INTRODUCTION

The terrestrial middle atmosphere comprises the region between roughly 200 and 0.01 mb — about 10 to 80 km. Its boundaries are not arbitrary; it is a statically stable region in which the effects of latent heat release and clouds cease to be important. It lies below that part of the atmosphere in which electromagnetic phenomena play a decisive role.

While a full understanding of the physics of the troposphere of necessity involves consideration of processes that are extremely difficult to model from first principles, this would seem not to be true of the middle atmosphere. It is therefore an ideal place to evaluate our present understanding of atmospheric physics and chemistry. There appear to be few places to hide here; no adjustable cloud amounts, surface drag coefficients, or sea-ice parameterizations are available as tuning knobs to allow us to bring theory into agreement with observations.

It is therefore of particular interest to examine how well our current generation of general circulation models (GCMs) do in simulating the middle atmosphere. By so doing, we may hope to get an indication of the strengths and weaknesses of the models. More important, we may, if we are lucky, learn something about how the real atmosphere works.

Of particular simplicity in the middle atmosphere is the calculation of diabatic heating, for this is largely due to the radiative effects of a few gases. Ozone, carbon dioxide, and water are the most important of these, with methane and the various oxides of nitrogen playing a smaller role. In the upper mesosphere, absorption of ultraviolet radiation by molecular oxygen is important, and in the lower stratosphere, aerosols can play a significant part.

ADVANCES IN GEOPHYSICS, VOLUME 28A

There has been a great deal of laboratory and theoretical work over the past 60 years with the goal of elucidating the basic spectroscopy of these gases. The subject is by no means closed; there remain uncertainties in the precise shape of the line profile, the behavior of line widths with temperature, and the nonadditivity of the absorption due to overlapping spectral lines, for example. Nonetheless, these are almost certainly of secondary importance in the middle atmosphere, and for a given specification of constituents, it is probably possible to calculate separate heating and cooling rates to within 10 or 20%. As we shall see presently, such accuracy is adequate for answering many, but not all, questions about the radiative–dynamical interactions in the middle atmosphere.

In an essay of this length, it is clearly impossible to discuss any subject both comprehensively and critically, nor am I qualified to do so. Rather, I shall concentrate on two sets of problems which seem to be of particular interest at present. These may be phrased roughly as follows:

(1) How far from a purely radiative state is the winter middle atmosphere, and why is it thus?
(2) What role, if any, is played by radiation in the dynamics of wave disturbances?

These questions are not as arbitrary as they may seem. They both address aspects of what has, in the past 10 years, come to be a central theme of middle atmospheric research — the interaction of waves with the mean flow [cf., for example, the article by Andrews (this volume)]. The manner in which this comes about can most easily be seen in the context of a simplified mathematical model similar to one discussed recently by Andrews *et al.* (1983). While an oversimplification of the true situation, the model serves well to illustrate the various ways in which radiation and dynamics can interact.

Andrews *et al.* consider quasi-geostrophic motion on an f plane. The time-evolving zonal-mean wind field is determined by the equation

$$\left[\frac{\partial^2}{\partial y^2} + \frac{\partial}{\partial p}\,\epsilon\,\frac{\partial}{\partial p}\right]\frac{\partial U}{\partial t} + \frac{\partial}{\partial p}\,\frac{\epsilon}{\tau_r}\,\frac{\partial}{\partial p}(U - U_r) = \frac{\partial^2}{\partial y^2}(\nabla \cdot \mathbf{F})$$

$$\epsilon^{-1} \equiv \frac{f^2}{N^2}\,\frac{gp^2}{RH^2} \quad (1.1)$$

In Eq. (1.1), y is the meridional coordinate, p the pressure, U the zonal wind, f the Coriolis parameter, and N^2 the Brunt–Vaisala frequency; U_r is the zonal mean wind determined from instantaneous radiative equilibrium, while τ_r is the radiative relaxation time. Finally, $\nabla \cdot \mathbf{F}$ is the Eliasson–Palm (EP) flux divergence, which represents the effect of the waves on the zonal mean.

The roles played by radiation in this model are therefore threefold:

(1)   Through U_r, it determines the state to which the mean flow will evolve in the absence of transience and wave forcing.

(2)   Through τ_r, it determines the size of the deviations from U_r brought about by transience and wave forcing; other things being equal, the smaller τ_r, the harder it will be to drive the system away from U_r.

(3)   The EP flux divergence $\nabla \cdot \mathbf{F}$ can be importantly affected by radiative processes. It has been recognized for many years that the mere presence of waves does not guarantee that they will influence the mean flow: one can have $\nabla \cdot \mathbf{F} = 0$ even when $\mathbf{F} \neq 0$. There is a relatively short catalog of mechanisms that yield a nonzero $\nabla \cdot \mathbf{F}$, and one of these is the radiative damping and forcing of the waves.

In the real atmosphere, $\mathbf{F}$ is influenced by factors other than radiation, including other sources of dissipation and the effects of transience, as well as the structure of the zonal mean wind U. Furthermore, radiative processes are more complex than (1.1) suggests; they are both nonlocal and nonlinear in general. A realistic model of the interplay of radiation and dynamics is therefore of necessity a complex one, in which both mean flow and waves are coupled to the radiative field.

An understanding of the middle atmosphere thus requires that we determine the relative importance of the various terms in Eq. (1.1). In what follows, we shall discuss several aspects of this problem and at the same time examine the success or failure of several GCMs to reproduce the observed balances.

2. RADIATIVE IMBALANCES IN THE WINTER MIDDLE ATMOSPHERE

There are several ways of addressing the question of the degree of radiative imbalance that exists in an atmosphere, and perhaps the simplest is to compare the observed thermal structure with that which would exist were all dynamical heating and cooling processes suppressed. While not the cleanest approach for some purposes, it provides a good starting point for further discussion.

Because radiative processes are essentially local horizontally, we may compute the radiatively determined temperature profile at a specified latitude as a function of time and height by use of the relation

$$(dT/dt)(\theta, z, t) = J_{SW}(\theta, z, t) - Q_{LW}[z, T, T_s(t)] \qquad (2.1)$$

Here, J_{SW} is the short-wave heating, due largely to absorption of solar radiation by ozone, and therefore requires for its computation a specification of

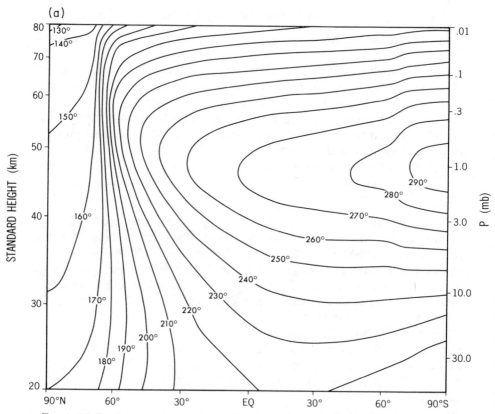

FIG. 1. (a) Zonal mean temperatures for 15 January calculated by using a time-marched radiative–convective–photochemical model. (The photochemistry is due to Drs. S. Liu and J. Macafee of the NOAA Aeronomy Laboratory.) (b) Zonal mean temperatures for January taken from CIRA (COSPAR, 1972)

the ozone profile; Q_{LW} is the long-wave cooling rate and depends, in principle, on the entire temperature profile $T(z)$. Finally, T_s is the surface temperature; since our interest here is in the middle atmosphere, we shall take it to be a specified function of time and latitude.

Figure 1a shows the latitude–height thermal structure obtained from these calculations for January 15; Fig. 1b is the observed values taken from CIRA (COSPAR, 1972).

The observed temperatures in the summer stratosphere agree well with those calculated by the radiative model. This suggests that dynamical heating [which is crudely measured by $(T_{obs} - T_{rad})/\tau_{rad}$] is less than 2° day^{-1} in this part of the atmosphere. Some caution is necessary, however, since the accuracy of T_{rad} in the summer depends strongly on the accuracy of the

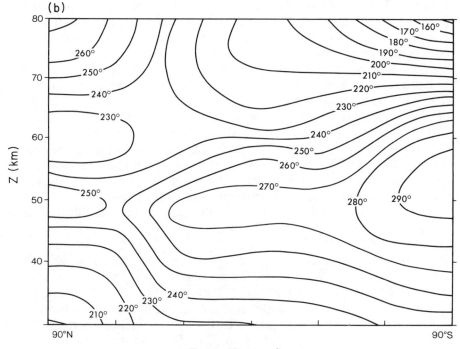

FIG. 1. *(Continued)*

ozone profile predicted by the model, as well as on that of the short-wave algorithm used.

Of the major discrepancies, one of the most dramatic is certainly the extremely cold polar night stratosphere in the radiative calculations: at 10 mb, these are too cold by 40° and at 1 mb by 80 to 90°! Equally spectacular is the failure of the model to produce a warm polar winter and cold solar summer mesosphere.

The huge radiative imbalance in the polar night is very difficult to explain as being due to inaccuracies in the radiative calculations. Since there is no solar heating in this part of the atmosphere, the actual temperature is determined by the balance between dynamical heating and IR cooling, the latter being predominantly due to the 15-μm band of CO_2. What sorts of errors might there be in this quantity?

The CO_2 transmittances used in these calculations are those described in Fels and Schwarzkopf (1981) and are based on the spectroscopic data of the Air Force Geophysical Laboratory (AFGL) compilation (Rothman, 1981). We took some care to calibrate our synthetic spectra by careful comparison with the laboratory data of Gryvnak and his co-workers (1976; Gryvnak and

Burch, 1978), but unfortunately the absorber amounts, temperatures, and pressures in the laboratory studies were not appropriate to the range of these parameters needed in the stratospheric polar night. On the other hand, cooling rates between 40 and 65 km depend on only two distributions: that of the line intensities S_i and of $S_i\alpha_i$, the product of the line intensities and the Lorentz width. In an important series of papers, Planet and his collaborators (1978; Planet and Tettemer, 1979) have measured the intensities and widths of selected CO_2 lines by using a tunable laser diode. They find values of S_i and α_i that differ from those used in the AFGL compilation by on the order of 7%. It is worth noting, however, that the discrepancies in the product $S_i\alpha_i$ are much less—about 2%. While these authors also find that the temperature variation of line width is stronger than that based on simple kinetic theory, this should not affect the transmittances by more than 10%.

It is therefore difficult to imagine that the CO_2 cooling rate calculations could be in error by more than 10–20%. Suppose, however, for the sake of argument that the errors were as large as 50%—how would this affect things? Such errors would be equivalent to a corresponding change in the CO_2 mixing ratio, and on the basis of the calculations described in Fels *et al.* (1980), the temperatures calculated at 50 km should change by 10 to 20°.

Is it possible that there are undetected radiative constituents that we have failed to include? Even were this to be the case, it could only make the situation worse at 50 km, since this would lead to even stronger cooling.

It is therefore quite clear that the polar night stratosphere must be very far from its radiatively controlled state. An appropriate measure of this is the dynamical heating required to account for the observed thermal structure. The first careful calculation of this quantity was carried out by Murgatroyd and Goody in 1958 and gave a value of $6-8°$ day^{-1} at the polar night stratopause. Similar calculations were later performed by London (1980), by Leovy and Wehrbein (1982), and Hamilton (1983). To a remarkable extent, these confirm the results found by Murgatroyd and Goody.

It is perhaps surprising, in light of the robustness of this result, that some mechanistic models have used radiative formulations that yield equilibrium temperatures for the polar night stratosphere much warmer than those shown earlier. As a result, these models give fairly realistic zonal wind and temperature profiles even though their dynamical heating is too small. The reason for this seems to be related to the use of a cooling formulation that is linear in T rather than in the Planck function and that, in addition, neglects the temperature dependence of line intensities.

The mechanism by which the middle and upper winter stratosphere is dynamically heated has not been fully resolved. The obvious candidates are the effects of planetary-scale waves, on the one hand, and those due to small-scale disturbances such as gravity waves, which are not resolved on synoptic maps, on the other hand. Hamilton (1983) has made an interesting attempt to diagnose the effects of planetary-scale waves on the winter stratospheric circulation. He finds that, at 1 mb and below, the Eliasson–Palm flux divergence due to the eddies resolved by the National Meteorological Center (NMC) weekly analysis is able to account for the radiative deficit but that, at 0.4 mb, this is not true. His results are therefore consistent with the theoretical ideas of Lindzen (1981) and Holton (1982), who suggest that the EP flux divergence due to gravity waves becomes important just above the stratopause.

Against this background, we may now examine the behavior of several GCMs in simulating the winter stratosphere. To my knowledge, there are only two such models that extend from the ground to the stratopause or above and for which there are published climatologies: those constructed by Mahlman and his collaborators at the Geophysical Fluid Dynamics Laboratory (GFDL) and that of Hansen and co-workers at the Goddard Institute for Space Studies (GISS) in New York. We shall come to these presently. There are, however, several other models that have one or more levels in the lower stratosphere: the Zodiac model of Manabe and Mahlman (1976), the M30 9-layer spectral model discussed by Manabe *et al.* (1979), the National Center for Atmospheric Research (NCAR) 12-layer model of Kasahara *et al.*, and the NCAR 9-layer Community Climate Model (CCM) are examples. It is instructive to examine these before going on to truly stratospheric models.

Even a cursory examination of Figs. 3.2 and 3.3 of Manabe and Mahlman (1976) shows the GCM temperatures to be much too "radiative," i.e., too cold in the polar night stratosphere. The model is too cold by 20 to 25° at 38 mb near the pole, for example. In the same region, the model dynamical heating is only a few tenths of a degree per day.

An interesting comparison can be made with the results from a seasonal simulation using an M30 *spectral* model with similar vertical resolution and radiative characteristics described by Manabe *et al.* (1979). They find that the model polar night temperature at 25 mb is close to 210°, in good agreement with observations. Since the radiative formulation used in both models is virtually identical, the comparison suggests that it is the model dynamics that are of decisive importance here.

Further evidence comes from recent experiments performed by Ramanathan and his co-workers at the NCAR (Ramanathan *et al.,* 1983; Pitcher *et al.,* 1983; Boville, 1984). In an interesting experiment using the CCM, they showed that the model generated a realistic polar night simulation if a sound radiative formulation was used. This radiation package was then degraded by making several changes, whose effect was twofold: the radiative equilibrium zonal wind was strengthened, primarily by altering the short-wave heating formulation, and the radiative relaxation time was shortened by ignoring the temperature dependence of the CO_2 hot bands. The resulting GCM simulation showed a dramatically colder polar night stratosphere — one whose temperature was not far from that of Manabe and Mahlman. The authors correctly emphasize the important difference between the nature of the thermal balance in the two cases: in the original run, there is about twice as much ($0.6°$ day^{-1}) dynamical heating as in the degraded case.

One must be careful in drawing general conclusions from this experiment. It is certainly true, as the authors state, that the stratospheric simulation is very sensitive to the radiative formulation used. However, Boville (1984) has shown that the CCM is also sensitive to the precise manner in which horizontal viscosity is incorporated in the model stratosphere, while D. L. Williamson (private communication, 1984) has found that the vertical difference scheme used is important. The CCM polar night stratosphere, in short, is apparently a very delicately poised state. Indeed, when a similar series of experiments used the NCAR 12-layer grid-point model, the use of the control radiation package yielded a polar night that was much too radiative.

It is of some interest to note the points of similarity and the differences between the "control" radiative transfer scheme used in the NCAR experiments and that used in the GFDL models described earlier. Careful comparisons carried out several years ago show that the CO_2 cooling rate formulations give results that agree to better than 10% in the stratosphere. This is much less than the difference of $0.3°$ day^{-1} between the control and degraded radiation runs discussed by Ramanathan *et al.* The NCAR scheme gives stratospheric cooling rates from water that are about $0.15°$ day^{-1} less than those for the GFDL models, primarily due to the low mixing ratio that was assumed. Finally, the NCAR scheme generates a somewhat smaller equator-to-polar short-wave heating gradient than does the GFDL scheme. Thus, were the CCM IR algorithm to be used in any of the GFDL models, it is unlikely that the polar temperature at 30 km would change by more than $10°$.

On the basis of both the GFDL and NCAR experience, therefore, it seems clear that the polar night temperature is very sensitive to the way in which the model dynamics is formulated. There is fragmentary evidence that suggests that spectral models are better able to simulate the EP flux divergence due to the large-scale eddies, perhaps due to the manner in which mechanical dissipation is included. The work of Ramanathan and his collaborators has also shown that in the CCM, at least, if the radiative "spring" pulling the model back toward radiative equilibrium is too strong, there will be a dramatic reduction in the amount of dynamical heating in the polar stratosphere. If this is not just an artifact of the particular model used but is characteristic of the real atmosphere, this result may have intriguing implications for the response of the stratosphere to increased CO_2 levels. We shall return to this question later.

The GFDL SKYHI GCM has 40 vertical levels and extends from the ground to 80 km. A brief description of the model is given in Fels et al. (1980), and discussions of more recent model results may be found in Andrews et al. (1983), Mahlman and Umscheid (1984), and Hayashi et al. (1984). The results described by Fels et al. are of only peripheral relevance to our present discussion, since the model they used employed annual-average radiation and in addition had extremely course ($\sim 9°$) horizontal resolution. Of much greater interest are the medium resolution ($\sim 5°$) seasonal experiments described by Mahlman and Umscheid.

A major event in this experiment was the occurrence of a dramatic warming episode in the mesosphere and upper stratosphere early in February. This is encouraging and represents a considerable achievement. We shall be perversely pessimistic to begin with, however, and concentrate on the prewarming climatology of the model, as exemplified in the January mean state. In so doing, we must recognize that the climatology of the real atmosphere includes such warming episodes, so that we are perhaps being somewhat harsh on the model.

The results are, at first blush, quite discouraging. The lower stratosphere is only slightly warmer than in the 1976 results of Manabe and Mahlman, and this "cold bias" becomes more pronounced as we continue upward; by the time 1 mb is reached, the model is too cold by about 60° at 85°N! What little dynamical heating there is (about 1° day^{-1}) has, indeed, raised the temperature about 30° above its radiative value, but this is not terribly impressive. Although misplaced by almost 20 km, the model does display a modest stratopause at 70 km; at this height, the GCM temperatures are some 55° above the purely radiative value.

In looking for possible causes of this major failure, it is useful to examine the effect of horizontal model resolution on the simulation. In this connection, we are fortunate that three separate and comparable seasonal runs have been performed, with horizontal resolution of about 9° (coarse), 5° (medium), and 3° (high). They are referred to as the N10, N18, and N30, respectively.

It is important to understand that these models all contain a scale-selective horizontal dissipation, which acts to prevent the accumulation of energy at the smallest resolved scale. As the model resolution is increased, the magnitude of the dissipation is correspondingly decreased. This has the effect of making the high-resolution model much less viscous at a given horizontal scale than that with low resolution.

In Fig. 2 we show the polar-night vertical temperature profiles for each of the three models. Figure 2a represents the December mean temperature at

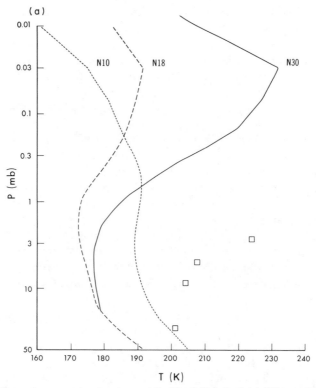

FIG. 2. (a) December mean temperatures at the North Pole in three different GFDL GCMs. Also shown are several observed values: squares are from Hamilton (1982). (b) As in (a), but for 62°N. The curve marked "radiative" is based on Eq. (2.1). (c) As in (a), but for January.

the polarmost point for each model, and Fig. 2b is the same thing at 62°N. Figure 2c is the polar point but for January.

The December profiles show a heartening improvement in the mesospheric temperatures as the resolution is increased. This is true at both the polar point above 62 km and at 62°N through the entire mesosphere and upper stratosphere. The improvement corresponds directly to an increase in the EP flux convergence that acts to decelerate the westerly jet. The dynamical heating produced by this effect in the N30 mesosphere is substantial — on the order of 15° day^{-1} at 70 km. As we descend, however, the picture deteriorates: dramatically at the pole and less so at 62°N. At the polar stratopause, even the high-resolution model yields only ~1° day^{-1} dynamical heating, in contrast with the 8° day^{-1} required by observations. Things are less bad at 62°N, where the calculated stratopause heating rates are 3–4°

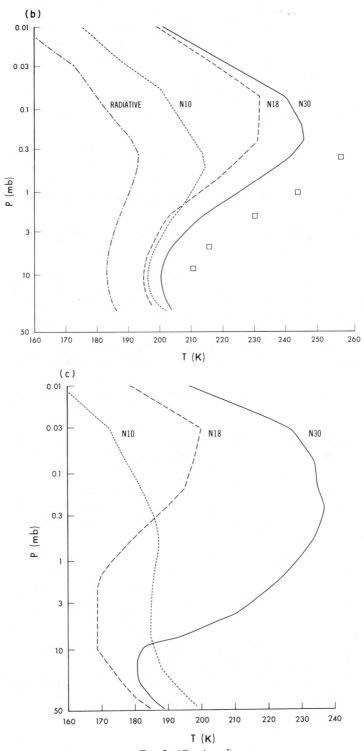

FIG. 2. *(Continued)*

day^{-1}. By the time the middle stratosphere is reached, however, the N18 and N30 are both decisively too cold. At 10 mb, for example, the observed temperature is 220°, and N30 gives only 200°.

We may summarize the situation for December, then, as follows:

(1) The winter mesopause improves with increasing resolution and is, for the N30 at least, approaching the observed temperature.

(2) The winter upper stratosphere remains too radiative at the pole but has improved substantially at 62°N.

(3) The entire winter lower and middle stratosphere is still much too cold; there has been only marginal improvement at 10 mb and 62°N and indeed marked deterioration at the pole.

The picture for January is somewhat more hopeful. The low-resolution results are about the same as those for December, and the medium-resolution mesosphere is somewhat warmer than the December case, while the middle and lower stratosphere is cooler. In this connection, we should note that, on the basis of radiation alone, the January middle atmosphere should be colder than that in December, so that both the low- and medium-resolution models are simply mimicking the radiative evolution in what is by now a depressingly familiar fashion. The high-resolution model, on the other hand, displays a dramatically warmer lower mesosphere and upper stratosphere; taken at face value, this is the first time that the model has come even close to a reasonable-looking zonal-mean temperature structure in this part of the atmosphere. Although there has been detectable improvement even at 10 mb, the lower stratosphere remains much too cold.

The great improvement in the January simulation is due largely to the occurrence of a strong warming event that takes place in the middle of the month and is even more dramatic than the one described by Mahlman and Umscheid. It is curious, and perhaps completely coincidental, that when the model is integrated for another full year beyond that described earlier, there takes place a major winter warming event that begins at about the same time as that in the previous year.

It seems that these simulations, even with their obvious shortcomings, hint at an interesting radiative-wave dynamical mechanism that may be at work in the real atmosphere. This relates to the possible existence of a certain critical amplitude for planetary waves, below which they become ineffective at heating the winter pole. In its original form, the idea is due to J. D. Mahlman.

We begin by noting that the radiative thermal structure near the pole is uniformly very cold until the edge of the polar night is reached, at which point there is a very sudden increase in temperature. If we now imagine the trajectory of a parcel of air in the presence of a small-amplitude planetary wave, it is clear that there exists a region in which the parcels never emerge from the polar night and therefore never experience solar heating. There are other trajectories, however, that do cross the terminator and hence transport heat very effectively. As a result, for waves of sufficiently small amplitude, there will be no dynamical heating near the pole but a sizable amount near the terminator. This is similar to what is observed in the model simulations and suggests that there, at least, the small-amplitude approximation is qualitatively correct.

As the wave amplitude increases, however, there eventually comes a point at which even those streamlines that pass over the pole cross the terminator and sample the portion of the atmosphere in direct sunlight. At this point, all portions of the polar cap are subject to dynamical heating. A very rough criterion for the critical wave amplitude is that the center of the perturbed polar vortex be displaced from the pole by something on the order of half the distance between the pole and the terminator—i.e., that it lie equatorward of about 80° in December and January.

It is important to understand that this process does not exist in the context of the usual small-amplitude theory. In such calculations, $\overline{v'T'}$ at some latitude θ_0 will involve $(dT^0/d\theta)(\theta_0)$, the temperature gradient *at that* latitude, since the amplitude of the wave is infinitesimal. If, however, the amplitude is such that the trajectories pass through regions in which $dT^0/d\theta$ is very different from $(dT^0/d\theta)(\theta_0)$, small-amplitude theory is not valid.

When we examine the climatology of planetary waves at 10 mb [cf., for example, the compilation of Labitzke (1972)], we find that their trajectory displacements are such as to put them in the large-amplitude regime. In the model simulations, on the other hand, the planetary waves are smaller than observed at 10 mb, even in the N30 case, and, as has already been stated, the models therefore lie in the small-amplitude range.

We should note that, even in the standard small-amplitude theory, the EP flux divergence depends strongly on the wave amplitude, so that in practice there may not exist as sharp a distinction between small- and large-amplitude waves as suggested earlier. Moreover, the more successful the waves are in smoothing out the sharp radiative terminator, the more applicable small-amplitude theory becomes.

The size of the trajectory displacement is influenced by the structure of the zonal wind U in two separate ways—one kinematic and one dynamical. For a wave of given geopotential amplitude Φ', the resulting meridional particle displacement is inversely proportional to U. Indeed, the strength of the planetary waves as simulated by the N30 model is approximately correct when measured by Φ' (D. S. Graves, private communication, 1984), and the too-zonal trajectories are therefore largely due to the excessive size of U. In addition to the above, Φ' itself is influenced by the mean zonal wind as first recognized by Charney and Drazin (1961). In general, this dynamical effect acts to increase the size of Φ' as U is reduced. Both mechanisms act in concert, therefore, to increase the zonal asymmetry of particle trajectories as the polar night temperature rises. If, as we have suggested, the size of the trajectory displacement is indeed important, there exists the potential for a strong amplification of any mechanism that acts to warm the polar night or equivalently to retard the polar-night jet.

The preceding discussion is, of course, no more than a hypothesis at this point, but it does seem to account for the overall features observed in the various experiments. In addition, it suggests that models that are only modestly different in the strength of their planetary waves (as measured by the displacement of trajectories) may differ strongly in their polar thermal structure.

Additional support for this idea comes from a simulation carried out with the 21-layer GISS model described by Rind *et al.* (1984). This GCM displays a relatively realistic January polar temperature structure, with T at 50 km of about 250°. Several points are relevant here: (1) there is an explicit drag formulation in the mesospheric layers that acts to reduce the zonal wind somewhat, even at 50 km; (2) the amplitude of the wave-number-one planetary wave at this height is about two geopotential kilometers, which is larger than that observed. Because the zonal wind is much smaller than in the GFDL models and the planetary wave is stronger, the displaced polar vortex is centered 10 to 15° off the pole, so that the flow is in what we have called the large-amplitude regime.

One of the most interesting aspects of the wave-heating mechanism is the strong dependence of the wave field on the structure of U. The fact that the N30 model undergoes warming episodes on the same date in two successive years may be coincidence, of course. It is also possible that it is a manifestation of the overly strong radiative control of the polar temperature.

In the real atmosphere, there is evidence that suggests that the occurrence of warmings depends on the existence of a suitably "preconditioned" structure — one in which vertical propagation of planetary waves near the pole is allowed (McIntyre, 1982). This favorable structure is thought to be the result of previously occurring wave activity in the form of "minor warmings." In the model simulation, on the other hand, the strong radiative control of the polar-night jet means that the ability of the stratosphere to propagate waves should be tightly locked to the annual cycle. It is thus not surprising should the occurrence of warmings in the model be more regular than in the atmosphere.

3. RADIATIVE DAMPING OF WAVES IN THE MIDDLE ATMOSPHERE

The trivial observation that warm air masses radiate more strongly than do cooler ones explains the mechanism by which atmospheric waves are damped radiatively, for there is associated with many (but not all) such disturbances a perturbation T' of the basic state temperature. This perturbation acts as a restoring force, and its reduction by radiation must act to damp the underlying wave. It is evident, therefore, that the importance of radiative dissipation must depend on the structure of the disturbance. Those whose dynamics depends only weakly on temperature perturbations (such as external Rossby waves) will be less susceptible to damping than will those for which bouyancy is essential (such as internal gravity waves).

A convenient measure of the effect of damping is the vertical decay length D, the e-folding distance due to radiation. One can show that for both gravity and Rossby waves,

$$D^{-1} = n_0/2\omega^*\tau_r \qquad (3.1)$$

Here, n_0 is the vertical wave number for the wave in the absence of damping, ω^* the local Doppler-shifted frequency, and τ_r the radiative damping time. Other things being equal, waves with large vertical wavelengths will be less strongly damped than those with shorter wavelengths.

As has already been pointed out, this damping process can have important effects on the zonal-mean circulation, since it is precisely the irreversible action of various dissipative mechanisms that lead to nonzero EP flux divergences. In recent years, therefore, interest in damped waves has been largely focused on their ability to drive zonal-mean flows. In the preceding section, we were primarily concerned with the radiative zonal state itself and paid less attention to the manner in which radiative processes affect the waves; in what follows, we shall look at this second role in more detail.

We have already discussed the part played by large-scale planetary waves in the general circulation, and we now recognize that by virtue of their large vertical wavelength, radiation does not damp them effectively. There are, however, several other interesting examples of wave–mean-flow interactions in which radiative processes may be important. Among these are the Holton–Lindzen (1972) theory of the tropical quasi-biennial oscillation (QBO) and the possible role of radiatively damped gravity waves in the general circulation of the mesosphere.

A brief consideration of either of these two problems shows that radiative wave–dynamical interactions differ from those discussed earlier in two important ways: the process is basically a linear one, and nonlocal effects can be very important. Linearity is a simple consequence of the smallness of most waves when measured by $\Delta T/T_0$, the fractional temperature perturbation. Nonlocality is more complicated and stems ultimately from the great range of monochromatic absorptivities present in the CO_2 spectrum. As a result, the exchange of photons between layers (which is the essence of radiative damping) can take place on many different length scales. In relatively transparent portions of the spectrum, distant layers can communicate radiatively, while, in the opaque portions, it is the local thermal gradients that are important.

The ideas of linearity and nonlocality are epitomized in the Curtis matrix (Curtis, 1956). In this formulation, one considers a discrete number of atmospheric layers (say, n of them), labeled by the index i. Let T_i^0 be some reference temperature profile, Q_i^0 the IR cooling rate associated with it, and $\Delta T_i \ll T_i^0$ the deviation of the true temperature from the reference state. We may then write the most general linear relationship between ΔT_i and Q_i as

$$Q_i = Q_i^0 + \sum_j M_{ij} \Delta T_j \qquad (3.2)$$

The Curtis matrix is just **M**. Instructive tables for **M** for CO_2 cooling have been given by Leovy and Wehrbein (1982).*

Even a cursory examination of the structure of **M** shows that while off-diagonal terms are important, their size falls off rapidly away from the main diagonal. This implies that if ΔT_j is in some loose sense slowly varying, it can be brought outside the summation and replaced by its value at level i:

$$Q_i - Q_i^0 = \Delta T_i \sum_j M_{ij} \qquad (3.3)$$

We notice that we are in effect assuming that the cooling rate perturbation at each level i can be calculated as though it were due to a *uniform* perturbation whose size is T_i. The approximation is local in the sense that the perturbation cooling at each level depends only on the temperature perturbation at that point.

The quantity $\tau_i^{-1}(\infty) = \Sigma_j M_{ij}$ evidently represents the decay time for vertical disturbances of very long scale; it is called the Newtonian damping rate and was first calculated in a form that was both accurate and practically useful in the well-known 1973 paper of Dickinson.

It is not surprising that waves begin to suffer important nonlocal radiative effects when their vertical wavelength λ_v becomes smaller than $2\pi \times$ the scale height H (Fels, 1982). Since the gross thermal structure of the middle atmosphere has a "half-wavelength" of about 60 km, it is often unnecessary

---

* There are some important errors in the tabulated values; these are referred to in Leovy (1984).

to consider nonlocal effects in computations of the zonal mean radiative structure.

Many important waves are "evanescent," or vertically trapped — most atmospheric normal modes are of this type. These disturbances are associated with thermal perturbations that either decay or grow with height less rapidly than $\exp(z/2H)$. For such waves, too, explicit calculations show that little error is committed by using the Newtonian damping rate.

The situation is quite different, however, for propagating waves. These have wavelengths ranging from > 50 km for large-scale planetary waves to < 1 km for internal gravity waves. For all of these, there are dynamically significant departures from the Newtonian results, and these are always such as to increase the damping rate.

There is a considerable literature dealing with the radiative damping of sinusoidal disturbances, and in the past several years, there have appeared a number of papers that give numerical results or parameterizations of particular use to dynamicists. These are Fels (1982, 1984), Shevd and Utyakovskiy (1983), Schoeberl et al. (1983), and Apruzese and Strobel (1984). All of these works are in good agreement, save that of Schoeberl et al., which gives radiative damping rates that are much too large for disturbances whose vertical wavelength is < 6 km.

Two important points emerge from these calculations:

(1) The dependence of damping times τ_r on the vertical wavelength is typically of the form $C\lambda_v^\beta$, with β between $\frac{1}{2}$ and 1. This is weaker than the λ_v^{+2} dependence due to diffusion, so that for small scales, radiation is of secondary importance.

(2) The damping rate depends strongly on the local reference temperature T^0, owing both to the variation of line intensities with temperature, and to the temperature dependence of the Planck function. Typically, damping rates at 300° are 2–3 times as large as those at 200° for the same pressure and vertical wavelength (Fels et al., 1980; Ramanathan et al., 1983).

One may legitimately ask whether scale-dependent radiative damping is of any dynamical importance, and in this connection, the two examples cited earlier are of interest.

In the original (1972) Holton–Lindzen (HL) model of the QBO, the entire EP flux divergence is due to the radiative damping of the Kelvin and mixed Rossby-gravity waves that propagate into the stratosphere. When first formulated, the dissipation used was based on so-called "photochemically accelerated" damping rates (Blake and Lindzen, 1973) that were greater than those of Dickinson by a factor of 2 to 4. The results from the dynamical model were very satisfactory; not only was the time evolution of the QBO well simulated, but so also was the vertical extent of the oscillation, which is observed to decay rapidly above 40 km.

It has become clear in the past decade, however, that the photochemical acceleration calculated by Blake and Lindzen is erroneously large and that for waves of large vertical scale the results of Dickinson are essentially correct (Hartmann, 1978; Strobel, 1979). Unfortunately, when the smaller damping rates are used in the dynamical model, the weaker dissipation allows the QBO to extend to 50 km (Hamilton, 1981).

One must recognize, however, that the waves involved have scales of less than 10 km, so that nonlocal radiative effects might be important. Indeed, when Hamilton used the parameterization of Fels (1982), the stronger damping due to scale dependence led to a QBO that did not extend above 40 km, just as in the original HL paper. The reason for this lies in the fortuitous agreement between the *non*-scale-dependent damping rates *with* photochemical acceleration (now believed to be wrong) and the relevant scale-dependent damping rates *without* photochemical acceleration. This is shown quite clearly in Fig. 3.

We have already suggested that internal gravity waves are particularly vulnerable to radiative damping, and this can have interesting consequences in the mesosphere, where such waves are believed to provide an important component of the EP flux divergence (Lindzen, 1981). This comes about not through the usual dissipative process, but by virtue of the growth of the waves to such a large amplitude that they become gravitationally unstable and break, much as do ocean waves on a beach. It is now thought that much of the zonal momentum sink required in the mesosphere is due to this process.

Underlying this mechanism is the growth of the wave with height due to the decrease in atmospheric density. This leads to an exponential increase in the temperature perturbation, T', with a scale height of $2H$—twice that for the mean-state pressure. It has been observed by Schoeberl et al. (1983), however, that since radiative processes act to cause such waves to decay, whether or not they ultimately break depends on whether the quantity $Hn_0/Uk\tau_r$ is greater or less than 1; i.e., whether

$$\frac{HN}{U^2\tau_r} \frac{\lambda_x}{2\pi} \left(\frac{\lambda_x^2}{\lambda_y^2} + 1\right)^{1/2} > 1 \tag{3.4}$$

Unfortunately, these authors used an incorrect parameterization for τ_r, so that their estimates for the critical values of n must be re-examined. As they correctly recognized, however, the dominant functional dependence in Eq. (3.4) comes from the n term, and the fact that their radiative parameterization is in error is not of great importance. Indeed, one finds that for $\lambda_x = \lambda_y = 100$ km, all waves with $|U - c| < 7$ m s^{-1} will decay, and for 1000 km, the critical value is 16 m s^{-1}. These are smaller than the values of 13 and

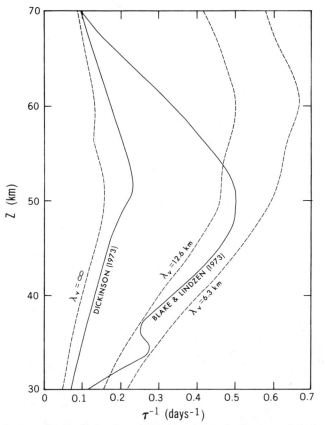

FIG. 3. Scale-dependent radiative damping rates compared with the scale-independent results from Dickinson (1973) and the photochemical calculations of Blake and Lindzen (1973). [From Fels (1982). Reproduced with permission from *Journal of the Atmospheric Sciences*, a publication of the American Meteorological Society.]

22 m s^{-1} found by Schoeberl *et al.* but do not obviate their conclusions. This does not mean, however, that one can be cavalier with the radiative parameterization chosen, since the height at which a given wave breaks can be very sensitive to the damping (Fels, 1984).

In summary, then, radiative damping is of secondary importance for most planetary waves, basically because of their very large vertical scale. This slow vertical variation has the further consequence that the Newtonian cooling approximation can be used without great error. For internal waves, and many of their equatorial cousins, however, an accurate representation of τ_r is important; for such disturbances, radiative damping can be the dominant dissipative process, and their wavelengths are such that the local approximation is very poor.

Before leaving this topic, we return briefly to our original theme, the successes and failures of GCMs in simulating the middle atmosphere. In particular, we may ask whether the present level of vertical resolution — typically 2 km at the smallest — introduces serious distortion of the radiative damping process.

The answer depends to some extent on the details of the radiative model and they way in which temperature is assumed to vary between levels. Nonetheless, it is reasonable to identify an effective maximum vertical wave number n as $2\pi/2\Delta z \sim 1.5$ km^{-1}. Damping times at this vertical scale are typically on the order of four to six times those for infinite wavelength, so that any well-constructed radiation algorithm will yield much greater damping of gravity and equatorial waves than would a scheme based on Newtonian cooling. It is also clear that the gain in radiative dissipation rate for increased vertical resolution beyond this will be relatively modest — doubling of n only increases τ_r by $\sim 40\%$ in this range. For those nonradiative processes that are diffusive, on the other hand, a decrease of Δz will be much more important. We expect, therefore, that, as is apparently the case in the real atmosphere, processes other than radiative ones will control the decay of waves of very short vertical scale (Fels, 1984).

Although a further increase in vertical resolution should be of little importance radiatively, it is curious that the same is not true for horizontal resolution. This follows directly from the result quoted previously, that waves of a given $|U - c|$ will only grow with height if λ_x is sufficiently small. For the N10, N18, and N30 models discussed in the preceding section, $\lambda_x = 2000$, 1200, and 650 km, respectively. On this basis, waves will only grow if

$$|U - c| > 30 \text{ m s}^{-1} \text{ in the N10 model}$$
$$> 18 \text{ m s}^{-1} \text{ in the N18 model}$$
$$> 12 \text{ m s}^{-1} \text{ in the N30 model}$$

Evidently, then, as we increase the horizontal resolution, we introduce more waves that can grow and therefore break in the upper part of the model. This might account for the dramatic improvement of winter mesospheric temperatures that we have commented on previously.

4. A FINAL SPECULATION

An essay of this sort can properly have no conclusion, but it is perhaps permissible to end by speculating once more — this time on a subject of more than scientific interest: the response of the middle atmosphere to a large increase in carbon dioxide. This is, of course, a question par excellence of radiative dynamical interaction. It is a problem whose solution, we think, may depend critically on our ability to simulate successfully the middle atmosphere with large-scale numerical models.

Joseph Smagorinsky has been closely identified with this endeavor for many years. The examination of this problem has been one of the strongest and best-known efforts of the laboratory that he founded. It is therefore appropriate (and perhaps inevitable) that we end with some remarks about this question.

The chief points have all been made already: that the polar-night strato-sphere is driven far from radiative equilibrium by the action of waves and that both the equilibrium state and the radiative restoring force can be reliably calculated. In terms of our original paradigm,

$$\frac{\partial}{\partial p} \frac{\epsilon}{\tau_r} \frac{\partial}{\partial p} (U - U_r) = \frac{\partial^2}{\partial y^2} (\nabla \cdot \mathbf{F}) \tag{4.1}$$

We have also seen evidence that the balance represented by the preceding equation is a precarious one, largely because of the great sensitivity of $\nabla \cdot \mathbf{F}$ to U itself—for several distinct reasons, decreasing U leads to an increase in $\nabla \cdot \mathbf{F}$. Indeed, the very failure of the GFDL models to reproduce the ob-served polar temperatures suggests that the balance is not robust.

How, then, might the temperature change if the carbon dioxide loading were to increase by a factor of 2? It is relatively easy to ascertain what the response of U_r and τ_r will be, for these are purely radiative quantities.

The polar-night radiative temperature will not change by very much, and in the sunlit regions it can be expected to drop by up to 12° (Fels et al., 1980). Since U_r depends on the horizontal gradient of the radiative temperature, we expect a decrease in the strength of the radiative polar-night jet of 10 to 20%. What about τ_r? Under a doubling of CO_2, this will decrease by about 23%; i.e., the radiative spring will become stronger. The response of $\nabla \cdot \mathbf{F}$ to the increase in CO_2, even holding other factors constant, is not obvious, but if $\nabla \cdot \mathbf{F}$ is largely due to planetary waves, the role played by radiation should be secondary. It is not unreasonable, then, to think in terms of a picture in which the dominant response of the stratosphere lies in a decrease in τ_r. Other things being equal then, $|U - U_r|$ should decrease by $\sim 20\%$; this would be the response predicted by assuming that the wave activity is not signifi-cantly altered by the change in U and is similar to the "fixed dynamical heating" response discussed by Fels et al. (1980).

It is not impossible, however, to imagine that the real atmosphere is as delicately poised as are some of the models and that the initial increase in U will be sufficient to lead to a large decrease in wave amplitude, with a concomitant further increase in U. In this scenario, the middle atmosphere would flip over into a state qualitatively similar to that of the at present too-radiative GFDL models! This new state would have a far colder polar vortex and a much more vigorous polar-night jet than the purely radiative response suggests. Should this rather unlikely eventuality occur, it would indeed be an interesting radiative dynamical interaction.

ACKNOWLEDGMENTS

I have profited greatly from discussions with Drs. I. Held, J. Mahlman, and S. Manabe, all of whom made useful comments on an earlier version of this essay. They should not be held responsible for the speculations, however, which are my own. I would also like to thank M. D. Schwarzkopf, L. Umscheid, and D. Graves for their help with various aspects of this work.

REFERENCES

Andrews, D. G., Mahlman, J. D., and Sinclair, R. W. (1983). Eliasson-Palm diagnostics of wave-mean flow interaction in the GFDL "SKYHI" general circulation model. *J. Atmos. Sci.* **40**, 2768–2784.

Apruzese, J. P., and Strobel, D. F. (1984). Radiative relaxation rates for individual CO_2 lines in the upper stratosphere and lower mesosphere. *JGR, J. Geophys. Res.* **89**, 7187–7194.

Blake, D., and Lindzen, R. S. (1973). The effect of photochemical equilibria and cooling rates in the stratosphere. *Mon. Weather Rev.* **101**, 783–802.

Boville, B. A. (1984). The influence of the polar night jet on the tropospheric circulation. *J. Atmos. Sci.* **41**, 1132–1142.

Charney, J. G., and Drazin, P. G. (1961). Propagation of planetary-scale disturbances from the lower into the upper atmosphere. *J. Geophys. Res.* **66**, 83–109.

COSPAR (1972). "COSPAR International Reference Atmosphere." Akademie-Verlag, Berlin.

Curtis, A. R. (1956). The computation of radiative heating rates in the atmosphere. *Proc. R. Soc. London, Ser. A* **236**, 156–159.

Dickinson, R. E. (1973). Method of parameterization for infrared cooling between the altitudes of 30 and 70 kilometers. *JGR, J. Geophys. Res.* **78**, 4451–4457.

Fels, S. B. (1982). A parameterization of scale-dependent radiative damping rates in the middle atmosphere. *J. Atmos. Sci.* **39**, 1141–1152.

Fels, S. B. (1984). The radiative damping of short vertical scale waves in the mesosphere. *J. Atmos. Sci.* **41**, 1755–1764.

Fels, S. B., and Schwarzkopf, M. D. (1981). An efficient, accurate algorithm for calculating CO_2 15 μm band cooling rates. *JGR, J. Geophys. Res.* **86**, 1205–1232.

Fels, S. B., Mahlman, J. D., Schwarzkopf, M. D., and Sinclair, R. W. (1980). Stratospheric sensitivity to perturbations in ozone and carbon dioxide: Radiative and dynamical response. *J. Atmos. Sci.* **37**, 2266–2297.

Gryvnak, D. A., and Burch, D. E. (1978). "Infrared Absorption by CO_2 and H_2O," AFGL Tech. Rep. AFGL-TR-78-0154. Air Force Geophys. Lab., Hanscom AFB, Bedford, Massachusetts.

Gryvnak, D. A., Burch, D. E., Alt, R. L., and Zgonc, D. K. (1976). "Infrared Absorption by CH_4, H_2O, and CO_2," AFGL Tech. Rep. AFGL-TR-76-0276. Air Force Geophys. Lab., Hanscom AFB, Bedford, Massachusetts.

Hamilton, K. P. (1981). The vertical structure of the Quasi-biennial oscillation: Observations and theory. *Atmos.-Ocean* **19**, 236–250.

Hamilton, K. P. (1982). "Stratospheric Circulation Statistics," NCAR Tech. Note TN-191-STR. National Center for Atmospheric Research, Boulder, Colorado.

Hamilton, K. P. (1983). Diagnostic study of the momentum balance of the northern hemisphere winter stratosphere. *Mon. Weather Rev.* **111**, 1434–1441.

Hartmann, D. L. (1978). A note concerning the effect of varying extinction on radiative-photochemical retardation. *J. Atmos. Sci.* **35**, 1125–1130.

Hayashi, Y., Golder, D. G., and Mahlman, J. D. (1984). Stratospheric and mesospheric Kelvin waves simulated by the GFDL "SKYHI" general circulation model. *J. Atmos. Sci.* **41**, 1971–1984.

Holton, J. R. (1982). The role of gravity wave induced drag and diffusion in the momentum budget of the mesosphere. *J. Atmos. Sci.* **39**, 791–799.

Holton, J. R., and Lindzen, R. S. (1972). An updated theory of the quasi-biennial oscillation of the tropical stratosphere. *J. Atmos. Sci.* **29**, 1076–1080.

Labitzke, K. (1972). "Climatology of the Stratosphere in the Northern Hemisphere, Part I. Meteorol. Abh., Vol. 100, No. 4. Verlag von Dietrich Reimer, Berlin.

Leovy, C. B. (1984). Infrared radiative exchange in the middle atmosphere in the 15 micron band of carbon dioxide. *In* "Dynamics of the Middle Atmosphere," pp. 355–366. Reidel Publ., Dordrect, Netherlands.

Leovy, C. B., and Wehrbein, W. M. (1982). An accurate radiative heating and cooling algorithm for use in a dynamical model of the middle atmosphere. *J. Atmos. Sci.* **39**, 1532–1544.

Lindzen, R. S. (1981). Turbulence and stress owing to gravity waves and tidal breakdown. *JGR, J. Geophys. Res.* **86**, 9707–9714.

London, J. (1980). Radiative energy sources and sinks in the stratosphere and mesosphere. *Proc. NATO Adv. Study Inst. on Atmos. Ozone: Its Variation and Human Influences* (A. Nicolet and A. C. Aiken, eds.) Rep. No. FAA-EE-80-20.

McIntyre, M. E. (1982). How well do we understand the dynamics of the stratosphere? *J. Meteorol. Soc. Jpn.* **60**, 37–65.

Mahlman, J. D., and Umscheid, L. J. (1984). Dynamics of the middle atmosphere: Successes and problems of the GFDL "SKYHI" general circulation model. *In* "Dynamics of the Middle Atmosphere," pp. 501–525. Reidel Publ., Dordrecht, Netherlands.

Manabe, S., and Mahlman, J. D. (1976). Simulation of the seasonal and interhemispheric variations in the stratospheric circulation. *J. Atmos. Sci.* **33**, 2185–2217.

Manabe, S., Hahn, D. G., and Holloway, J. L. (1979). Climate simulations with the GFDL spectral models of the atmosphere: Effects of spectral truncation. *GARP Publ. Ser.* **22**.

Murgatroyd, R. J., and Goody, R. M. (1958). Sources and sinks of radiative energy from 30 to 90 km. *Q. J. R. Meteorol. Soc.* **84**, 225–234.

Pitcher, E. J., Malone, R. C., Ramanathan, V., Blackmon, M. L., Puri, K., and Bourke, W. (1983). January and July simulations with a spectral general circulation model. *J. Atmos. Sci.* **40**, 580–604.

Planet, W. G., and Tettemer, G. L. (1979). Temperature-dependent intensities and widths of N_2-broadened CO_2 lines at 15 μm from tunable laser measurements. *J. Quant. Spectrosc. Radiat. Transfer* **22**, 345–354.

Planet, W. G., Tettemer, G. L., and Knoll, J. S. (1978). Temperature dependence of intensities and widths of N_2-broadened lines in the 15 μm CO_2 band from tunable laser measurements. *J. Quant. Spectrosc. Radiat. Transfer* **20**, 547–556.

Ramanathan, V., Pitcher, E. J., Malone, R. C., and Blackmon, M. L. (1983). The response of a spectral circulation model to improvements in radiative processes. *J. Atmos. Sci.* **40**, 605–630.

Rind, D., Suozzo, R., Lacis, A., Russell, G., and Hanson, J. (1984). 21 Layer troposphere-strato-sphere climate model. *J. Atmos. Sci.* (submitted for publication).

Rothman, L. S. (1981). AFGL atmospheric absorption line parameters compilation: 1980 version. *Appl. Opt.* **20,** 791–795.

Schoeberl, M. R., Strobel, D. F., and Apruzese, J. (1983). A numerical model of gravity wave breaking and stress in the mesosphere. *JGR, J. Geophys. Res.* **88,** 5249–5259.

Shevd, G. M., and Utyakovskiy, D. P. (1983). Radiative damping of temperature perturbations in the Earth's upper atmosphere, taking into account the breakdown of local thermody-namic equilibrium. *Izv., Acad. Sci. USSR, Atmos. Oceanic Phys. (Engl. Transl.)* **19,** 353–357.

MECHANISTIC INTERPRETATION OF STRATOSPHERIC TRACER TRANSPORT

J. D. Mahlman

Geophysical Fluid Dynamics Laboratory/NOAA
Princeton University
Princeton, New Jersey

1. Introduction

"The wind blows where it wills, and you hear the sound of it, but you do not know whence it comes or whither it goes" (John 3:8). This biblical quotation suggests that it has long been recognized that a stationary observer's perspective on transport has its limitations. It seems to imply that if one could "ride along" an air parcel, some of the mysteries might be clarified.

This paper is an update on this question as applied to the stratosphere. The approach will be personal in the sense that the material presented will represent some of my extended struggles to reduce our perspective on stratospheric transport to its simplest essence.

In 1970 I was invited by Joseph Smagorinsky to come to the Geophysical Fluid Dynamics Laboratory (GFDL) to work on the problem of trace constituent transport in the stratosphere. By that time Joe had already made a substantial commitment to this problem through support of the pioneering general circulation model (GCM) transport work of Hunt and Manabe (1968).

On my arrival at GFDL, I found Joe to be very interested in tracer behavior as a signature of important dynamical processes. He, of course, came from a rich background of Eulerian diagnostic experience as strongly evidenced in his classic paper (Smagorinsky, 1963). At that time, however, he was highly intrigued by the potential power of using Lagrangian diagnostic methods. On the other hand, I had been working mainly with Lagrangian methods and had been rather discouraged by the tendency of parcel trajectories to accumulate serious ambiguities after a few days or so.

301

After much discussion the two of us did agree that probably long-term numerical integrations are best accomplished by using Eulerian methods. This is especially so if one considers the problems of modeling dissipative processes, as well as chemical sources and sinks. However, we also agreed that, in a number of ways, "Lagrangian" can be a less ambiguous way of thinking about the mechanics of transport.

In the more than a decade that has elapsed since those philosophical conversations, Lagrangian perceptions have become almost fashionable. For example, the Lagrangian dynamical techniques that have produced important generalizations of the so-called nonacceleration theorems (Andrews and McIntyre, 1976, 1978a,b) have become accepted by a large community of stratospheric dynamicists. In fact, for a period it looked as though all things "Eulerian" were destined to have an "old-fashioned" label. However, as in most revolutions, the momentum carried too far. Soon it was realized (McIntyre, 1980) that Lagrangian diagnostic techniques were beset with serious technical difficulties when applied to nonidealized problems.

That realization led to a mild retreat into "Lagrangian insight"-oriented Eulerian diagnostic techniques. The most notable of these is the strong use of the Eliassen–Palm "transformed Eulerian" diagnostics introduced by Andrews and McIntyre (1976a) [e.g., Edmon et al. (1980), Dunkerton et al. (1981), Palmer (1981), O'Neill and Youngblut (1982), Andrews et al. (1983), and Mahlman and Umscheid (1984)].

It was soon realized in a variety of contexts that circumstances leading to "nonacceleration" conditions (e.g., nondissipative, steady waves) also imply a "nontransport" situation (Andrews and McIntyre, 1976b; Clark and Rogers, 1978; Wallace, 1978; Plumb, 1979; Holton, 1980; Mahlman et al., 1980; Matsuno, 1980; Pyle and Rogers, 1980). In this context, nontransport implies that stratospheric air particles are following closed orbits in their quasi-zonal motions. These realizations opened up a number of new approaches to understanding the mechanisms of stratospheric tracer transport. One approach [e.g., Holton (1980)] was to use the transformed Eulerian equations applied to the tracer zonal-mean balances. This has the advantage of retaining the practical applicability of Eulerian calculations, but it avoids the most obvious mistake of Eulerian diagnostics—the large cancellation between zonal-mean and eddy contributions to the zonal-average balances.

In a similar spirit, Mahlman et al. (1981, 1984a) and Tung (1982, 1984) argued that stratospheric tracer transport becomes conceptually simpler when viewed in isentropic (θ) coordinates. This is because the wave-induced indirect meridional circulation disappears in this framework (Mahlman et al., 1981). The only systematic meridional circulation in this system results from the presence of nonadiabatic motion across θ surfaces. The isentropic coordinate is sometimes called a quasi-Lagrangian one because the θ surfaces become material surfaces for adiabatic motions in a stratified atmosphere. Isentropic coordinates were used by Mahlman *et al.* (1980) to illustrate the character of "nontransport" under nonacceleration conditions, even at finite amplitude. The θ coordinate was used by Andrews (1983) to produce a finite-amplitude Eulerian generalization of earlier nonacceleration/nontransport theorems.

Mahlman *et al.* (1981, 1984a) argue that the annual average nonadiabatic motions in the stratosphere must ultimately result from the effects of dissipating disturbances propagating from the troposphere. They point out that meridional gradients of diabatic heating must lead to meridional gradients of a given trace constituent on θ surfaces. The presence of such tracer gradients implies that essentially adiabatic processes (e.g., wave transience or wave "breaking") can lead to irreversible mixing essentially along the isentropic surfaces. They contend, using conceptual arguments, that the equilibrium meridional slopes of stratospheric tracers must result from a competition between these two processes. The diabatic circulation acts to steepen the slope of tracer surfaces relative to θ surfaces, while wave-induced mixing acts to "flatten" the slope of tracer surfaces back to that of the θ surfaces. The calculations to be presented here can be considered as an examination of this conceptual perspective.

It is perhaps surprising that the use of isentropic coordinates is offered here as a way to enhance physical understanding of transport, since the advocacy of isentropic coordinates is more than a half-century old. Coordinate details were worked out by Rossby, Montgomery, Starr, and others in the 1930s and 1940s. As a practical tool, however, θ coordinates were abandoned until the mid-1950s when Reed (1955), Danielsen (1959), and Reed and Danielsen (1959) made systematic use of θ coordinates in their seminal studies of stratosphere – troposphere mass exchange. Later, detailed analyses were performed by Staley (1960, 1962), Reiter and Mahlman (1965), Danielsen *et al.* (1962), Mahlman (1965), and Danielsen (1968). The θ coordinate has also been used in numerical models by Danielsen and Diercks (1967), Eliassen and Raustein (1968), and Bleck (1973), with special emphasis on the upper troposphere frontogenesis problem.

The use of θ coordinates in stratospheric dynamics and transport has been much less common. Isentropic trajectories were computed by Berggren and Labitzke (1968) to aid in the construction of synoptic charts of ozone mixing ratio and by Mahlman (1970) to understand the polar heating mechanisms in a sudden stratospheric warming. Similar calculations were performed in a mechanistic model of sudden warming by Hsu (1980). McIntyre and Palmer (1983) have performed potential vorticity analyses on θ surfaces to provide a more physical view of stratospheric planetary wave dynamics, especially "saturation" and "wave-breaking" phenomena.

It is an easy prediction that such Lagrangian-oriented diagnostic perspectives will see increasing use in future stratospheric research. In that spirit the intent of this paper is to present some 3-D model calculations of transport that are designed to take advantage of the sharpened insights available from this quasi-Lagrangian isentropic coordinate perspective.

2. Model Description and Design of Experiments

We now begin to design a strategy to explore some of the quasi-Lagrangian, isentropic coordinate insights outlined in the preceding section. This will be accomplished by formulating two numerical experiments designed to simplify the analysis of tracer transport when viewed from the isentropic coordinate perspective.

The model to be used is the GFDL general circulation/tracer model described in detail by Mahlman and Moxim (1978) and as modified in Levy *et al.* (1982). The 3-D tracer model uses time-dependent input winds from the GFDL Zodiac GCM. This GCM is perhaps the most successful in GFDL history; certainly it is the most thoroughly analyzed and documented. Meteorological analyses of this GCM are available in a wide variety of publications [e.g., Hayashi (1974), Manabe *et al.* (1974), Hahn and Manabe (1975), Manabe and Holloway (1975), Manabe and Mahlman (1976), Hayashi and Golder (1977), Mahlman (1979), and Blackmon and Lau (1980)]. Also, the model has been applied to problems of meteorological network sampling (Oort, 1978) and total ozone network sampling (Moxim and Mahlman, 1980).

This general circulation/tracer model has been applied to a number of trace constituent transport and chemistry problems: stratospheric nuclear debris (Mahlman, 1973, 1976; Mahlman and Moxim, 1978), ozone (Mahlman *et al.*, 1980; Liu *et al.*, 1980; Levy *et al.*, 1984), nitrous oxide (Levy *et al.*, 1979, 1982), and reactive nitrogen (Levy *et al.*, 1980).

In this work, two new tracer experiments have been designed to illustrate the physical processes outlined in the preceding section. In both experiments, there are no chemical source or sink terms anywhere. The only processes modeled are three-dimensional advection (strictly speaking, flux divergence) and sub-grid-scale diffusion. These experiments can be thought of as initial value problems in the sense that, at infinite time, the only solution is constant tracer mixing ratio equal to the global average of the initial condition.

The first tracer experiment is designed with a very simple initial condition. The tracer mixing ratio R_θ is set on model date 1 January to be equal at every point to the *local* value of potential temperature (θ). Thus, at initial time t_0

the R_θ distribution is such that there are no gradients of R_θ along model isentropic surfaces. This experiment is therefore designed to examine transport from the point of view of how the tracer R_θ acts to systematically cross isentropic θ surfaces. This is designated as the THETA experiment.

The second experiment is given an even simpler initial condition. Here the initial tracer mixing ratio R_ϕ is set on model date 1 January to be equal to the local value of the latitude ϕ (in degrees) at every grid box plus an arbitrary constant of value 1000.

The constant is just to keep the range of mixing ratios small and all the values positive. In all pictures shown, the constant is subtracted off so that mixing ratios have a direct labeling of latitude corresponding to that original value. At time t_0 the R_ϕ field has no vertical gradients anywhere. This experiment can thus be thought of as being set up to explore the mechanisms leading to horizontal tracer dispersion along isentropic surfaces. In this sense, the lack of any significant vertical tracer gradients avoids the confusion produced in many tracer problems by the effect of vertical tracer advection through the isentropic surfaces. This will be called the PHI experiment.

3. THE THETA TRACER EXPERIMENT

In this experiment, many aspects of the interpretation are particularly simple when the tracer R_θ is compared against the contours of the potential temperature θ. Shown in Fig. 1 are monthly averages of zonal-mean potential temperature for January, February, April, and June. Note the generally poleward–upward slopes of the θ surfaces in the troposphere and the poleward–downward slopes in the lower stratosphere. An exception to this occurs in the winter polar stratosphere where the slopes are again poleward–upward. This is related to the cold polar vortex in winter. The slope is somewhat exaggerated due to the excessively cold polar temperatures in the GCM (Manabe and Mahlman, 1976).

Figure 2 shows the distribution of monthly averages of zonal mean R_θ for the same months of January, February, April, and June. To increase ease of interpretation, the $R_\theta = 500$ and 700 lines are given in dark, solid lines, while the positions of the $\theta = 500$- and 700-K lines are noted as dashed lines. Thus the drift of the R_θ isolines relative to their original θ surfaces can be readily visualized. Already in the first month, R_θ shows significant systematic departures from the θ surfaces. In particular, higher northern latitudes show R_θ dipping below θ, while in the tropics the opposite occurs. In the Southern (summer) Hemisphere, almost no difference is seen. This behavior already shows the direct relevance of diabatic processes in producing long-term vertical tracer transport. The "diabatic" circulation is apparently acting to

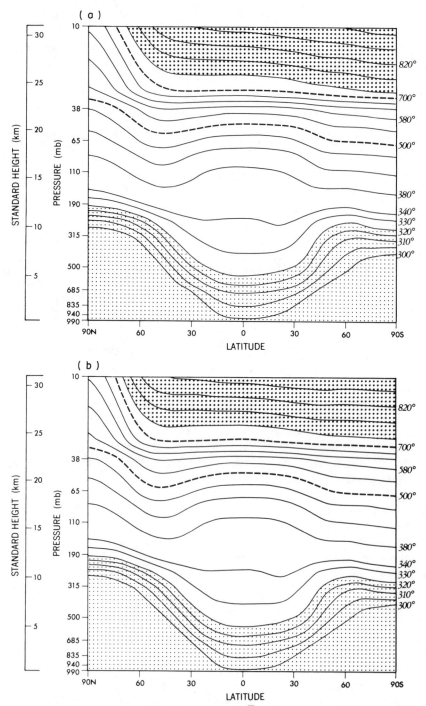

FIG. 1. Model zonal-mean potential temperature (θ) in kelvin for the months of (a) January, (b) February, (c) April, and (d) June. Vertical coordinate is log pressure; standard heights are given on left. The $\theta = 500$ K and 700 K lines are dashed for reference to Fig. 2.

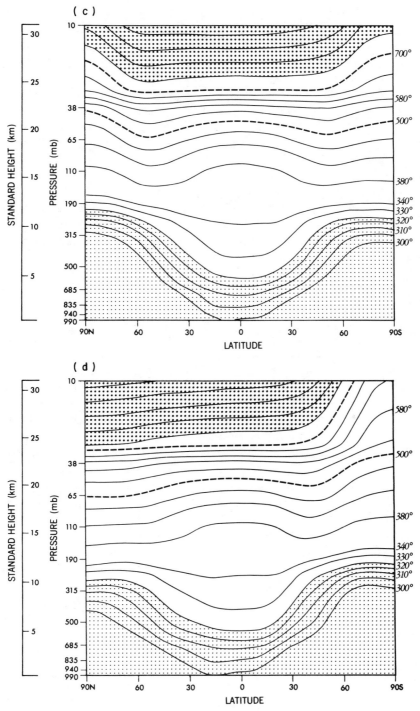

Fig. 1. *(Continued)*

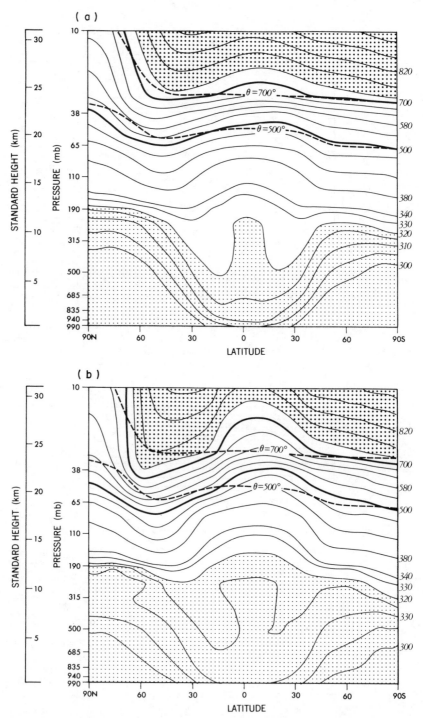

FIG. 2. Zonal-mean tracer mixing ratio R_θ from the "THETA" model experiment for the months of (a) January, (b) February, (c) April, and (d) June. The $R_\theta = 500$ and 700 lines are thicker, while the $\theta = 500$ K and 700 K from Fig. 1 are given as dashed lines.

308

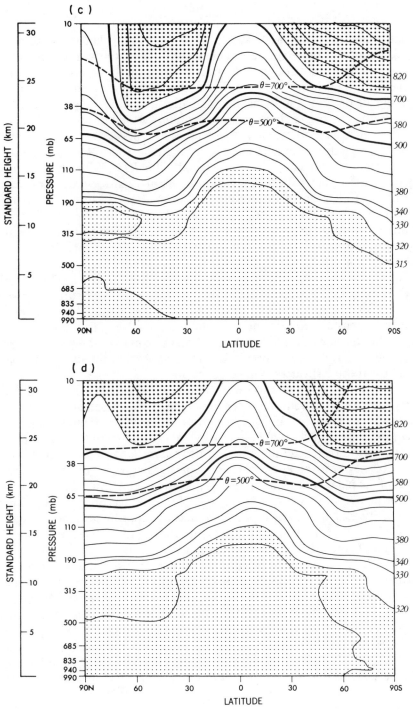

FIG. 2. *(Continued)*

produce upward motion through the θ surfaces in low latitudes and downward motion through θ surfaces in higher latitudes of the winter hemisphere. In the Southern Hemisphere, the summertime easterly flow is very nearly in radiative equilibrium. Thus, it is in the sunlit, strongly heated hemisphere that the air motion is most nearly adiabatic.

By February, Fig. 2 shows a more pronounced picture of the same processes evident in January. In this picture the slope-steepening effect of the diabatic circulation is much more apparent. In the troposphere for February, some remarkable changes have occurred. The $R_\theta = 320$ line has moved upward in the tropics from about 5 km to about 12 km. On the other hand, the $R_\theta = 310$ line has moved downward from about 3 km to ground level. Such behavior is quite incompatible with the idea of a simple movement relative to a mean θ surface. In fact, it is much more compatible with a transport dominated by local vertical mixing rather than zonal-mean vertical advection.

Such behavior is not that surprising when the tropics are considered to be a place dominated by deep moist convection. Also, it is not so surprising when one considers the tropical lower troposphere as a place roughly characterized by nearly constant equivalent potential temperature with altitude. In this sense, the strong vertical θ gradients shown there in Fig. 1 are quite misleading. The effective stratification is actually very weak; thus strong mixing of R_θ across those θ surfaces is to be expected.

By April, Fig. 2 shows a troposphere that is essentially well mixed and a stratosphere R_θ that is an enhancement of the February pattern in equatorial and northern latitudes. In southern latitudes, however, a large change has occurred, showing apparent large downward movement of R_θ relative to θ. A more careful look reveals that this is somewhat misleading. It is actually the θ lines that have moved away from R_θ. This has happened due to the strong onset of the polar cooling in early winter leading to an upward movement of isentropic surfaces. Thus, a conceptual disadvantage of the θ-coordinate perspective has appeared. In this case it is the coordinate that moved (in physical space) relative to the tracer. Thus, the interpretative advantage of θ coordinates converts to a disadvantage at this limit.

In northern latitudes for April, something remarkable has occurred. Although the R_θ slopes are steeper here (than in February) relative to the θ surfaces, those R_θ's are virtually unchanged from those of March (not shown). Did the diabatic circulation cease? The answer is no; the cooling rates in higher latitudes are as large as for previous months. What has happened here is that the R_θ surfaces have come close to what we shall call "slope equilibrium." Roughly, the slope-steepening effect of the diabatic circulation has produced large gradients of R_θ along isentropic surfaces. This leads to a slope-flattening opposition mechanism. One effect of the approximately adiabatic disturbances propagating from the troposphere is to induce irreversible horizontal mixing of R_θ, essentially *along* isentropic surfaces. This competing process will be investigated in the PHI tracer experiment.

This behavior is quite consistent with the conceptual framework offered in Section 2. Thus, the equilibrium slope of vertically stratified trace surfaces in the lower stratosphere results from a competition between the slope-steepening effect of the diabatic circulation and the slope-flattening effect of irreversible diffusive-type processes acting essentially along isentropic surfaces.

For June, Fig. 2 shows a continuation of processes previously mentioned. The Northern Hemisphere transition to summer conditions has led to large warmings in the polar regions (Fig. 1). This produces a marked lowering of the θ surfaces relative to the R_θ surfaces. Note also, though, the very strong poleward-downward movement of the $R_\theta = 700$ line at high northern latitudes. This irreversible transfer is caused by large meandering eddies appearing in association with the seasonal transition from westerlies to easterlies.

In the troposphere, note that the R_θ slopes are poleward–downward, even though the θ slopes are poleward–upward. Note also that R_θ there is now rather well mixed in the vertical, especially in comparison to θ. This shows that the radiative re-establishment of the θ field is a strong process. Thus, the concept of isentropic motion can only be valid on the very short (~days) time scale.

In the Southern Hemisphere, the most pronounced effect is again the movement of θ relative to R_θ. In a radiatively controlled (nondynamical) atmosphere, this would be the only effect since essentially no real transfer of R_θ would take place. Interestingly, the Southern Hemisphere stratosphere of this model is near that limit, since the dynamically induced diabatic heating rates (those that are not associated with the annual cycle of insolation) are rather small there.

The preceding results are relevant to a recent comparison of an N_2O simulation using this model (Mahlman *et al.*, 1985) with an observational study of long-lived trace gases (Bacmeister *et al.*, 1985). Their comparison shows conclusively that the model meridional N_2O slopes are less steep than observed slopes by about 25%. Thus, the steep R_θ slopes shown in Fig. 2 must be considered as underestimates of that expected from the real stratosphere.

In the context of the R_θ results given here, the obvious conclusion is that the slope-steepening effect of the diabatic circulation is not strong enough in this model. Because the diabatic circulation intensity is due to the degree of forcing from the troposphere (Mahlman *et al.*, 1981, 1984), this means that the GCM is not "dynamical" enough. This is in the sense that the role of disturbances in this context is to propagate to the stratosphere, decelerate the zonal flow, warm up the polar regions (to maintain thermal wind balance), and thus excite polar diabatic cooling.

Thus, the model deficiency producing meridional tracer slopes that are not steep enough is directly related to a common deficiency of this and other GCMs. That is, the polar cap region is too cold (in all but midsummer conditions) and the associated zonal winds are too strong. Thus, eventual solution of the "cold-bias" problem is required before the "flattened R-slope" problem can be solved. This hypothesis has already received strong support through a series of GCM experiments using the GFDL 40-level SKYHI model [first results reported in Andrews *et al.* (1983) and Mahlman and Umscheid (1984)]. In those calculations, as the degree of forcing from the troposphere (as measured by the magnitude of the Eliassen–Palm flux convergence) gets larger, the polar vortex gets warmer, and the meridional slopes of an accompanying passive N_2O tracer get steeper.

A final consideration for this experiment centers about the character of the inferred diabatic circulation. Earlier, Dunkerton (1978) argued that a Lagrangian-mean circulation could be identified with the implied circulation associated with the zonal-mean diabatic heating rate. A crude check on this hypothesis can be obtained here by comparing the early movement of the R_θ isolines in the THETA experiment against the prediction that they will be displaced vertically at the zonal-mean diabatic vertical velocity

$$W_{\text{diab}} \approx \frac{\overline{Q^\lambda}/c_p}{g/c_p + \partial \overline{T^\lambda}/\partial z} \tag{3.1}$$

where Q/c_p is the diabatic heating rate, g/c_p the adiabatic lapse rate, $\partial T/\partial z$ the local lapse rate, and $(\quad)^\lambda$ is the zonal averaging operator. This is compatible with the hypothesis of Dunkerton (1978) and as implied much earlier in the work of Murgatroyd and Singleton (1961), Danielsen *et al.* (1962), and Matsuno (1972).

A comparison of W_{diab} against the displacements of R_θ from the initial position on 1 January to 15 February for a number of latitude–altitude intersections reveals an interesting behavior. The actual stratospheric displacements of R_θ from the model exceed those "predicted" by W_{diab} by values ranging from ~ 20 to $\sim 75\%$ in the winter hemisphere. Thus, W_{diab} predicts the sign of the displacements correctly (in sharp contrast to the thermally indirect Eulerian meridional circulation of the model), but the magnitude is significantly underestimated. This result is compatable with a similar estimate made by Mahlman *et al.* (1980), who used the eddy-temperature variance equation. The argument they gave explaining this effect still seems relevant in the current context: upward-propagating long-wave disturbances from the troposphere induce a poleward eddy heat flux. These eddy temperatures are associated with an eddy diabatic heating. Values warmer than the zonal mean are associated with eddy diabatic cooling, and vice versa. Because the warmer air is generally moving poleward (and thus perturbation Q/c_p is negative), the air parcels are generally "sliding under" the mean θ surfaces during a typical poleward leg of a parcel trajectory. The generally heating equatorward trajectories produce the opposite effect; air parcels rise up through the mean θ surfaces. For disturbances of large meridional scale, the effect is to enhance net downward movement of tracers in higher latitudes and upward movement in lower latitudes. Thus the eddy effect appears to enhance the net efficiency of the extratropical diabatic circulation by an average factor of, say, 40 ± 20%. A more accurate determination is beyond the scope of this analysis. Nevertheless, it appears that the eddy diabatic effect introduces a significant correction to the Dunkerton (1978) hypothesis.

4. THE PHI TRACER EXPERIMENT

In this experiment, the lack of initial vertical gradients of R_ϕ leads to a much simplified perspective on the details of horizontal tracer structure. This is because the small vertical gradients of R_ϕ strongly reduces the relative contribution of vertical advection of R_ϕ through isentropic surfaces.

Shown in Fig. 3 is a wind vector-streamline horizontal chart on the 480-K ($\approx$ 65-mb) isentropic surface for model date 1 January. Many of the features to be shown can be interpreted relative to this flow pattern. On this date there is significant westerly flow in both model hemispheres. In the Pacific near 30°N is a pronounced anticyclone. At higher elevations this feature becomes the well-known Aleutian high. The tropics are characterized by a complex but generally easterly flow. In the Southern Hemisphere mid-latitudes, waves can be seen that are essentially remnants of well-formed tropospheric extratropical cyclones.

Also given in Fig. 3 are vector-streamline charts at $\theta = 480$ K for model dates 5 and 9 January. Although the flow appears approximately stationary during this period, two events near 9 January will prove to be of interest. In the western Pacific near 30°N, a second anticyclone has formed, splitting the Aleutian high into two distinct cells. In the Southern Hemisphere mid-latitude near 180°W a distinct ridge has formed, terminating a wide region of northwesterly flow west of the trough near 70°E.

Figure 4 presents a sequence of PHI mixing ratios from 1 – 11 January on the $\theta = 480$ K isentropic surface. The initial condition on day 0 (1 January) shows height-independent zonal isolines. Picked for special emphasis are

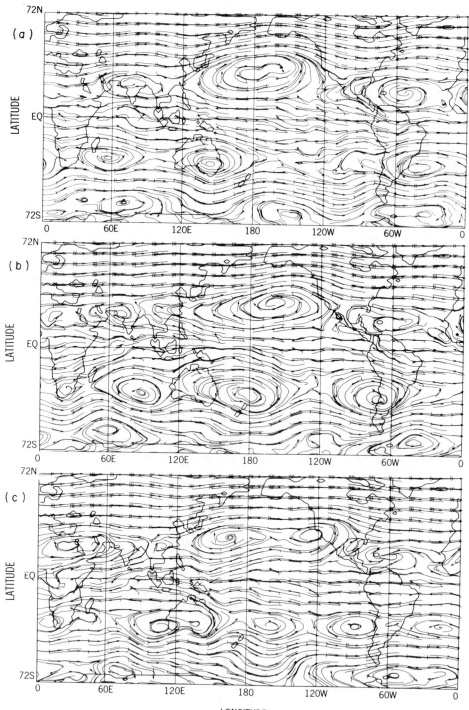

LONGITUDE

"tubes" of tracer material initially at 48–54°S, 18–24°N, and 48–54°N, respectively.

By day 1 (2 January, Fig. 4a) the tracer tubes are beginning to distort, particularly in the vicinity of the "Aleutian" high. On day 2 (3 January) the 18–24°N tube is starting to bulge northward to the west of the Aleutian high, while an elongated streamer from the 48–54°N tube is being stretched southwestward around the high. By day 3 (4 January, Fig. 4b), this streamer has almost disappeared. This brings up a point of caution in interpreting the model results. It is always tempting to think of these tubes as material ones "marked" by the boundaries of a "conservative" tracer on an isentropic surface. What has actually happened here is the streamer has stretched out sufficiently that one of its horizontal scales is of the order of the grid size itself. Thus the model's highly scale-selective sub-grid-scale horizontal diffusion (Mahlman and Moxim, 1978) becomes activated. As a result, this local mixing ratio maximum starts to diffuse away and disappear. Presumably, this process is similar to that expected in the real atmosphere; as elements stretch to smaller scales, they begin to be acted on by motions of smaller scale. Thus, such stretching events should ordinarily be regarded as being essentially irreversible. This leaves a picture of the mixing processes as being both advective and diffusive in character. It is the advective processes, particularly in the form of transient events, that ultimately make the smaller-scale diffusive type processes effective [see also Dunkerton (1980)].

By day 4 (5 January, Fig. 4b) a number of important processes are beginning to be evident. The 48–54°N tube shows very little structure and evolution. In this region, the model shows a tendency for a Lagrangian convergence of particles into the polar-night jet stream [see Mahlman et al. (1980)]. This convergence acts to suppress the tendency for individual blobs to disperse.

In sharp contrast the day 4 tube for 48–54°S shows a great deal of structure. To the west of the trough near 50°S, 120°W, the tube has contracted in meridional scale by about a factor of 3. This arises from the isentropic convergence there. To the east of the trough, isentropic divergence has spread the tube laterally by more than a factor of 2. This lateral spreading suggests caution in interpreting regions of weak gradients as being due to "wave breaking," or "mixing."

The 18–24°N tube has undergone an important transformation by day 4. The poleward-moving element has now "broken off" and separated from

FIG. 3. Instantaneous Mercator vector-streamline charts on the $\theta = 480$ K isentropic surface for model dates 1, 5 and 9 January [(a), (b), and (c), respectively]. The arrow gives wind direction, while each barb indicates a wind speed of 5 m s^{-1}.

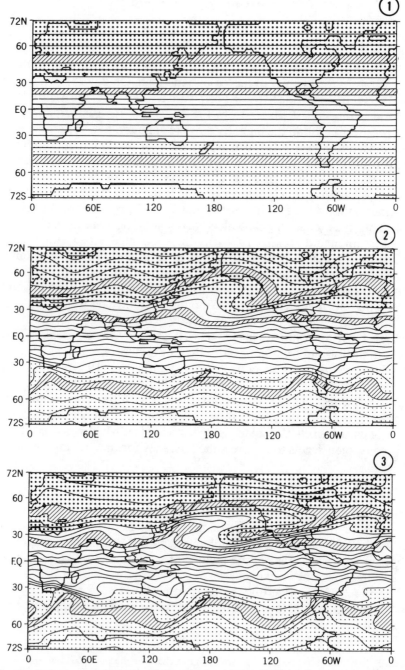

FIG. 4a. Instantaneous Mercator charts of R_ϕ on the $\theta = 480$ K isentropic surface for model dates 1, 2, and 3 January (①, ②, and ③, respectively). The 1 January chart represents the PHI experiment initial condition with highlighted tracer tubes at 48–54°S (top cross-hatching), 18–24°N (middle), and 48–54°N (bottom).

316

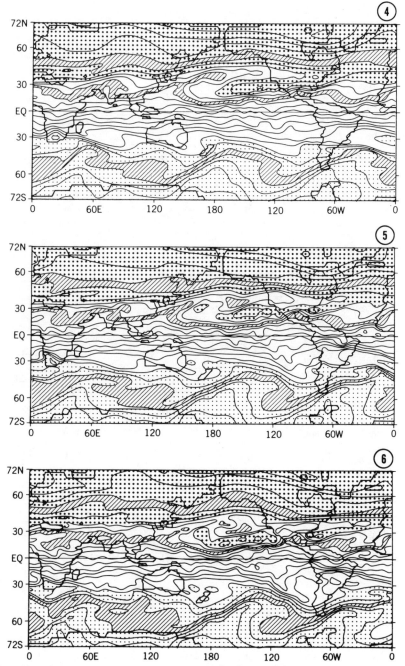

FIG. 4b. As in (a) except for 4, 5, and 6 January (④, ⑤, and ⑥, respectively). *(Continued on next page)*

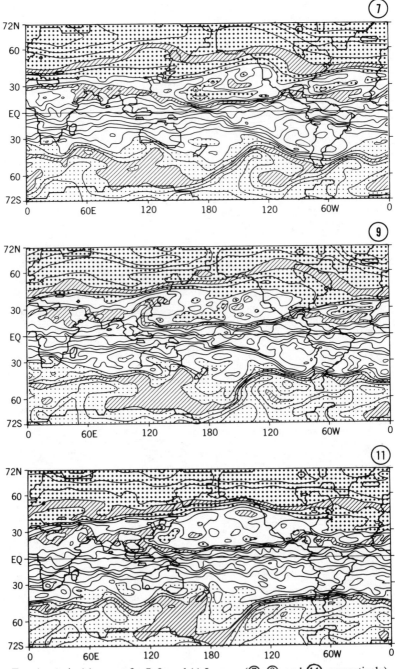

FIG. 4c. As in (a) except for 7, 9, and 11 January (⑦, ⑨, and ⑪, respectively).

the main tube and is rotating around the Aleutian high. On day 5 (6 January) the same processes are evident, but in a more developed state.

In Fig. 4c the sequence now shifts to 2-day intervals. On day 6 (7 January, Fig. 4c) there is a remarkable structure in the 48–54°S "tube." An element near 120°W is in the process of stretching and breaking away from the main body. Near 100–160°E a significant isentropic divergence of the 48–54°S tube is evident. By day 8 the element near 120°W has completely broken off and is recirculating back toward the main tube.

Also on day 8 (9 January) a new blob of the 18–24°N tube is stretching poleward near 120°E. This is associated with a developing high in the western Pacific near 30°N (see Fig. 3). As this transient disturbance grows, it pulls the tracer elements along with it. By day 10 (11 January) these elements have broken off and, in fact, form the center of the western Pacific anticyclone.

This is a phenomenon that has been observed earlier in analysis of this model. As argued in Mahlman (1979), the extremely low potential vorticities in model troposphere blocking anticyclones come from transient blobs of low-latitude air being deposited irreversibly into the blocking region. Thus, in both cases the amplifying anticyclone is "fed" by transient injections of low potential vorticity air from lower latitudes.

The last chart in the sequence is given for day 10 (11 January). By 10 days it is difficult to tell whether there has been a significant meridional drift of the tubes (compare with initial condition in Fig. 4a). However, there is a suggestion of a drift toward polar regions in each hemisphere. Perhaps more striking is the large degree of dispersion evident in the 48–54°S and 18–24°N tubes. Even more obvious is the large degree of tracer homogenization that has occurred in the vicinity of the Aleutian high, while gradients remain large near both the southern and northern edges. This provides an interesting contrast to the relatively small degree of dispersion that has occurred near the 48–54°N tube. This contrast is quite compatible with the drastic gradient in effective lateral diffusivity for the two-dimensional subset of this model as diagnosed by Plumb and Mahlman (1985).

5. SUMMARY

As a means of simplifying understanding of stratospheric tracer transport, a Lagrangian-type perspective is offered through use of isentropic diagnostic techniques. The GFDL general circulation/tracer model is employed to run two tracer experiments designed to explore the power of this viewpoint.

The first experiment (THETA) is a conservative (no chemistry) tracer designed so that at the initial instant (1 January), the tracer mixing ratio is equal to the local potential temperature at every point in the model. This experiment is designed to examine the systematic movement of air across isentropic surfaces in the stratosphere.

The second experiment (PHI) is designed such that the initial tracer values are a linear function of latitude only. This allows a simplified perspective on processes leading to meridional exchange of air essentially along isentropic surfaces.

The THETA experiment shows a systematic evolution of tracer relative to isentropic surfaces, compatible with a downward mass flow in high latitudes and an upward one in low latitudes. In the first couple of months this flux is larger than that implied by the zonal-mean diabatic circulation alone. An argument is presented on how an "eddy diabatic" effect can systematically augment the transport by the zonal-mean diabatic circulation.

By the fourth month the steepening of tracer slopes in the meridional plane comes to an abrupt halt. This arises because the slope-steepening effect of the diabatic circulation becomes balanced by an equivalent slope-flattening process: the effective down-gradient dispersion/diffusion of tracer mixing ratio essentially along isentropic surfaces.

Such exchange on the model isentropic surfaces is examined in some detail in the PHI experiment. The analysis indicates that this process is rather complex. The dominant process is mixing induced by stretching and shearing of tracer elements down to horizontal scales small enough to be irreversibly mixed by diffusive processes.

ACKNOWLEDGMENTS

I am grateful to Joseph Smagorinsky for his patience in allowing this kind of work to mature at GFDL and to Dr. S. Manabe for the leadership he provided in designing the GCM and the concept of the tracer model used in this study. Useful comments on the work were provided by I. M. Held, N.-C. Lau, and R. A. Plumb. Research assistance was provided by W. J. Moxim, while technical assistance was offered by J. Kennedy and P. Tunison.

REFERENCES

Andrews, D. G. (1983). A finite-amplitude Eliassen-Palm theorem in isentropic coordinates. *J. Atmos. Sci.* **40**, 1877–1883.

Andrews, D. G., and McIntyre, M. E. (1976a). Planetary waves in horizontal and vertical shear: The generalized Eliassen-Palm relation and the mean zonal acceleration. *J. Atmos. Sci.* **33**, 2031–2048.

Andrews, D. G., and McIntyre, M. E. (1976b). Planetary waves in horizontal and vertical shear: An asymptotic theory for equatorial waves in weak shear. *J. Atmos. Sci.* **33**, 2049–2053.

Andrews, D. G., and McIntyre, M. E. (1978a). Generalized Eliassen-Palm and Charney-Drazin theorems for waves in axisymmetric mean flows in compressible atmospheres. *J. Atmos. Sci.* **35**, 175–185.

Andrews, D. G., and McIntyre, M. E. (1978b). An exact theory of nonlinear waves on a Lagrangian mean flow. *J. Fluid Mech.* **89,** 609–646.

Andrews, D. G., Mahlman, J. D., and Sinclair, R. W. (1983). Eliassen-Palm diagnostics of wave mean-flow interaction in the GFDL "SKYHI" general circulation model. *J. Atmos. Sci.* **40,** 2768–2784.

Bacmeister, J. T., Albritton, D. L., and Mahlman, J. D. (1985). Toward a stratospheric climatology of long-lived trace gases. In preparation.

Berggren, R., and Labitzke, K. (1968). The distribution of ozone on pressure surfaces. *Tellus* **20,** 88–97.

Blackmon, M., and Lau, N.-C. (1980). Regional characteristics of the Northern Hemisphere winter circulation: A comparison of the simulation of a GFDL general circulation model with observations. *J. Atmos. Sci.* **37,** 497–514.

Bleck, R. (1973). Numerical forecasting experiments based on the conservation of potential vorticity on isentropic surfaces. *J. Appl. Meteorol.* **12,** 737–752.

Clark, J. H. E., and Rogers, T. G. (1978). The transport of conservative gases by planetary waves. *J. Atmos. Sci.* **35,** 2232–2235.

Danielsen, E. F. (1959). The laminar structure of the atmosphere and its relation to the concept of a tropopause. *Arch. Meteorol. Geophys. Bioklimatol., Ser. A* **11,** 293–332.

Danielsen, E. F. (1968). Stratospheric-tropospheric exchange based on radioactivity, ozone and potential vorticity. *J. Atmos. Sci.* **25,** 502–518.

Danielsen, E. F., and Diercks, J. W. (1967). "A Study of the Tropopause Based on Numerical Integration of the Potential Vorticity Equation," Final Rep., Part 1, Contract AT(30-1)-3317. U.S. At. Energy Comm., Washington, D.C.

Danielsen, E. F., Bergman, K. H., and Paulson, C. A. (1962). "Radioisotopes, Potential Temperature and Potential Vorticity—A Study of Stratospheric-tropospheric Exchange Processes." Dep. Meteorol. Climatol., University of Washington, Seattle.

Dunkerton, T. (1978). On the mean meridional mass motions in the stratosphere and mesosphere. *J. Atmos. Sci.* **35,** 2325–2333.

Dunkerton, T. (1980). A Lagrangian-mean theory of wave, mean-flow interaction with applications to nonacceleration and its breakdown. *Rev. Geophys. Space Phys.* **18,** 387–400.

Dunkerton, T., Hsu, C.-P. F., and McIntyre, M. E. (1981). Some Eulerian and Lagrangian diagnostics for a model stratospheric warming. *J. Atmos. Sci.* **38,** 819–843.

Edmon, H. J., Jr., Hoskins, B. J., and McIntyre, M. E. (1980). Eliassen-Palm cross sections for the troposphere. *J. Atmos. Sci.* **37,** 2600–2616; corrigendum: **38,** 1115.

Eliassen, A., and Raustein, E. (1968). A numerical integration experiment with a model atmosphere based on isentropic coordinates. *Meteorol. Ann.* **5,** 45–63.

Hahn, D. G., and Manabe, S. (1975). The role of mountains in the South Asian monsoon circulation. *J. Atmos. Sci.* **32,** 1515–1541.

Hayashi, Y. (1974). Spectral analysis of tropical disturbances appearing in a GFDL general circulation model. *J. Atmos. Sci.* **31,** 180–218.

Hayashi, Y., and Golder, D. G. (1977). Space-time spectral analysis of mid-latitude disturbances appearing in a GFDL general circulation model. *J. Atmos. Sci.* **34,** 237–262.

Holton, J. R. (1980). Wave propagation and transport in the middle atmosphere. *Philos. Trans. R. Soc. London, Ser. A* **296,** 73–85.

Hsu, C.-P. F. (1980). Air parcel motions during a numerically simulated sudden stratospheric warming. *J. Atmos. Sci.* **37,** 2768–2792.

Hunt, B. G., and Manabe, S. (1968). Experiments with a stratospheric general circulation model. II. Large-scale diffusion of tracers in the stratosphere. *Mon. Weather Rev.* **96,** 503–539.

Levy, H., II, Mahlman, J. D., and Moxim, W. J. (1979). A preliminary report on the numerical simulation of the three-dimensional structure and variability of atmospheric N_2O. *Geophys. Res. Lett.* **6**, 155–158.

Levy, H., II, Mahlman, J. D., and Moxim, W. J. (1980). A stratospheric source of reactive nitrogen in the unpolluted troposphere. *Geophys. Res. Lett.* **7**, 441–444.

Levy, H., II, Mahlman, J. D., and Moxim, W. J. (1982). Tropospheric N_2O variability. *JGR, J. Geophys. Res.* **87**(C4), 3061–3080.

Levy, H., II, Mahlman, J. D., W. J. Moxim, and Liu, S.-C. (1985). Tropospheric ozone: The role of transport. *JGR, J. Geophys. Res.* **90**(C4), 3753–3772.

Liu, S.-C., Kley, D., McFarland, M., Mahlman, J. D., and Levy, H., II (1980). On the origin of tropospheric ozone. *JGR, J. Geophys. Res.* **85**(C12), 7546–7552.

McIntyre, M. E. (1980). Towards a Lagrangian-mean description of stratospheric circulations and chemical transports. *Philos. Trans. R. Soc. London, Ser. A* **296**, 129–148.

McIntyre, M. E., and Palmer, T. N. (1983). Breaking planetary waves in the stratosphere. *Nature (London)* **305**, 593–600.

Mahlman, J. D. (1965). Relation of stratospheric-tropospheric mass exchange mechanisms to surface radioactivity peaks. *Arch. Meteorol., Geophys. Bioklimatol. Ser. A* **15**, 1–25.

Mahlman, J. D. (1970). Eddy transfer processes in the stratosphere during major and "minor" breakdowns of the polar night vortex. *J. Geophys. Res.* **75**, 1701–1705.

Mahlman, J. D. (1973). Preliminary results from a three-dimensional general circulation/tracer model. *Proc. Conf. Clim. Impact Assess. Program, 2nd, 1972*, DOT-TSC-OST-73-4, pp. 321–337 (NTIS PB-221 16612).

Mahlman, J. D. (1976). Some fundamental limitations of simplified-transport models as implied by results from a three-dimensional general circulation/transport model. *Proc. Conf. Clim. Impact Assess. Program, 4th, 1975*, DOT-TSC-OST-75-38, pp. 132–146 (NTIS AD-A068982).

Mahlman, J. D. (1979). Structure and interpretation of blocking anticyclones as simulated in a GFDL general circulation model. *Proc. Stanstead Sem., 13th, Bishops Univ., Lennoxville, Quebec, Canada,* Dept. of Meteorol., McGill Univ., Montreal, Meteorology paper No. 123, pp. 70–76.

Mahlman, J. D., and Moxim, W. J. (1978). Tracer simulation using a global general circulation model: Results from a midlatitude instantaneous source experiment. *J. Atmos. Sci.* **35**, 1340–1374.

Mahlman, J. D., and Umscheid, L. J. (1984). Dynamics of the middle atmosphere: Successes and problems of the GFDL "SKYHI" general circulation model. *In* "Dynamics of the Middle Atmosphere" (J. R. Holton and T. Matsuno, eds.), pp. 501–525. Terra Sci. Publ. Co., Tokyo.

Mahlman, J. D., Levy, H., II, and Moxim, W. J. (1980). Three-dimensional tracer structure and behavior as simulated in two ozone precursor experiments. *J. Atmos. Sci.* **37**, 655–685.

Mahlman, J. D., Andrews, D. G., Dutsch, H. U., Hartmann, D. L., Matsuno, T., and Murgatroyd, R. J. (1981). Transport of trace constituents in the stratosphere. Report of Study Group 2. "Middle Atmosphere Program, Handbook for MAP," Vol. 3, pp. 14–43. Published for ICSU Scientific Committee on Solar-Terrestrial Physics (SCOSTEP).

Mahlman, J. D., Andrews, D. G., Dutsch, H. U., Hartmann, D. L., Matsuno, T., and Murgatroyd, R. J. (1984). *In* "Dynamics of the Middle Atmosphere" (J. R. Holton and T. Matsuno, eds.), pp. 387–416. Terra Sci. Publ. Co., Tokyo.

Mahlman, J. D., Levy, H., II, and Moxim, W. J. (1985). Three-dimensional simulations of stratospheric N_2O: Predictions for other trace constituents. *JGR, J. Geophys. Res.* (submitted for publication).

Manabe, S., and Holloway, J. L., Jr. (1975). The seasonal variation of the hydrologic cycle as simulated by a global model of the atmosphere. *JGR, J. Geophys. Res.* **80**, 1617–1649.

Manabe, S., and Mahlman, J. D. (1976). Simulation of seasonal and interhemispheric variations in the stratospheric circulation. *J. Atmos. Sci.* **33**, 2185–2217.

Manabe, S., Hahn, D. G., and Holloway, J. L., Jr. (1974). The seasonal variation of the tropical
circulation as simulated by a global model of the atmosphere. *J. Atmos. Sci.* **31**, 43–83.

Matsuno, T. (1972). Stratospheric transport. Paper presented at the CIAP Workshop on Computational Modeling of the Atmosphere, Pacific Grove, California.

Matsuno, T. (1980). Lagrangian motion of air parcels in the presence of planetary waves. *Pure
Appl. Geophys.* **118**, 189–216.

Moxim, W. J., and Mahlman, J. D. (1980). Evaluation of various total ozone sampling networks using the GFDL 3-D tracer model. *JGR, J. Geophys. Res.* **85**(C8), 4527–4539.

Murgatroyd, R. J., and Singleton, F. (1961). Possible meridional circulations in the stratosphere
and mesosphere. *Q. J. R. Meteorol. Soc.* **87**, 125–135.

O'Neill, A., and Youngblut, C. E. (1982). Stratospheric warmings diagnosed using the transformed Eulerian-mean equations and the effect of the mean state on wave propagation. *J.
Atmos. Sci.* **39**, 1370–1386.

Oort, A. H. (1978). On the adequacy of the rawinsonde network for global circulation studies
tested through numerical model output. *Mon. Weather Rev.* **106**, 174–195.

Palmer, T. N. (1981). Diagnostic study of a wavenumber-2 stratospheric sudden warming in the
transformed Eulerian-mean formalism. *J. Atmos. Sci.* **38**, 844–855.

Plumb, R. A. (1979). Eddy fluxes of conserved quantities by small amplitude waves. *J. Atmos.
Sci.* **36**, 1699–1704.

Plumb, R. A., and Mahlman, J. D. (1985). The zonally averaged transport characteristics of the
GFDL general circulation/transport model.

Pyle, J. A., and Rogers, C. F. (1980). Stratospheric transport by stationary waves — The importance of chemical processes. *Q. J. R. Meteorol. Soc.* **106**, 421–446.

Reed, R. J. (1955). A study of a characteristic type of upper-level frontogenesis. *J. Meteorol.* **12**,
226–237.

Reed, R. J., and Danielsen, E. F. (1959). Fronts in the vicinity of the tropopause. *Arch. Meteorol., Geophys. Bioklimatol., Ser. A* **11**, 1–17.

Reiter, E. R., and Mahlman, J. D. (1965). Heavy radioactive fallout over the southern United
States. *J. Geophys. Res.* **70**, 4501–4520.

Smagorinsky, J. (1963). General circulation experiment with the primitive equations. I. The
basic experiment. *Mon. Weather Rev.* **91**, 99–164.

Staley, D. O. (1960). Evaluation of potential vorticity changes near the tropopause and the
related vertical motions, vertical advection of vorticity, and transport of radioactive debris
from stratosphere to troposphere. *J. Meteorol.* **17**, 591–620.

Staley, D. O. (1962). On the mechanism of mass and radioactivity transport from stratosphere
to troposphere. *J. Atmos. Sci.* **19**, 450–457.

Tung, K. K. (1982). On the two-dimensional transport of stratospheric trace gases in isentropic
coordinates. *J. Atmos. Sci.* **39**, 2230–2355.

Tung, K. K. (1984). Modeling of tracer transport in the middle atmosphere. *In* "Dynamics of
the Middle Atmosphere" (J. R. Holton and T. Matsuno, eds.), pp. 417–444. Terra Sci.
Publ. Co., Tokyo.

Wallace, J. M. (1978). Trajectory slopes countergradient heat fluxes and mixing by lower
stratospheric waves. *J. Atmos. Sci.* **35**, 554–558.

Part III

PLANETARY ATMOSPHERES

THE GENERAL CIRCULATION OF MARS: MODELS AND OBSERVATIONS

Conway B. Leovy

*Department of Atmospheric Sciences and
Graduate Program of Geophysics
University of Washington
Seattle, Washington*

1. Why Model Mars?

One of the hallmarks of Joseph Smagorinsky's leadership of the Geophysical Fluid Dynamics Laboratory (GFDL) has been the broadly based character of the research. Although Earth's atmosphere is the primary focus, the GFDLs program has encompassed problems in all areas of geophysical fluid dynamics, including planetary atmospheres. In an early review of the use of general circulation models (GCMs), Smagorinsky wrote, "It is quite clear to me that the next more fundamental step in general circulation research is to encompass planetary atmospheres in general. This is not a new idea, but I do wish to emphasize its inevitability" (Smagorinsky, 1970, p. 36). Geophysical Fluid Dynamics Laboratory scientists have made notable contributions to the field [e.g., Williams (1978, 1979); Williams and Holloway (1982); Fels (1977); Rossow and Williams (1979), Crisp (1983)] with a resulting enrichment of the entire GFDL program. The study of the planets, and of planetary atmospheres in particular, allows us to stretch our theories and models into unfamiliar territory and in the process provides clues and inspirations that can deepen our understanding of fundamental processes taking place on Earth.

Among the planets, Mars is particularly amenable to study. Relatively close, its surface is visible through a thin but significant atmosphere so that, as on Earth, atmospheric heating arises mainly from solar radiation absorbed at the surface and transferred back into the atmosphere. It is also similar to Earth in rotation rate, axial tilt, and size (Table I). The rotation rate, planetary size, and heating distribution are probably the most impor-

327

TABLE I. PLANETARY AND ATMOSPHERIC PARAMETERS FOR EARTH AND MARS

Quantity	Units	Value for Mars	Value for Earth
Equatorial radius a	Kilometers	3394	6369
Acceleration of gravity g	Meters per square second	3.72	9.81
Orbital eccentricity	—	0.093	0.017
Orbital inclination	Degrees	25	23.5
Length of day	Seconds	88,775	86,400
Length of year	Earth days	687	365
Rotation rate Ω	Seconds^{-1}	0.709×10^{-4}	0.729×10^{-4}
Surface pressure, p_s[a]	Millibars	6–8	1013
Atmospheric visible[b] optical depth	—	0.1–10	0.2–100
Atmospheric thermal[b] IR emissivity ϵ	—	0.15–0.8	0.4–1.0
Planetary equilibrium temperature T_e	Kelvin	210	256
Mean scale height H[c]	Kilometers	10.0	7.8
Adiabatic lapse rate	Kelvin per kilometer	4.5	9.8
Mean lapse rate	Kelvin per kilometer	2.5	6.5
External rotational Froude number $\Omega a/\sqrt{gH}$[d]	—	1.3	1.7
Internal rotational Froude number $\Omega a/\sqrt{NH}$	—	4.0	5.3
Dimensionless radiative time constant $(\Omega\tau_r) = \Omega p_s/C_p T_e/(g\epsilon\sigma T_e^4)$[d]	—	70	1000

[a] The Martian surface pressure range is due to the seasonal CO_2 cycle and corresponds to the mean surface elevation.

[b] The indicated variations of visible optical depth and thermal IR opacity are due primarily to dust (Mars) and water clouds (Earth).

[c] Atmospheric scale heights and lapse rates correspond to the lower atmospheres (the troposphere for Earth, and the region below 15 km for Mars).

[d] The external and internal rotational Froude numbers $\Omega a/\sqrt{gH}$ and $\Omega a/\sqrt{NH}$, and the dimensionless radiative time scale $\Omega\tau_r$ important for dynamical similarity, are defined in terms of rotation rate Ω, radius a, gravitational acceleration g, scale height H, surface pressure p_s, planetary equilibrium temperature T_e, specific heat at constant pressure C_p, Stefan–Boltzmann constant σ, emissivity ϵ, and buoyancy frequency N ($N = [gT_e^{-1}(\partial T/\partial z + gC_p^{-1})]^{1/2}$).

tant factors controlling the general circulation of a planetary atmosphere. The external and internal rotational Froude numbers, measuring the ratios of characteristic external and internal gravity-wave speeds to the planetary rotational speeds are nearly the same on the two planets, but Mars has a shorter radiative time scale, so its atmosphere responds more quickly and more directly to thermal forcing. As a consequence of the general similarities between the atmospheres of Earth and Mars, studies of the Martian general circulation require a stretch of our Earth-based imaginations, but not too much of a stretch.

There is another and perhaps more interesting reason for studying the Martian general circulation. Because the heating is sensitive to the dust load of the atmosphere and the dust load varies from time to time both within individual years and between years, by studying Mars we can study the response of the general circulation of an Earth-like atmosphere to a wide range of heating distributions. It is almost like a laboratory situation except that nature, not a human investigator, controls the knob labeled "heating rate."

2. Early Models: A Flat Mars

The first attempt to piece together a picture of the circulation of the Martian atmosphere was by Seymour Hess (1950). Working with scattered ground-based measurements of cloud drift and thermal emission temperatures measured by Coblentz and Lampland (1927), Hess constructed an illustrative "synoptic" weather map. Using the temperatures to fill in thermal winds between the few cloud drift measurements, he produced a map showing Earth-like features: subtropical anticyclones, prevailing westerlies in mid-latitudes, and sharp troughs resembling fronts embedded in the westerlies.

By 1961, the age of planetary exploration had begun. The first planetary probe, Mariner 2, was launched the following year to Venus, and the first successful Mars probe, Mariner 4, was launched two years later. It was clear that detailed data on the planets would eventually become available, and a few meteorologists had begun to turn their attention toward planetary atmospheres. Yale Mintz of UCLA was the first to apply the rich body of meteorological theory that had been developed over the preceding 15 years to Mars (Mintz, 1961). At that time it was generally accepted that the mean surface pressure on Mars was about 80 mb, 10 times the actual value. Nevertheless, Mintz recognized that the thin, almost cloud-free atmosphere and desertlike surface implied a short atmospheric thermal response time, so that the meridional gradients of atmospheric temperature should be closely tied to the seasonally varying gradients of surface temperature, with the latter responding immediately to the imposed solar radiation at the top of the atmosphere. With this idea in mind, Mintz reasoned from the properties of the quasi-geostrophic two-level model that the Martian atmosphere ought to be baroclinically stable during summer but baroclinically unstable during winter. He deduced that the dominant zonal wave number of the baroclinic disturbances should be about four. These predictions have proven to be remarkably accurate, so that both Mintz's basic assumptions and the applicability of the simplified quasi-geostrophic theory have been justified by subsequent observations. Interestingly, Mintz also attempted a preliminary assessment of the general circulation of Venus, but there he was less successful; Venus's general circulation is much harder to understand and, despite recent advances, the underlying mechanisms are still unclear.

Mintz's main interest was in the development of general circulation models as tools for simulation experiments in geophysical fluid dynamics, and he saw application of these models to planetary atmospheres as a way of broadening our understanding of the processes governing the general circulation and climate of Earth. In 1965, the author began collaborating with Mintz in an application to Mars of the general circulation model he had recently developed with Akio Arakawa. This grid-point model had two dynamically active layers, a dynamically passive but radiatively active stratosphere, and a finite differencing scheme that had recently been invented by Arakawa (Arakawa, 1966; Mintz, 1965). This scheme had the important property, novel at the time, of conserving enstrophy, thereby suppressing aliasing of small-scale vorticity patterns without requiring large explicit dissipation.

Application of this model to Mars was motivated by Mintz's earlier result that suggested an Earth-like dynamical regime for which the two-layer model was appropriate. For Mars, the model had to incorporate the thermal drives due to absorption and emission of radiation by CO_2, convective transfer from the surface, and convective exchange between layers (Gierasch and Goody, 1968). A convective heat flux formulation obtained by combining Great Plains data and data from a California dry lake with data from free convection laboratory experiments was employed and the diurnal cycle was explicitly simulated (Leovy, 1969).

By the time the model was run, Mariner 4 had flown past Mars (July 14, 1965) and had shown that the surface pressure was in the neighborhood of 7 mb, confirming and refining a new estimate based on ground-based spectroscopy that was published during the preceding year (Kaplan et al., 1964). The implied small atmospheric heat capacity led Leighton and Murray (1966) to conclude that the polar caps were solid CO_2, not water ice as had been generally believed, and that the regular seasonal variations of the caps in response to the seasonal radiation regime represented a substantial exchange of the atmosphere's major constituent with the surface. Leighton and Murray were also influenced by the Mariner 4 pictures that showed a heavily cratered moonlike surface. Accordingly, the Mintz–Arakawa model was modified to allow for CO_2 condensation and sublimation at the surface and this aspect of the model proved to have novel dynamical consequences.

Simulations for northern winter solstice and northern spring equinox were carried out at the Jet Propulsion Laboratory in 1966, but the results were not published until three years later (Leovy and Mintz, 1969). These results supported the assumption of Leighton and Murray that atmospheric heat transport could not prevent or seriously inhibit condensation of CO_2 in the seasonal polar caps. Moreover, the meridional mass flux arising from sublimation and condensation was shown to have a substantial effect on the momentum balance during solstice seasons, contributing to the development of surface westerly winds during winter. Aside from this mass flow, the circulation resembled a continental Earth, with a strong meridional temperature gradient and baroclinic wave cyclones during winter and a flat temperature gradient during summer. A synoptic example, a rapidly growing baroclinic wave cyclone from the solstice simulation, is shown in Fig. 1. The solstice simulation also produced a well-developed cross-equatorial Hadley circulation, extending poleward to about 30° in each hemisphere. Relatively weak meridional temperature gradients and baroclinic waves were obtained in the equinox run, but it was recognized that this simulation might be unrealistic because of the neglect of the thermal memory retained by the retreating spring polar cap.

The simulations also produced thermal tides, and despite the severe constraints of the two-layer model, the diurnal surface pressure oscillation turned out to be in quite good agreement with later calculations and observations (Zurek, 1976; Leovy, 1981).

These simulation results supported Mintz's earlier reasoning. Indeed, they tended to confirm the view that Mars is like a continental version of Earth whose general circulation and climate are relatively easy to understand and simulate. However, a complication was threatening this simple view. In 1967, the first direct radar measurements of surface topography were obtained, and although restricted to the sub-Earth latitudes on Mars, they immediately showed large-scale topographic variations of surprisingly large amplitude. The altitude range in the accessible latitude band exceeded one scale height (Pettingill *et al.*, 1969; Rogers *et al.*, 1970). Planetwide relief was revealed by a surface pressure map produced from Mariner 9 infrared measurements that showed deep basins, high volcanic uplands, and broad sloping plains covering much of the planet (Conrath *et al.*, 1973).

3. MARS WITH TOPOGRAPHY

These findings led Blumsack (1971a,b) and later Webster (1977) to attempt systematic analyses of the topographically induced circulation systems. Blumsack argued that uplands would correspond to thermal lows in

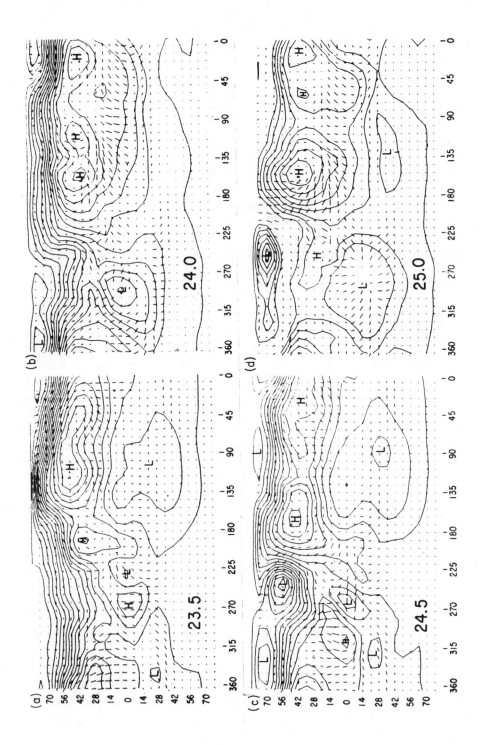

much the same way that the Rocky Mountain and Himalayan plateau regions correspond to summer thermal low-pressure areas on Earth. The
isothermal surfaces tend to be closely tied to ground temperature so that
wherever temperature decreases upward, isothermal surfaces bend, con-
forming to the topography and producing warm anomalies over uplands and
cold anomalies over lowlands. The resulting circulation pattern has cyclonic
low-level inflow and weak anticyclonic upper-level outflow in the warm
anomalies, with the reverse pattern in cold anomalies. Webster, who used a
linearized two-level model, showed that the topographic response in the
equatorial zone was likely to have a Kelvin wave character, with much
stronger zonal than meridional winds. He also showed that the response at
high latitudes should have the characteristics of Rossby waves with strong
response in westerly winds and weak and localized response in easterlies. At
high latitudes during winter, there is little or no vertical temperature gradient
so that the topography produces mechanical forcing but not differential
heating.

In addition, as Blumsack et al. (1973) pointed out, the topography would
produce diurnally varying slope winds like those that occur over large gently
sloping regions of Earth, for example, the North American Great Plains.
This diurnal wind pattern is characterized by a clockwise rotating wind with
upslope wind in the evening and downslope wind in the morning.

Mariner 9 also showed that dust storms ranging in area from a few thousand square kilometers to the entire planet as well as variable surface albedo
markings apparently produced by shifting dust or sand were common and
could account for the secular variability of Mars's appearance that had long
been reported by ground-based observers. Because of the very low atmospheric density, much stronger winds are required to raise particles on Mars
than on Earth. These facts led Carl Sagan and some of his colleagues to
speculate that extremely high winds might be widespread on Mars (Sagan et
al., 1971; Gierasch and Sagan, 1971). Sagan was particularly intrigued with
the possibility that the enormous smooth-floored impact basin Hellas might
be perpetually filled with dust stirred up by winds of near sonic speed racing
up and down its sloping walls. Indeed, there was some observational evi-

FIG. 1. Surface weather maps at half-day (Mars) intervals from the solstice simulation of
Leovy and Mintz (1969), showing the development of a baroclinic cyclone (upper left, maps c
and d). Maps show isobars at 0.1-mb intervals and wind vectors scaled to a maximum of about
60 m s^{-1} and approximately following the isobars in the manner of the geostrophic wind. The
numbers correspond to the Martian day number from the start of the simulation. On days 23.5
and 24.5, the sun is overhead on the 180th meridian at 25°S latitude; on days 24.0 and 25.0, it is
on the prime meridian. [From Leovy and Mintz (1969). Reproduced with permission from
Journal of the Atmospheric Sciences, a publication of the American Meteorological Society.]

dence from Mariner 9 that the atmospheric opacity due to suspended particles was larger in Hellas than elsewhere (Hanel et al., 1972).

Motivated by a desire to test these ideas, Cliff Mass, then an undergraduate
student at Cornell, developed a quasi-geostrophic two-level model for Mars
that incorporated topography. This model, applied only to the Southern
Hemisphere, showed that topography, and particularly the Hellas basin, did
indeed have a strong influence on the flow, but it did not produce the
extreme surface winds anticipated by Sagan (Mass and Sagan, 1976).

During this period, preparations were under way for the Viking missions
to Mars. One of the many concerns of the mission designers was the possibility of high surface winds at touchdown. Because of the low atmospheric
density, the landers were not sensitive to wind speeds below about 70 m s^{-1},
but they could have been damaged by higher winds. The observations of dust
storms and variable surface features together with the estimates of very high
surface winds by Sagan and others was a cause for concern. At the same time,
James Pollack at the NASA Ames Research Center was working with a
version of the Mintz–Arakawa model with the aim of re-examining the
Martian general circulation, this time with the observed topography. Mintz
and I were collaborating with Pollack and a graduate student, P. W. Greiman, in this effort. Our aim was to further assess the role of topography in the
general circulation. In addition to the incorporation of realistic topography,
this model contained several improvements over the earlier Mintz–
Arakawa model. There were three layers instead of two, improved horizontal
resolution, finite differencing by a new scheme better suited to modeling
geostrophic adjustment (Arakawa, 1972), and an explicit diurnally varying
convective boundary layer. We were interested primarily in improving our
understanding of Mars's general circulation, but the effort was also of interest to the Viking mission designers who wanted reassurance that the landings
could be made safely, at least at selected sites that were deemed to be safe
from hazards other than wind. Consequently, the first reported results from
this simulation were framed as a kind of "wind forecast" for various possible
Viking landing sites (Pollack et al., 1976). In keeping with the tradition
established with the previous version of this model, the major scientific
findings were not published until much later (Pollack et al., 1981). The early
model results predicted relatively mild surface winds, but the Viking mission
planners remained understandably nervous. Fortunately, the actual winds at
both landing sites turned out to be comfortably light and generally consistent
with the theory of Blumsack et al. (Hess et al., 1977).

Zonally averaged meridional wind, temperature, and zonal wind from this
simulation are shown in Fig. 2. A limited number of meridional temperature
cross sections can be constructed from the Mariner 9 infrared measurements
(Hanel et al., 1972; Conrath, 1981), and one of these is also shown in Fig. 2

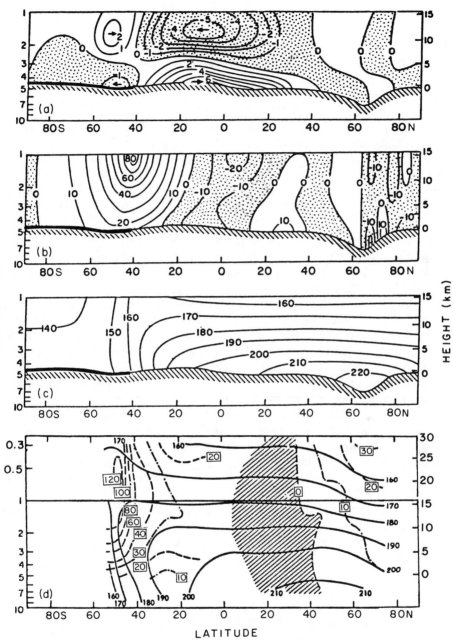

FIG. 2. Simulated zonally averaged meridional wind (a), zonal wind (b), and temperature (c) from the northern summer solstice simulation of Pollack *et al.* (1981). Cross section of temperature and thermal zonal wind (d) from Mariner 9 infrared interferometer spectrometer data for $L_s = 43$–54 (late southern autumn). Units are meters per second and Kelvin. Shaded areas correspond to southward and westward winds. The heavy lines correspond to the location of the seasonal CO_2 cap. [After Pollack, Leovy, Greiman, and Mintz (1981). Reproduced with permission from *Journal of the Atmospheric Sciences,* a publication of the American Meteorological Society.]

together with the derived zonal thermal winds. The observed and simulated cross sections both show strong meridional and weak vertical temperature gradients in middle latitudes of the winter hemisphere with a strong baroclinic westerly jet in winter mid-latitudes. Both show relatively weak horizontal temperature gradients and thermal winds in the summer hemisphere. Some minor differences, the latitude of the jet, for example, can be attributed to a difference in season; the observations correspond to late northern spring rather than northern summer solstice. Significantly the model simulated static stability in the tropics and summer hemisphere was only about half as great as that observed. This can probably be attributed to the absorption of solar radiation by dust, which is not included in the model (Pollack *et al.,* 1979).

Topography influenced the simulated circulation very much as had been anticipated by Blumsack and Webster: in the tropics, thermal lows over uplands alternated with thermal highs over lowlands; while at high latitudes of the winter hemisphere, there was a barotropic mechanically forced Rossby wave response in the westerlies. As in the simulation with the earlier version of the Mintz–Arakawa model, traveling baroclinic wave cyclones were produced in the winter hemisphere and, in agreement with the earlier results, the dominant zonal wave number was four. More significantly, the amplitude as well as the zonal wave number agreed well with those of traveling waves observed at the Viking lander sites (Ryan *et al.,* 1978; Barnes, 1980, 1981). The Viking lander observations confirmed the absence of summer baroclinic wave activity in middle latitudes, but some Viking images have shown small cyclonic cloud systems at very high northern latitudes during summer (Hunt and James, 1979). These systems were seen adjacent to the edge of the residual summer polar cap, which is composed of water ice, and they resemble the small but intense polar cyclones found on Earth near the edge of polar sea ice.

This simulation also produced a thermally forced diurnal tide, in this case modulated by the topography. Qualitatively at last, the surface pressure response of this tide was in good agreement with detailed linearized tidal calculations of Zurek (1976), with the largest amplitude occurring over upland longitudes.

4. Mariner and Viking Observations: The Role of Dust

Ground-based observers have seen dust storms on Mars for many years (Slipher, 1962; Capen and Martin, 1972; Martin, 1974), but our present understanding of these storms has been derived largely from Mariner 9 and Viking data. When Mariner 9 arrived at Mars, shortly before perihelion and northern winter solstice, the planet's surface was almost completely obscured by a thick layer of globally dispersed dust (Masursky *et al.*, 1972). During four northern winters in which Viking Lander 1 (VL-1, located at 22.5°N latitude and 48°W longitude) operated on the surface of mars, several such global scale dust storms occurred (Leovy *et al.*, 1984).

One of the surprising atmospheric results from Viking was the finding that there is a significant amount of dust in the atmosphere even during the clearest periods (Pollack *et al.*, 1977, 1979). Since it is an effective absorber of solar radiation, this suspended dust strongly affects the general circulation. The dust effects can be seen clearly in the thermal structure; as the suspended dust load increases, the atmosphere as a whole is heated and its static stability increases (Conrath, 1975; Pollack *et al.*, 1979; Martin and Kieffer, 1979; and Martin, 1981). Figure 3, based on data from Martin (1981), shows how the 15-μm-band atmospheric emission temperature varied as a function of latitude and season during the year following the Viking landings. This temperature corresponds to a very broad atmospheric weighting function centered near 25 km altitude. The generally higher temperatures during northern

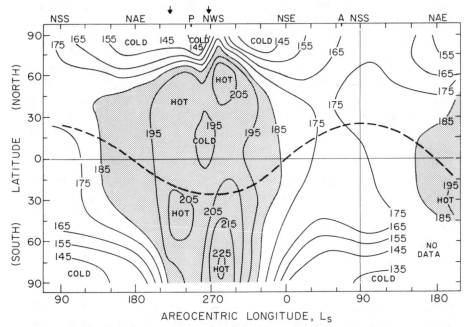

FIG. 3. Distribution with season and latitude of atmospheric thermal emission temperatures from the data of Martin (1981). Dates identified at the top are northern summer solstice (NSS), northern autumn equinox (NAE), northern winter solstice (NWS), northern spring equinox (NSE), perihelion (P), and aphelion (A). Arrows mark the onsets of two global dust storms.

winter were partly due to the eccentricity of the orbit; Mars makes its closest approach to the sun shortly before the northern winter solstice. However, the highest temperatures were due in large part to two global dust storms that occurred during this particular year, one near $L_s = 210$, the other near $L_s = 270$.* Each storm produced a rapid rise in atmospheric temperature followed by a more gradual decrease lasting 60–90 days together with a drop in near-surface temperature and a corresponding marked increase in static stability (Ryan and Henry, 1979). Figure 3 shows that the highest temperatures occurred at high latitudes in both winter and summer hemispheres rather than at the subsolar latitude.

The winter high latitude warm belt is particularly striking during the second dust storm, and it is interpreted as evidence for subsidence in an expanded and intensified cross-equatorial Hadley circulation. This interpretation is supported by changes in surface winds and surface pressures at the lander sites; a trade-wind regime appeared to expand poleward past the latitude of Viking Lander 2 (VL-2, latitude 48°W) during the peak phase of the second storm (Leovy, 1979). Such large and intense Hadley circulations forced by strong heating offset from the equator are consistent with theoretical models of the Hadley circulation in the quasi-inviscid limit (Held and Hou, 1980; Schneider, 1983).

Dust heating drives intensified diurnal and semidurnal thermal tides, but these two modes of circulation differ in their responses to the heating: the diurnal tide responds locally to shallow and/or latitudinally confined heat sources while the semidiurnal tide responds to deep, globally distributed heat sources (Zurek, 1980). This behavior is similar to that of tides on Earth, and it is a consequence of the much larger vertical and horizontal scales of the semidiurnal tidal modes compared with the diurnal modes. During Mars's global dust storms, dust tends to be distributed more or less uniformly to altitudes of 50 km or so except in the polar regions (Anderson and Leovy, 1978), so these storms effectively excite the semidiurnal tide. Using the theory of the semidiurnal tide, the global mean dust optical depth at visible wavelengths can be deduced quite accurately from VL-1 pressure data (Zurek and Leovy, 1981).

The surface pressure signature of the global dust storms is illustrated in Fig. 4. Large-amplitude low-frequency oscillations of daily mean pressure are produced by condensation and sublimation of CO_2 (Briggs, 1974). The seasonal maximum occurs after sublimation of the south polar cap and before condensation of the north polar cap. Near this maximum in the first year of the Viking record, there are two large sawtooth features, most prominent at VL-1, in the standard deviation of pressure about the daily mean.

---

* L_s, the areocentric longitude of the sun, is the seasonal index. $L_s = 0°$ corresponds to northern spring equinox. Because of the orbital eccentricity, the relationship between L_s and time is significantly nonlinear.

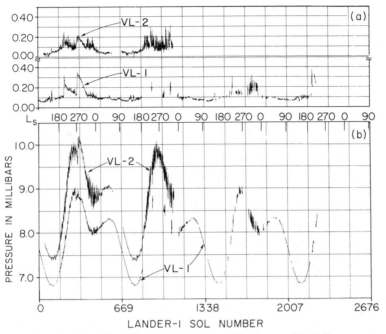

FIG. 4. (a) Standard deviation of pressure about the daily mean and (b) daily mean pressures at the Viking lander sites. Gaps correspond to periods when no data were acquired. The difference in mean pressure between the two sites is due primarily to elevation difference.

These are due primarily to the sudden onset and gradual decay of the semi-diurnal pressure oscillation produced by two global dust storms. The signature of the third global dust storm can be seen less clearly near the end of the record during the fourth winter. Pressure standard deviation maxima can also be seen in the other two winters, but these are associated with enhancements of the diurnal tide and day-to-day variability rather than the semidiurnal tide, and they do not have the characteristic sawtooth signature of the global storms.

In Table II, maximum semidiurnal tidal amplitudes and the inferred optical depths are given for three seasons, autumn (A), winter (W), and spring (S), in four Martian years. The diurnal tidal amplitude and a representative optical depth deduced from sun diode measurements or images taken at the VL-1 site are also given (Pollack *et al.*, 1977, 1979; Arvidson *et al.*, 1983). The semidiurnal tidal data clearly indicate that two global dust storms occurred during the first year observed by Viking, none in the second and third, and a third global dust storm, the largest of the three, in the fourth autumn (Leovy *et al.*, 1985).

The period from late autumn to early spring at VL-1 was very dusty in every year in which Viking data were obtained, whether or not any global

TABLE II. BAROCLINIC WAVE RMS PRESSURE VARIATIONS, TIDAL PRESSURE
AMPLITUDES, AND OPTICAL DEPTHS AT THE VIKING LANDER SITES[a]

		Baroclinic wave rms pressure amplitude[d]		Diurnal tide amplitude[d]		Semidiurnal tide amplitude[d]		In situ optical depth at 0.5 μm	
Year	Season[b,c]	VL-1	VL-2	VL-1	VL-2	VL-1	VL-2	VL-1	VL-2
1	A*	0.008	0.017	0.022	0.018	0.036	0.010	>3	>2
	W*	0.003	0.007	0.031	0.020	0.039	0.014	>4	>2
	S	0.007	0.020	0.016	0.011	0.014	0.009	1	0.5–1
2	A	—	0.020	0.019	0.014	0.015	0.011	—	—
	W, S	0.015	0.021	0.020	0.013	0.016	0.006	—	—
3	A	—	—	0.024	—	0.020	—	—	—
	W, S	0.018	—	0.027	—	0.021	—	4	—
4	A*	0.004	—	0.024	—	0.044	—	>4	—

[a] Data are from Barnes (1980, 1981), Leovy (1981), Leovy et al. (1985), Pollack et al. (1979), and J. B. Pollack (personal communication).

[b] Data are for various Mars years (1, 2, 3, 4) and seasons: A (autumn, $L_s \approx 190$–250), W (winter, $L_s \approx 250$–310), S (spring, $L_s \approx 310$–010).

[c] Global dust storms occurred in seasons with *.

[d] Pressure variances and amplitudes are normalized by the mean pressure.

dust storms occurred. Not only were high optical depths due to dust directly observed at the site, but the large amplitudes of the diurnal tide compared with the amplitude observed during the relatively clear summer half-year indicate that dust was sufficiently widespread to excite this tide, but not sufficiently widespread to excite the semidiurnal tide. Another interesting aspect of the winter season meteorological data at both VL-1 and VL-2 is the anticorrelation between dust storms and traveling baroclinic waves. These waves, whose centers normally move eastward in a latitude band slightly poleward of the VL-2 site, are strongly suppressed whenever there is a global dust storm (Barnes, 1980, 1981). They are responsible for the high-frequency variability of daily mean pressure shown in Fig. 4. Note the suppression of this signal during the second of the three global dust storms at both sites and its large amplitude at VL-1 near $L_s = 300$ of the third winter when there was no global dust storm. In years without global dust storms, these systems become intense enough to generate local dust storms in the latitude band containing both landers. Winds in the neighborhood of 30–40 m s^{-1} are apparently capable of raising dust at the sites (Arvidson et al., 1983; Leovy et al., 1985), and the strongest winds often seem to occur in cold air outbreaks associated with these systems (Briggs and Leovy, 1974).

Thus there is evidence for a bimodal weather pattern during Mars's northern winter season. In some years, there are global dust storms that spread over most of the planet carrying dust to very high altitudes. The dust heats and stabilizes the atmosphere, apparently strengthening and expanding the cross-equatorial Hadley circulation and strongly suppressing baroclinic wave activity. In other years, no global dust storms occur, but the northern winter baroclinic waves are very strong and raise considerable dust within a limited latitude belt in the winter hemisphere.

The global dust storms themselves appear to arise in the following sequence. As the large seasonal south polar cap recedes, the strong surface outflow winds deflected toward the west by the coriolis acceleration generate numerous dust storms (Briggs et al., 1979; Haberle et al., 1979; Kahn, 1983). Some of this dust remains in the atmosphere and enhances the heating due to absorption of solar radiation as Mars approaches perihelion. As a consequence, localized dust storms occur near perihelion in the vicinity of the subsolar latitude. There is evidence that both the diurnal thermal tide and topography influence the timing and location of these storms (Briggs et al., 1979; Peterfreund and Kieffer, 1979). A global dust storm is produced as these localized storms enlarge, coalesce, and the dust from the affected latitude belt is transported to high altitude and then rapidly swept meridionally over most of the planet. Why this sequence of events is followed in some years but not in others remains a mystery.

Modeling of these complex dust storm processes presents a challenge. Diagnostic models based on Mariner 9 data suggested that the enhanced thermally forced Hadley circulation and enhanced thermal tides are a major factor in these storms (Conrath et al., 1973; Leovy et al., 1973). Figure 1 shows how the cross-equatorial Hadley circulation and the diurnal tide can cooperate to produce strong surface winds during the daytime at northern winter solstice. Zurek (1976, 1980) showed that the diurnal tide and especially the semidiurnal tide are strongly driven by dust heating. Moriyama and Iwashima (1980; also see Iwashima et al., 1979) have used a low-order spectral balanced flow model limited to one hemisphere to investigate the circulation of the dusty Martian atmosphere. Their model included topography. Under very dusty conditions this model produced intense thermal tides strongly modulated by topography. Zurek, on the other hand, found that topographic modulation of the tides decreases as the dust heating increases. Because of the low spectral order of their model and the restriction to a single hemisphere, Moriyama and Iwashima were not able to investigate the behavior of baroclinic waves or the cross-equatorial Hadley circulation.

The cross-equatorial Hadley circulation was investigated in a series of two-dimensional (meridional plane) model calculations by Haberle et al. (1982). The model used was patterned after the Mintz–Arakawa model used by Pollack et al. (1981) and extended to six layers. It was driven by the diurnally averaged heating generated by the complete diurnal cycle of a radiative–convective model and included heating due to dust. For clear conditions at northern winter solstice (the global dust storm season), this model produced zonally averaged temperatures and meridional and zonal winds in good agreement with those generated by the solstice simulation of Leovy and Mintz. As the amount of dust in the atmosphere was increased, the atmospheric temperature and static stability and the size and intensity of the Hadley circulation increased, in qualitative agreement with the observations. However, the northward expansion of the Hadley cell was not as great as that apparently observed, and the north polar region atmospheric temperatures in the model remained well below those observed.

In a series of further calculations designed to investigate the mechanisms of global dust storms, Haberle *et al.* were able to show that the Hadley circulation intensifies rapidly if transport of dust raised within a limited latitude belt near the subsolar point is simulated. Apparently the positive feedback between dust heating and the Hadley circulation plays an important role in distributing the suspended dust to great heights over the planet during these storms.

5. LESSONS FROM MARS

The development of our understanding of the Martian general circulation has benefited from a well-proportioned mixture of theory, observations, and a heirarchy of models, including general circulation models. Even before the beginning of the era of spacecraft exploration, the body of quasi-geostrophic theory and the ideas and techniques of general circulation modeling were available. These were applied early in the era to address specific issues such as the existence and dynamical implications of a mass flow circulation produced by the seasonal polar cap cycle and the existence and properties of baroclinic waves. Final resolution of these issues required further observations, but the modeling studies helped sharpen the questions asked of these observations. As new data about Mars revealed further complexities, for example, the existence of large amplitude large scale topography, the dynamical implications were analyzed first with comparatively simple (but still quite sophisticated) models that provided physical insights, and later with a general circulation model that sharpened these insights and increased our confidence in them. Thermal tides were thought to be important on Mars and appropriate models for investigating tidal behavior had been applied to Mars well before the first Martian data showing tides were obtained. These modeling studies focused the questions, and as a result, analysis of the data from the two Viking weather stations has proven to be remarkably revealing.

Of course, Mars is a cooperative planet, it fits our Earth-based theories well. Moreover, the two Viking landers seem to have been particularly for-tuitously located to obtain revealing data about the general circulation. Nevertheless, the prior theoretical and modeling studies have greatly facili-tated the interpretations of these data in terms of the polar cap mass flow, baroclinic waves, the Hadley circulation, topographically controlled flow, and thermal tides. In retrospect, the most surprising results are that the Martian atmosphere appears to have two sharply differentiated modes of behavior, either with or without global dust storms, and that a single, well-sit-uated surface weather station can be used to diagnose both the global and regional states of the atmosphere with respect to dust storms.

The obvious next step is to apply a full general circulation model to the dusty Martian atmosphere. Such an application should provide further in-sight into the behavior of the Hadley circulation and the baroclinic waves in response to dust loading, and in particular, it could illuminate the feedback between dust loading and the general circulation that apparently produces the rapid spread of dust as the global dust storms develop. One such model is under development by Pollack and his collaborators. Development of this model is in a leapfrog mode; the physics, including friction as well as heating, has been drawn largely from the six-layer model of Haberle *et al.* The fric-tional parameterization includes a Richardson-number-dependent vertical momentum exchange that may be vital in the dusty atmosphere since the dust-driven heating can be strong enough to drive vigorous inertial instabil-ity. This instability can be controlled in a physically plausible way with a vertical momentum exchange that tends to adjust the Richardson number toward stable values.

Beyond the problems of the interaction between dust and the general circulation, modeling studies might address the atmospheric transport of water that is of considerable planetological interest (Jakosky and Farmer, 1982) and the role of breaking gravity waves and tides as sources and sinks of momentum. Theoretical studies indicate that gravity wave breaking is im-portant on Earth (Lindzen, 1981; Matsuno, 1982; Holton, 1982) and break-ing tidal waves may be a very important momentum source for Mars's atmosphere above 30 km (Hamilton, 1982).

By the early 1990s, a new body of spacecraft data for Mars should be available. The Mars Geochemistry and Climatology orbiter, now being planned by NASA, is expected to be the first spacecraft at Mars in a low polar orbit. It is to be equipped with a full compliment of atmospheric remote-sensing instruments and should be able to provide data for the first true synoptic maps of the Martian atmosphere.

Have we learned anything from all of this that helps us to understand the weather and climate of Earth? To me, the most interesting result is the evidence that the Hadley circulation expands and contracts in response to the thermal forcing. True, this is only consistent with theory, but it is very encouraging to discover an actual planetary example of this process. This result may have implications for paleo-climate, and it has already influenced studies of the "nuclear winter" phenomenon (Turco *et al.*, 1983; Covey *et al.*, 1984). The body of observational, modeling, and theoretical results concerning the Martian atmosphere is a rich one, and one can hardly doubt that this material and the future additions to it will provide other clues and inspirations that will enhance our understanding of Earth's atmosphere.

ACKNOWLEDGMENT

I am indebted to Terry Martin and James Tillman for providing the data shown in Figs. 3 and 4.

REFERENCES

Anderson, E., and Leovy, C. (1978). *J. Atmos. Sci.* **35**, 723–734.
Arakawa, A. (1966). *J. Comput. Phys.* **1**, 119–143.
Arakawa, A. (1972). "Design of the UCLA General Circulation Model" Tech. Rep. No. 7. Dep. Meteorol., University of California, Los Angeles.
Arvidson, R. E., Guiness, E. A., Moore, H. J., Tillman, J. E., and Wall, S. D. (1983). *Science* **222**, 463–468.
Barnes, J. R. (1980). *J. Atmos. Sci.* **37**, 2002–2015.
Barnes, J. R. (1981). *J. Atmos. Sci.* **38**, 225–234.
Blumsack, S. L. (1971a). *J. Atmos. Sci.* **28**, 1134–1143.
Blumsack, S. L. (1971b). *Icarus* **15**, 429–442.
Blumsack, S. L., Gierasch, P. J., and Wessel, W. R. (1973). *J. Atmos. Sci.* **30**, 66–82.
Briggs, G. A. (1974). *Icarus* **23**, 167–191.
Briggs, G. A., and Leovy, C. B. (1974). *Bull. Am. Meteorol. Soc.* **55**, 278–296.
Briggs, G. A., Baum, N. A., and Barnes, J. (1979). *JGR, J. Geophys. Res.* **84**, 2795–2820.
Capen, C. F., and Martin, L. J. (1972). *Sky Telescope* **43**, 276–279.
Coblentz, W. W., and Lampland, C. O. (1927). Further radiometric measurements and temperature estimates of the planet Mars. *Sci. Pap, Bu. Stand.* **22**, 237–276.
Conrath, B. J. (1975). *Icarus* **24**, 36–46.
Conrath, B. J. (1981). *Icarus* **48**, 246–255.
Conrath, B. J., Curran, R., Hanel, R., Kunde, V., Maguire, W., Pearl, J., Pirraglia, J., Welker, J., and Burke, T. (1973). *JGR, J. Geophys. Res.* **78**, 4267–4278.
Covey, C., Schneider, S. H., and Thompson, S. L. (1984). *Nature (London)* **38**, 21–31.
Crisp, D. A. (1983). Ph.D. Thesis, Geophysical Fluid Dynamics Program, Princeton University, Princeton, New Jersey.
Fels, S. B. (1977). *J. Atmos. Sci.* **34**, 419–514.
Gierasch, P. J., and Goody, R. M. (1968). *Planet. Space Sci.* **16**, 615–646.
Gierasch, P. J., and Sagan, C. (1971). *Icarus* **14**, 312–318.
Haberle, R. M., Leovy, C., and Pollack, R. M. (1979). *Iscarus* **39**, 151–183.
Haberle, R. M., Leovy, C. B., and Pollack, J. B. (1982). *Icarus* **50**, 322–368.

Hamilton, K. (1982). *J. Atmos. Sci.* **39**, 481–485.
Hanel, R. B., Conrath, W., Hovis, W., Kunde, V., Lowman, P., Lowman, W., McGuire, W., Pearl, J., Pirraglia, J., Prabhakara, C., Schlachman, B., Levin, G., Straat, P., and Burke, T. (1972). *Icarus* **17**, 423–442.
Held, I. M., and Hou, A. Y. (1980). *J. Atmos. Sci.* **37**, 515–533.
Hess, S. L. (1950). *J. Meteorol.* **7**, 1–13.
Hess, S. L., Henry, R. M., Leovy, C. B., Ryan, J. A., and Tillman, J. E. (1977). *JGR, J. Geophys. Res.* **82**, 4559–4574.
Holton, J. R. (1982). *J. Atmos. Sci.* **39**, 791–799.
Hunt, G. E., and James, P. B. (1979). *Nature (London)* **278**, 531–532.
Iwashima, T., Moriyama, S., and Yamamoto, R. (1979). *J. Meteorol. Soc. Jpn.* **57**, 97–111.
Jakosky, B., and Farmer, C. B. (1982). *JGR, J. Geophys. Res.* **87**, 2999–3019.
Kahn, R. (1983). *JGR, J. Geophys. Res.* **88**, 10,189–10,209.
Kaplan, L. D., Muench, G., and Spinrad, H. (1964). *Astrophys. J.* **139**, 1–15.
Leighton, R. B., and Murray, B. C. (1966). *Science* **153**, 136–144.
Leovy, C. B. (1969). *J. Geophys. Res.* **74**, 3313–3321.
Leovy, C. B. (1979). *Annu. Rev. Astron. Astrophys.* **17**, 387–413.
Leovy, C. B. (1981). *J. Atmos. Sci.* **38**, 30–39.
Leovy, C. B., and Mintz, Y. (1969). *J. Atmos. Sci.* **26**, 1167–1190.
Leovy, C. B., Zurek, R. W., and Pollack, J. B. (1973). *J. Atmos. Sci.* **30**, 749–762.
Leovy, C. B., Tillman, J. E., Guest, W. R., and Barnes, J. R. (1985). *In* "Dynamics of Planetary Atmospheres" (G. E. Hunt, ed.). Cambridge Univ. Press, London and New York (in press).
Lindzen, R. S. (1981). *JGR, J. Geophys. Res.* **86**, 9707–9714.
Martin, L. J. (1974). *Icarus* **23**, 108–115.
Martin, T. Z. (1981). *Icarus* **45**, 427–446.
Martin, T. Z., and Kieffer, H. H. (1979). *JGR, J. Geophys. Res.* **84**, 2843–2852.
Mass, C. and Sagan, C. (1976). *J. Atmos. Sci.* **33**, 1418–1430.
Masursky, H., Batson, R., McCauley, J., Soderblom, L., Wildey, R., Carr, M., Milton, D., Wilhelms, D., Smith, B., Kirby, T., Robinson, J., Leovy, C., Briggs, G., Duxbury, T., Acton, C., Murray, B., Cutts, J., Sharp, R., Smith, S., Leighton, R., Sagan, C., Veverka, J., Noland, M., Lederberg, J., Levinthal, E., Pollack, J., Moore, J., Hartmann, W., Shipley, E., de Vaucouleurs, G., and Davies, M. (1972). *Science* **175**, 294–305.
Matsuno, T. (1982). *J. Meteorol. Soc. Jpn.* **60**, 215–226.
Mintz, Y. (1961). *NAS-NRC, Publ.* **944**, 107–146.
Mintz, Y. (1965). *Meteorol. Monogr.* **8**, No. 30, 20–36.
Moriyama, S., and Iwashima, T. (1980). *JGR, J. Geophys. Res.* **85**, 2847–2860.
Peterfreund, A. R., and Kieffer, H. H. (1979). *JGR, J. Geophys. Res.* **84**, 2853–2863.
Pettengill, F. G., Counselman, C. C., Rainville, L. F., and Shapiro, I. I. (1969). *Astron. J.* **74**, 461–482.
Pollack, J. B., Leovy, C. B., Mintz, Y., and van Camp, W. (1976). *Geophys. Res. Lett.* **3**, 479–483.
Pollack, J. B., Colburn, D., Kahn, R., Hunter, J., Van Camp, W., Carlston, C., and Wolf, M. (1977). *JGR, J. Geophys. Res.* **82**, 4479–4496.
Pollack, J. B., Colburn, D. S., Flasar, F. M., Kahn, R., Carlston, C. E., and Pidek, D. (1979). *JGR, J. Geophys. Res.* **84**, 2929–2945.
Pollack, J. B., Leovy, C. B., Greiman, P. W., and Mintz, Y. (1981). *J. Atmos. Sci.* **38**, 3–29.
Rogers, A. E., Ash, M. E., Counselman, C. C., Shapiro, I. I., and Pettengill, F. G. (1970). *Radio Sci.* **5**, 465–473.
Rossow, W. B., and Williams, G. P. (1979). *J. Atmos. Sci.* **36**, 377–389.
Ryan, J. A., and Henry, R. M. (1979). *JGR, J. Geophys. Res.* **84**, 2821–2829.

Ryan, J. A., Hess, S. L., Henry, R. M., Leovy, C. B., and Tillman, J. E. (1978). *Geophys. Res. Lett.* **5,** 715–718.
Sagan, C., Veverka, J., and Gierasch, P. J. (1971). *Icarus* **15,** 253–278.
Schneider, E. D. (1983). *Icarus* **55,** 302–331.
Slipher, E. C. (1962). "The Photographic Story of Mars." Sky Publishing Corp., Cambridge, Massachusetts.
Smagorinsky, J. (1969). *In* "The Global Circulation of the Atmosphere" (G. A. Corby, ed.), pp. 24–41. R. Meteorol. Soc., London.
Turco, R. P., Toon, O. B., Ackerman, T., Pollack, J. B., and Sagan, C. (1983). *Science* **222,** 1283–1292.
Webster, P. J. (1977). *Icarus* **30,** 626–649.
Williams, G. P. (1978). *J. Atmos. Sci.* **35,** 1399–1426.
Williams, G. P. (1979). *J. Atmos. Sci.* **36,** 932–968.
Williams, G. P., and Holloway, J. L. (1982). *Nature (London)* **297,** 295–299.
Zurek, R. W. (1976). *J. Atmos. Sci.* **33,** 321–337.
Zurek, R. W. (1980). *J. Atmos. Sci.* **37,** 1132–1136.
Zurek, R. W., and Leovy, C. B. (1981). *Science* **213,** 437–439.

ATMOSPHERIC CIRCULATION
OF VENUS

WILLIAM B. ROSSOW

NASA Goddard Space Flight Center
Institute for Space Studies
New York, New York

1. INTRODUCTION

Laboratory experiments with, and theoretical studies of, differentially heated, rotating fluids have illuminated the basic baroclinic instability process that replaces a simple thermal Hadley circulation with a fully turbulent, horizontal flow that has most of its momentum directed perpendicular to the pressure gradient direction [e.g., Fultz *et al.* (1959), Hide (1977), and Spence and Fultz (1977)]. The geostrophically balanced zonal flow in Earth's atmosphere has superimposed on it a spectrum of planetary scale wave motions that play a major role in the heat and angular momentum budgets: only at low latitudes does a Hadley circulation become important in these budgets (Oort and Rasmussen, 1971). Understanding how rotational effects influence these characteristics of Earth's atmospheric circulation is basic to understanding how our atmosphere might change when perturbed (the climate problem). A natural laboratory for study of rotational effects on atmospheric circulations is provided by the planets in our solar system (Williams and Holloway, 1982), where Venus provides an example of the slowly rotating regime to be contrasted with Earth's rapidly rotating regime.

In slow rotation experiments in laboratory fluids, the thermal circulation is a simple axisymmetric Hadley cell. Observations of Venus, however, show

347

that the circulation there involves fully developed turbulent motions and strong zonal flow, in contrast to the laboratory circulations, suggesting a more complicated heat and momentum balance. Two differences between the slowly rotating laboratory fluid and a slowly rotating atmosphere are the much larger difference in horizontal and vertical length scales and the spherical geometry. The former property may require more than one dynamic mode to be involved in the thermal balance. The latter property results in large zonal wind speeds near the pole produced by the momentum conserving Hadley cell motions. Numerical simulations (Geisler *et al.,* 1983) find no axisymmetric flow regime for slow rotation and large temperature gradients in spherical geometry, suggesting that the zonal flow must be unstable even at slow rotation rates. However, the instability processes that lead to the wave motions in a slowly rotating atmosphere are not well understood and the role played by them in the heat and momentum budgets is not yet known. Understanding of rotational effects on atmospheric circulations is not complete, therefore, without understanding the slowly rotating regime as well as the rapidly rotating regime.

In this paper, we consider these issues by highlighting developments in understanding of the Venus circulation. At all stages of this development, the facts available to describe the Venus atmosphere have been limited and the available theoretical models rather simple. Recent spacecraft missions have provided many new facts, but analysis and modeling studies exploiting this new information are not yet complete. Key developments in the study of Venus are discussed in Section 2. Limitations of currently available data and theory are discussed in Section 3. The new observations and some recent modeling studies suggest new formulations of the basic dynamical questions posed by Venus. In Section 4, we outline our view of these new questions, which address many of the limitations discussed in Section 3, and suggest subjects for further study. Section 5 provides a summary.

2. DEVELOPMENT OF THE PROBLEM

Early ground-based observations of Venus suggested that the amount of sunlight absorbed by the completely cloud-covered planet was probably less than that of the Earth [e.g., Sinton (1963)], even though it is closer to the sun. Nevertheless, the surface temperature appeared to be more than twice that of Earth (Barath *et al.,* 1963). Other observations show a rotation period of the solid planet of more than 200 days (Shapiro, 1968) but an apparent rotation period of the atmosphere at cloud levels of less than about 5 days (Boyer and Guerin, 1966). These two puzzles have continued to serve as the focus of Venus investigations, but they actually constitute two pieces of the single problem of understanding the general circulation of the Venus atmosphere, that is, how the atmosphere achieves *both* an energy and a momentum balance.

The intimate connection between the energy and momentum budgets can be seen in the equations of motion, here expressed in spherical coordinates (λ, θ, z) as conservation of angular momentum, meridional momentum, and potential temperature (or entropy), plus hydrostatic balance:

$$\frac{\partial}{\partial t}(\rho M) + \left[\frac{1}{a \cos \theta} \frac{\partial}{\partial \lambda}(\rho M u) + \frac{1}{a \cos \theta} \frac{\partial}{\partial \theta}(\rho M v \cos \theta) + \frac{\partial}{\partial z}(\rho M w) \right]$$

$$= -\frac{\partial p}{\partial \lambda} + T_\lambda \tag{2.1}$$

$$\frac{\partial}{\partial t}(\rho v) + \left[\frac{1}{a \cos \theta} \frac{\partial}{\partial \lambda}(\rho v u) + \frac{1}{a \cos \theta} \frac{\partial}{\partial \theta}(\rho v^2 \cos \theta) + \frac{\partial}{\partial z}(\rho v w) \right]$$

$$= -\frac{\sin \theta}{a^3 \cos^3 \theta}[M^2 - \Omega^2 a^4 \cos^4 \theta] - \frac{1}{a}\frac{\partial p}{\partial \theta} \tag{2.2}$$

$$\frac{\partial p}{\partial z} = -\rho g \tag{2.3}$$

$$\frac{\partial}{\partial t}(\rho \Theta) + \left[\frac{1}{a \cos \theta} \frac{\partial}{\partial \lambda}(\rho \Theta u) + \frac{1}{a \cos \theta} \frac{\partial}{\partial \theta}(\rho \Theta v \cos \theta) + \frac{\partial}{\partial z} \right]$$

$$= \left(\frac{p_0}{p}\right)^\kappa \left(\frac{Q}{C_p}\right) \tag{2.4}$$

where $M = ua \cos \theta + \Omega a^2 \cos^2 \theta$ is the absolute angular momentum per unit mass, Ω is the planetary rotation rate, T_λ is the torque exerted by "friction" processes, $\Theta = T(p_0/p)^\kappa$ is the potential temperature (entropy per unit mass), and Q is the *net* radiative heating (or cooling). Other symbols have their conventional meanings.

Stone's (1975) estimates of the magnitudes of the quantities in Eqs. (2.1)–(2.4) can be refined by more recent observations to give (from lower atmosphere to near cloud tops when a range is given): length scale $L \sim 10^7$ m (Rossow *et al.*, 1980a), velocity scale $u \sim 10$–100 m s$^{-1} \sim 5$–$50\ \Omega a$ (Counselman *et al.*, 1980), dynamic time scale $\sim 10^6$–10^5 s [see also, Rossow and Williams (1979)], length of solar day, $\tau_{day} \sim 10^7$ s, $\gamma \equiv \tau_{dyn}/\tau_{day} \sim 10^{-1}$–$10^{-2}$, horizontal temperature contrast $\delta\Theta_H \sim 0.01$–$0.1\ \Theta$ (Seiff *et al.*, 1980), radiative time constant $\tau_{rad} \sim 10^9$–10^5 s, $\delta \equiv \tau_{rad}/\tau_{day} \sim 10^{-3}$–$10^1$, vertical temperature contrast $\delta\Theta_v \lesssim 0.1\ \Theta$, and depth of atmosphere below clouds in scale heights $D \sim 6H$.

The observed meridional and zonal wind speeds (Counselman *et al.*, 1980; Rossow *et al.*, 1980a) and the observed temperature contrasts (Seiff, 1983) suggest from (2.2) that the zonal and time-averaged zonal flow is in cyclostrophic balance (Leovy, 1973); however, a dynamic flux of angular momentum is still required to balance the torques of any "friction" processes in (2.1). If the atmosphere were in local radiative equilibrium, $Q = 0$ and $\delta\Theta_H \sim \Theta$, however, the latter fact means that $\delta p/\delta\theta \neq 0$, requiring motions in the atmosphere. If the energy transporting efficiency of these motions is small compared to that of radiation, then the dynamic heat flux on the left in (2.4) does not alter the temperature distribution and the energy and momentum balances can be considered independently. However, the observed $\delta\Theta_H \lesssim 0.1\ \Theta$ means that the dynamic effects are dominant and that these two balances cannot be uncoupled. The nonlinear cyclostrophic balance [see Eq. 2.6)] makes consideration of the circulation more difficult than for the case of the linear geostrophic balance (see Section 3.2.1). Consequently, separate consideration of the momentum and energy balance may be very misleading on Venus.

2.1. Puzzle of the Hot Surface

The presence of large amounts of CO_2 (Dunham, 1952) and some H_2O (Belton et al., 1968) in the atmosphere of Venus suggested a "greenhouse" explanation of the high surface temperatures (Sagan, 1962), but this required that some sunlight penetrate through the complete cloud cover to the bottom of a dense atmosphere. Without any evidence for sunlight pentration, Goody and Robinson (1966) suggested a dynamical analogy with the ocean in which heat energy is transported from the surface into the interior by the circulation. Although subsequent dynamical models, which included proper atmospheric density stratification, showed that this explanation was unrealistic (Kalnay de Rivas, 1973, 1975), Goody and Robinson's focus on the interaction of dynamical and radiation processes to determine the thermal structure and their emphasis on the key role of the clouds still seem appropriate. Scale analyses, like that made following (2.1–2.4) (Gierasch et al., 1970; Stone, 1974, 1975), show that large-scale dynamics must play a primary role in determining the horizontal thermal structure, but circulation model results suggest that the vertical distribution of radiative forcing may determine the vertical structure of the dynamics (Kalnay de Rivas, 1975; Rossow, 1983). In other words, the thermal structure and dynamics cannot be determined independently of each other because the energy balance may involve different dynamic modes in the horizontal and vertical directions.

The first Venera probes into the atmosphere below the clouds showed that sunlight does, indeed, penetrate to the surface (Ekonomov et al., 1983), but that most of the sunlight is absorbed in the clouds. Current estimates are that about 60% of the total absorbed solar energy is deposited in the clouds (40% above 65 km) and 25% of the total at the surface and in the lower atmosphere

(Tomasko *et al.,* 1980; Tomasko, 1983). Pioneer Venus probes also detected another important source of infrared opacity for the greenhouse, namely SO_2 (Hoffman *et al.,* 1980). The Pioneer Venus radiation and composition measurements, together with theoretical calculations (Pollack *et al.,* 1980) strongly support the greenhouse explanation of the high surface temperature; but the complicated temperature distribution observed in the atmosphere (Seiff *et al.,* 1980; Taylor *et al.,* 1980; Kliore and Patel, 1980; Seiff, 1983; Newman *et al.,* 1984) raises many new questions about the heat budget.

Four features of the temperature distribution are particularly intriguing: (1) positive latitudinal temperature gradients in low latitudes at 20 to 50 km (Seiff *et al.,* 1980) and above the clouds to about 90 km at higher latitudes (Taylor *et al.,* 1980), (2) strong latitudinal temperature gradients (~ 20 K) and a temperature inversion forming a temperature minimum in high latitudes at cloud levels (Kliore and Patel, 1980), (3) a shallow neutrally stable layer near the cloud base lying above a deep statically stable layer (Seiff *et al.,* 1980), and (4) complicated vertical structures in the Pioneer Venus night probe net flux profile (Suomi *et al.,* 1980).

While purely radiative explanations have been offered for (3) (Pollack *et al.,* 1980) and (4) (Suomi *et al.,* 1980), (1) cannot be readily explained by radiative forcing [cf. Crisp (1984), Fels *et al.* (1984)] and is probably dynamically produced. Because the polar cloud properties are different from those in lower latitudes (Kawabata *et al.,* 1980), (2) may also have a radiative explanation, but the associated dynamical features in IR observations of the polar regions (Taylor *et al.,* 1980) suggest a strong dynamical element as well. The general circulation model (GCM) of Rossow (1983) suggests an alternative dynamical explanation for (1) and (3) involving convection near the surface and in the clouds coupled by vertically propagating gravity waves that redistribute the radiative heating to produce the observed gradients. If such a process were operative on Venus, it might also explain (4) in that alternating regions of heating and cooling would be associated with the propagating waves' temperature perturbations. All of these structures suggest that the planetary thermal budget is probably not just differential radiative heating and cooling balanced by simple Hadley circulation heat transports [see also, Tomasko (1983)]. In particular, heat transport by propagating waves can produce unanticipated thermal structures by heating regions not directly forced by solar radiation absorption (Fels *et al.,* 1984).

2.2. Puzzle of the Fast Winds at Cloud Levels

In the absence of any information about atmospheric motions above or below the clouds, early investigators visualized explanations of the flow, taken to a be a simple rotation of the atmosphere at cloud levels, in terms of local accelerations balanced by "friction." The first suggestions again focused on the importance of the radiation absorbed by the clouds: (1) increasing phase lag of the diurnal heating variations with depth below the clouds forces tilted convective motions that accelerate the flow in the heated region (Schubert and Whitehead, 1969), (2) buoyancy driven convective motions become "tilted" in a sheared zonal flow reinforcing the shear of the zonal flow (Thompson, 1970), and (3) vertically propagating thermal tides transport momentum into the cloud level where they originate (Fels and Lindzen, 1974). Gierasch (1975) proposed that the thermally driven mean meridional circulation (MMC) could accelerate cloud-level zonal flow if eddy mixing processes were mostly horizontal and served to eliminate horizontal gradients of angular velocity like molecular viscosity. All of these models of the cloud-level winds use some *ad hoc* diffusive process for momentum balance.

Even though the earlier Venera probe wind measurements near the equator provided some hints, it was the more detailed and widely dispersed Pioneer Venus probe results, sampling 60° of latitude, that revealed a very different and more complex picture of the zonal flow on Venus (Counselman *et al.,* 1980): most of the momentum and kinetic energy in the flow is actually concentrated near 20 km altitude (Fig. 1) with the whole atmosphere above that level contributing very little to the total (Schubert *et al.,* 1980). Instead of a localized zonal flow at (and possibly above) cloud levels, the whole atmosphere is superrotating. From this perspective, the atmosphere above 20 to 30 km appears only to be "along for the ride" rather than the primary locus of the acceleration. Nevertheless, despite the small amount of momentum in the upper-level flow, the large vertical shear in the rotation rate (Fig. 2) does require a process actively maintaining it.

The entry probe wind measurements also show that the lower atmospheric zonal flow resembles rigid shell rotation (based on four widely spaced probes) (Fig. 2), whereas differential rotation occurs at higher altitudes. Differential rotation near cloud tops is also observed in the motions of small-scale ultraviolet cloud features; four years of observations from the Pioneer Venus Orbiter are summarized in Fig. 3. [See Limaye and Suomi (1981) for Mariner 10 results.] Inferences about the zonal flow derived from the radio occultation measurements of temperature suggest increasing differential rotation above the clouds producing a strong jet (Fig. 4) associated with a steeper horizontal temperature gradient in the polar regions (Newman *et al.,* 1984). These variations of the horizontal distribution of the zonal flow suggest changes in the momentum balance with altitude.

Observations also clearly indicate the presence of planetary-scale turbulent motions at cloud tops (Rossow *et al.,* 1980a; Del Genio and Rossow, 1982a). All the probe wind measurements (Kerzhanovich and Marov, 1983;

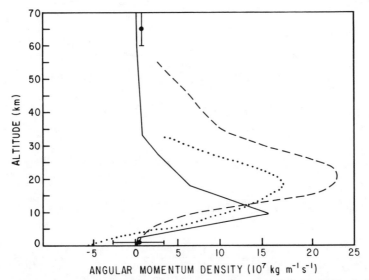

FIG. 1. Global-mean angular momentum density as a function of altitude for Venus ($\times 10^{-1}$, dashed), Earth ($\times 10^4$, dotted), and a numerical model (solid). Dot with error bar at top indicates measurements from cloud-tracked winds (Rossow *et al.,* 1980a). Earth profile has vertical scale twice the actual scale for comparison.

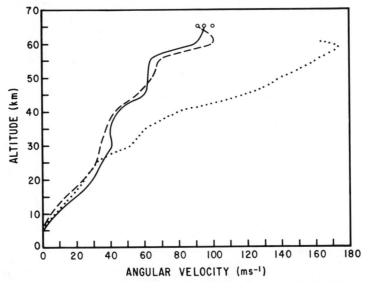

FIG. 2. Vertical profiles of angular velocity (divided by planetary radius) of the zonal flow measured by the four Pioneer Venus entry probes. Open circles indicate cloud-tracked wind measurements at comparable latitudes in the Southern Hemisphere. (——, sounder, equator; ------, day–night, 30°; ⋯⋯, north, 60°.)

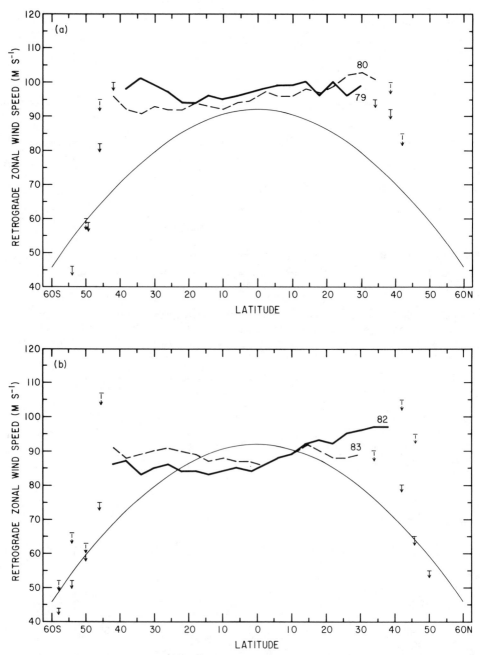

FIG. 3. Mean zonal flow at cloud tops as inferred from tracking the motion of UV cloud features in Pioneer Venus Orbiter images. Results are shown for four time periods in early (a) 1979 and 1980, (b) 1982 and 1983. The reference solid body rotation curve has an equatorial velocity of 92 m s^{-1}.

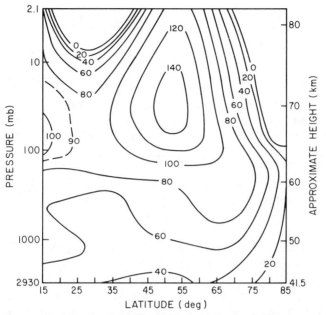

FIG. 4. Mean zonal flow deduced from Pioneer Venus radio occultation temperature field by assuming cyclostrophic balance. Velocity in direction of planetary rotation shown in meters per second. [After Newman, Schubert, Kliore, and Patel (1984). Reproduced with permission from *Journal of the Atmospheric Sciences,* a publication of the American Meteorological Society.]

Schubert, 1983), taken together with probe temperature measurements (Seiff, 1983), suggest variability of the zonal flow in the lower atmosphere that may be associated with wave motions. As with the heat budget, all of the characteristics of the momentum distribution suggest a more complex balance that cannot be understood in isolation from the thermal balance. The presence of propagating wave modes, in particular, creates the possibility for their playing a role in the momentum budget far from their source region.

3. LIMITATIONS OF FACT AND THEORY

3.1. Limitations of Fact

3.1.1. Net Radiative Forcing. The specific features of the Venus atmospheric circulation and thermal structure, highlighted above, provide intriguing hints as to the nature of the dynamical balances; however, investigation of these problems will be hindered by lack of some fundamental facts. Probably the most important of these is the vertical and horizontal distribution of net radiative heating. Venera and Pioneer Venus entry probes have sketched out the qualitative vertical distribution of solar energy deposition (Tomasko *et al.*, 1980; Ekonomov *et al.*, 1983; Tomasko 1983), but little is known about the variation of this structure with latitude. That it must vary with latitude (and time) is apparent at least from the observed cloud structure variations (Ragent and Blamont, 1980; Kawabata *et al.*, 1980). Furthermore, though some spectral distribution information is available at low latitudes (Ekonomov *et al.*, 1983), the radiation absorbing processes at different levels in the atmosphere are not well enough understood for accurate determinations of solar flux divergences, especially near cloud tops and in the lower atmosphere. The flux divergence structure of the thermal radiation is even more problematical because it is probably sensitive to small spectral variations in gaseous infrared opacities or to details in cloud composition (Tomasko, 1983). Again qualitative information is available, but the Pioneer Venus probe (Suomi *et al.*, 1980; Revercomb *et al.* 1982) and orbiter observations (Taylor *et al.*, 1980) revealed many complex, dynamic structures in the thermal radiation field. Uncertainties in the abundance of key trace gases, particularly H_2O, further complicate interpretation because the thermal radiation in the atmosphere below the clouds may have strong spectral variation with altitude [Pollack *et al.* (1980), see, e.g., Young (1982)].

These limitations prevent accurate calculation of the net radiative flux divergences, making it difficult to determine the radiative contribution to each of the features of the thermal structure listed in Section 2. This can be crucial because some of these features appear in regions where the solar contribution to Q in (2.4) is small. For example, the processes responsible for the deep, stable layer below the clouds and the shallow, neutrally stable layer near the cloud bottom (Seiff *et al.*, 1980) are important because the suggested explanation involving heating by the thermal radiation from below has important implications for the coupling of the upper and lower atmospheres. If the heating producing this neutrally stable layer in the clouds is primarily radiation from the surface at wavelengths shorter than 3 μm, where CO_2 is relatively transparent and the cloud opaque, then the relevant time constant for changes in thermal structure at cloud levels could be very much longer than that estimated from local atmospheric properties. Both the heat balance and the nature of the dynamic motions excited by solar absorption in the clouds would be altered.

3.1.2. Mean Zonal Flow. The second limitation of facts is uncertainty in the mean wind speeds above and below the clouds. Most of the information about the zonal wind structure comes from inferences based on the cyclostrophic relationship between temperature and zonal wind gradients (Seiff *et al.*, 1980; Schubert *et al.*, 1980; Newman *et al.*, 1984), plus a number of direct probe measurements (Kerzhanovich and Marov, 1983; Schubert, 1983). However, careful examination of the cyclostrophic wind results (Fig. 4) shows several regions in which the relationship breaks down completely, indicating either that some other dynamic process is involved in the pressure gradient balance, that the measured temperature field does not accurately represent the *mean* state of the atmosphere, or both (see discussion in Section 3.2.2). Different analyses of the same data (Newman *et al.*, 1984; Limaye, 1984) suggest that the quantitative effect of wave motions present in the observations may be important. Differences between probe wind measurements (Kerzhanovich and Marov, 1983; Schubert, 1983), the probe net thermal flux structures (Suomi *et al.*, 1980), and observations of motions near cloud tops (Apt and Leung, 1982; Del Genio and Rossow, 1982a) all suggest that large-scale wave effects might be responsible for this breakdown. The natural inference is that the zonal wind structure deduced from the temperature measurements may not describe the zonal flow structure with high accuracy.

Determination of the true zonal-mean flow from the more extensive cloud-tracked winds measurement available from Pioneer Venus Orbiter is also made difficult by the large-scale wave motions present in the flow. Since the measurements are limited to the illuminated hemisphere and the wave motions are predominantly planetary in scale (Del Genio and Rossow, 1982a), averaging the data in time must replace the desired longitudinal averaging to obtain the zonal-mean flow. The estimated wave-phase speeds (Del Genio and Rossow, 1982a) suggest that an averaging time period of at least 30 days is required to eliminate transient eddy effects; thus measurement of time variations of the zonal mean and eddy motions on time scales $< 10^7$ s is not possible. That variations in the zonal flow occur on longer time scales is illustrated by the Pioneer Venus Orbiter results obtained over four years (Fig. 3).

Two important regions in which even qualitative zonal wind speed information is lacking are near the surface and in the polar regions. Comparison of results from several numerical models (Hunt, 1979; Williams and Holloway, 1982; Geisler *et al.*, 1983; Rossow, 1983) indicates that the mean zonal wind *direction* at the surface, as a function of latitude, can be diagnostic of the momentum balance in an atmosphere, particularly the role of eddies (Rossow, 1983). If the Venus atmospheric angular momentum is in equilibrium with the surface, then the sum of the surface torques on the atmosphere must be zero, requiring zonal winds in both eastward and westward directions. Figure 1 suggests that this distribution on Venus is also equivalent to a very small relative angular momentum near the surface, in strong contrast to Earth's atmosphere at low latitudes (Rossow, 1983). The zonal flow very near the poles is important for understanding the momentum balance because of the potential importance of waves produced by zonal-flow instabilities at high latitudes in the global balance.

3.1.3. Waves. A final limitation of facts is the lack of meaningful information about waves in all parts of the atmosphere except near cloud tops. Although there are many hints that wave motions are present everywhere (Rossow *et al.,* 1980a; Kerzhanovich and Marov, 1983; Schubert *et al.,* 1980; Schubert, 1983), most of these observations will not allow identification of wave types and diagnosis of their properties. Ongoing analysis of the cloud-top observations has provided some results of this type for one atmospheric level (Del Genio and Rossow, 1982a,b), but interpretation of the global significance of these observations will remain difficult.

3.2. Limitations of Theory

The Soviet space program continues a steady pace of probe and orbiter missions to Venus that will slowly accumulate more information about the deep atmosphere, but long-lived orbiter missions to obtain climatological data are apparently not being planned. Enough information is available now to characterize the general dynamical regime that exists on Venus, though probably not enough to diagnose processes directly. Theoretical studies of the general processes that can occur in slowly rotating atmospheres can be fruitful; however, substantive progress requires tackling several difficult problems for which current theory is not adequate. In addition, some key process parameterizations, commonly used in numerical dynamical models, must be generalized.

Early studies of the Venus circulation regime employed "scaling analyses" to estimate the magnitude of particular terms in (2.1)–(2.4) [see review by Stone (1975)]; these results were then used to define simplified models of the circulation. This approach assumes that the properties of the circulation can be estimated using a balance composed of only the leading magnitude terms; but as discussed below this may not be adequate for all aspects of the circulation on Venus.

3.2.1. Cyclostrophic Balance. Observation of large zonal flow speeds near cloud tops led Leovy (1973) to suggest a balance of the centrifugal force acting on the mean zonal flow and the equator-to-pole pressure gradient produced by differential solar heating, analogous to the geostrophically balanced zonal flow on Earth. If (2.2) is written in pressure coordinates, then the balance of the two terms on the right can be expressed, using (2.3), as

$$\frac{\sin \theta}{a^3 \cos^3 \theta} \frac{\partial}{\partial p} [M^2 - \Omega^2 a^4 \cos^4 \theta] = \frac{R}{ap} \frac{\partial T}{\partial \theta} \qquad (3.1)$$

Since on Venus $u \gg \Omega a$, the term on the left in (3.1) can be reduced to

$$\frac{\tan \theta}{a} \frac{\partial}{\partial p} (u^2) = \frac{R}{ap} \frac{\partial T}{\partial \theta} \qquad (3.2)$$

While this balance is between the two largest terms in (2.2), it does not explain how the mean flow is maintained or even how it will respond to a perturbation. As discussed following (2.1)–(2.4), the horizontal temperature gradient on Venus is controlled by a balance of dynamic heat fluxes and net radiative heating/cooling, but the dynamics involved in this energy balance must also play a part in balancing the torques acting on the zonal flow. In other words *reactions* to perturbations bring in the other constraints on the mean circulation thereby involving *all* motions in the adjustments: the reaction is determined by the small magnitude terms in (2.1)–(2.4) [see similar discussion for Earth circulation in Rind and Rossow (1984)].

Even in the absence of dynamic feedbacks, the balance in (3.2) is nonlinear (in contrast to geostrophic balance); consequently, the *mean* temperature distribution is not directly related to the *mean* zonal flow as it is on Earth. To see this, take the zonal and time average of (3.2), where a variable $A = [A] + A'$ (zonal mean plus variation) and $B = \bar{B} + B^*$ (time mean plus variation):

$$\frac{\tan \theta}{a} \frac{\partial}{\partial p} \overline{[u][u]} + \overline{[u]^*[u]^*} + \overline{[(u)'(u)']} = \frac{R}{ap} \frac{\partial}{\partial \theta} \overline{[T]} \qquad (3.3)$$

The two additional contributions to the balance between the mean centrifugal force and the equator-to-pole temperature gradient are the time-averaged variations of the zonal-mean flow and the time and zonal-averaged eddy motions. Observations of the motions near cloud tops suggest not only significant eddy motions on the largest scales but also possible time variations of the mean zonal flow (Rossow *et al.,* 1980a; Del Genio and Rossow, 1982a,b, and Fig. 3). Note that the contribution to the balance of these variations in the flow can be more or less important if their vertical distribution is different from that of the mean zonal flow. The form of (3.3) shows the fundamental complexity of the slow rotation regime and suggests a basic uncertainty in determining the mean zonal flow from temperature measurements.

3.2.2. Hadley Cell Extent. Held and Hou (1980) derive a simple expression, relating the latitudinal extent of the Hadley circulation to the planetary rotation rate, the depth of the circulation, and the magnitude of differential radiative heating, by assuming an energy balance involving only the MMC and radiation and a momentum balance expressed by the thermal wind relation for the zonal flow. Surface friction is included implicitly in the bottom boundary condition of zero wind speed. Schneider (1977) makes different assumptions about the radiative forcing and obtains an expression that also depends on the static stability. In both cases the latitudinal extent is dependent on the energy balance. Hunt (1979) suggests instead that the extent is controlled by rotation rate, only, i.e., by momentum balance considerations. These simple expressions and the laboratory experiments all imply an equator-to-pole Hadley cell at Venus's rotation rate. However, these simple relationships neglect any eddy transports of heat and momentum that can alter the mean zonal flow and temperature distribution, as well as the heat and momentum transporting efficiency and extent of the Hadley circulation, itself. That these alterations will not cancel can be seen from (3.3), which replaces the thermal wind relation on Venus: eddy motions can contribute directly to the left side of this expression without altering the right side. Rind and Rossow (1984) illustrate changes in Hadley cell extent in model experiments where static stability, circulation depth, rotation rate, and radiative forcing are all constant, which suggests that a balanced circulation has additional constraints that must be considered as well. Various other model results, using different assumptions about "eddy friction," show conflicting results. Kalnay de Rivas (1973, 1975) neglects eddies but does not get an equator-to-pole cell at Venus rotation rates; Taylor (1980) gets an equator-to-pole cell for an Earth rotation rate without eddy mixing. Held and Hou (1980) appear to get equator-to-pole cells in Earth models with very strong friction, while Taylor (1980) gets a cell of limited extent when eddy effects are added. Variable rotation experiments with the Goddard Institute for Space Science (GISS) GCM of Earth (Fig. 5) agree only qualitatively with Held and Hou's expression and differ between hemispheres (Del Genio *et al.*, 1983). The implication is that, since the eddy motions can alter the momentum balance both by direct momentum transport and by heat transport alteration of the MMC, different parameterizations of the eddy processes lead to different model behavior. This more complicated linkage between the two budgets, mediated by the eddies (Rind and Rossow, 1984), makes suspect the use of simple scaling relationships for predicting the properties of the MMC under different conditions.

3.2.3. Other Scaling Analyses. Other scaling analyses (Golitsyn, 1970; Stone, 1974) have focused on the energy balance in a circulation in order to estimate the wind and temperature contrast magnitudes. Golitsyn's (1970) similarity theory, that the dimensionless numbers defined by the external parameters are nearly constant from one atmosphere to another, is equivalent to assuming that dynamic energy transport efficiency is roughly constant; whereas Gierasch *et al.* (1970) argue that the magnitude of the same key dimensionless number, $\epsilon = \gamma/\delta = \tau_{dyn}/\tau_{rad}$ [see Stone (1975)], simply indicates how efficient the dynamic energy transport actually is. Golitsyn's

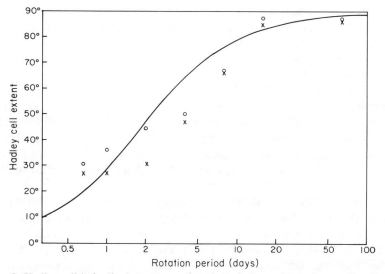

FIG. 5. Hadley cell latitudinal extent as a function of planetary rotation rate in the GISS GCM [X, Northern Hemisphere; O, Southern Hemisphere; ——, Held and Hou (1980), $H = 12$ km, $\Delta_H = \frac{1}{3}$.] [After Del Genio *et al.* (1983).]

(1970) approach predicts that the circulation on Venus should have about half the kinetic energy of the circulation on Earth, whereas observations show about 100 times more kinetic energy. Hunt (1979) obtains a similar contradiction between his model and the similarity relation between kinetic energy and planetary rotation rate. The kinetic energy in the GISS GCM (Del Genio *et al.*, 1983) and that of Williams and Holloway (1982) peaks at a rotation rate intermediate between that of Earth and Venus, in contradiction of the scaling results.

Stone (1974) estimates wind speeds for the MMC and temperature contrasts by assuming energy balance between the MMC and radiation. However, this balance is altered in the GCM of Rossow (1983) by the effects of the zonal flow and eddy heat and momentum transports. Not only can eddy motions alter the heat transport of the MMC by changing the temperature contrasts directly by transporting heat, but they also alter the drive for the MMC, the terms on the right in (2.2), through alterations of the zonal flow by transporting momentum. The scaling analyses neglect these nonlinear interactions between the MMC, zonal flow and eddies. Even if the MMC energy fluxes are the dominate terms in (2.4), the eddies can significantly alter the relationship between Q, Θ, v, and w because the MMC is driven by the *small* difference between the two *large* terms on the right in (2.2) and because Q is the *net* radiative flux divergence involving differences of large fluxes. Studies of Earth's circulation illustrate these same general conclusions (Rind and Rossow, 1984) and demonstrate the necessity of considering both the heat and momentum effects of eddies to diagnose their total effect on the mean circulation (Andrews *et al.*, 1983).

3.2.4. Large-Scale Wave Transports.

When Gierasch (1975) proposed his theory for the cloud-level winds on Venus, he envisioned an interaction between a single, surface-to-cloud top Hadley cell and planetary waves, represented by horizontal momentum diffusion, which act to eliminate gradients of angular velocity. Kalnay de Rivas (1975) showed that another necessary condition for this process to work is that the Prandtl number of the eddy mixing must be very large; otherwise the eddy heat transport replaces that by the Hadley circulation (Gierasch included no diffusion terms in his energy equation). Rossow and Williams (1979) demonstrated that two-dimensional barotropic waves could provide this type of momentum mixing and Rossow (1983) demonstrated the presence of such waves in a three-dimensional circulation as a consequence of the efficient heat transport by the Hadley circulation. This quasi-barotropic momentum mixing implies an equatorward transport of angular momentum against the latitudinal gradient of absolute angular momentum, whereas baroclinic eddies on Earth are responsible for a poleward transport of angular momentum with the gradient (Oort and Rasmussen, 1971). Thus some fundamental transition in the behavior of large-scale eddy motions is required as planetary rotation rate decreases.

The consequences of these two different eddy momentum transports can be illustrated by Fig. 6 and an extension of the discussion given by Held and Hou (1980) [attributed to Hide (1969)]. If Eq. (2.1) is written in zonally averaged form for a steady circulation, then

$$\nabla \cdot [\rho M][\mathbf{V}] + \nabla \cdot [(\rho M)'(\mathbf{V})'] = [T_\lambda] \qquad (3.4)$$

where contributions to $[T_\lambda]$ are considered from surface drag only. The zonal wind distribution with surface drag and no eddy transports (Fig. 6a) is similar to that obtained in Held and Hou's inviscid analysis: contant absolute angular momentum aloft and vertical wind shear to the low speed winds near the surface. However, the requirement that $[T_\lambda]$ be zero in a global average requires both easterly and westerly zonal winds near the surface; thus, the constant angular momentum distribution aloft must be composed of easterly and westerly flow. (Held and Hou's zero wind speed boundary condition satisfies this condition differently, producing westerly flow everywhere.) Addition of poleward eddy momentum transport would tend to exaggerate the easterly/westerly contrast (Fig. 6b), thereby increasing differential rota-

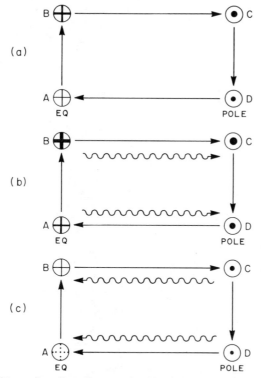

FIG. 6. Cartoon illustrating effect of large-scale eddy momentum transport on the zonal wind distribution. In (a) the Hadley cell in frictional contact with a surface produces winds in the direction of planetary rotation (out of the page — dot) at the pole and in the opposite direction at the equator (into the page — cross). Relative magnitudes are indicated by symbol thickness. Poleward eddy momentum transport (b) increases both the polar and equatorial wind speeds, while equatorward eddy transport (c) reduces them.

tion, while addition of equatorward transport would decrease this contrast (Fig. 6c) and the differential rotation.

  However, this analysis does not account for the effects of eddy heat transport on the momentum balance because it considers the MMC transports as fixed. Eddy heat transport in (2.4) changes the temperature distribution, which requires a change in the zonal flow to maintain the geostrophic or cyclostrophic balance in (2.2). The change is accomplished by a change in the MMC, the terms on the left in (2.2). For example, poleward heat transport by eddies on Earth decelerates westerly flow in opposition to the acceleration implied by their momentum transport; in the stratosphere, at least, the heat transport effect seems predominant (Andrews *et al.*, 1983).

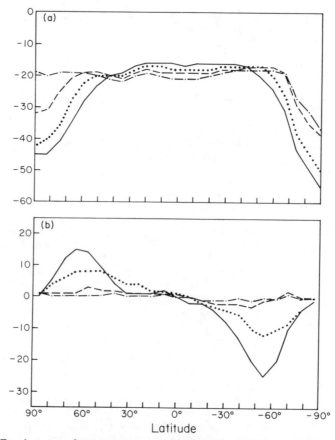

FIG. 7. Zonal mean surface temperature distribution (°C) at 500 mb (a) and the distribution of horizontal transport of dry static energy by eddies (10^{14} W) (b) as a function of planetary rotation rate in the GISS GCM [period (days): ——, 4; ······, 8; ------, 16; · – · – · –, 64.] [After Del Genio *et al.* (1983).]

The transition in the character of eddy transports with decreasing planetary rotation rate is illustrated in Figs. 7 and 8; these results are from a "dry" version of the GISS GCM [Del Genio *et al.* (1983); see Hansen *et al.* (1983), for a complete description of the model]. As rotation rate decreases, eddy heat transports decrease in relation to MMC transports. Eddy momentum transport is generally poleward until the rotation period increases beyond 8 days. At the same time that eddy momentum transport changes direction, the eddy heat transport ceases. The primary source of eddy energy at fast rotation rates is baroclinic instability of the zonal flow; at slow rotation rates the source is barotropic instability of the zonal flow. The same switch in behavior appears in the model experiments of Williams and Holloway (1982). The dependence of this transition on the other physical processes in an atmosphere remains to be explored, however.

3.2.5. Vertical Propagation of Waves. The problem of wave interactions with the mean flow in Venus's upper atmosphere is at least as difficult, we believe, as the modeling of Earth's stratosphere; but the strong vertical wind shear prevents similar separation of the vertical and horizontal parts of the solution. Proper modeling of propagating wave modes, including thermal tides, gravity waves, and other planetary-scale wave modes, is crucial to understanding both of these upper atmospheric dynamic regimes. This is

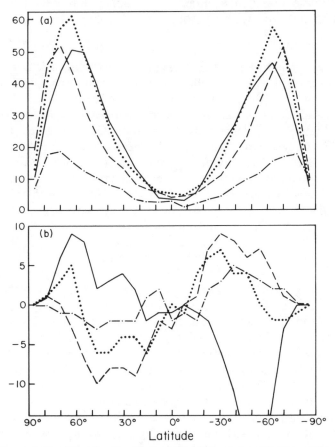

FIG. 8. Same as Fig. 7 but for the zonal wind at 300 mb (m s^{-1}) (a) and the northward transport of angular momentum by eddies (10^{18} J) (b). [After Del Genio *et al.* (1983).]

especially true for the cloud-level zonal flow on Venus, which could be maintained by a balance of very weak vertical momentum fluxes by different wave modes. Fels (1977) and Fels et al. (1984) discuss two such possibilities. Linearized calculations of thermal tides in a strong, vertically sheared flow show that these modes can also play a role in the horizontal momentum flux balance, similar to the barotropic waves (Pechman, 1983). [Williams and Holloway (1982) exhibit a similar role played by large amplitude diurnal waves.] The changes in wave propagation with rotation rate illustrated by Hunt's (1979) results and the complex propagating behavior of waves produced by barotropic instability in the results of Rossow (1983), all point to a very complex, possibly unanticipated behavior for planetary-scale wave modes in the slowly rotating regime. Proper treatment of these processes is a challenge to the numerical accuracy of the models and to the fidelity of the parameterizations of key energy source – sink processes [see e.g., Rind et al. (1984)].

3.2.6. Convection. The crucial role played by small scale convection in the GCM results of Rossow (1983) suggests that this process must also be better understood and represented in models before they can be considered definitive. A similar conclusion has been reached with regard to convection and its influence on Earth's climate sensitivity (Hansen et al., 1984). The problem for Venus research (and for other deep planetary atmospheres) is to generalize what we know about convection in laboratory fluids to different *atmospheric* dynamical settings [see Fein et al. (1983)]. Two particular concerns for Venus are raised by Rossow's model results, but similar issues have been raised for Earth's atmosphere [e.g., Rind and Rossow (1984)]. The first issue is the interaction between small-scale convection and the Hadley circulation. In the model, even though radiation destabilizes almost the whole of the lower atmosphere (actually $\pm 70°$ of latitude), convection is confined to $\pm 15°$; whereas, the pattern of heating and cooling by the MMC and convection (Fig. 9) suggests that the convection has altered the vertical structure of the MMC (Rossow, 1983). In other words, the distribution of the convection and the structure of the MMC are interdependent: neither can be determined alone. This result points to a fundamental distinction between laboratory fluids and actual atmospheres; namely, the thermally driven convective motions are expressed in two modes of vastly different scale in atmospheres, rather than one. The determination of the structure of generalized convective circulations in atmospheres is, consequently, more complex.

The second issue concerns the interaction between small-scale convection and large-scale waves, especially vertically propagating waves. In Rossow's model results, this interaction allowed for a coupling between the deep atmosphere and cloud levels resulting in a strong downward transport of

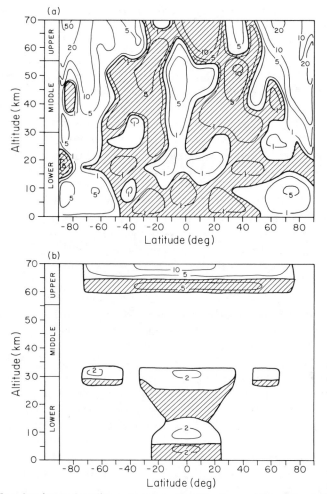

FIG. 9. Mean heating and cooling patterns produced by the meridional circulation (10^{-6} K s^{-1}) (a) and small-scale convection (10^{-6} K s^{-1}) (b) in GCM of Rossow (1983). Cooling is indicated by shading.

momentum and an upward transport of heat (Rossow, 1983). In the slow rotation rate experiments with the GISS GCM, convection is the process that opposes the MMC vertical momentum transport to produce a balance (Del Genio *et al.*, 1983). In Earth's tropics, the interaction of horizontally propagating waves with convection is implicated in the formation of tropical storms [e.g., Riehl (1983)]. Our theoretical understanding of these types of dynamical interactions is poor, which will limit progress in understanding the upper atmosphere of Venus.

3.2.7. Turbulence. Another way of viewing all of these complex wave interactions is to consider the atmospheric motions as fully turbulent and attempt to treat the statistics of the motions. Direct molecular diffusion and friction at solid surfaces are weak processes, hence, the bulk of the atmospheric motions can be considered inviscid. However, the smaller-scale turbulent motions connect these two processes to larger scales of motion and so these smaller-scale motions are usually treated in numerical models as a kind of macro-diffusion that dissipates energy analogously to molecular diffusion. In so doing these motions also transport momentum and heat energy, but not necessarily in a way similar to molecular diffusion. Behavior that is at odds with the diffusion formulation can occur because the constraints on the circulation and nonlinear coupling to other modes of motion lead to different kinds of eddy transport for different quantities [e.g., Rhines (1979), Rossow and Williams (1979), Stone (1978), and Stone and Carlson (1979)]. A particular example of this behavior discussed here is the opposing effects of baroclinic eddy heat and momentum transports on the mean zonal flow [see Andrews *et al.* (1983)]. Turbulence theories have been developed with some application to small-scale convection [e.g., Lumley and Panofsky (1964)] and certain simple cases for large-scale atmospheric and oceanic motions (Rhines, 1979). However, these theories do not yet address the problem of forced motions that are usually encountered in planetary problems [see, however, Canuto and Goldman (1984)].

Mixing-length theory, developed to describe the heat transport by free convection in stellar interiors, is an intuitively attractive formulation of three-dimensional turbulent transport; however, this theory is limited to *free* convection and the transport of *conserved* quantities. Transport by forced convection or other wave motions in an atmosphere with variable static stability, phase changes, or wind shears is not necessarily represented by the mixing-length formulation. Many authors invoke mixing-length theory to justify their use of particular diffusion parameterizations of small-scale turbulent transport; however, they mistakenly apply this formulation to simplified equations for quantities that are not conserved (e.g., diffusion of wind speed in deep atmospheres). These formulations produce very different consequences, though the differences are not often recognized. For study of Venus's zonal flow, the neglect of density effects, e.g., can produce spurious body force terms that might accelerate the flow in a model (Rossow *et al.,* 1980b). These formulations can be accepted as *ad hoc* representations of turbulent transports, but then almost any momentum or heat balance can be obtained in a model by suitable tuning of the coefficients or changes of the form of the equations. For Venus's upper atmosphere, in which the balance may involve very weak momentum transports (Rossow, 1983), use of such *ad hoc* diffusion in models may overwhelm the other dynamic transports.

4. New Formulation of Venus Questions

In understanding the momentum balance on Venus, determination of the relative efficiency of momentum and heat transport by different dynamic modes is crucial and requires a complete treatment of the coupled heat and momentum budgets. Simplified theoretical treatments, when compared to more complex models, argue for the fundamental nonlinearity of these problems on Venus; i.e., eddy processes are crucial to the results obtained, but our understanding of these processes in the slowly rotating regime is not general enough. Furthermore, use of *ad hoc* formulations can completely alter the results obtained in models, leaving their general validity in doubt. With observational information for Venus remaining incomplete, theoretical work should focus on careful process and parameter studies to identify and elucidate general properties of slowly rotating atmospheres. In this section, we will propose some speculative conclusions in order to pose questions for further research. Much remains to be done to exploit fully recent spacecraft observations and to understand more thoroughly the tantalizing model results.

4.1. Deep Atmosphere

Observations show that most of the zonal flow momentum and kinetic energy is found in the lowest two scale heights, that both quantities are concentrated in a layer near 20 km altitude (a little more than one scale height above the surface), and that the zonal flow distribution appears to be that of rigid shell rotation at each level up to about 25 km altitude. Numerical circulation model results suggest that the first two facts are a consequence of momentum transport by a thermally driven MMC with (relatively) strong horizontal mixing of momentum by planetary-scale waves (Williams and Holloway, 1982; Rossow, 1983), which is the process proposed by Gierasch (1975). Rossow's model results, together with studies by Kalnay de Rivas (1973, 1975), further suggest that the depth of the flow is controlled by the vertical distribution of net radiative forcing. This appears consistent with Pioneer Venus probe observations of the vertical distributions of solar heating (Tomasko, 1983). However, the only model results that "explain" the third fact are those of Williams and Holloway (1982) using an unrealistically strong diurnal forcing. That is, the source of the eddy mixing needed to complete the story cannot yet be attributed to waves produced solely by zonal flow shear instability, as suggested by Rossow and Williams (1979), because the factors that control the relative efficiencies of these waves and the MMC have not been determined as yet. Numerical model characteristics or parameter assumptions may well explain why no model has yet produced this rigid shell flow. The Williams and Holloway (1982) results at least indicate the sensitivity of the horizontal distribution of angular momentum to the relative eddy mixing efficiency.

The complexity of the wave transports illustrated in the model of Rossow (1983) shows that there is a lot to learn yet about the "simple" barotropic waves produced by zonal flow horizontal shear instability. Other zonal flow shear instabilities may come into play as well, including Kelvin – Helmholtz, symmetric [cf. Stone's (1976) discussion for Jupiter] and inertial instability. The low values of the Coriolis parameter and the static stability (though this is uncertain) could make the zonal flow in Venus's lower atmosphere very susceptible to a number of these shear instabilities. Indeed, the multiple Hadley cells that result from inertial instability in some models of Earth's tropical upper atmosphere (Hunt, 1981; Rind et al., 1984) suggest an interesting analogy between Earth's tropics and Venus. This dynamic regime is unfamiliar, both as a consequence of the slow planetary rotation and because of the relation between the radiative and dynamical time constants (Stone, 1975) that makes accurate calculation of the radiative forcing more critical.

Another source of planetary-scale waves could be the diurnal forcing, which is usually neglected for the deep atmosphere because the length of the day is almost 100 times smaller than the radiative time constant for one scale height. However, as Dobrovolskis and Ingersoll (1980) show, this fact does not eliminate tidal forcing but serves to concentrate the amplitude of the response at the surface. Generally, forcing confined to such a narrow layer is not effective for driving the propagating planetary-scale modes that have larger vertical wavelengths; however, coupling to convection in a nearly neutrally stable atmosphere could provide another way for this forcing to interact with the planetary-scale modes. Such coupling occurs in Rossow's model, though not necessarily in a realistic way, and plays an important role in the model momentum balance (Rossow, 1983). This sort of coupling with convection could produce diurnal waves that are more effective than anticipated from simple scaling arguments, with important consequences for the deep or cloud-level circulation.

We believe the deep atmospheric circulation (below about 30 km) is probably produced by a process like that proposed by Gierasch (1975). The heat transporting efficiency of the Hadley circulation (relative to radiation) is likely to be very high [as Stone (1974) suggested], resulting in a nearly barotropic lower atmosphere. Consequently, planetary scale wave motions can mix momentum as suggested by Rossow and Williams (1979), producing nearly rigid shell rotation and a concentration of momentum at the top of the Hadley cell as observed (Rossow, 1983). The operation of these processes may be a general consequence of slow planetary rotation, as the GCM results seem to indicate (Figs. 7 and 8). The fact that these models do not obtain a strong enough zonal flow may suggest that the relative eddy mixing efficiency may be dependent on the specific properties of an atmosphere that determine the radiative forcing, surface friction effects and the amplitude of forced wave modes. No model has yet produced a Venus-like zonal flow in the lower atmosphere, except for the experiments with unrealistically large diurnally forced waves (Williams and Holloway, 1982). The dependence of the zonal flow distribution on specific atmospheric properties, which controls the relative strength of different dynamic processes, requires consideration of the complete circulation problem including both heat and momentum budgets. Process studies can, therefore, be useful to study different types of wind shear instabilities in the slowly rotating regime with varying atmospheric characteristics. These studies are also needed to generalize understanding of the kinds of dynamic instabilities that occur in this regime to produce a fully turbulent flow in contrast to laboratory fluids.

4.2. Cloud-Level Atmosphere

The small amount of momentum contained in the flow at cloud levels, not only makes it difficult to accurately determine the vertical distribution from currently available data, but also suggests that the dynamic balance responsible for the zonal flow may be composed of very weak transports. The former makes observational diagnosis difficult because even the sign of the vertical gradient of momentum density at each altitude is not well determined. The latter means that numerical modeling of dynamic processes with sufficient accuracy is a challenge. In particular, use of crude parameterizations for small-scale convection or of ad hoc diffusion processes in models may significantly alter the momentum budget at these levels away from what would occur if only large-scale motions were involved. The complex vertical structure of atmospheric stability and wind shear also challenges the accuracy of propagating wave calculations, particularly the coupling of wave modes of various kinds at and across the narrow, neutrally stable layer. For example, this layer could produce a partial isolation of deep and upper atmospheric waves from each other (Covey and Schubert, 1982) or provide some (weak) coupling through convection (Rossow, 1983). This layer might also serve as a source of wave energy if baroclinic instability is possible (Young et al., 1984). The details of such a weak process may be sensitive to the distribution of cloud-induced radiative heating and, therefore, could undergo slow changes with time as the clouds vary.

In addition to the dynamic coupling provided by propagating waves and the thermally driven mean circulation, radiative coupling with the deep atmosphere is possible if the spectral dependence of the infrared opacity allows a significant leak of energy from deeper levels. If enough energy from deeper levels is deposited in the clouds in this fashion, then the radiative time constant will be lengthened, similar to the effect of the ocean on Earth's atmosphere, and additional nonlinear feedbacks between dynamics and cloud structure become possible.

Study of the circulation at and above cloud levels also involves several interesting problems of cloud-radiative–dynamical feedback and the interaction of the MMC and propagating planetary waves forced by solar heating variations. A proposed simplification of the dynamics in this region is to treat the total angular momentum in the local cloud-level flow as fixed, much like a planetary rotation, so that the dynamics can be treated as quasi-geostrophic. In other words, in (2.1)–(2.4), replace u by $u_0 + u$, where u_0 is a constant, representing the time-averaged zonal flow at cloud levels. This approach must be carefully scrutinized, however, because of the nonlinear contributions to the pressure gradient balance expressed in (3.3). Since time variations of the zonal flow on a time scale shorter than the radiative time can contribute to this balance, the adjustment time scale for restoring the perturbed zonal flow momentum may actually be larger than this "geostrophic" approximation assumes. This approach may also neglect the interaction between the cloud-radiative processes and whatever process is responsible for maintaining the zonal flow at these levels.

The role of the clouds in all of these problems seems to be pivotal, suggesting, we believe, that the particular characteristics of the upper atmosphere circulation on Venus may be a consequence of specific conditions there, rather than the general consequence of slow planetary rotation. In other words, the maintenance of a strong vertical shear in the zonal flow into the upper atmosphere may be caused primarily by the presence of the cloud layer there. Cloud-radiative heating of these levels may also be responsible for the efficient horizontal mixing concentrating the flow momentum at the equator at these levels. This conclusion does not automatically implicate any particular process as being responsible for the "four-day wind," however, since the enhanced radiative heating produced by the cloud's solar and infrared absorption can be responsible for increases in amplitude of all circulation components relative to a clear atmosphere.

4.3. Upper Atmosphere

The circulation of the atmosphere above the clouds is largely unobserved, though the observed temperature structure suggests a general decrease of wind speeds through the cyclostrophic relationship. However, the temperature structure requires a dynamic explanation [e.g., Crisp (1984), and Fels *et al.* (1984)], which may mean that cyclostrophic balance is not accurate in this region. Propagation of several different types of wave into this region has been suggested (Fels and Lindzen, 1974; Taylor *et al.*, 1980; Covey and Schubert, 1983; Del Genio and Rossow, 1982a; Fels *et al.*, 1984) suggesting that the upper atmosphere circulation may be completely dominated by energy and momentum imported from the lower atmosphere by waves. Better understanding of our atmosphere at similar pressure levels may be a necessary precursor to study of this part of Venus's atmosphere.

5. SUMMARY

5.1. New Questions and Work Needed

A key issue in further study of the processes that produce the Venus general circulation is the distribution of net radiative forcing. Direct probe observations of the spectral dependence of solar and infrared net flux divergences as a function of altitude and latitude are crucial to progress, but better laboratory understanding of H_2SO_4, CO_2, SO_2, and H_2O would also allow for better theoretical treatment of this problem. Sensitivity studies of the variations of radiative forcing with cloud structure variations can be guided by the variations suggested in available data. Now that the basic greenhouse explanation for the high surface temperature is established, the new questions concern (1) determination of the amount of radiative coupling between the clouds and the deeper atmospheric levels, which is equivalent to a determination of the cloud contribution to the total greenhouse effect, and (2) determination of the radiative contribution to the static stability distribution, particularly near the surface and in the clouds.

The most important feature of the Venus general circulation to be explained is the superrotation of the whole lower atmosphere with a concentration of the flow near 20 km altitude. This superrotation may well be a general feature of all slowly rotating atmospheres, though the magnitude and the latitudinal uniformity of the angular velocity may be dependent on specific properties of the atmosphere that govern the efficiency of eddy mixing relative to that of the MMC. Direct probe measurements of *mean* surface wind *direction* at different latitudes could be diagnostic of the momentum balance in the whole lower atmosphere. The basic dynamical process responsible for this style of circulation seems to be that proposed by Gierasch (1975); however, a general understanding of the behavior of planetary-scale waves and convection in a slowly rotating atmosphere is lacking. Theoretical studies should focus on understanding (1) the change in behavior of planetary waves with changing planetary rotation rate, with particular attention to the variations of dynamic instability processes and (2) the interaction of small-scale convection with large-scale convection (the MMC) and its dependence on planetary rotation rate. Determining the rotation rate at which the large-scale waves switch from baroclinic to barotropic behavior is crucial for study of Titan's atmosphere (rotation rate is 15 days) (Flasar *et al.,* 1981).

In our opinion the "four-day wind" on Venus may not be a general feature of slowly rotating atmospheres, but a specific feature associated with the presence of the planetwide cloud layer and the radiative forcing that it produces. Even though the bulk of the zonal momentum and kinetic energy resides in the lower atmosphere, the apparent change in sign of the vertical shear of the zonal wind near cloud tops still strongly suggests a relation between cloud-radiative forcing of the circulation at this level and the maintenance of the wind shear above 30 km. However, the weakness of the transports required to explain the zonal flow at cloud levels precludes direct observational diagnosis of the key processes or identification of the process in current numerical models with crude parameterizations of wave processes and kinetic energy dissipation processes. Observations of this region are difficult, but a combination of UV and IR imagery with microwave temperature sounding from a long-lived polar orbiter might provide sufficient vertical detail on mean and wave motions to constrain modeling results. Improved calculations of cloud-radiative forcing could make models more realistic. Theoretical studies should focus on improvements in understanding several general processes: (1) propagating planetary-scale waves in the presence of vertical variations of radiative forcing, static stability, and wind shear, with particular attention to mode coupling to convection or other smaller-scale gravity waves, (2) zonal flow and planetary-scale wave instability processes in a heated layer, with no solid surface, like the cloud layer on Venus, and (3) convection in an isolated, neutrally stable layer with no solid surface, with particular attention to interactions with vertically propagating planetary-scale waves.

5.2. Conclusions

Consideration of Venus and Earth general circulations raises a number of questions about atmospheric dynamical processes, in particular, the role of planetary rotational effects on the heat and momentum budgets established in atmospheres. Three crucial issues are apparent.

(1) The distinction between small-scale convection and Hadley circulations, though real in a length scale sense, may be somewhat artificial since

most atmospheres have both vertical and horizontal variations of radiative forcing, especially with solid surfaces present. The relative importance of these two interrelated modes of thermal convection is not generally understood.

(2) The change in planetary wave–MMC interactions with decreasing planetary rotation rate needs to be understood in the broader context of planetary-scale wave instability processes for different dynamic regimes. The distinction between baroclinic and barotropic instability, which makes sense for quasi-geostrophic circulations, may not be so clear at slower rotation rates. Furthermore, other types of dynamic instability, such as inertial or Kelvin–Helmholtz instability, have not received as much attention as these two. The "instability regime diagram" that we all envision for atmospheres is actually based on laboratory experiments with fluids that do not exhibit fully turbulent flow in the slowly rotating regime, in contrast to slowly rotating atmospheres [see Geisler *et al.* (1983)].

(3) General understanding of fully turbulent atmospheric circulations is poor. Coupling between various scale, forced, and free modes mediates all sorts of energy transfers that are not possible (or are less efficient) when only a single mode is present. Stratospheric dynamics on Earth and Venus is probably dominated by the importation of momentum and energy from other portions of the atmosphere by various propagating and interacting dynamic modes. Use of the concept of a local balance between two (or more) explicit types of dynamic modes, without the use of any *ad hoc* diffusion, seems to be a necessary next step in our modeling of these regions.

ACKNOWLEDGMENTS

The planetary atmospheres available for our study stimulate a broad investigation of dynamical problems. The desire to understand climate change on Earth also requires a more general understanding of our own circulation beyond that required for mere simulation of observed motions. When the GFDL was established under Joseph Smagorinsky's leadership, he set a course of research that adopted this broader view of atmospheric and oceanic science, which has been very successful. I am grateful to Joe for nurturing some of my work on these problems. I also thank A. D. Del Genio, M. Allison, D. Rind, and L. Travis for helpful discussion; L. Del Valle for drafting; and D. Smith and A. Calarco for typing.

REFERENCES

Andrews, D. G., Mahlman, J. D., and Sinclair, R. W. (1983). Eliassen–Palm diagnostics of wave–mean flow interaction in the GFDL "SKYHI" general circulation model. *J. Atmos. Sci.* **40**, 2768–2784.

Apt., J., and Leung, J. (1982). Thermal periodicities in the Venus atmopshere. *Icarus* **49**, 423–427.

Barath, F. T., Barrett, A. H., Copeland, J., Jones, D. C., and Lilley, A. (1963). Microwave radiometers, part of Mariner II: Preliminary reports on measurements of Venus. *Science* **139**, 908–909.

Belton, M. J. S., Hunten, D. M., and Goody, R. (1968). Quantitative spectroscopy of Venus in the region 8,000–11,000Å. *In* "The Atmospheres of Venus and Mars" (J. C. Brandt and M. B. McElroy, eds.), pp. 69–98. Gordon & Breach, New York.

Boyer, C., and Guérin, P. (1966). Mise en évidence discrète, per la photographie d'urve rotation retrograde de Venus en 4 Jours. *C. R. Hebd. Seances Acad. Sci.* **263**, 253–255.

Canuto, V. M., and Goldman, I. (1984). Analytical model for large scale turbulence. *Phys. Rev. Lett.* **54**, 430–433.

Counselman, C. C., Gourevitch, S. A., King, R. W., and Loriot, G. B. (1980). Zonal and meridional circulation of the lower atmosphere of Venus determined by radio interferometry. *JGR, J. Geophys. Res.* **85**, 8026–8030.

Covey, C. C., and Schubert, G. (1982). Planetary scale waves in the Venus atmosphere. *J. Atmos. Sci.* **39**, 2397–2413.

Crisp, D. (1984). Radiative forcing of the Venus mesosphere. Ph.D. Thesis, Princeton University, Princeton, New Jersey.

Del Genio, A. D., and Rossow, W. B. (1982a). Temporal variability of ultraviolet cloud features in the Venus stratosphere. *Icarus* **51**, 391–415.

Del Genio, A. D., and Rossow, W. B. (1982b). Power spectrum analysis of Pioneer Venus extended mission UV images. *Bull. Am. Astron. Soc.* **14**, 740.

Del Genio, A. D., Meccage, J. K., Suozzo, R., Opstbaum, R., Rind, D., Rossow, W. B., Russell, G., and Travis, L. D. (1983). Variable rotation rate experiments with the GISS general circulation model. *Bull. Am. Astron. Soc.* **15**, 821.

Dobrovolskis, A. R., and Ingersoll, A. P. (1980). Atmospheric tides and the rotation of Venus. I. Tidal theory and the balances of torques. *Icarus* **41**, 1–17.

Dunham, T. (1952). Spectroscopic observations of the planets at Mount Wilson. *In* "Atmospheres of the Earth and Planets" (G. P. Kuiper, ed.), pp. 288–305. Univ. of Chicago Press, Chicago, Illinois.

Ekonomov, A. P., Golovin, Yu. M., Moroz, V. I., and Moshkin, B. Ye. (1983). Solar scattered radiation measurements by Venus probes. *In* "Venus" (D. M. Hunten, L. Colin, T. M. Donahue, and V. I. Moroz, eds.), pp. 632–649. Univ. of Arizona Press, Tucson.

Fein, J. S., Stephens, P. L., and Loughran, K. S. (1983). The Global Atmospheric Research Program: 1979–1982. *Rev. Geophys. Space Phys.* **21**, 1076–1096.

Fels, S. B. (1977). Momentum and energy exchanges due to orographically scattered gravity waves. *J. Atmos. Sci.* **34**, 499–514.

Fels, S. B., and Lindzen, R. S., (1974). The interaction of thermally excited gravity waves with mean flows. *Geophys. Fluid Dyn.* **6**, 149–191.

Fels, S. B., Schofield, J. T., and Crisp, D. (1984). Observations and theory of the solar semidiurnal tide in the mesosphere of Venus. *Nature (London)* **312**, 431–434.

Flasar, F. M., Samuelson, R. E., and Conrath, B. J. (1981). Titan's atmosphere: Temperature and dynamics. *Nature (London)* **292**, 693–698.

Fultz, D., Long, R., Owens, G., Bohen, W., Kaylor, R., and Weil, J. (1959). "Studies of Thermal Convection in a Rotating Cylinder with some Implications for Large-Scale Atmospheric Motions," Meteorol. Monogr. No. 21. Am. Meteorol. Soc., Washington, D.C.

Geisler, J. E., Pitcher, E. J., and Malone, R. C. (1983). Rotating-fluid experiments with an atmospheric general circulation model. *JGR, J. Geophys. Res.* **88**, 9706–9716.

Gierasch, P. J. (1975). Meridional circulation and the maintenance of the Venus atmospheric rotation. *J. Atmos. Sci.* **32**, 1038–1044.

Gierasch, P. J., Goody, R. M., and Stone, P. H. (1970). The energy balance of planetary atmospheres. *Geophys. Fluid Dyn.* **1**, 1–18.

Golitsyn, G. S. (1970). A similarity approach to the general circulation of planetary atmospheres. *Icarus* **13**, 1–24.

Goody, R. M., and Robinson, A. R. (1966). A discussion of the deep circulation of the atmosphere of Venus. *Astrophys. J.* **146**, 339–353.

Hansen, J., Russell, G., Rind, D., Stone, P., Lacis, A., Lebedeff, S., Ruedy, R., and Travis, L. (1983). Efficient three dimensional global models for climate studies: Models I and II. *Mon. Weather Rev.* **111**, 609–662.

Hansen, J., Lacis, A., Rind, D., Russell, G., Stone, P., Fung, I., Ruedy, R., and Lerner, J. (1984). Climate sensitivity: Analysis of feedback mechanisms. *In* "Climate Processes and Climate Sensitivity" (J. E. Hansen and T. Takahashi, eds.), Maurice Ewing Ser. No. 5, pp. 130–163 Am. Geophys. Union, Washington, D.C.

Held, I. M., and Hou, A. Y. (1980). Nonlinear axially symmetric circulations in a nearly invisid atmosphere. *J. Atmos. Sci.* **37**, 515–533.

Hide, R. (1969). Dynamics of the atmospheres of the major planets with an appendix on the viscous boundary layer at the rigid boundary surface of an electrically conducting rotating fluid in the presence of a magnetic field. *J. Atmos. Sci.* **26**, 841–853.

Hide, R. (1977). Experiments with rotating fluids. *Q. J. R. Meteorol. Soc.* **103**, 1–28.

Hoffman, J. H., Oyama, V. I., and von Zahn, U. (1980). Measurements of the Venus lower atmosphere composition: A comparison of results. *JGR, J. Geophys. Res.* **85**, 7871–7881.

Hunt, B. G. (1979). The influence of the Earth's rotation rate on the general circulation of the atmosphere. *J. Atmos. Sci.* **36**, 1392–1408.

Hunt, B. G. (1981). The maintenance of the zonal mean state of the upper atmosphere as represented in a three-dimensional general circulation model extending to 100 km. *J. Atmos. Sci.* **38**, 2172–2186.

Kalnay de Rivas, E. (1973). Numerical models of the circulation of the atmosphere of Venus. *J. Atmos. Sci.* **30**, 763–779.

Kalnay de Rivas, E. (1975). Further numerical calculations of the circulation of the atmosphere of Venus. *J. Atmos. Sci.* **32**, 1017–1024.

Kawabata, K., Coffeen, D. L., Hansen, J. E., Lane W. A., Sato, M., and Travis, L. D. (1980). Cloud and haze properties from Pioneer Venus polarimetry. *JGR, J. Geophys. Res.* **85**, 8129–8140.

Kerzhanovich, V. V., and Marov, M. Ya. (1983). The atmospheric dynamics of Venus according to doppler measurements by the Venera entry probes. *In* "Venus" (D. M. Hunten, L. Colin, T. M. Donahue, and V. I. Moroz, eds.), pp. 766–778. Univ. of Arizona Press, Tucson.

Kliore, A. J., and Patel, I. R. (1980). The vertical structure of the atmosphere of Venus from Pioneer Venus orbiter radio occultations. *JGR, J. Geophys. Res.* **85**, 7957–7962.

Leovy, C. (1973). Rotation of the upper atmosphere of Venus. *J. Atmos. Sci.* **30**, 1218–1220.

Limaye, S. S. (1984). Venus atmospheric circulation from near cloud top level to the surface. *Venus International Reference Atmosphere Workshop* (A. Kliore, V. I. Morse, and G. M. Keating, eds.), Pergamon, New York (in press).

Limaye, S. S., and Suomi, V. E. (1981). Cloud motions on Venus: Global structure and organization. *J. Atmos. Sci.* **38**, 1220–1235.

Lumley, J. L., and Panofsky, H. A. (1964). "The Structure of Atmospheric Turbulence." Wiley (Interscience), New York.

Newman, M., Schubert, G., Kliore, A. J., and Patel, I. R. (1984). Zonal winds in the middle atmosphere of Venus from Pioneer Venus radio occultation data. *J. Atmos. Sci.* **41**, 1901–1913.

Oort, A. H., and Rasmussen, E. (1971). "Atmospheric Circulation Statistics," NOAA Prof. Pap. No. 5. U.S. Dept. of Commerce, Washington, D.C.

Pechman, J. B. (1983). Thermal tides in the atmosphere of Venus. Ph.D. Thesis, California Institute of Technology, Pasadena.

Pollack, J. B., Toon, O. B., and Boese, R. (1980). Greenhouse models of Venus' high surface temperature, as constrained by Pioneer Venus measurements. *JGR, J. Geophys. Res.* **85**, 8223–8231.

Ragent, B., and Blamont, J. (1980). Structure of the clouds of Venus: Results of the Pioneer Venus nephelometer experiment. *JGR, J. Geophys. Res.* **85**, 8089–8105.

Revercomb, H. E., Sromovsky, L. A., and Suomi, V. E. (1982). Reassessment of net radiation measurements in the atmosphere of Venus. *Icarus* **52**, 279–300.

Rhines, P. B. (1979). Geostrophic turbulence. *Annu. Rev. Fluid Mech.* **11**, 401–441.

Riehl, H. (1983). "Climate and Weather in the Tropics." Academic Press, New York.

Rind, D., and Rossow, W. B. (1984). The effects of physical processes on the Hadley circulation. *J. Atmos. Sci.* **41**, 479–507.

Rind, D., Suozzo, R., Lacis, A., Russell, G., and Hansen, J. (1984). 21-layer-troposphere-stratosphere climate model. NASA Tech. Memo. 86183.

Rossow, W. B., 1983: A general circulation model of a Venus-like atmosphere. *J. Atmos. Sci.* **40**, 273–302.

Rossow, W. B., and Williams, G. P. (1979). Large-scale motion in the Venus stratosphere. *J. Atmos. Sci.* **36**, 377–389.

Rossow, W. B., Del Genio A. D., Limaye, S. S., Travis, L. D., and Stone P. H. (1980a). Cloud morphology and motions from Pioneer Venus images. *JGR, J. Geophys. Res.* **85**, 8107–8128.

Rossow, W. B., Fels, S. B., and Stone, P. H. (1980b). Comments on "A three-dimensional model of dynamical processes in the Venus atmosphere." *J. Atmos. Sci.* **37**, 250–252.

Sagan, C. (1962). Structure of lower atmosphere of Venus. *Icarus* **1**, 151–169.

Schneider, E. K. (1977). Axially symmetric steady-state models of the basic state for instability and climate studies. Part II. Nonlinear calculations. *J. Atmos. Sci.* **34**, 280–296.

Schubert, G. (1983). General circulation and the dynamical state of the Venus atmosphere. *In* "Venus," (D. M. Hunten, L. Colin, T. M. Donahue and V. I. Moroz, eds.), pp. 681–765. Univ. of Arizona Press, Tucson.

Schubert, G., and Whitehead, J. (1969). Moving flame experiment with liquid mercury: Possible implications for the Venus atmosphere. *Science* **163**, 71–72.

Schubert, G., Covey, C., Del Genio A., Elson, L. S., Keating, G., Seiff, A., Young, R. E., Apt, J., Counselman, C. C., Kliore, A. J., Limaye, S. S., Revercomb, H. E., Sromovsky, L. A., Suomi, V. E., Taylor, F., Woo, R., and von Zahn, U. (1980). Structure and circulation of the Venus atmosphere. *JGR. J. Geophys. Res.* **85**, 8007–8025.

Seiff, A. (1983). Thermal structure of the atmosphere of Venus. *In* "Venus" (D. M. Hunten, L. Colin, T. M. Donahue, and V. I. Moroz, eds.), pp. 215–279. Univ. of Arizona Press, Tucson.

Seiff, A., Kirk, D. B., Young, R. E., Balanchard, R. C., Findlay, J. T., Kelly, G. M., and Sommer, S. C. (1980). Measurements of thermal structure and thermal contrasts in the atmosphere of Venus and related dynamical observations: Results from the four Pioneer Venus probes. *JGR, J. Geophys. Res.* **85**, 7903–7933.

Shapiro, I. I. (1968). Spin and orbital motions of the planets. *In* "Radar Astronomy" (J. V. Evans and T. Hagfors, eds.), pp. 143–185. McGraw-Hill, New York.

Sinton, W. M. (1963). Infrared observation of Venus. *In* "Proceedings of the Eleventh International Astrophysical Symposium, The Physics of Planets." pp. 300–310. Univ. of Liege, Belgium.

Spence, T. W., and Fultz, D. (1977). Experiments on wave-transition spectra and vacillation in an open rotating cylinder. *J. Atmos. Sci.* **34**, 1261–1285.

Stone, P. H. (1974). The structure and circulation of the deep Venus atmosphere. *J. Atmos. Sci.* **31**, 1681–1690.

Stone, P. H. (1975). The dynamics of the atmosphere of Venus. *J. Atmos. Sci.* **32**, 1005–1016.

Stone, P. H. (1976). The meteorology of the Jovian atmosphere. *In* "Jupiter" (T. Gehrels, ed.), pp. 586–618. Univ. of Arizona Press, Tucson.

Stone, P. H. (1978). Baroclinic adjustment. *J. Atmos. Sci.* **35**, 561–571.

Stone, P. H., and Carlson, J. H. (1979). Atmospheric lapse rate regimes and their parameterizations. *J. Atmos. Sci.* **36**, 415–423.

Suomi, V. E., Sromovsky, L. A., Revercomb, H. E. (1980). Net radiation in the atmosphere of Venus: Measurements and interpretation. *JGR, J. Geophys. Res.* **85**, 8200–8218.

Taylor, F. W., Beer, R., Chahine, M. T., Diner, D. J., Elson, L. S., Haskins, R. D., McCleese, D. J., Martonchik, J. V., Reichley, P. E., Bradley, S. P., Delderfield, J., Schofield, J. T., Farmer, C. B., Froidevaux, L., Leung, J., Coffey, M. T., and Gille, J. (1980). Structure and meterology of the middle atmosphere of Venus: Infrared remote sensing from the Pioneer orbiter. *JGR, J. Geophys. Res.* **85**, 7963–8006.

Taylor, K. E. (1980). The roles of mean meridional motions and large-scale eddies in zonally averaged circulations. *J. Atmos. Sci.* **37**, 1–19.

Thompson, R. (1970). Venus' general circulation is a merry-go-round. *J. Atmos. Sci.* **27**, 1107–1116.

Tomasko, M. G. (1983). The thermal balance of the lower atmosphere of Venus. *In* "Venus" (D. M. Hunten, L. Colin, T. M. Donahue and V. I. Moroz, eds.), pp. 604–631. Univ. of Arizona Press, Tucson.

Tomasko, M. G., Doose, L. R., Smith, P. H., and Odell, A. P. (1980). Measurements of the flux of sunlight in the atmosphere of Venus. *JGR, J. Geophys. Res.* **85**, 8167–8186.

Williams, G. P., and Holloway, J. L. (1982). The range and unity of planetary circulations. *Nature (London)* **297**, 295–299.

Young, L. G. (1982). Transmission of CO_2 in the atmosphere of Venus for the spectral region near 7 microns. *Icarus* **51**, 606–609.

Young, R. E., Houben, H., and Pfister, L. (1984). Baroclinic instability in the Venus atmosphere. *J. Atmos. Sci.* **41**, 2310–2333.

JOVIAN AND COMPARATIVE ATMOSPHERIC MODELING

GARETH P. WILLIAMS

Geophysical Fluid Dynamics Laboratory/NOAA
Princeton University
Princeton, New Jersey

Princeton, New Jersey

1. INTRODUCTION

In this chapter, we describe the recent development of a Jovian meteorology and assess its impact on the evolution of comparative meteorology. The classical rationale for conducting comparative studies was given, long ago, by Edward Tyson (1651–1708), the founder of comparative anatomy, who wrote[†]

> Nature when more shy in one, hath more freely confest and shown herself in another. The anatomy of one animal will be the key to open several others, and until such time as we can have the whole completed 'tis very desirable to have as many as we can of the most different and anomalous.

[†] From "Anatomy of a Porpess." Tyson's studies of the porpoise—a mammal—also revealed the danger of classifying objects by their external appearance alone.

ADVANCES IN GEOPHYSICS, VOLUME 28A

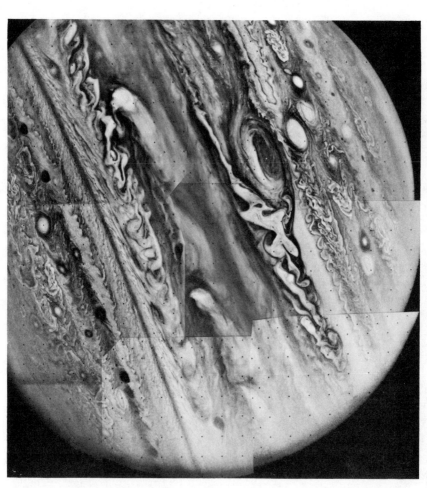

FIG. 1. A mosaic of Jupiter assembled from photographs taken through a violet filter by Voyager 1 in February 1979. A Large Oval passes just below the Great Red Spot while smaller ovals pass below it. Three plumes are apparent in the equatorial zone. Features as small as 150 km are resolved. (Photograph courtesy of Jet Propulsion Laboratory.)

1.1. Development of the Terrestrial Connection

1.1.1. Toward Unity. In the past decade, our view of Jupiter (and Saturn) has undergone a radical change. We no longer consider the Jovian circulation as being unique, steadily axisymmetric, and of uncertain dynamics but, rather, as a seething turbulent system with conventional meteorological processes at play and having close dynamical ties with Earth's atmosphere and oceans. These changes have been wrought mainly by theoretical developments in geophysical fluid dynamics (GFD), with high-resolution spacecraft measurements acting to substantiate the new view (Fig. 1.).

The pre-1975 theories all assume that some form of axisymmetric instability is responsible for the quasi-symmetric banded form of the circulation. All these theories had major defects — see Stone (1976) for their review. The modern GFD view of the circulation began when fundamental studies of planetary β turbulence revealed that zonally aligned flows are the preferred end state of eddy-driven quasi-horizontal nonlinear cascades on a rapidly rotating planet (Rhines, 1975; Williams, 1975a,b, 1978). Studies of quasi-geostrophic (QG) turbulence then showed that baroclinic instability could energize the eddies that drive the Jovian jets if the planetary baroclinicity $(\Delta T)_p$ (the isobaric pole-to-equator temperature difference) lies in the 5–60-K range (Williams, 1979a). These studies also showed that the energy de-cascade to larger scales barotropized the motions — particularly the jets — so that details of the vertical variation of the atmosphere (an unknown) may not be crucial to an understanding of the cloud-level circulation.

The QG studies also imply that in mid-latitudes Jupiter behaves like a larger, faster-spinning Earth (Williams, 1979b). Increasing the rotation rate in a global circulation model for Earth's atmosphere (ECM) produces powerful equatorial westerlies resembling Jupiter's, so the analogy also holds in the tropics (Williams and Holloway, 1982, 1985). Further calculations with the ECM suggest that Venus's circulation may have much in common with that of a very slowly rotating, diurnally heated Earth while Mars has connections with a moisture-eliminated Earth atmosphere. These analogies suggest that perhaps every planetary circulation has some elements that are universal and some that are unique. Physical generalities can compensate for observational deficiencies in developing an understanding of a particular planet.

While the Jovian planets are worthy of individual examination, the study of their connections with each other and with other rapidly rotating planets is vital to comparative meteorology. Such unity is sought mainly to simplify issues and to generalize the terrestrial paradigm but also because we prefer theories that connect hitherto unrelated problems. Meteorological similarities within the solar system could be merely coincidental (but convenient), or they could be intrinsic by virtue of a common planetary origin and evolution (Pollack and Yung, 1980). Earth's atmosphere and oceans share a common GFD (Charney and Flierl, 1981), despite vast differences in their constituents, configurations, and thermodynamics, so there are already indications that disparate bodies can have a comparable dynamics.

All planets have special features that add individuality to their meteorologies: Venus has a dense cloudy atmosphere and a very slow rotation, Mars has a thin condensing atmosphere that exchanges mass with its polar caps, and Jupiter has an internal heat source and an indeterminate vertical structure. The main problem is to determine whether these factors provide merely a minor influence on the dynamics of the motion or whether they induce uniqueness. The movement toward a unified theory for the circulations of all planetary atmospheres and oceans is part of the credo of GFD (Pedlosky, 1979, p. 1; Charney and Flierl, 1981). The richness and complexity of Earth's atmosphere and oceans have led to concepts of such generality that they may suffice for explaining much that is seen on other planets.

The GFD view of the Jovian planets discussed in this article depends on the basic assumption that their atmospheres† are thin relative to their sublayers and are driven by differential solar heating. Theories based on this idea are successful in that they provide an explanation for the following aspects of Jupiter's motions: (1) the scale, amplitude, and zonality of the jets; (2) the scale, origin, waviness, and turbulence of the small eddies; and (3) the origin, longevity, form, anticyclonic bias, drift, scale and scale variations, uniqueness or multiplicity, and localization of the large coherent vortices—the Great Red Spot (GRS) and Large Ovals. All of these theories are mutually consistent and are also relevant to our understanding of Earth's atmosphere and oceans. We can thus claim to have a viable model of most of the major aspects of Jupiter's cloud-level circulation, one that has the full weight of meteorological principles behind it. These basic principles and their Jovian implications are discussed in detail in a companion review entitled "Circulation Dynamics" (hereafter CD85). In this paper, we concentrate only on modeling and observational developments and issues.

1.1.2. Unity or Uniqueness? Alternative views of Jupiter are still pursued. In particular, the classical view assumes that the planet is unique, that its atmosphere is thick and indistinguishable from its envelope, and that the motions are convectively driven, in astrophysical fashion, by internal heating (Busse, 1983; Ingersoll and Pollard, 1982). [See Iavorskaya and Belyaef (1983) for a review.] The main difficulties with this view are that to test it observationally requires probes that penetrate deep into the planet's interior and that modeling it requires a fundamental understanding of thermal tur-

† For convenience, we regard the "atmosphere" as being the solar-influenced, meteorologically active layer and the rest of the envelope as the "sublayer."

bulence. Neither is possible at present so the hypothesis has little practical value.

Linear analyses of the convection hypothesis are totally dependent on the eddy viscosity parameterizations of the thermal turbulence and so lack intrinsic significance. These formulations imply that alternating axisymmetric cylinders of motion exist throughout the planetary interior, extending from one hemisphere to the other (Busse, 1983). Motions at the tops of the cylinders are equated with the observed zonal flows. The analyses do not explain what determines the scale and amplitude of the jets or why the corresponding jets in opposite hemispheres differ. Neither do they explain the existence of the coherent vortices, the waves, and the turbulent eddies, nor their relationship to the jets. The idea of motions retaining their identity and momenta over the vast range of pressures in the planet's interior is difficult to justify. The convection hypothesis does not constitute a "model" of the circulation in the accepted sense of the term.

The real advantage of the thin atmosphere view has been in bringing Jovian studies into the mainstream of meteorological and oceanographical thought, to open them up to the powerful concepts and tools of GFD, and to make these planets relevant to terrestrial studies and comparative meteorology. The GFD view is simpler to pursue, generates richer possibilities, has a larger number of new consequences, and so can be tested more stringently. Conversely, to insist on the uniqueness of Jovian dynamics denies such advantages and condemns such studies to a meteorological pathology.

Before 1975, the real reason Jupiter was not understood was because Earth was not fully understood. If we had asked why Earth has only one (or two) jets per hemisphere, why the jets are azonal, and if we had systematically evaluated ECMs in parameter space, the Jovian connection would have been readily realized even though GFD theory was not then adequate for understanding the relationship. Reversing the usual rationale for planetary study, it is now clear that to understand Jupiter we need to understand Earth better.

1.1.3. Toward Coherence. Limitations in GFD theory also delayed our understanding of coherent vortices such as the Great Red Spot and Large Ovals. Resolution of this problem came finally from progress related to the study of long-lived ocean eddies. Jovian motions have much in common with oceanic ones: strong energy conversion by the small eddies, activity over a wide range of scales, weak dissipation, turbulent and coherent forms, and similar nondimensional parameter ranges. Differences occur not so much in the basic dynamical modes, but rather in their forcing mechanisms.

Initial developments in the modern explanation of the Jovian vortices began — when viewed with hindsight — with the suggestion (Golitsyn, 1970) that, because of the low dissipation level of quasi-horizontal motions in an unbounded atmosphere, the GRS could be a free vortex. The problem was to explain how the rapid wave dispersion endemic to a rapidly rotating planet could be contained. One mechanism capable of balancing weak Rossby-wave dispersion is the weak nonlinear steepening provided by the meridional momentum transport induced by solitary waves in a latitudinal shear zone (Long, 1964). These Rossby shear-solitons have been applied to Jupiter (Maxworthy and Redekopp, 1976), but they differ from Jovian vortices in many ways: they are not oval in shape, they propagate very rapidly (Beaumont, 1980), they are weak vortices, and they have counter vortices lying beneath them (Flierl *et al.,* 1983).

No attempt has been made to simulate Rossby shear-solitons numerically so their stability and existence remains uncertain. Numerical studies of solitary Rossby waves were first made 30 years ago when they were first suggested as a cause of blocking (Yeh, 1949; Bolin, 1956). Those calculations indicated that quasi-geostrophic solitary waves disperse rapidly in a uniform environment but that divergence effects can greatly reduce the rate of dispersion, a result that has been recently exploited.

The early Jovian vortex theories conflict with the GFD view for the zonal circulation, which requires that quasi-geostrophic eddies be turbulent, not coherent, to drive the jets. It is not clear how turbulence and coherence can exist within the *same* dynamical regime. The resolution of this problem and the next development came with the realization that the Jovian vortices, because of their great size, are not quasi-geostrophic but lie in the divergence-dominated intermediate-geostrophic (IG) regime that occurs between the smaller QG and the larger planetary-geostrophic (PG) scales (see Section 3.2.1 for details). Long-lived, anticyclonic solitary vortices are the fundamental mode in the IG regime and occur readily at such scales. Nonlinear steepening of the fluid interface (or isotherms) balances dispersion in these solitary waves, which because they exhibit coalescence during collisions, not soliton behavior, are known as IG vortices or Rossby density-vortices (Williams and Yamagata, 1984; Williams and Wilson, 1985). Such vortices have also been produced in laboratory experiments (Antipov *et al.,* 1982).

When zonal currents become barotropically unstable at the IG scale, they produce solitary vortices in contrast to the periodic waves seen at QG scales. Just as the study of normal mode Rossby waves led to the discovery of barotropic instability, so has the study of solitary waves led to the discovery of the solitary instability (Williams and Yamagata, 1984). Thus the isolation of a vortex from its environment is no longer considered essential for vortex longevity. Jupiter's GRS and Large Ovals appear to be the Rossby vortices produced by weakly unstable zonal currents. Studies are now being made to determine whether solitary baroclinic instabilities can occur. Again, these discoveries could have been made 20 years ago by a systematic evaluation of simple models in parameter space.

Coherence and turbulence are thus seen to coexist by occurring at widely separated scales. Barotropic and baroclinic instabilities coexist in the same way. Thus, small, turbulent QG-scale eddies, energized by baroclinic instability, drive zonal currents that can become barotropically unstable at the larger IG scale and produce coherent IG vortices that help equilibrate the jets.

1.2. Planetary Comparisons

1.2.1. Earth and Jupiter. The main problem in defining Jupiter's meteorology is that the nature and extent of the atmosphere and its motions are not known for the region below the clouds. Theories for the planet's interior [e.g., Stevenson (1982)] suggest that no solid surfaces exist except at great depth. It is in this absence of a lower surface that Jupiter's atmosphere differs most from Earth's atmosphere, while in its confinement of the motions by the thermal structure it most resembles the ocean.

Both atmospheres are partially heated from below, Jupiter by internal heating and Earth by surface heating due to atmospheric transparency to solar heating. Earth's winter hemisphere also experiences an internal heat source due to ocean storage. The primary interaction between atmosphere and ocean occurs in the tropics, where the ocean is statically stable and reacts more shallowly and rapidly and where the atmosphere is statically unstable and reacts more deeply and completely to convection. The distribution of the Jovian internal heat flux is unknown.

The sublayer heating on Earth produces small-scale moist convection that drives the lapse rate toward the moist adiabat. Jupiter's internal heat may also produce this effect, since there may be water clouds in the lower troposphere. Both atmospheres could thus be stable for large-scale processes. This stability could be enhanced by the baroclinic instabilities produced by differential heating. Above the tropopause, the stability is increased by the absorption of solar radiation by ozone on Earth and by methane and dust on Jupiter.

Both atmospheres experience a latitudinal gradient in solar heating. For Earth, baroclinicity levels are of the order of 30 K, while for Jupiter estimates vary from 3 to 30 K (Williams, 1979a; Branscome, 1982). The uncertainties occur because little is known about the absorption of solar heating below the clouds. Weak baroclinicities are effective in driving strong motions on Jupiter because they are associated with the gas constant for hydrogen, which is 14 times greater than the value for air; i.e., the gas is light.

These baroclinicities can produce single or multiple QG jets in the mid-latitudes of both planets (Williams, 1979a,b). On Earth, the mid-latitudinal jet overlaps the zonal flow associated with the Hadley circulation. On Jupiter, this overlap will be confined to a small region — if a Hadley circulation exists—and the other QG jets will be unaffected. Regions of strong rising motion are usually confined to the hot towers of the Intertropical Convergence Zone (ITCZ) and determine the extent of the tropical region—30° latitude on Earth. A tropical regime may exist on Jupiter to about 10° latitude, but the form of a Hadley circulation in the absence of a lower surface is uncertain.

Separate heat sources in Earth's stratosphere produce a different type of circulation in that region, with large qualitative seasonal changes and a transfer of momentum and energy (by wave action) from the troposphere. On Jupiter, the absence of seasonal, topographic, and orographic forcing implies a simple stratospheric continuation of tropospheric motion, but convective forcing may induce some differences.

The turbulent eddies in both systems are due to baroclinic instability and they occur at the scale of the radius of deformation, $L_R = NH/f$. For Earth, the instability is of the Charney type and is greatly influenced by thermal gradients at the ground. For Jupiter, the instability is most likely to be that of the internal (Holton, 1975), interface (McIntyre, 1972; Simmons, 1974; Phillips, 1954), or unbounded (Dickinson, 1973) type. In the ocean, the simplest instabilities are of the Charney type, but mixed barotropic–baroclinic instabilities prevail in the Gulf Stream (Holland and Haidvogel, 1980). Ocean eddies, generated in the thermocline near the surface, penetrate into the deep ocean, where they generate currents (Holland et al., 1984). Jovian eddies could act in this way and extend motions into regions well below those heated by the sun.

The terrestrial eddies have been identified by their statistical properties rather than by their linear characteristics [e.g., Gall (1976)]. A similar statistical identification of Jovian eddies has been attempted by Mitchell (1982). The radius of deformation is of 0(1000 km) for both atmospheres; for Jupiter, this is relatively small and produces nondimensional parameter values comparable to those given by $L_R \sim 0(100 \text{ km})$ for the ocean. Numerical modeling of Jupiter and the ocean thus requires great resolution and computational power.

Coherent vortices occur in the ocean and on Jupiter at scales that are large relative to L_R. This scale separation does not exist in Earth's atmosphere to the same extent, and the only phenomenon of the same relative scale as the GRS is the Aleutian high [see Mahlman and Moxim (1978, Fig. 4.2)]. Whether blocking events are due to coherent vortices is unknown. Coherent vortices are less likely to occur in Earth's atmosphere because of strong dissipation in the boundary layer, unless they also have a strong energy source, as do hurricanes, for example.

Dissipation in the Jovian atmosphere can only occur through turbulent friction. Details of the dissipation mechanism are not important as its time

TABLE I. Classification of Planets According to Rotation Rate
(or Period) and Obliquity[a]

Rotation rate (circulation type) Ω	Obliquity (degree of seasonal variation) θ_p		
	Low	Medium	High
Low (meridional)	Mercury[b] 0°, 59^d Venus[c] 3°, −244^d	Titan 27°, 16^d	Pluto[b] > 50°, 6^d
Medium (hybrid: meridional and zonal)		Earth 23°, 24^h Mars[b] 24°, 25^h	
High (zonal)	Jupiter 3°, 10^h	Saturn[d] 27°, 10^h Neptune[d] 29°, 15^h	Uranus 82°, −15^h

[a] From Williams and Holloway (1985).
[b] Seasonal variation enhanced by large orbital eccentricity.
[c] Circulation influenced by diurnal cycle.
[d] Seasonal variation reduced by interior heat source.

scale is relatively long, as in the ocean. This makes modeling simpler than for Earth's atmosphere where the planetary boundary layer must be dealt with, but it is nonetheless subject to the ambiguity of the subgrid closing parameterization. Changes in the Jovian jets are probably balanced by changes in the weak meridional cells and in the coherent vortices. Earth's jet is equilibrated by the transfer of momentum to the ground by the strong meridional circulation.

1.2.2. Saturn (Titan), Uranus, and Neptune. The other Jovian planets are considered to be essentially the same as Jupiter in structure and meteorology unless upcoming spacecraft encounters prove otherwise. [See Golitsyn (1979) and Trafton (1981) for details.] Jupiter, Saturn, and Neptune all have internal sources of heat of the same magnitude as their solar fluxes. This coincidence suggests that solar input controls the internal and meteorological heat transfers, not vice versa. Uranus has no internal heat source — perhaps because its extreme obliquity and seasonal variation have allowed the complete loss of internal energy via the unlit winter hemisphere. It is in their obliquities that the Jovian planets differ the most, Table I.

The radiative time scales[†] also differ greatly: 10 years for Jupiter and Saturn, 600 years for Uranus, and 2000 years for Neptune (Stone, 1973). These slow response times could insulate the atmospheres from seasonal changes or conversely limit dynamical activity to the uppermost regions.

[†] Ratio of thermal energy to solar heating flux.

The cloud-level circulation of Saturn exhibits multiple zonal jets that are stronger (400 m s^{-1} versus 100 m s^{-1}), wider, and more westerly in form than Jupiter's. These differences could be due to Saturn having a deeper atmosphere and to an inappropriate rotational reference frame. Saturn also displays coherent and turbulent eddies, though in less abundance or with less visibility. There is some evidence for bands on Uranus and for a tropical jet of 140 m s^{-1} on Neptune.

Titan, a satellite of Saturn, has an appreciable atmosphere. A slow rotation rate makes Venus its closest analog.

1.3. Modeling Problems and Strategy

A hierarchy of numerical models has been developed for terrestrial studies. According to Smagorinsky (1974) "the ultimate model of such a hierarchy could be conceived as one appropriate to any planetary atmosphere." In this section, we assess the planetary application of these models and the feasibility of developing a universal model.

1.3.1. Limitations.
Direct simulations of nonterrestrial circulations have been realized for Mars (Leovy, 1979), Venus (Rossow, 1983), and Jupiter (Williams, 1979a). But it is not obvious that such modeling is justifiable in Jupiter's case. Given that we know only the cloud-level flow, is it really possible to develop an understanding of the atmospheric circulation? What sort of modeling is possible under these circumstances? What is the least level of observation below which we would be attempting the impossible?

The answer to these questions depends on whether Jupiter is unique or possesses universal characteristics. If the GFD paradigm applies, then there is no reason why we cannot use it to construct a reasonable range of possible descriptions of the complete circulation. For this we must assume a thin atmosphere. If we believe Jupiter is unique, then only extensive observation can reveal its nature and modeling is impossible at this time. We can proceed only because we believe general principles are at work.

The situation resembles, in some ways, the early stages of terrestrial studies in which efforts were made to construct circulation theories based only on ground-level data for the atmosphere and surface data for the ocean. Although those studies also had the advantage of knowing the baroclinicity and lapse rate for the atmosphere, they produced erroneous results. We have fewer data for Jupiter, but we now know better how the basic mechanisms work and how to avoid the main error of earlier studies — ignoring or underestimating the eddies. We proceed with optimism, but history suggests caution.

1.3.2. Model Types. For atmospheric and oceanic studies, numerical process and predictive (GCM) models have been found to be useful. Process models are simplified models that analyze the behavior of a single, idealized but complex (usually nonlinear) mechanism in isolation. An atmosphere or ocean contains many complex mechanisms. Process models allow us to determine the characteristics of each one and to estimate their relative importance. Basic process models are thus the first in a hierarchy of models that usually culminate in a comprehensive, synthesizing predictive model. Process models can thus help describe and reveal what happens in nature and in predictive models. Nothing is ever fully understood or explained; we achieve only levels of understanding or explanation. Process models provide the first and simplest level of such a hierarchy of explanations. Analytical models (e.g., turbulence closure theory) deepen our understanding of basic mechanisms. Idealized concepts provide a language for discussion rather than a true explanation. Modeling of Jupiter has been mainly at the process level.

Predictive models are for direct simulations, i.e., comparison with nature. They can be constructed when all the basic parameters and all the important complex processes are known. Such models are only possible for Earth, Mars, and perhaps Venus. They can also be used for comparative modeling to estimate how a representative atmosphere behaves when its parameters and physics are varied. Comparative modeling generates a large set of circulations that can be used to generalize terrestrial issues, to reveal analogs among planets, and to broaden the base from which to extrapolate. To date, such modeling has been limited to the evaluation of an ECM that, unfortunately, lacks universality in its vertical and sublayer structure. Earth's atmosphere and oceans present us with two quite different types of vertical structure to guide our ideas and prompt our imagination toward a more general conception.

1.3.3. Predictive Model Design. Process and comparative models have already given some indication of how a predictive Jovian circulation model (JCM) could be assembled. In particular, studies of β and QG turbulence reveal similarities between Earth and Jupiter in mid-latitudes, while comparative models reveal tropical connections. The similarities between the GRS and IG vortices only exist under conditions that place constraints on the vertical structure. Exploring the conditions under which the similarities and differences occur in greater detail could suggest a preferred vertical structure for the JCM. Thermodynamical modeling will require even greater ingenuity.

Circulation modeling began with the barotropic and quasi-geostrophic models of Charney and Phillips. These led to the primitive equation model of Smagorinsky, which in turn led to the development of the Mars and Venus circulation models (MCM, VCM). The development at GFDL of a Jupiter circulation model (JCM) has followed the same systematic hierarchial evolution.

The construction of a JCM constitutes a major step in achieving the ultimate meteorological goal (Smagorinsky, 1974): the development of a general planetary model (GPM). To be dynamically universal such a model must be capable of describing either a semi-infinite or an unbounded atmosphere, but thermodynamical generality is harder to define. The high level of planetary observation, theoretical understanding, and computational power make such a model possible and worthwhile. It seems certain that all planetary models will be based on the pioneering ECM of Smagorinsky (1963) and its descendants.

2. Observations for Dynamical Modeling

For Jupiter and Saturn, some of the most basic items needed for dynamical modeling and verification are not available, but estimates are possible and are discussed below. Titan has a better-defined atmosphere and may be more easily modeled.

2.1. Stratification

2.1.1. Static Stability. The planetary scale dynamics of an atmosphere or ocean is primarily determined by the value and form of the Brunt Väisälä frequency $N(z)$, where $N^2/g = \theta^{-1}\theta_z = T^{-1}(T_z + \Gamma)$ is the static stability and Γ/c_p the adiabatic lapse rate (notation is standard unless defined). For planetary waves, the amplitude of N determines their scale while the form of $N(z)$ determines their vertical structure and their propagation characteristics. On Jupiter, motions could be trapped between a very stable stratosphere and a stable water cloud at the 5-bar level or, perhaps, by a stratification of the form $\mathrm{sech}^2 \, m(z - z_0)$ [cf. Pfister (1979)], where z_0 lies in the 1–5-bar region. Kinetic energy is confined to surface layers in the ocean by such distributions of $N(z)$ [e.g., Philander and Pacanowski (1980)]. Baroclinic instability cannot arise without wave trapping (Holton, 1974; Lindzen *et al.*, 1980), so its occurrence suggests the existence of appropriate forms of $N(z)$.

2.1.2. Clouds. Clouds have a major influence on the radiation balance and the formation of the stratification. In the most-accepted model of the gross vertical structure (Weidenschilling and Lewis, 1973), clouds form at three levels, a scale height apart, due to the condensation of ammonia, ammonia hydrosulphide, and water into ice crystals (Fig. 2). All are white

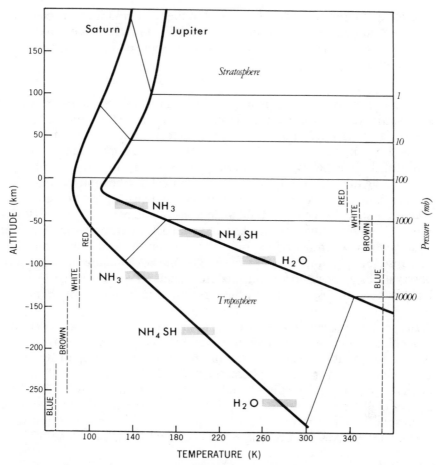

FIG. 2. Vertical profiles of temperature, cloud, and color for the upper atmospheres of Jupiter (on the right) and Saturn (on the left) as estimated from measurements in the radio and infrared wavelengths. [After Hunt and Moore (1982) and Hunt (1983).]

substances. The coloring is due to compounds of sulphur and phosphorus and depends on pressure, temperature, height, and latitude in a complex and poorly understood manner (Owen and Terrile, 1981) but may be approximately as shown in Fig. 2.

Most of the observed motions occur in the high ammonia cirrus clouds. The formation of the clouds may be attributed simply to geostrophic pressure variations (Williams, 1979a) or less simply to the vertical motions associated with the indirect (Ferrel) cells that equilibrate baroclinic jets (Williams and Holloway, 1985) and with direct (Hadley) cells. The first view is more consistent with the fact that the clouds disclose the horizontal motions so directly, motions that easily overwhelm the weak updrafts expected on a rapidly rotating planet. On Saturn, the cloud albedo varies more weakly with latitude, which suggests that the cloud formation process is dynamically unimportant.

2.1.3. Lapse Rates. The hydrogen–helium mix of Jupiter and Saturn is sufficiently well known that their lapse rates, 1.9 and 0.9 K km^{-1}, and their scale heights, 22 and 38 km, may be considered accurate [e.g., Hunt (1983)]. In Fig. 2, the dry adiabatic lapse rate is used to yield an approximate temperature distribution below the ammonia clouds. In reality this distribution could be significantly modified through nonadiabatic heating by condensation, radiation, and convection. The major condensing gases are ammonia and water so latent heating could yield a moist adiabat in the lower atmosphere. The thermodynamical disequilibrium of the para and ortho forms of hydrogen at low temperatures could alter the specific heat c_p and influence the lapse rate (Conrath and Gierasch, 1984). Above the ammonia clouds, observations in the radio and infrared frequencies reveal a tropopause and a highly stable stratosphere (due to absorption of radiation by methane and haze).

In the theoretical cloud models, the strongest stratification occurs in the water cloud and most of the radiation is absorbed in the region above it, so it is not unreasonable to expect deviations in the lapse rate of up to 10% from the dry adiabat in the troposphere. Such values ($\theta_z = 0.2$ K km^{-1}) can be observed just above the clouds (Lindal *et al.*, 1981) and give $N^2 \sim 3 \times 10^{-5}$ s^{-2} (as in the ocean) and $L_R \sim 1000$ km (as in the waves). In the lower stratosphere, values of $N \sim 5 \times 10^{-4}$ s^{-2} and $L_R \sim 400$ km are suggestive of smaller-scale waves but these have not been detected (Branscome, 1982).

2.2. Baroclinicity and Barotropy

2.2.1. Heat Sources. The brightness temperatures of Jupiter and Saturn, 124 and 94 K, reflect internal heat sources that are $\frac{2}{3}$ and $\frac{4}{3}$ of the solar input. These source values are substantially smaller than earlier estimates (Hanel *et al.*, 1983). The latitudinal distribution of the internal heat flux at the base of the atmosphere is unknown and is not necessarily uniform. This heat source, like that of Earth's ocean, reduces the imbalance in the solar heating but is unlikely to completely eliminate the need for meridional atmospheric transport. Our lack of knowledge about the value of $(\Delta T)_p$, the baroclinicity, below the clouds poses a major modeling problem.

2.2.2. Global Temperature Variation. The observed latitudinal and longitudinal variations in the infrared brightness temperature relate to thermal emission from above the ammonia cloud decks. For Jupiter, they indicate a cloud-level temperature difference $(\Delta T)_{\text{CL}}$ of 5 K between high and low latitudes. Local variations are also about 5 K at the cloud top (800 mb) and at the tropopause (150 mb) and they have some correlation with the visible features, i.e., the albedo. For example, the GRS is slightly cooler and therefore higher than its environment (Hanel *et al.,* 1979). For Saturn, seasonal variations result in a $(\Delta T)_{\text{CL}}$ of 10 K in the Northern (winter) Hemisphere and a much smaller value in the Southern Hemisphere (Conrath and Pirraglia, 1983). Longitudinal variations of 1 to 2 K reflect eddy activity in both planets.

2.2.3. Baroclinicity Estimates. It is unlikely that the observed (nonisobaric) temperature differentials $(\Delta T)_{\text{CL}}$ are an accurate indicator of the baroclinicity below the clouds. Although baroclinicities of 5 K are sufficient for energizing an atmosphere with a weak dissipation and a large specific heat, it is likely that larger values occur. On Earth, the $(\Delta T)_{\text{p}}$ of the lower troposphere is much larger than the ΔT along the tropopause. The small values of $(\Delta T)_{\text{CL}}$ on Jupiter could be due to variations in cloud height: if the clouds in high latitudes are a half-scale height lower than those near the equator, then a $(\Delta T)_{\text{p}} \sim 30$ K ensues (Gehrels, 1976). If the polar region receives only internal heat while the equatorial region gets both internal and solar heat, then $\Delta T \sim 30$ K is predicted. So far, it has not been possible to narrow the estimated baroclinicity range of 5–30 K.

2.2.4. Thermal Wind Fallacies. The main diagnostic tool used—and misused—to probe below the clouds is the thermal wind relationship

$$\hat{\mathbf{v}} = \mathbf{v}(p_2) - \mathbf{v}(p_1) = \frac{R}{f} \ln \frac{p_1}{p_2} \mathbf{k} \times (\nabla \tilde{T})_{\text{p}} \qquad (2.1)$$

where $(\hat{\ })$, $(\tilde{\ })$ denote the barotropic and baroclinic components. This connects the winds at two pressure levels with isobaric variations in the vertically averaged temperature $\tilde{T}$ using the geostrophic and hydrostatic relationships

$$\mathbf{v} = \frac{1}{f} \mathbf{k} \times (\nabla \Phi)_{\text{p}}, \qquad \Phi(p_2) - \Phi(p_1) = R \ln \frac{p_2}{p_1} \tilde{T} \qquad (2.2)$$

respectively [e.g., Houghton (1977, p. 80)]. The thermal wind relationship has been used in two ways: (1) to estimate the depths of the Jovian atmospheres using the observed cloud-level velocities and temperatures $\mathbf{v}_{\text{CL}}$ and

$T_{\rm CL}$ (Lorenz, 1953; Smith *et al.*, 1982) and (2), inversely, to estimate the flow
below the clouds using the observed $T_{\rm CL}$ and a presupposed depth (Conrath
and Pirraglia, 1983; Flasar *et al.*, 1981b). Such applications are fraught with
danger and error and are the cause of much misunderstanding.

All applications of the Eq. (2.1) set $\mathbf{v}(p_2) = \mathbf{v}_{\rm CL}$, and assume that $\mathbf{v}(p_1) = 0$
at a so-called "level of no motion." This representation of the baroclinic
component of the wind $\hat{\mathbf{v}}$ is only meaningful when $\hat{\mathbf{v}}$ is fairly uniform and is
comparable with or larger than the barotropic component $\tilde{\mathbf{v}}$. The application
of the thermal wind relation gives meaningless results if the motions are
predominantly barotropic, which they are in weakly dissipative systems such
as the ocean and Jupiter, where it is possible for weak baroclinicities to pump
up large quasi-barotropic currents with $\tilde{\mathbf{v}} \gg \hat{\mathbf{v}}$ [e.g., Williams, (1979a, Fig.
8)]. Then $\mathbf{v}_{\rm CL}$ indicates $\tilde{\mathbf{v}}$, not $\hat{\mathbf{v}}$. It should be noted that oceanographers have
recently realized the error of this approach: "One regrets that the barotropic
field was for so long obscured as a level of no motion" (Rhines, 1979). The
problem can be overcome using the β-spiral method (Stommel and Schott,
1977), but this requires temperature data in the vertical and horizontal
directions. These criticisms also apply to analyses based on the cyclostrophic
wind relation.

Applications of the geostrophic relation [Eq. (2.2)] to Saturn's cloud-level
winds have also been misinterpreted. When the relation is integrated over
latitude, it produces a large value for the pole-to-equator gradient in the
geopotential height $\Delta\Phi$. However, $\Delta\Phi$ is also a measure of the net angular
momentum, which for a weakly dissipative atmosphere should be very
small. This contradiction implies that the reference frame used in defining
the (excessively prograde) winds is incorrect [cf. Allison and Stone (1983)]
and that the tropical jet is strongly baroclinic. It does not imply that the
atmosphere is very deep [cf. Smith *et al.* (1982)].

2.2.5. Evidence for Barotropy. The fact that the Jovian jets are so stable
and so constant suggests that they are predominantly barotropic and thus
have great inertia to baroclinic changes. Weak baroclinicity is only influential if it acts for a long time. Barotropy is also suggested by the close relationship between jet widths and bands via the expression produced by barotropic
β-turbulence theory, $L_\beta = (U/\beta)^{1/2}$, where U is the velocity scale. Such jets
could penetrate to a depth of $h_\beta = (f/N)L_\beta$ while baroclinic eddies penetrate
to $h_{\rm R} = (f/N)L_{\rm R}$ [cf. Holland *et al.* (1984)]. Assuming possible values of
$N^2 = 3 \times 10^{-5}$ s^{-2}, $L_{\rm R} = 1000$ km, and $L_\beta = 5000$ km gives $h_\beta = 200$ km
and $h_{\rm R} = 40$ km. The Phillips criterion for baroclinic instability requires a
critical shear of $\hat{u} = \beta L_{\rm R}^2$, which equals 1 m s^{-1} per scale height and implies
that $\hat{u} \ll \tilde{u}$. Thus in a weakly dissipative system the barotropic components

of the circulation could be substantially stronger, wider, and deeper than the baroclinic ones.

2.3. Cloud-Level Circulation

2.3.1. Rotation Rate. In defining the cloud-level circulation, ambiguities arise due to uncertainties as to which rotating reference frame is the most appropriate and as to which height the cloud-tracked winds refer. The latter problem is not serious if the winds are strongly barotropic. However, the observed motions define a very relative circulation.

The customary rotation rate is based on the radio frequency and gives velocities relative to the so-called System III reference frame. However, the bulk of the planet (and its magnetic field) need not rotate at the radio frequency. In addition, dynamical models of the GRS and Large Ovals suggest that these vortices are moving more rapidly westward by 5 to 15 m s^{-1} than System III implies (Williams and Yamagata, 1984), while the observed prograde bias in Saturn's jets suggests that the winds be made 70 m s^{-1} more easterly to achieve momentum balance. These problems indicate that reference frames — say System IV — with rotation periods that are about 1 min and 5 min shorter than System III be used for Jupiter and Saturn.

2.3.2. Jets and Bands. The high-resolution zonal winds obtained from tracking cloud features as small as 100–200 km over short time intervals (about 1 day) in Voyager spacecraft data have essentially the same structure (Fig. 3) as the winds derived from Earth-based tracking of larger clouds over lengthy periods. Now, however, the finer details of the motions, the rapid variations of the turbulent eddies and their interactions with the coherent vortices can be followed in remarkable detail for both Jupiter (Beebe *et al.,* 1980; Ingersoll *et al.,* 1981; Limaye *et al.,* 1982) and Saturn (Smith *et al.,* 1982; Sromovsky *et al.,* 1983).

The Voyager data indicate that the amplitudes of the jets are somewhat greater than originally thought but that the amplitudes vary little in time. The observations also reveal that alternating easterly and westerly jets, with amplitudes of up to 20 m s^{-1}, extend as far as 72° latitude (the observational limit) in both hemispheres (Beebe, personal communication, 1984) — even though cloud banding ends at 45° latitude. The jets are fairly symmetric between hemispheres but the bands are not, and the latter provide a more sensitive measure of temporal variations.

The bands (color, albedo) of Jupiter have changed continuously over the years. Between the Pioneer and Voyager encounters, a period of 4 years, one

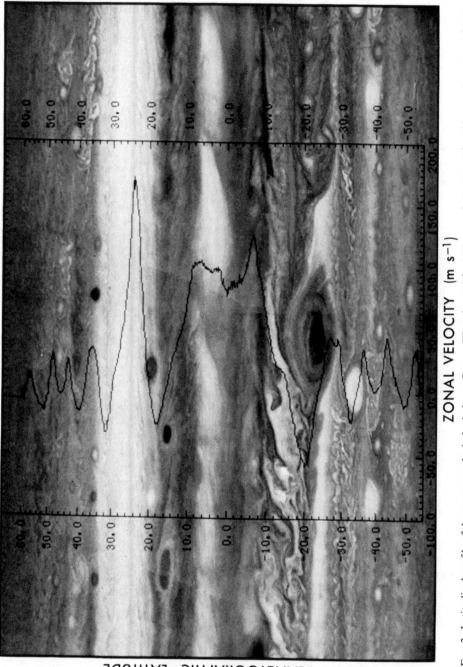

ZONAL VELOCITY (m s^{-1})

Fig. 3. Latitudinal profile of the mean zonal wind relative to System III, estimated from Voyager 2 cloud tracking. [Prepared courtesy of S. S. Limaye (1985).]

zone doubled in size and another halved. But during the two Pioneer encounters (1 year apart) there was little change in cloud structure. Bands appear to vary significantly with periods of 4 to 5 years but occasionally change in only 1 year, reflecting perhaps different phases of an energy cycle.

The correlation between the unchanging jets and the variable bands is thus not as simple as once thought. On Jupiter, there is still a reasonable correlation between the zonal motion and the bands, with jet maxima coinciding with belt–zone interfaces; but, on Saturn a correlation exists only for the mid-latitudinal jets, with extrema coinciding with the centers of the bands (Smith *et al.*, 1982). However, the correlation between temperature variations near the tropopause and the visible markings of Jupiter is clearcut (Hanel *et al.*, 1979). All of these relations are consistent with the idea that the jets are predominantly barotropic while the bands depend more on baroclinic factors.

2.3.3. Eddies and Vortices. Spacecraft observations have revealed the flow fields inside the long-lived, coherent vortices — the GRS, Large Ovals, and Small Ovals — that occur at latitudes 22°, 33°, and 41° (Mitchell *et al.*, 1981). These anticyclonic eddies are all very similar in form, environment and parameter values. They are strong vortices: the relative vorticity of the GRS exceeds the ambient vorticity by a factor of 4 and wind speeds exceed 100 m s^{-1} near the periphery. Flow is along closed symmetric ellipses so interaction with the zonal flow is limited. Between the two Voyager encounters (5 months) considerable changes occurred in the flow just west of the GRS and resembled the breaking of a PG-scale planetary wave.

In contrast to the Large Ovals, the GRS appears to have its vorticity concentrated near its outer boundary and to possess a quiescent interior. These differences could be due to the greater size of the GRS (Williams and Wilson, 1985), or, alternatively, the variations could be due more to vertical shears in the winds than to real differences in horizontal structure, especially if the winds peak at the height of the peripheral clouds and decay above it. There is no direct evidence of organized vertical motion within the vortices.

The GRS has been observed since the invention of the telescope and the Large Ovals since their birth in 1938. The formation of the Large Ovals is well documented — they took 15 years to develop into strong vortices — and is consistent with the behavior of weak barotropic instability at the IG scale (Williams and Wilson, 1985). Both the GRS and Large Ovals have contracted in longitude, the former from 40,000 to 24,000 km in this century. According to theory, this indicates increased amplitude and steepening, as energy is extracted from narrowing jets, and not vortex decay.

The longitudinal drift of the GRS has varied over the past 150 years, changing direction every 50 years in System III coordinates. On top of its recent drift at 5 m s^{-1}, the GRS oscillates in longitude with an amplitude of 0.9° and a period of 90 days (Solberg, 1969). According to theory, such variations could be related to changes in vortex amplitude, current amplitude, or the radius of deformation. However, theoretical vortices only propagate westward, so changes in direction in System III really indicate changes in speed in System IV.

Persistent coherent cyclonic eddies also occur. In the Southern Hemisphere (Mitchell *et al.*, 1979), they are induced in cyclonic shear regions by the GRS and Large Ovals. In the Northern Hemisphere at 14° latitude, the cyclonic "barges" (Hatzes *et al.*, 1981) are primary vortices that drift eastward at 2 to 5 m s^{-1} in System III. According to theory, cyclonic vortices are long-lived only when they lie in a strong easterly flow. The flow at 14°N could be easterly if averaged vertically in System IV.

Disturbances peculiar to the tropics are the so-called "plumes" that form the centers of a wavelike train of features moving with the 100 m s^{-1} westerly jet at 10°N (Fig. 1). Some plumes are brighter and more structured than others and have been described as "active convective centers," 1000–2000 km long (Hunt and Müller, 1979; Hunt *et al.*, 1981, 1982). Smaller (gravity?) waves are seen in the tails of the plumes. The tropical wave containing the plumes has the same scale as the GRS and could be generated by disturbances emanating from that vortex. Because of its size, the GRS can generate waves capable of propagating beyond the critical latitude at 10°S but which would be trapped at 10°N [cf. Williams and Yamagata (1984, Fig. 8)]. It seems unlikely that wave-CISK—which requires low ventilation rates for moisture accumulation (Grey, 1978)—could arise in such rapidly moving currents, especially in latitudes in which the downward branch of a Hadley cell might occur.

Saturn's eddies resemble Jupiter's in form and behavior but are generally smaller and shorter lived (Sanchez-Lavega, 1982; Sromovsky *et al.*, 1983). At the Voyager encounter, three brown Ovals with diameters of 5000 km existed at 42°N and a solitary 10,000 km Oval existed at 72°N. The complex interaction of two small white vortices was observed in fine detail (Sromovsky *et al.*, 1983) and it more closely paralleled the oblique collisions of IG vortices [cf. Williams and Yamagata (1984, Fig. 10)] than the collisions of the vorticity concentrations generated by turbulence (McWilliams, 1984).

Disturbances said to be peculiar to Saturn may just be poorly resolved vortices (Sanchez-Lavega, 1982). These so-called Great White Spots have occurred 5 times in 80 years with diameters as large as 25,000 km in both the tropics and mid-latitudes. More than one type of vortex may be involved. Their lives are short (months). They sometimes expand longitudinally to fill the whole zone and generate other spots, actions consistent with the development of barotropic instability (Williams and Wilson, 1985). The "ribbon wave" observed at 46°N, with cyclones to the north and anticyclones to the south, is suggestive of barotropic instability at the QG scale [cf. Williams and Yamagata (1984, Fig. 17)]. A similar, but nonwavy, thin brown line or ribbon occurs in the center of a similar westerly jet at 25°N on Jupiter and could be a barotropically stable version of such cloud formation.

2.4. Data Analysis

2.4.1. Quasi-Geostrophic Instabilities. The necessary condition for the instability of zonal flows involves the potential vorticity gradient, which for QG scales, can be written as

$$q_y = \beta + \tilde{q}_y + \hat{q}_y, \qquad \tilde{q}_y = -\tilde{u}_{yy}, \qquad \hat{q}_y = -\hat{u}_{yy} - \frac{1}{\rho_s}\left(\frac{\rho_s}{S}\hat{u}_z\right)_z + \frac{\hat{u}_z}{S}\delta \quad (2.3)$$

where δ denotes interface contributions.

Estimates of the barotropic term $\beta + \tilde{q}_y$ using cloud-level winds are error prone as the winds may not give a good measure of the vertically averaged flow, and their second derivatives cannot be accurately calculated. One set of estimates from Voyager data suggests that Jupiter's jets are mildly barotropically unstable or mildly baroclinic (Ingersoll *et al.*, 1979; Mitchell *et al.*, 1981), while a second set suggests that all easterly jets are strongly unstable or strongly baroclinic (Ingersoll *et al.*, 1981; Limaye *et al.*, 1982). Although both hemispheres appear to be equally unstable (or baroclinic), the coherent vortices generated by barotropic instability only occur in the Southern Hemisphere (SH). This suggests that either (1) the SH is marginally unstable and the Northern Hemisphere (NH) marginally stable or (2) the instabilities are in the shear zones in the SH but in the jet maxima in the NH and hence less visible, except as ribbon waves (see Section 2.3.3). For Saturn, the noise level in the winds precludes meaningful estimates of $\beta + \tilde{q}_y$ [cf. Smith *et al.* (1981) and Sromovsky *et al.* (1983)].

The QG form of $\hat{q}_y$ is not really appropriate for Jupiter, given the large scales of the jets. At such scales, divergence effects due to the displacement of free surfaces shared with deeper underlying or overlying layers are important and instability depends on the expression $\beta - \tilde{u}_{yy} + (\tilde{u}/L_D^2)$, where L_D is the external radius of deformation (Lipps, 1963). This criterion has not been estimated for the data.

In the barotropic β-turbulence theory, jets generated by *homogeneous* forcing attain a state of neutral stability with $\tilde{u}_{yy} = \beta$ (Rhines, 1975). In a baroclinic atmosphere, forcing by baroclinic instabilities (in the jet maxima) is inhomogeneous and can produce barotropically unstable jets. Thus the two forms of instability can coexist, at vastly different scales L_R and

L_β [cf. Brown (1969)]. Estimates of the eddy energy conversion (Section 2.4.2) fail to discriminate between opposing contributions at the two scales and appear to be dominated by the more easily measured small-scale components.

The baroclinic term $\hat{q}_y$ is significant if the ratio $\alpha = f^2 u_{zz}/\beta N^2$ is large. If we chose $u_{zz} \approx u_z/H$ (to avoid the errors noted in Section 2.2.4), then $\alpha = h/H$, where $h = f^2 u_z/\beta N^2$ is the eddy penetration scale (Held, 1978). The shear u_z can be estimated from thermal data for the upper troposphere, where a close correlation between u_z and u indicates that most jets gain strength below the clouds (Pirraglia et al., 1981). The observations give $u_z H = -10$ m s^{-1}, $N^2 = 3 \times 10^{-5}$ s^{-2} and thence $\alpha = 5$. So subcloud baroclinic instability is indicated.

2.4.2. Kinetic Energy Conversion. The equation for eddy kinetic change in a barotropic fluid is best written as

$$\overline{K'_t} = C_1 - (\overline{v'p'} + \overline{v'K'})_y$$

where $K'(y) = \bar{u}u' + \frac{1}{2}(u'^2 + v'^2)$ and $C_1(y) \equiv \bar{u}(\overline{u'v'})_y$. According to the nonacceleration theorem, these forms of the conversion and flux divergence terms are preferred over those in which the conversion term is written as $C_2(y) \equiv -\overline{u'v'} \cdot \bar{u}_y$. This is because only the former are identically zero for a steady wave propagating in a sheared environment and so only they are locally meaningful. With the first forms the error of identifying regions in which $C_2 > 0$ and $(\overline{v'p'})_y > 0$ as barotropically unstable can be avoided.

Several evaluations of the expression $C_2(y)$ have been attempted that use Voyager cloud-level winds observed over a 30-hr interval. Such estimates are useful provided no local (in latitude) or climatological significance is attached to them. One set of estimates (Beebe et al., 1980; Ingersoll et al., 1981), in which the cloud-level winds are assumed to penetrate to the 2.5-bar level, produces large positive values of C_2 that imply the mean flow will double or be replenished in 3 months by using 10% of the solar energy input. This unrealistic result suggests that the estimates are inaccurate. A second set of estimates (Limaye et al., 1982) eliminates the systematic sampling errors of the first (by using lower resolution) and yields $C_2 \approx 0$. A third estimate (Mitchell, 1982), using uniform sampling and high resolutions, again gives large positive values of C_2.

Thus there are contradictory indications that the eddies occasionally supply energy to the mean flow at cloud level, but there are no estimates of behavior in the more important lower atmosphere. Oceanographic evaluations of local energy balances have also been interpreted as indicating that the Gulf Stream is accelerated by the eddies. However, the cross-stream-averaged value of $\overline{u'v'} \cdot v_x$ is nearly zero, so such results may indicate the transfer of energy from one side of a jet to the other and not mean flow generation [cf. Charney and Flierl (1981, p. 507)].

2.4.3. Equilibrium and Dissipation. There are three possible mechanisms for jet equilibrium: (1) dissipation by gravity waves or by exchanges with the sublayer, (2) loss of energy to the coherent vortices by barotropic instability, or (3) balance by the induced meridional circulation. The momentum equation

$$-f\bar{v}_a + (\overline{u'v'})_y = D \tag{2.4}$$

summarizes these effects at the quasi-geostrophic level, where v_a is the ageostrophic flow. Observations give no clue as to which process prevails, if any.

The dissipation mechanism operates in Earth's stratosphere and if we adopt the stratospheric dissipation coefficients (Schoeberl and Strobel, 1978) a dissipation time scale of 900 days is predicted (Branscome, 1982). This value is consistent with our suggestion that there is a wide separation between the dynamical (50-day) and dissipative time scales. Equilibration by mechanism (2) requires a balance between the baroclinic eddy source term $[(\overline{u'v'})_y]^{L_R}$ and barotropic eddy loss term $[(\overline{u'v'})_y]^{L_\beta}$, where brackets denote averaging over scales close to L_R or L_β. The absence of coherent vortices in many regions suggests this is not the main control process. No estimates of the scale dependence of the eddy conversion have been made.

With mechanism (3), a meridional circulation of about 0.1 m s^{-1} could balance the eddy fluxes estimated by Mitchell (1982). Thus the cells would be much weaker than those of Earth's atmosphere, and if they are primarily induced by baroclinic instability, they would be confined to the jet extrema and be narrower than the jets ($L_R \ll L_\beta$) — as are some of the bands. There may be no meridional circulation in the region between these cells. Estimates of the mean meridional wind $\bar{v}$ from Voyager data produce values of about 1 m s^{-1}, but these cannot be accurate given that the rms winds have values up to 10 m s^{-1}.

2.4.4. Spectra. Spectral analyses of the Voyager cloud-level winds produce such noisy spectra that it is impossible to detect a simple wave number relationship of the form k^{-n}, although—like for Earth—a k^{-3} result has been claimed (Mitchell, 1982). The best indication of the nature and dimensionality of the nonlinear exchanges is the close relationship between jet widths and amplitudes via the L_β expression of β turbulence. The steadiness of the jets also reflects the barotropization associated with β-turbulence effects.

Recent numerical studies of two-dimensional and β turbulence (see CD85) yield spectral slopes with powers ranging from $n = 3$ to 6 in the enstrophy cascading scales, with the actual value depending on the forms of the forcing and dissipation. The absence of simple turbulence behavior makes data interpretation very difficult.

2.5. New Worlds: Titan

2.5.1. Significance. A bonus from the spacecraft encounters is the discovery that Titan, Saturn's largest satellite (2575-km radius) has a substantial (1.6-bar) nitrogen atmosphere and perhaps a methane ocean (Smith *et al.,* 1981, 1982). Clearly Titan is a planet of physical relevance to terrestrial studies and possesses great modeling potential. The planet has dynamical relevance for Venus because of the length of its rotational period (15.9 days) and for comparative meteorology it is an invaluable addition to the meager category of slowly rotating systems.

2.5.2. Stratification. The atmosphere has observed temperatures of 94 K at the surface, 71 K at the tropopause level (43 km, 140 mb), and a 170-K limit in the upper stratosphere (200 km) (Fig. 4) (Lindal *et al.,* 1983). With $g = 135$ cm s^{-2}, the scale height is 18 km. The lapse rate has the adiabatic value for dry nitrogen, 1.4 K km^{-1}, only near the surface and drops sharply to 0.9 K km^{-1} at the top of the boundary layer (3.5 km). Methane makes up 1% of the atmospheric mass but its moist adiabat, 0.3 K km^{-1}, is not observed so saturation is absent. There are methane clouds in the troposphere and an aerosol layer plus two haze layers in the stratosphere (Samuelson *et al.,* 1981, Fig. 2; Smith *et al.,* 1981, 1982). Carbon dioxide is another important minor constituent (Samuelson *et al.,* 1983).

2.5.3. Global Temperature Variation. The observed brightness temperatures indicate pole-to-equator temperature differences of 3 K near the surface, 1 K at the tropopause, and 20 K in the stratosphere (at 0.3 mb) (Flasar *et al.,* 1981a). Hemispheric asymmetries occur in the stratospheric temperatures due to seasonal effects, but no diurnal effects have been detected. The radiative time scale thus exceeds a Titan day in the stratosphere and reaches an estimated 140 years in the troposphere.

Ground-based observations have revealed dramatic seasonal variations in the planet's overall appearance [cf. Sromovsky *et al.* (1981)]. If the troposphere is involved, the efficient dynamical heat transports of the Hadley cell that occurs at low rotation rates could be important to these secular albedo changes.

2.5.4. Circulation. Visually, Titan is bland because of the opaque stratospheric hazes. No surface or cloud features have been seen so there are no

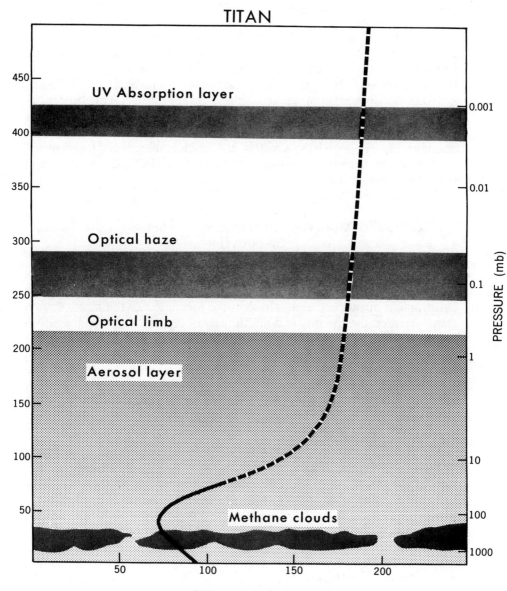

FIG. 4. Vertical profile of temperature and clouds in Titan's atmosphere. [After Hunt and Moore (1982).]

wind estimates. The large stratospheric temperature gradients could produce superrotating cyclostrophic winds of 100 m s^{-1} near the 1-mb level (Flasar *et al.*, 1981a). Titan's circulation should have much in common with the slowly rotating Earth circulation models of Williams and Holloway (1982, Fig. 3; 1985). If so, maximum westerly winds should occur near 75° latitude with jets just below the tropopause and in the stratosphere. The latter could be associated with the observed dark polar collar (Smith *et al.*, 1981). Easterlies could occur in the summer hemisphere toward solstice. Baroclinic instability should be absent, and indeed no longitudinal variations in brightness temperature have been observed. Temperature inversions at the top of the boundary layer (to which the equatorward flow is confined) and low-temperature gradients between the equator and pole occur in both the model and the atmosphere.

3. Numerical Modeling: Planetary Turbulence, Coherence, Circulations

The basic ideas and modeling results mentioned in the Introduction are discussed in greater detail in this section. We begin by reviewing the nature of barotropic β turbulence and its role in the formation of the major Jovian characteristics: the zonality and multiplicity of the jets. Barotropic β turbulence underlies all forms of planetary turbulence as barotropic β waves can occur in any form of atmosphere (semi-infinite, unbounded, etc.). We then describe QG turbulence, noting how and when baroclinic flows behave like forced barotropic flows and the conditions under which it produces Jupiter-like circulations. The origin and existence of coherent features are described using the shallow water (SW) model, the simplest system to incorporate the necessary divergence effects.

The turbulence studies indicate that in mid-latitudes Jupiter is analogous to a more rapidly rotating Earth. To see whether this analog holds in equatorial regions and to see whether any analogs exist with other planets, ECMs have been evaluated for a wide range of parameter values. The ECM solutions also provide a basis for comparative modeling and for circulation theory, and we end with a brief discussion of their character.

3.1. Planetary Turbulence

3.1.1. Barotropic β Turbulence. Barotropic flows behave like two-dimensional (2D) turbulence on the smaller scale, $M \equiv L_\beta^2/L^2 > 1$, where M is the wave steepness factor. Recent studies, while confirming the well-known tendency of the stream function toward larger scale and the vorticity toward smaller scale, have revealed that interactions are far more intermittent in space and time than originally thought. These result in the formation of coherent, small-scale, high-vorticity regions and enstrophy cascade spectra that range from k^{-3} to k^{-6}, depending on the form of energy input and dissipation (Fornberg, 1977; Basdevant et al., 1981; McWilliams, 1984). Theories based solely on spectral decomposition no longer provide an adequate description of turbulence.

On the larger scale, $M < 1$, barotropic flows display a β-wave dynamics that interacts with the turbulent dynamics only at the transitional scale L_β (Rhines, 1975). At this scale, β-wave dispersion interrupts the expansion of the 2D eddies to retard the energy decascade and to create resonant triads that focus the energy into alternating east–west zonal jets. The anisotropy of the eddies and the zonality of the final flow are mainly due to the anisotropy of the dispersion relation for β waves. At the equator, the nondispersive form of the Kelvin wave relation implies that Kelvin waves cannot be energized by 2D energy decascades even though it also implies that Kelvin waves triads are always resonant and potentially dominant. However, Kelvin waves become dispersive in the presence of shear (Boyd, 1984) so Kelvin turbulence may be possible even though β turbulence normally prevails globally.

The generation of zonal jets is not fully understood. In resonant triads, fully zonal flows cannot gain or lose energy and only act as a catalyst in the exchange between the other two waves (Longuet-Higgins and Gill, 1967; Gill, 1974). However, near-zonal flows can be energized by triad resonances, while near-resonant and sideband interactions can bridge the gap to full zonality (Yamagata and Kono, 1976).

Homogenously forced β turbulence produces alternating jets that are barotropically stable (Rhines, 1975), but inhomogenous forcing produces westerlies — that could become unstable — in the forcing latitudes and easterlies in the unforced regions. The character of locally forced zonal flows can be explained either deterministically using vortex separation ideas based on helicity transfer (Kuo, 1950) or statistically using potential vorticity mixing (Eady, 1954). The latter shows that steady forcing leads to easterlies of magnitude $\bar{u} = -(1/2\beta)\overline{q^2}$, which translates in the Lagrangian view to $\bar{u} = -\frac{1}{2}\beta y_m^2$, where $q = \beta y_m$ and y_m is the latitudinal mixing length. For Jupiter, the observed winds of $\bar{u} \sim 20$ m s^{-1} (and $\beta = 4 \times 10^{-9}$ km^{-1} s^{-1}) imply a mixing length of 3000 km, a value consistent with the observed eddy sizes.

The development of anisotropy and zonality from freely evolving homogeneous eddy fields and from forced homogenous and inhomogenous eddy fields has been demonstrated both in laboratory experiments (Whitehead, 1972; de Verdiere, 1980; McEwan et al., 1980) and in numerical studies with Jovian and terrestrial parameters (Rhines, 1975, 1977; Williams, 1975a,b, 1978; Basdevant *et al.*, 1981; Haidvogel and Rhines, 1983). Eddy forcing is normally based on simple Markovian closure schemes that represent the growth and decay of baroclinic instabilities in midlatitudes and that represent waves created by convection in the tropics.

A solution with Jovian parameters in Fig. 5 reflects the globally homogenous forcing during the early stages. As the energy level increases and energy decascades to larger scales, β-wave propagation sets in, with the steepness of the waves indicating their nonlinear origin. The eddies cease growing as wave propagation takes over. Alternating stable, zonal currents of scale L_β develop from the waves, with the associated waves and currents moving in the same direction, and the system eventually equilibrates. Equatorial jets can be produced by enhanced tropical forcing that is symmetrical about the equator (as are β waves), (Williams, 1978, Fig. 18). Coherent vortices are absent from the flow in Fig. 5 because divergence effects are excluded. Calculations with the more general SW model remedy this deficiency (Williams and Wilson, 1985).

3.1.2. QG Turbulence. Although QG flows possess a 3D vortex stretching mechanism they behave more like 2D flows — when β and boundary effects are negligible — because of analogous potential enstrophy and total energy constraints. Charney (1971) has suggested that QG turbulence could be isotropic if the potential vorticity is defined in terms of the stretched vertical coordinate zN/f and that this results in the available potential and kinetic energies being equipartitioned and having κ^{-3} spectra, where κ is the total wave number. Spectral closure analyses (Herring, 1980) confirm that flows that are initially homogenous become isotropic at the small scales, barotropic at the large scales and baroclinic at the scale of the energy peak L_0. The barotropization is due to the energy decascade toward larger stretched-vertical and horizontal scales.

A serious limitation with the Charney theory is that there is no way of achieving the vertical homogenization of the initial state from more general states (Herring, 1980). This problem arises because the mixing is two-dimensional even though the potential vorticity is three-dimensional.

More realistic and amenable views of QG turbulence have been obtained using the two-level approximation. The equations for QG_2 turbulence can be written in the barotropic, baroclinic forms

$$\nabla^2 \tilde{\psi}_t + J(\tilde{\psi}, \nabla^2 \tilde{\psi} + f) + J(\hat{\psi}, \nabla^2 \hat{\psi}) = 0 \qquad (3.1)$$

$$(\nabla^2 - k_R^2)\hat{\psi}_t + J(\tilde{\psi}, (\nabla^2 - k_R^2)\hat{\psi}) + J(\hat{\psi}, \nabla^2 \tilde{\psi} + f) = 0 \qquad (3.2)$$

where k_R is the deformation wave number. These equations immediately reveal the main characteristic of QG_2 flows: baroclinic flows can generate barotropic flow, but barotropic initial states remain barotropic.

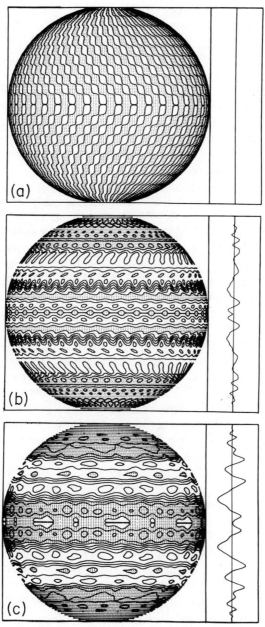

FIG. 5. Formation of multiple zonal currents in a forced barotropic β-turbulence model with Jovian parameters. (a) Day 4.6, (b) day 46, (c) day 161. The flow initially reflects the homogeneous eddy forcing and then develops Rossby waves and finally alternating zonal currents. The contour interval of the stream function, 40 km² s⁻¹, is doubled in (c), and negative values are shaded. The zonal wind profile has a scale of ±100 m s⁻¹ and a zero value at the center line. [After Williams (1978). Reproduced with permission from *Journal of the Atmospheric Sciences*, a publication of the American Meteorological Society.]

Analysis of the resonant wave triads of these equations indicate that barotropic primary waves prefer to interact in pure barotropic triads at all scales, whereas baroclinic primary waves prefer to interact in pure baroclinic triads only at small scales and in mixed barotropic–baroclinic triads at large scales (Yamagata, 1976, 1977; Kim, 1978; Jones, 1978; Salmon, 1978, 1980). The barotropic–baroclinic interaction is only really effective at L_R, a scale that provides the valve through which baroclinicity flows into barotropy — but not vice versa. Thus, QG_2 turbulence theory also predicts large-scale barotropy and small-scale isotropy.

How QG_2 flows evolve depends on their initial configuration and on the scale of the energy input relative to L_R and L_β. Rhines (1977, Fig. 19) describes the five basic paths. In general, when the dominant eddy scale L is less than L_R, the two layers are decoupled and each exhibits a separate 2D turbulence; but when $L > L_R$, the layers lock together and behave as a single barotropic layer with the eddies expanding until β-wave effects are felt.

Numerical studies of both freely evolving flows (Rhines, 1975, 1977, 1979) and of equilibrated flows with atmospheric and oceanic forms of forcing and geometry and with idealized (doubly periodic) domains (Steinberg, 1973; Barros and Wiin-Nielsen, 1974; Williams, 1975b, 1979a; Holland, 1978; Holland and Rhines, 1980; Salmon, 1980; Haidvogel and Held, 1980; McWilliams and Chow, 1981) all display the elementary QG_2 turbulent processes described above. The differences between turbulence in heat-driven atmospheric and wind-driven oceanic channels are minor [cf. Williams (1979b) with McWilliams and Chow (1981)]. Ocean basins behave uniquely, however, with eddies acting to limit the wind driven mean flow in the upper layer by producing a downward momentum flux that induces a mean flow in the lower layer (Holland, 1978; Holland and Rhines, 1980).

For Jupiter, QG_2 turbulence models are forced by weak heating functions that crudely represent the latitudinal imbalance of radiative, convective, and internal heating and that produce baroclinicities ranging from 2 to 40 K and instability wavelengths ranging from 2000 to 9000 km. The QG_2 process model is relevant to Jupiter as it represents all forms of baroclinic instability (internal, unbounded, etc.) except the surface type.

Jovian QG_2 flows, Fig. 6, take about 10 years to spin up because of the weak heating rate and go through alternating phases of baroclinic instability and quiescence. The nonlinear cascades and β effects eradicate all traces of the initial Hadley circulation (with its 2 m s^{-1} uniform zonal wind) and generate a series of highly zonal, alternating easterly and westerly jets that are strongly barotropic and whose scale is close to L_β, not L_R. The intermittent baroclinic instabilities eventually pump the jets up to speeds exceeding 100 m s^{-1}.

No organized meridional cells occur in the QG_2 solutions. Similarities

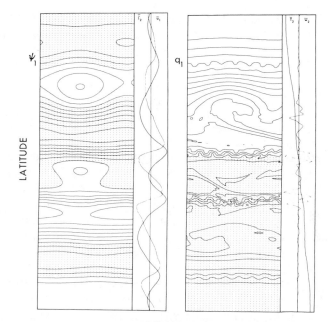

LONGITUDE

FIG. 6. Formation of multiple zonal currents in a QG_2 turbulence model with Jovian parameters and heating function. The stream function and zonal wind indicate the alternating jets 1773 days into the spinup, while the potential vorticity indicates the scale of the baroclinic instability. The large gyre is a standing neutral baroclinic wave. Negative values are shaded. The zonal wind profile has a scale of ± 160 m s^{-1}. [After Williams (1979a). Reproduced with permission from *Journal of the Atmospheric Sciences,* a publication of the American Meteorological Society.]

between the stream function — rather than temperature or vertical motion — and Jupiter's bands imply that the larger-scale clouds are primarily correlated with horizontal variations in pressure, as befits a quasi-barotropic circulation. Such mechanically induced clouds resemble terrestrial cirrostratus and make the motions remarkably visible.

3.2. Planetary Coherence

3.2.1. Geostrophic Regimes. Most planetary-scale motions are governed by geostrophy, but their characteristics can vary widely depending on their scale relative to the deformation scale L_R. The simplest system capable of describing all the geostrophic regimes (i.e., types of motion) is the shallow-

water (SW) model, whose equations reduce under geostrophy to a single
equation for the geopotential height — the general geostrophic equation

$$h_t - \nabla \cdot \left(\frac{h}{f^2} \nabla h_t \right) + \frac{h}{m} h_x (f^{-1})_y - J\left(h, \frac{h}{f^2} \zeta \right) - J\left(\frac{h}{f}, K \right) = 0 \quad (3.3)$$

where $\zeta \equiv \nabla \left((1/f) \nabla h \right)$, $K \equiv (1/2f^2)(\nabla h)^2$, $J(h, \alpha) \equiv m^{-1} (h_x \alpha_y - h_y \alpha_x)$,
$(x, y) = a(\lambda, \theta)$, and $m = \cos \theta$ (Williams, 1985). If Eq. (3.3) is nondimen-
sionalized and parametric ordering relationships are chosen, we obtain the
planetary geostrophic (PG), intermediate-geostrophic (IG), and the QG sets
of subequations that describe motions at the large, intermediate, and synoptic scales. Intermediate motions occur near the scale $L_I = (L_D^2 L_B)^{1/3}$, where
$L_D = (gH)^{1/2}/f$ and $L_B = f/\beta$ (Charney and Flierl, 1981). Dispersion (second
term) and vorticity advection (fourth term) dominate in the QG regime;
nonlinear divergence due to interface displacement (third term) dominates
in the PG regime while dispersion and divergence act in balance in the IG
regime.

The two types of nonlinearity in the above equation act in different ways.
That due to divergence acts at IG scales to preserve correlations and phase
information against dispersion, thereby producing such highly predictable
phenomena as solitary waves. That due to vorticity advection acts at QG
scales as a turbulent scrambler of information. Coherence and turbulence
may thus coexist by occurring at widely separated scales.

3.2.2. Coherent Features. Coherent features are essentially of two forms:
(1) analytical solitary waves and (2) multivalued modons. Planetary features
may be further categorized by dynamical balance, scale, amplitude, symmetry, and location [e.g., Rizzoli (1982)].† The description of modons requires multivalued functions that contain finite discontinuities in the radial
vorticity gradient so their physical significance has been questioned. The
relevance of a theoretical vortex depends on how readily it can occur, an
issue that has only recently been addressed for both analytical forms (Williams and Yamagata, 1984) and multivalued forms (Flierl *et al.*, 1983).

The long-lived, coherent vortices that occur at IG scales are based on
solitary Rossby waves travelling westward at close to the long-wave speed
$c_\beta = -\beta L_D^2$. In mid-latitudes they coalesce during collisions and are sometimes referred to as Rossby density-vortices (Clarke, 1971) to distinguish
them from the Rossby shear-solitons of Long (1964). At the equator, the
solitary waves do not coalesce and behave like the Rossby density-soliton of
Boyd (1980). The IG balance between dispersion and nonlinear steepening

---

† Hurricanes differ from most other isolated features in that their strong external energy
sources and sinks, rather than their internal inertial balances, hold them together.

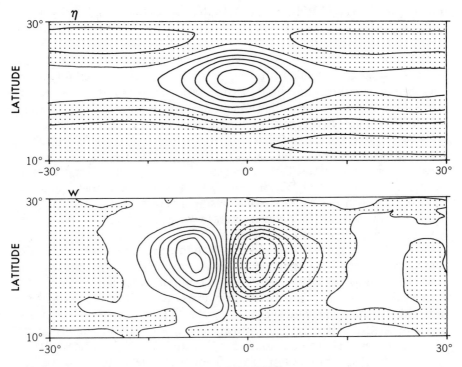

LONGITUDE

FIG. 7. Closeup of flow near a GRS-like anticyclonic IG vortex located in an anticyclonic shear zone, from the shallow-water model of Williams and Yamagata (1984). Diagram shows height variations and vertical motion after 5 years of evolution. The contour intervals are 1 km and 0.1 cm s^{-1} and negative values are shaded. Computational domain extends over 180° longitude. Such vortices have been maintained in numerical solutions for periods in excess of a century. [After Williams and Yamagata (1984). Reproduced with permission from *Journal of the Atmospheric Sciences,* a publication of the American Meteorological Society.]

due to divergence holds more readily for anticyclonic motion than for cyclonic. However, long-lived coherent cyclones can occur in strong easterly currents (Williams and Yamagata, 1984).

3.2.3. Jovian Vortices. Integrating the SW equations with Jovian parameters shows that vortex behavior varies with latitudinal location and zonal flow environment (Williams and Wilson, 1985). In mid-latitudes (30–60°), IG vortices exist indefinitely but in the subtropics (10–30°) vortex existence is conditional: in the absence of zonal flows they decay in about 1000 days by generating equatorial disturbances, but when Jupiter-like zonal flows are introduced, the vortices can exist indefinitely. A GRS-like vortex has been simulated for 10 years (Fig. 7) and for over 100 years in a less-dissipative model (Williams and Wilson, 1985). In the tropics (0 – 10°), Boyd's (1980) solitary β waves occur readily in the SW model and also in the ocean, but apparently not on Jupiter.

Coherent vortices are generated when barotropic instability occurs at the IG scale, whereas periodic disturbances are generated by instability at the QG scale. The number of solitary vortices produced depends on the criticality of the anticyclonic shear zone and on the form of the initial perturbation. Moderately unstable currents produce a small number of well-spaced vortices resembling the Large Ovals (Fig. 8). To produce a *single* permanent vortex, like the GRS, requires a weak instability acting over a long time† in a weakly dissipative atmosphere. This genesis is more convincingly demonstrated in Williams and Wilson (1985) than in Williams and Yamagata (1984). During the development of an instability, perturbations can progress from periodic waves to modulated waves to wave packets to multiple solitary vortices and finally to single solitary vortices.

According to the preceding numerical studies, the uniqueness of the GRS can be attributed to the weakness of the generating instability, the width of the zone, and to the inhomogeneity of the initial perturbation. This is the only theoretical explanation for the uniqueness of the GRS that has been put forward. The modeling also suggests that the 40 to 25° longitudinal shrinkage of the GRS and changes in its drift rate could be due to very small changes in zone width. The vertical motion associated with IG vortices (Fig. 7) provides an observational test of the theory, but the weakness of vertical motions compared to horizontal ones makes detection difficult. To explain the amplitude of the cloud-level winds in the GRS requires models with continuous stratification and with baroclinicity.

3.3. Comparative Global Circulations

3.3.1. Circulation Theory. Although GFD concepts explain many of the regional aspects of planetary circulations, no comprehensive global views have been developed other than the ECM syntheses developed by Smagorinsky *et al.* (1965). Substantial theories have, however, been developed for quasi-geostrophic scale motions in the mid-latitudes of Earth's atmosphere and oceans.

Ocean theories proceed by exploiting the vast difference between the response times of the wind-driven circulations (10 years) and the thermohaline circulations (10^3 years). The wind-driven circulation theories can assume a known stable stratification and can then describe the flow by evaluating the mixing of potential vorticity along density surfaces (Holland *et al.,*

† About 10 years, the time scale for Large Oval development and for zonal flow buildup in circulation models.

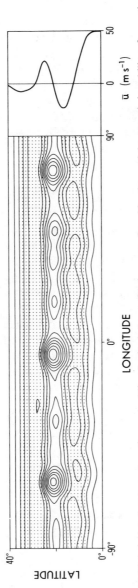

FIG. 8. Multiple isolated, coherent vortices resembling Jupiter's Large Ovals are produced by the weak barotropic instability of an anticyclonic shear zone acting on the IG scale. The height variations and zonal wind profile are produced by a shallow water model with Jovian parameters. The contour interval is 1.5 km and negative values are shaded. [After Williams and Yamagata (1984). Reproduced with permission from *Journal of the Atmospheric Sciences*, a publication of the American Meteorological Society.]

1984). These theories indicate that upper level motions penetrate downward to a depth h_β. Perhaps Jovian dynamical and thermodynamical problems can be similarly segregated.

Atmospheric circulations are turbulent, the fundamental description of which requires that time variations be treated equally with spatial variations. Only the two-point, two-time spectral closure models for velocity variance and Green's function, derived from the direct interaction approximation of Kraichnan† (1959), achieve this fundamental level of description (Kraichnan and Montgomery, 1979; Rose and Sulem, 1978). The spectral closure models for QG_2 turbulence (Salmon, 1978, 1980) indicate the degree of complexity and insight needed to develop a fundamental understanding of atmospheric and oceanic circulations. Simpler parameterizations and climate models avoid the basic dynamical issues.

3.3.2. QG₂ Circulations. The QG_2 model (Phillips, 1956) indicates how mid-latitudinal circulations depend on the basic external parameters f_0, β, and N. For the normal heating rate and surface drag, the circulation changes from an axisymmetric flow at $\Omega^* \leq \frac{1}{4}$, to a wavelike jet at $\Omega^* = \frac{1}{2}$, to an irregular jet at $\Omega^* = 1$, and to double jets at $\Omega^* = 4$, where $\Omega^* = \Omega/\Omega_E$ is the rotation rate relative to the existing value Ω_E (Williams and Holloway, 1985). When drag is removed the double jets coalesce into a stronger and wider jet in keeping with the L_β relation, while the two sets of baroclinic eddies become one without changing scale. This clearly indicates that barotropic processes, not baroclinic ones, determine jet scales. When $\beta = 0$ no jets occur at any value of f_0, only intense irregular eddy motion; this contrasts with annulus circulations where zonal flows always occur because the geometry inhibits nonlinear eddy development. When both β and drag are absent, large gyres occur (Williams, 1979b).

Predictability should be greater on the larger QG scales‡ than on the smaller because of the β blocking effect at L_β—but only if the surface drag is weak and the baroclinic eddies are small, as on Jupiter. For Earth, the surface drag is a major source of flow irregularity on both the turbulent and wave scales (Williams, 1979b), and it is debatable whether predictability on the wave scales is greater (Basdevant *et al.,* 1981) or the same (McWilliams and Chow, 1981) as on the turbulent scales. Flows are more predictable when baroclinic waves fill the domain and thereby limit nonlinear exchanges, as on Mars.

---

† Kraichnan's creation of the spectral turbulence models ranks as one of the great achievements of modern theoretical physics. It is regretable that its planetary assimilation has been so limited.

‡ Divergence gives motions coherence and predictability on the even larger (IG) scale.

3.3.3. Moist Circulations. When an idealized ECM—with moisture, a swamp surface, and annual mean heating parameters [see Holloway and Manabe (1971) for details]—has its relative rotation rate varied from $\Omega^* = 0$ to 8, its circulations also go from quasi-symmetric to multijet, but they also incorporate a tropical regime. The circulation at $\Omega^* = 4$ is analogous to Jupiter's (Fig. 9) [Williams and Holloway (1982, 1985), see also Hunt (1979)]. These circulations are made up of two types of quasi-geostrophic flow (QG_A, QG_B) and a tropical flow. The QG_A type has an eddy angular momentum transport traversing a diffuse jet in high latitudes, while QG_B has an eddy transport converging on a sharp jet in mid-latitudes (Fig. 9). Nonlinear and linear baroclinic instabilities have similar distinctions (Simmons and Hoskins, 1980). Both types have three meridional cells, two direct and one indirect. The tropical flow has upper-level westerlies and surface easterlies and is due to Hadley cell deflection and to tropical eddy action. The Hadley circulation only extends to about $10°$ latitude when $\Omega^* = 4$, compared to about $30°$ when $\Omega^* = 1$, in keeping with the Ω^{-1} relation of Held and Hou (1980). The three forms of jet overlap extensively at $\Omega^* = 1$ to give Earth a most complex meteorology.

Below $\Omega^* = \frac{1}{4}$ baroclinic instability is absent, surface torques are weaker by a factor of 10 and the easterly trade winds vanish. Comparing flows with rotation rates above and below $\Omega^* = \frac{1}{4}$ makes it apparent that waves propagating from the baroclinic eddies create the easterlies in the tropics, as in β turbulence. At the transitional value of $\Omega^* = \frac{1}{4}$, baroclinic instability is shallow and only occurs in the lower troposphere, in keeping with the decline in penetration depth, $h = f^2 u_z / \beta N^2$, as Ω decreases (Held, 1978).

3.3.4. Dry Circulations. If moisture dynamics is excluded from the ECM, the tropical form of circulation does not materialize and the meridional and zonal flows are much weaker near the equator, at all Ω^* values. The tropical cell is just the secondary direct circulation associated with the Ferrel cell of the mid-latitudinal jet. Strong motions only occur in the tropics if the heating is enhanced there, either by moisture or by internal heating. If surface drag is omitted, only easterly winds occur in the tropics (Williams and Holloway, 1985).

3.3.5. Moist Axisymmetric Circulations. Natural Hadley circulations occur when $\Omega^* < \frac{1}{4}$ but they are not axisymmetric—except when time averaged—as longitudinally varying convective and dissipative eddies remain. To estimate the role of baroclinic instability at $\Omega^* = 1$, attempts have been made to define an "ideal" or axisymmetric Hadley circulation in which all longitudinal variations are artificially suppressed. Unfortunately, this

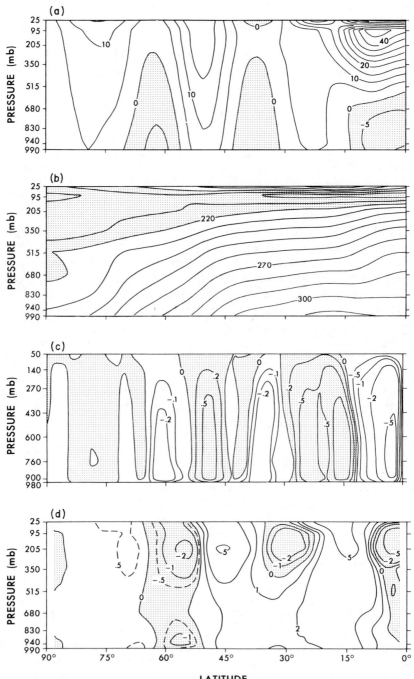

FIG. 9. The time and longitudinally averaged fields of the circulation of an idealized Earth-like model atmosphere when the rotation rate is 4 times the normal value, i.e., $\Omega^* = 4$. Diagram shows zonal motion (a), temperature (b), meridional stream function (c), and northward eddy angular momentum transport (d), with units of m s^{-1}, K, 10^{13} g s^{-1}, 10^7 m^3 s^{-2}, respectively. The three basic types of circulation occur: the tropical up to 10° latitude and types QG$_B$, QG$_A$ at 50°, 80°. [After Williams and Holloway (1982, 1985).]

action also eliminates the natural dissipation and dispersion mechanisms that must then be replaced by ambiguous vertical mixing representations. Axisymmetric circulations are crucially dependent on these dissipation schemes and thus appear to be of marginal physical significance, although they remain of great historical interest.

A better way of gauging the role of the eddies — other than by altering Ω^* — is by reducing their size and strength artificially by using small global sectors. "Small-eddy" circulations can be made to approach the ideal Hadley circulation gradually while retaining natural dissipation and mixing.

Moist axisymmetric ECM flows are dominated by subgrid transports (convection, dissipation) so their meridional circulations lack simplicity and uniqueness (Williams and Holloway, 1985). At the lower rotation rates ($\Omega^* \leq 1$) the zonal flow consists of a single broad westerly jet while at higher rotation rates it consists of two westerly jets, one in the tropics and one in mid-latitudes. The tropical jet has the same width and amplitude as in the natural system but the mid-latitude jet is broader and stronger (60 m s^{-1} compared to 15 m s^{-1}).

If the axisymmetric westerlies are stronger than the natural westerlies, is it correct to conclude that eddies reduce the zonal momentum in mid-latitudes [cf. Schneider and Lindzen (1977)]? The answer is no, on two counts. First, the axisymmetric winds are stronger because the axisymmetric thermal gradients are stronger. Second, the time required to create the axisymmetric flow is much longer than the time required by the eddies to create the natural jets. Thus, the natural state does not sense the axisymmetric state, just as synoptic states do not sense the seasonal cycle.

3.3.6. Diurnal Circulations. As the rotation rate drops below the transitional value of $\Omega^* = \frac{1}{4}$, the kinetic energy of the ECM continues to increase and the axis of the Hadley jet moves poleward until a limit is reached near 75° latitude (Williams and Holloway, 1982). Kinetic energy peaks at $\Omega^* = \frac{1}{8}$ and then decreases as cyclostrophy takes over from geostrophy.

A second transition occurs at $\Omega^* = \frac{1}{16}$ when diurnal heating variations become important. The equatorward transport of angular momentum and heat by the diurnal eddies changes the narrow polar jets of the nondiurnal state into broad global superrotating currents resembling those of Venus. Below $\Omega^* = \frac{1}{64}$, the diurnal variations dominate rather than modify the circulations and produce subsolar to antisolar flows.

3.3.7. Oblique (Seasonal) Circulations. Seasonal variations illustrate most simply the sensitivity of ECM behavior to thermodynamical forcing. Varying the planetary obliquity θ_p up to 90° latitude gives the full range of response. Without ocean heat storage, temperature maxima occur in mid-latitudes when $\theta_p = 10°$ and at the pole when $\theta_p \geq 20°$ —a typical planetary value (Table I).

Zonal flows are generally easterly in the summer hemisphere and westerly in the winter hemisphere as a result of these temperature gradients (Williams and Holloway, 1982, 1985; Hunt, 1982). The easterlies are produced by Hadley circulations, which straddle the equator symmetrically from $\pm 30°$ when $\Omega^* = \frac{1}{2}$ to $\pm 15°$ when $\Omega^* = 4$ for most θ_p values. Only in an extreme case ($\Omega^* = \frac{1}{2}$, $\theta_p = 90°$) does the cell extend from pole to pole and do unique diagonal convective bands occur in the summer tropics. Normally eddies are most active in the winter hemisphere.

Hadley circulations cool the summer hemisphere and heat the winter tropics, which is then cooled by eddies transferring heat to the winter pole. Angular momentum balance is achieved globally with the meridional circulation providing the exchange between the positive surface torque in the winter hemisphere and the negative torque in the summer hemisphere.

3.3.8. Planetary Implications. The ECM solutions suggest that when a simplified, Earth-like atmosphere is placed in the rotational configuration of another planet it displays that planet's form of motion despite thermodynamical and other differences. Table I contains a preliminary classification of planetary circulations by rotation rate and obliquity.

For Earth, the solutions indicate that the poleward eddy momentum transport is a consequence of the hybrid mix of three circulation types. Mars has a strong seasonal variation because it lacks oceanic thermal inertia and so its circulation resembles those of our simple ECM at $\Omega^* = 1$ (Williams and Holloway, 1982, Fig. 2c). Venus appears to lie in the narrow range of Ω values where diurnal effects modify rather than dominate the circulation.

Both Jupiter and the moist ECM at $\Omega^* = 4$ have pre-eminent tropical jets and multiple, highly zonal, extratropical jets, plus assorted eddies [cf. Williams and Holloway (1982, Fig. 4)]. If the analog is completely valid, Jupiter should have easterly trade winds in the lower tropics. However, the analog is weakest in the tropics because it is uncertain whether moisture and surface stress occur on Jupiter or whether enhanced internal heating and cumulus friction can act in an equivalent way. Tropical westerly jets can be produced either by Hadley circulations or by enhanced eddy activity in β-turbulence cascades. Further studies are needed to determine which process, if either, occurs.

Saturn, Uranus, and Neptune should resemble Jupiter at equinox but during solstice their summer hemispheres should contain easterly winds. Internal heating could reduce seasonal variations on Saturn and Neptune. On Uranus, diagonal convective bands could occur in the summer tropics while a Hadley cell straddles the equator to about $\pm 20°$ latitude — unless the rotational influence is unexpectedly weak, in which case it could go from pole to pole.

4. PLANETARY PROSPECTS

4.1. Observations

The upcoming Voyager encounters with Uranus (in 1986) and Neptune (in 1989) will complete the recent *reconnaissance* of the solar system by some two dozen spacecraft (Kondratyev and Hunt, 1982; Beatty *et al.,* 1981) and reveal whether or not these planets fit into the general scheme. Although planetary *exploration* appears to be no more than a remote possibility at this time, detailed monitoring of Jupiter is imminent.

The long period, high-resolution observation of Jupiter by the Galileo orbiter and by the Space Telescope should yield details of wave and eddy interactions that, if imaginatively analyzed, could reveal the vertical structure of the atmosphere. For example, baroclinic instabilities have speeds and growth rates that vary as u_z and u_z/N, so the shear and stability could be estimated from temporal data. Instabilities may also be absolute or advective and exhibit spatial or temporal growth depending on the ratio of $\hat{u}/\tilde{u}$ (Farrell, 1982, 1983). In absolute (advective) instabilities the front and rear edges of a pulse move in opposite (identical) directions. Thus the study of wave packet evolution could also give a value for the vertical shear.

The Galileo probe of Jupiter's equatorial atmosphere should test for moisture, vertical motion, and vertical shear to determine whether a Hadley circulation exists. Deeper probes are needed to explore the lower atmosphere, while multiple mid-latitudinal probes are needed to measure baroclinicity.

4.2. Modeling

The completion of the class of circulations generated by the ECM for a semi-infinite atmosphere requires the evaluation of models for vertically unbounded fluids. Such models should also reveal how baroclinic instabilities, Hadley circulations, etc., behave in the absence of a surface. Evaluating ocean models as a function of Ω^* would supplement and guide such calculations.

The existence of Rossby vortices and solitons in models with a continuous stratification needs to be studied to help circumscribe the vertical form of the atmosphere. Then JCMs can be designed to synthesize the results from the different models for the different phenomena. Our understanding of Jupiter's, jets, vortices, and eddies is good at the basic level and should be greatly enhanced in this decade.

4.3. Theory

To deepen our understanding of the various circulations requires that some basic GFD problems concerning geostrophic regimes, waves, instabilities, and turbulence be resolved (see CD85). Perhaps the most important immediate problem is to determine the influence of nonlinear divergence on the energy decascade into zonal flow at the IG scales and at the equator.

To improve numerical models, we need to discover which methods best describe the intermittent, part random, part coherent nature of the 2D exchanges that underlie much of planetary turbulence and must be allowed for in subgrid closure schemes. Can renormalized perturbation schemes be created for the planetary subgrid scales? Can fractal dimensions really describe the space occupied by dissipative eddies and explain intermittency (Rose and Sulem, 1978)? Or can the successive averaging methods of renormalized group theory be used to design layers of subgrid scales to give better eddy representations (Rose, 1977)? The original nonlinear viscosity designed for planetary modeling (Smagorinsky, 1963) appears to have "succeeded brilliantly" (Leslie, 1982) for 3D turbulence — more so, perhaps, than for quasi-2D motions. Perhaps direct simulations with resolutions greater than the 256^3 and 256^2 modes used for quasi-3D turbulence (Brachet et al., 1983) and 2D turbulence (Frisch and Sulem, 1984) will answer some of these questions.

5. Conclusion

Fool: "The reason why the seven stars are no more than seven is a pretty reason."
Lear: "Because they are not eight."
Fool: "Yes indeed. Thou woulds't make a good fool."

W. Shakespeare

In this article we have tried to indicate how meteorological unity might exist among the planets of the solar system and how it can be used to construct preliminary or provisional models for individual planets. The reason the unity exists is because no disunity is apparent. Whether this attempt to recreate the solar system in Earth's image has any more merit than previous views only time, observation, and better theory will decide. For now, its advantage appears to be that it yields explanations — where none existed before — of various phenomena without apparent inconsistencies and with verifiable (or falsifiable) predictions.

For Jupiter, the main implication of the GFD view is that the zonally banded form of circulation, with its multiple easterly and westerly jets, is essentially a characteristic of quasi-horizontal turbulence on a rapidly rotating sphere. The flow is energized by small-scale (L_R) baroclinically unstable eddies that cascade energy toward the large scale (L_β), where they generate the Rossby waves that evolve into zonal currents. These jets can become barotropically unstable and produce solitary waves resembling the Great Red Spot and Large Ovals. The greatest uncertainties at present concern the extent to which eddy action or Hadley cell deflection produce the tropical jet and the extent to which baroclinicity influences the GRS.

In the past decade, modeling and observation have drastically altered our perspective of Earth and our view of the solar system. There are indeed connections between the terrestrial and planetary meteorologies, but these are often subtle and involve great parametric changes. The planets are no longer semimythical bodies, glimpsed "through a glass, darkly" by inadequate telescopes or ideas, but real worlds demanding imaginative interpretation.

ACKNOWLEDGMENTS

My planetary studies have been greatly influenced by the ideas and philosophy of Joseph Smagorinsky, from the time he gave the 1963 Symons memorial lecture as meteorological spokesman for the New Frontier to his present role as senior meteorological statesman. His credo of parametric, computational, and cultural freedom and his belief that meteorologists could contribute to the exploration of space have been a constant source of encouragement and enlightenment.

This paper would never have materialized without Syukuro Manabe, who persuaded me that reviewing the unknown was possible and who accepted that it took longer. I am also grateful to Leith Holloway and John Wilson for collaboration in developing many of the ideas in this paper, to Joan Pege for typing, to Phil Tunison for drafting, and to Sanjay Limaye for preparing Fig. 3.

REFERENCES

Allison, M., and Stone, P. H. (1983). Saturn meteorology: A diagnostic assessment of thin-layer configurations for the zonal flow. *Icarus* **54**, 296–308.

Antipov, S. V., Nezlin, M. Y., Snezhkin, E. N., and Trubnikov, A. S. (1982). Rossby soliton in the laboratory. *JETP* **82**, 145–160 [in Russian].

Barros, V. R., and Wiin-Nielsen, A. (1974). On quasi-geostrophic turbulence: A numerical experiment. *J. Atmos. Sci.* **31,** 609—621.

Basdevant, C., Legras, B., Sadourny, R., and Beland, M. (1981). A study of barotropic model flows: Intermittency, waves and predictability. *J. Atmos. Sci.* **38,** 2305–2326.

Beaumont, D. N. (1980). Solitary waves on an unsymmetrical shear flow with applications to Jupiter's Great Red Spot. *Icarus* **41,** 400–408.

Beatty, J. K., O'Leary, B., and Chaikin, A. (1981). "The New Solar System." Sky Publishing, Cambridge, Massachusetts.

Beebe, R. F., Ingersoll, A. P., Hunt, G. E., Mitchell, J. L., and Müller, J. P. (1980). Measurements of wind vectors, eddy momentum transports, and energy conversions in Jupiter's atmosphere from Voyager 1 images. *Geophys. Res. Lett.* **7,** 1–4.

Bolin, B. (1956). An improved barotropic model and some aspects of using the balance equation for three-dimensional flow. *Tellus* **8,** 61–75.

Boyd, J. P. (1980). Equatorial solitary waves. Part 1: Rossby solitons. *J. Phys. Oceanogr.* **10,** 1699–1717.

Boyd, J. P. (1984). Equatorial solitary waves. Part 4: Kelvin solitons in a shear flow. *Dyn. Atmos. Oceans* **8,** 173–184.

Brachet, M. E., Meiron, D. I., Orszag, S. A., Nickel, B. G., Morf, R. H., and Frisch, U. (1983). Small-scale structure of the Taylor-Green vortex. *J. Fluid Mech.* **130,** 411–452.

Branscome, L. E. (1982). Jovian dynamics and cloud features. Unpublished manuscript, Department of Meteorology, MIT, Cambridge, Massachusetts.

Brown, J. A. (1969). A numerical investigation of hydrodynamic instability and energy conversions in a quasi-geostrophic atmosphere: Part 1. *J. Atmos. Sci.* **26,** 352–365.

Busse, F. H. (1983). A model of mean zonal flows in the major planets. *Geophys. Astrophys. Fluid Dyn.* **23,** 153–174.

Charney, J. G. (1971). Geostrophic turbulence. *J. Atmos. Sci.* **28,** 1087–1095.

Charney, J. G., and Flierl, G. R. (1981). Oceanic analogues of large scale atmospheric motions. *In* "Evolution of Physical Oceanography" (B. A. Warren and C. Wunsch, eds.), pp. 504–548. MIT Press, Cambridge, Massachusetts.

Clarke, R. A. (1971). Solitary and cnoidal planetary waves. *Geophys. Fluid Dyn.* **2,** 343–354.

Conrath, B. J., and Pirraglia, J. A. (1983). Thermal structure of Saturn from Voyager infrared measurements: Implications for atmospheric dynamics. *Icarus* **53,** 286–292.

Conrath, B. J., and Gierasch, P. J. (1984). Global variation of the para hydrogen fraction in Jupiter's atmosphere and implications for dynamics on the outer planets. *Icarus* **57,** 184–204.

De Verdiere, A. C. (1980). Quasi-geostrophic turbulence in a rotating homogeneous fluid. *Geophys. Astrophys. Fluid Dyn.* **15,** 213–251.

Dickinson, R. E. (1973). Baroclinic instability of an unbounded zonal shear flow in a compressible atmosphere. *J. Atmos. Sci.* **30,** 1520–1527.

Eady, E. T. (1954). The maintenance of the mean zonal surface currents. *Proc. Toronto Met. Conf., 1953,* pp. 124–128. Roy. Met. Soc., London.

Farrell, B. F. (1982). Pulse asymptotics of the Charney baroclinic instability problem. *J. Atmos. Sci.* **39,** 507–517.

Farrell, B. F. (1983). Pulse asymptotics of three dimensional baroclinic waves. *J. Atmos. Sci.* **40,** 2202–2210.

Flasar, F. M., Samuelson, R. E., and Conrath, B. J. (1981a). Titan's atmosphere: Temperature and dynamics. *Nature (London)* **292,** 693–698.

Flasar, F. M., Conrath, B. J., Pirraglia, J. A., Clark, P. C., French, R. G., and Gierasch, P. J. (1981b). Thermal structure and dynamics of the Jovian atmosphere. 1. The Great Red Spot. *JGR, J. Geophys. Res.* **86,** 8759–8767.

Flierl, G. R., Stern, M. E., and Whitehead, J. B. (1983). The physical significance of modons: Laboratory experiments and general integral constraints. *Dyn. Atmos. Oceans* **7**, 233–263.

Fornberg, B. (1977). A numerical study of 2-D turbulence. *J. Comp. Phys.* **25**, 1–31.

Frisch, U., and Sulem, P. L. (1984). Numerical simulation of the inverse cascade in two-dimensional turbulence. *Phys. Fluids* **27**, 1921–1923.

Gall, R. L. (1976). A comparison of linear baroclinic instability theory with the eddy statistics of a general circulation model. *J. Atmos. Sci.* **33**, 349–373.

Gehrels, T. (1976). The results of the imaging photopolarimeter on Pioneers 10 and 11. *In* "Jupiter" (T. Gehrels, ed.), pp. 531–563. Univ. of Arizona Press, Tucson, Arizona.

Gill, A. E. (1974). The stability of planetary waves on an infinite beta-plane. *Geophys. Fluid. Dyn.* **6**, 29–47.

Golitsyn, G. S. (1970). A similarity approach to the general circulation of planetary atmospheres. *Icarus* **13**, 1–24.

Golitsyn, G. S. (1979). Atmospheric dynamics on the outer planets and some of their satellites. *Icarus* **38**, 333–341.

Grey, W. M. (1978). Hurricanes: Their formation, structure and likely role in the tropical circulation. *In* "Meteorology over the Tropical Oceans" (D. B. Shaw, ed.), pp. 155–218. Roy. Met. Soc., London.

Haidvogel, D. B., and Held, I. M. (1980). Homogeneous quasi-geostrophic turbulence driven by a uniform temperature gradient. *J. Atmos. Sci.* **37**, 2644–2660.

Haidvogel, D. B., and Rhines, P. B. (1983). Waves and circulation driven by oscillatory winds in an idealized ocean basin. *Geophys. Astrophys. Fluid Dyn.* **25**, 1–63.

Hanel, R. A., Conrath, B. J., and 11 co-authors (1979). Infrared observations of the Jovian system from Voyager 1. *Science* **204**, 972–976.

Hanel, R. A., Conrath, B. J., Kunde, V. G., Pearl, J. C., and Pirraglia, J. A. (1983). Albedo, internal heat flux, and energy balance of Saturn. *Icarus* **53**, 262–285.

Hatzes, A., Wenkert, D. D., Ingersoll, A. P., and Danielson, G. E. (1981). Oscillations and velocity structure of a long-lived cyclone spot. *JGR, J. Geophys. Res.* **86**, 8745–8749.

Held, I. M., (1978). The vertical scale of an unstable baroclinic wave and its importance for eddy heat flux parameterizations. *J. Atmos. Sci.* **351**, 572–576.

Held, I. M., and Hou, A. Y. (1980). Nonlinear axially symmetric circulations in a nearly inviscid atmosphere. *J. Atmos. Sci.* **37**, 515–533.

Herring, J. R. (1980). Statistical theory of quasi-geostrophic turbulence. *J. Atmos. Sci.* **37**, 969–977.

Holland, W. R. (1978). The role of mesoscale eddies in the general circulation of the ocean: Numerical experiments using a wind-driven quasi-geostrophic model. *J. Phys. Oceanogr.* **8**, 363–392.

Holland, W. R., and Haidvogel, D. B. (1980). A parameter study of the mixed instability of idealized ocean currents. *Dyn. Atmos. Oceans* **4**, 185–215.

Holland, W. R., and Rhines, P. B. (1980). An example of eddy-induced ocean circulation *J. Phys. Oceanogr.* **10**, 1010–1031.

Holland, W. R., Keffer, T., and Rhines, P. B. (1984). Dynamics of the oceanic general circulation: The potential vorticity field. *Nature (London)* **308**, 698–705.

Holloway, J. L., and Manabe, S. (1971). Simulation of climate by a global general circulation model. *Mon. Weather Rev.* **99**, 335–370.

Holton, J. R. (1974). On the trapping of unstable baroclinic waves. *J. Atmos. Sci.* **31**, 2220–2222.

Holton, J. R. (1975). "The Dynamic Meteorology of the Stratosphere and Mesosphere." Meteorol. Monogr. 37, Am. Met. Soc., Boston, Massachusetts.

Houghton, J. T. (1977). "The Physics of Atmospheres." Cambridge Univ. Press, Cambridge.

Hunt, B. G. (1979). The influence of the Earth's rotation rate on the general circulation of the atmosphere. *J. Atmos. Sci.* **36**, 1392–1408.

Hunt, B. G. (1982). The impact of large variations of the Earth's obliquity on the climate. *J. Met. Soc. Japan* **60**, 309–318.

Hunt, G. E. (1983). The atmospheres of the outer planets. *Annu. Rev. Earth Planet. Sci.* **11**, 415–459.

Hunt, G. E., and Müller, J.-P. (1979). Voyager observations of small scale waves in the equatorial region of the Jovian atmosphere. *Nature (London)* **280**, 778–780.

Hunt, G. E., and Moore, P. (1982). "Saturn." Roy. Astron. Soc. and Rand-McNally, London.

Hunt, G. E., Conrath, B. J., and Pirraglia, J. A. (1981). Visible and infrared observations of Jovian plumes during the Voyager encounter. *JGR, J. Geophys. Res.* **86**, 8777–8781.

Hunt, G. E., Müller, J.-P., and Gee, P. (1982). Convective growth rates of equatorial features in the Jovian atmosphere. *Nature (London)* **295**, 491–494.

Iavorskaya, I. M., and Belyaef, Yu. N. (1983). Convective motions in rotating fluid layers. *Advances in Science and Technology of VINITI, Mechanics of Fluids and Gases* **17**, 2–85 [in Russian].

Ingersoll, A. P., and Pollard, D. (1982). Motion in the interiors and atmospheres of Jupiter and Saturn: Scale analysis, anelastic equations, barotropic stability criterion. *Icarus* **52**, 62–80.

Ingersoll, A. P. *et al.* (1979). Zonal velocity and texture in the jovian atmosphere inferred from Voyager images. *Nature (London)* **280**, 773–775.

Ingersoll, A. P., Beebe, R. F., Mitchell, J. L., Garneau, G. W., Yagi, G. M., and Müller, J.-P. (1981). Interaction of eddies and zonal mean flow on Jupiter as inferred from Voyager 1 and 2 images. *JGR, J. Geophys. Res.* **86**, 8733–8743.

Jones, S. (1978). Interactions and instabilities of barotropic and baroclinic Rossby waves in a rotating, two layer fluid. *Geophys. Astrophys. Fluid Dyn.* **11**, 49–60.

Kim, K. (1978). Instability of baroclinic Rossby waves: energetics in a two-layer ocean. *Deep-Sea Res.* **25**, 795–814.

Kondratyev, K. Y., and Hunt, G. E. (1982). "Weather and Climate on Planets." Pergamon Press, Oxford.

Kraichnan, R. H. (1959). The structure of isotropic turbulence at very high Reynolds numbers. *J. Fluid Mech.* **5**, 497–543.

Kraichnan, R. H., and Montgomery, D. (1979). Two-dimensional turbulence. *Rep. Prog. Phys.* **43**, 547–619.

Kuo, H.-L. (1950). The motion of atmospheric vortices and the general circulation. *J. Meteor.* **7**, 247–258.

Leovy, C. B. (1979). Martian Meteorology. *Annu. Rev. Astron. Astrophys.* **17**, 387–413.

Leslie, D. C. (1982). Simulation methods for turbulent flows. *In* "Numerical Methods for Fluid Dynamics" (K. W. Morton and M. J. Baines, eds.), pp. 63–80. Academic Press, New York.

Limaye, S. S. (1985). New estimates of the mean zonal flow on Jupiter. *Icarus* (in press).

Limaye, S. S., Revercomb, H. E., and 6 co-authors. (1982). Jovian winds from Voyager 2. Part 1: Zonal mean circulation. *J. Atmos. Sci.* **39**, 1413–1432.

Lindal, G. F. *et al.* (1981). The atmosphere of Jupiter: An analysis of the Voyager radio occultation measurements. *JGR, J. Geophys. Res.* **86**, 8721–8727.

Lindal, G. F., Wood, G. E., Hotz, H. B., Sweetnam, D. N., Eshleman, V. R., and Tyler, G. L. (1983). The atmosphere of Titan: An analysis of the Voyager 1 radio occultation measurements. *Icarus* **53**, 348–363.

Lindzen, R. S., Farrell, B., Tung, K.-K. (1980). The concept of wave overreflection and its application to baroclinic instability. *J. Atmos. Sci.* **37**, 44–63.

Lipps, F. B. (1963). Stability of jets in a divergent barotropic fluid. *J. Atmos. Sci.* **20**, 120–129.

Long, R. R. (1964). Solitary waves in the westerlies. *J. Atmos. Sci.* **21**, 197–200.

Longuet-Higgins, M. S., and Gill, A. E. (1967). Resonant interactions between planetary waves. *Proc. Roy. Soc.* **A299**, 120–140.

Lorenz, E. N. (1953). The vertical extent of Jupiter's atmosphere. *In* "The Study of Planetary Atmospheres" (E. C. Slipher, ed.), pp. 136–145. Lowell Observatory Rep. AF19(122)-162, Flagstaff, Arizona.

Mahlman, J. D., and Moxim, W. J. (1978). Tracer simulation using a global general circulation model: Results from a midlatitude instantaneous source experiment. *J. Atmos. Sci.* **35**, 1340–1374.

Maxworthy, T., and Redekopp, L. G. (1976). A solitary wave theory of the Great Red Spot and other observed features of the Jovian atmosphere. *Icarus* **29**, 261–271.

McEwan, A. D., Thompson, R., and Plumb, R. A. (1980). Mean flows driven by weak eddies in rotating systems. *J. Fluid Mech.* **99**, 655–672.

McIntyre, M. E. (1972). Baroclinic instability of an idealized model of the polar night jet. *Quart. J. Roy. Meteor. Soc.* **98**, 165–174.

McWilliams, J. C. (1984). The emergence of isolated coherent vortices in turbulent flow. *J. Fluid Mech.* **146**, 21–43.

McWilliams, J. C., and Chow, J. H. S. (1981). Equilibrium geostrophic turbulence 1: A reference solution in a β-plane channel. *J. Phys. Oceanogr.* **11**, 921–949.

Mitchell, J. L. (1982). "The Nature of Large-Scale Turbulence in the Jovian Atmosphere." NASA/JPL Publication 82–34, Pasadena, California.

Mitchell, J. L. *et al.* (1979). Jovian cloud structure and velocity fields. *Nature (London)* **280**, 776–778.

Mitchell, J. L., Beebe, R. F., Ingersoll, A. P., and Garneau, G. W. (1981). Flow fields within Jupiter's Great Red Spot and White Oval BC. *JGR, J. Geophys. Res.* **86**, 8751–8757.

Owen, T., and Terrile, R. J. (1981). Colors on Jupiter. *JGR, J. Geophys. Res.* **86**, 8797–8814.

Pedlosky, J. (1979). "Geophysical Fluid Dynamics." Springer-Verlag, New York.

Pfister, L. (1979). A theoretical study of three-dimensional barotropic instability with applications to the upper stratosphere. *J. Atmos. Sci.* **36**, 908–920.

Philander, S. G. H., and Pacanowski, R. C. (1980). The generation of equatorial currents. *JGR, J. Geophys. Res.* **85**, 1123–1136.

Phillips, N. A. (1954). Energy transformations and meridional circulations associated with simple baroclinic waves in a two-level, quasi-geostrophic model. *Tellus* **6**, 273–286.

Phillips, N. A. (1956). The general circulation of the atmosphere: A numerical experiment. *Quart. J. Roy. Met. Soc.* **82**, 123–164.

Pirraglia, J. A., Conrath, B. J., Allison, M. D., and Gierasch, P. J. (1981). Thermal structure and dynamics of Saturn and Jupiter. *Nature (London)* **292**, 677–679.

Pollack, J. B., and Yung, Y. L. (1980). Origin and evolution of planetary atmospheres. *Annu. Rev. Earth Planet Sci.* **8**, 425–487.

Rhines, P. B. (1975). Waves and turbulence on a beta plane. *J. Fluid Mech.* **69**, 417–443.

Rhines, P. B. (1977). The dynamics of unsteady currents. *In* "The Sea," Vol. 6 (I. N. McCane, J. J. O'Brien, and J. M. Steele, eds.), pp. 189–318. Wiley, New York.

Rhines, P. B. (1979). Geostrophic Turbulence. *Annu. Rev. Fluid Mech.* **11**, 401–441.

Rizzoli, P. M. (1982). Planetary solitary waves in geophysical flows. *Adv. Geophys.* **24**, 147–224.

Rose, H. A. (1977). Eddy diffusivity, eddy noise and subgridscale modelling. *J. Fluid Mech.* **81**, 719–734.

Rose, H. A., and Sulem, P. L. (1978). Fully developed turbulence and statistical mechanics. *J. de Phys.* **39**, 441–484.

Rossow, W. B. (1983). A general circulation model of a Venus-like atmosphere. *J. Atmos. Sci.* **40**, 273–302.

Salmon, R. (1978). Two-layer quasi-geostrophic turbulence in a simple special case. *Geophys. Astrophys. Fluid Dyn.* **10**, 25–52.

Salmon, R. (1980). Baroclinic instability and geostrophic turbulence. *Geophys. Astrophys. Fluid Dyn.* **15**, 167–211.

Samuelson, R. E., Hanel, R. A., Kunde, V. G., and Maguire, W. C. (1981). Mean molecular weight and hydrogen abundance of Titan's atmosphere. *Nature (London)* **292**, 688–693.

Samuelson, R. E., Maguire, W. C., and 5 co-authors (1983). CO_2 on Titan. *JGR, J. Geophys. Res.* **88**, 8709–8715.

Sanchez-Lavega, A. (1982). Motions in Saturn's atmosphere: Observations before Voyager encounters. *Icarus* **49**, 1–16.

Schneider, E. K., and Lindzen, R. S. (1977). Axially symmetric steady-state models of the basic state for instability and climate studies. Part 1: Linearized calculations. *J. Atmos. Sci.* **34**, 263–279.

Schoeberl, M. R., and Strobel, D. F. (1978). The zonally averaged circulation of the middle atmosphere. *J. Atmos. Sci.* **35**, 577–591.

Simmons, A. J. (1974). Baroclinic instability at the winter stratopause. *Quart. J. Roy. Meteor. Soc.* **100**, 531–540.

Simmons, A. J., and Hoskins, B. J. (1980). Barotropic influences on the growth and decay of nonlinear baroclinic waves. *J. Atmos. Sci.* **37**, 1679–1684.

Smagorinsky, J. (1963). General circulation experiments with the primitive equations. 1. The basic experiment. *Mon. Weather Rev.* **91**, 99–164.

Smagorinsky, J. (1974). Global atmospheric modeling and the numerical simulation of climate. *In* "Weather and Climate Modification" (W. N. Hess, ed.), pp. 633–686. Wiley, New York.

Smagorinsky, J., Manabe, S., and Holloway, J. L. (1965). Numerical results from a nine-level general circulation model of the atmosphere. *Mon. Weather Rev.* **93**, 727–768.

Smith, B. A., Soderblom, L., and 25 co-authors (1981). Encounter with Saturn: Voyager 1 imaging science results. *Science* **212**, 163–191.

Smith, B. A., Soderblom, L., and 27 co-authors (1982). A new look at the Saturn system: The Voyager 2 images. *Science* **215**, 504–537.

Solberg, H. G. (1969). A three-month oscillation in the longitude of Jupiter's Red Spot. *Planet. Space Sci.* **17**, 1573–1580.

Sromovsky, L. A. *et al.* (1981). Implications of Titan's north–south brightness asymmetry. *Nature (London)* **292**, 698–702.

Sromovsky, L. A., Revercomb, H. E., Krauss, R. J., and Suomi, V. E. (1983). Voyager 2 observations of Saturn's northern midlatitude cloud features: Morphology, motions and evolution. *JGR, J. Geophys. Res.* **88**, 8650–8666.

Steinberg, H. L. (1973). Numerical simulation of quasi-geostrophic turbulence. *Tellus* **25**, 233–246.

Stevenson, D. J. (1982). Interiors of the giant planets. *Annu. Rev. Earth Planet. Sci.* **10**, 257–295.

Stommel, H., and Schott, F. (1977). The beta spiral and the determination of the absolute velocity field from hydrographic station data. *Deep-Sea Res.* **24**, 325–329.

Stone, P. H. (1973). The dynamics of the atmospheres of the major planets. *Space Sci. Rev.* **14**, 444–459.

Stone, P. H. (1976). The meteorology of the Jovian atmosphere. *In* "Jupiter" (T. Gehrels, ed.), pp. 586–618. Univ. Arizona Press, Tucson, Arizona.

Trafton, L. (1981). The atmospheres of the outer planets and satellites. *Rev. Geophys. and Space Phys.* **19**, 43–89.

Weidenschilling, S. J., and Lewis, J. S. (1973). Atmospheric and cloud structures of the Jovian planets. *Icarus* **20**, 465–476.

Whitehead, J. A. (1972). Observations of rapid mean flow produced in mercury by a moving heater. *Geophys. Fluid. Dyn.* **3**, 161–180.

Williams, G. P. (1975a). Some ocean-Jupiter connections. *Mode News,* No. 78, 1–4.

Williams, G. P. (1975b). Jupiter's atmospheric circulation. *Nature (London)* **257**, 778.

Williams, G. P. (1978). Planetary circulations: 1. Barotropic representation of Jovian and terrestrial turbulence. *J. Atmos. Sci.* **35**, 1399–1426.

Williams, G. P. (1979a). Planetary circulations: 2. The Jovian quasi-geostrophic regime. *J. Atmos. Sci.* **36**, 932–968.

Williams, G. P. (1979b). Planetary circulations: 3. The terrestrial quasi-geostrophic regime. *J. Atmos. Sci.* **36**, 1409–1435.

Williams, G. P. (1985). Geostrophic regimes on a sphere and a beta plane. *J. Atmos. Sci.* **42**, 1237–1243.

Williams, G. P., and Holloway, J. L. (1982). The range and unity of planetary circulations. *Nature (London)* **297**, 295–299.

Williams, G. P., and Holloway, J. L. (1985). Global circulations. *J. Atmos. Sci.* (in press).

Williams, G. P., and Yamagata, T. (1984). Geostrophic regimes, intermediate solitary vortices and Jovian eddies. *J. Atmos. Sci.* **41**, 453–478.

Williams, G. P., and Wilson, R. J. (1985). Rossby vortices, solitons and turbulence. *J. Atmos. Sci.* (in press).

Yamagata, T. (1976). Stability of planetary waves in a two-layer system. *J. Oceanog. Soc. Japan* **32**, 116–127.

Yamagata, T. (1977). Stability of planetary waves in a two-layer system (small M limit). *J. Met. Soc. Japan* **55**, 240–247.

Yamagata, T., and Kono, J. (1976). On energy and enstrophy transfer in two-dimensional non-divergent waves on a beta-plane. *J. Met. Soc. Japan* **54**, 454–456.

Yeh, T.-C. (1949). On energy dispersion in the atmosphere. *J. Meteorol.* **6**, 1–16.

Part IV

OCEAN DYNAMICS

MODELING OCEAN CIRCULATION

Kirk Bryan

Geophysical Fluid Dynamics Laboratory/NOAA
Princeton University
Princeton, New Jersey

AND

Jorge L. Sarmiento

Geophysical Fluid Dynamics Program
Princeton University
Princeton, New Jersey

1. Introduction

Modeling the ocean circulation is entering a new era due to two major technical developments. One of these developments is the satellite-borne altimeter, which can provide a nearly synoptic view of the sea-surface elevation of the World Ocean. Several altimeters will be deployed at the end of this decade. The data from these instruments with the addition of a large number of subsurface measurements, which are planned as part of WOCE (World Ocean Circulation Experiment), will provide oceanographers with data sets nearly equivalent to those available on a routine basis for the atmosphere. The second technological development is the decreasing cost of large-scale computation. It will soon be possible to attain a level of modeling and analysis commensurate with the horizontal detail seen in good synoptic data sets of the upper ocean.

As we proceed into this new era it is important to review the present status of three-dimensional models of ocean circulation. A great deal of interesting work has been carried out with quasi-geostrophic models of the ocean, and

ADVANCES IN GEOPHYSICS, VOLUME 28A

these models have been particularly valuable for determining the role of mesoscale eddies in ocean circulation [see Holland *et al.* (1984) for a recent review]. However, this review will be confined to three-dimensional models based on the primitive equations of motion. At present, these models are the only type that is suitable for studying many problems related to global climate and have been the focus for most of the research carried out at the Geophysical Fluid Dynamics Laboratory (GFDL). Early studies carried out with these models were aimed at studying ocean circulation in the simplest possible context (Bryan and Cox, 1967, 1968). Both the basin geometry and boundary conditions were highly idealized. The first attempt to couple a three-dimensional ocean model with an atmospheric model (Manabe and Bryan, 1969) was also done in an idealized geometry. Since that time, these studies have been extended to the geometry of actual ocean basins. Recently, attempts have been made to model the entire World Ocean as a single unit specifying observed data at the upper boundary (Bryan and Lewis, 1979; Meehl *et al.,* 1982; Han, 1984).

The three-dimensional models, which are similar to current atmospheric circulation models, are general enough to treat a wide variety of time scales. For example, on a time scale of a few seasons, the ocean thermocline is effectively specified from initial conditions, and interactions among major ocean basins have little importance. Cox's (1970) study of the monsoon-driven circulation of the Indian Ocean was one of the first models of this type, taking advantage of the excellent data set produced by the Indian Ocean Expedition. Recently, interest in the El Niño phenomenon has spurred modelers to make more studies of this kind and to examine seasonal or slightly longer time scales in tropical ocean circulation. Tropical circulation modeling is being reviewed in this volume by Philander. Motivation for studying longer time scales of response has stemmed from the CO_2/climate question and related problems. In this case water formation at high latitudes must be taken into account. The data sets based on measurements of bomb-produced tritium in the upper ocean has provided a new basis for verification of water mass formation in models. Renewed interest in thermocline formation has also led to the development of some important new concepts. It seemed appropriate to revisit numerical models of the ocean circulation with a simple, idealized geometry and to re-examine the dependence of the solutions on governing parameters. The CDC Cyber 205 acquired by the Geophysical Fluid Dynamics Laboratory provided an ideal opportunity for carrying out much higher resolution calculations than had been possible in the earlier studies.

Rhines and Young (1982) have demonstrated some very interesting mechanisms related to the mixing of potential vorticity in the subtropical gyre. They point out that even weak mixing is sufficient to homogenize potential vorticity (or any other tracer) on isopycnal surfaces within a region of closed trajectories. They divide the subtropical thermocline into a "pool region" of closed trajectories and an inactive region in which the geostrophic contours are blocked by the meridional boundaries. These ideas are nicely demonstrated in numerical experiments with quasi-geostrophic models (Holland *et al.*, 1984). Luyten *et al.* (1983), by using a three-dimensional model, introduced the idea of a "ventilated region" in the eastern part of the subtropical gyre in which waters in contact with the surface are swept down into the thermocline. From a climate standpoint the ventilation process is particularly interesting because it describes how water masses can be formed outside of polar regions.

Cox and Bryan (1984) attempt to provide a more complete framework for testing the dynamical consistency of these ideas within the context of a numerical model with high vertical (15 levels) and high horizontal (1° latitude × 1° longitude) resolution. The geometry of the model is shown in Fig. 1a. A great advantage of the numerical model compared with the analytic models is the ability to include convection, which is found to play a key role in creating low potential vorticity. In addition, the solutions indicate a new downward pathway in the subtropical thermocline adjacent to the eastern boundary allowed by a dissipative layer at the wall. High-vorticity waters derived from downwelling at the wall move into the interior adjacent to the low-vorticity waters of the ventilated region. Pedlosky (1983) has recently incorporated this wall-ventilated region into the analytic ventilated thermocline model, producing a much more realistic density structure near the eastern boundary.

In this review we shall present some additional analysis of the solutions of Cox and Bryan (1984) that bring out some of the relationships among the mass, heat, and vorticity balances of the large-scale circulation of the model. This is followed by a discussion of the vertical structure of the pycnocline, and the role of wind in modifying it. The final sections deal with the transient response of similar models to anomalies of heat applied to the upper surface. The penetration of active thermal anomalies is compared with the penetration of passive tracers with no dynamical feedback. The most critical test of the transient behavior of an ocean model is provided by the tracer data sets, particularly the tritium data sets taken at 10-year intervals after the large-scale injection of bomb-produced tritium into the oceans in the late 1950s and early 1960s. A final section deals with a model simulation of the tritium entry into the North Atlantic Ocean.

2. THE MODEL

The results of several closely related models will be cited and compared in this study, but as a convenient frame of reference we will refer to the simpli-

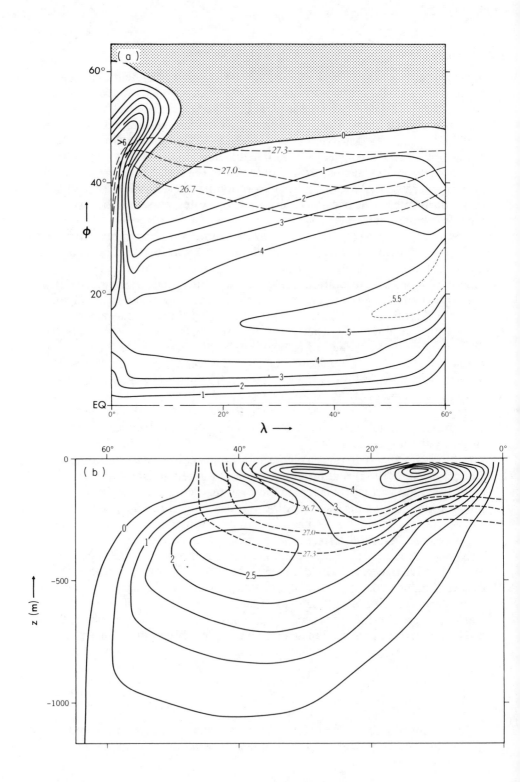

(a)

(b)

fied model of the recent study by Cox and Bryan (1984). The governing equations are quite standard for problems of large-scale flow in the ocean. The fluid is assumed to be Boussinesq and in hydrostatic equilibrium. The metric terms that are usually retained in atmospheric problems can be omitted in the ocean case, since the Rossby number defined with a planetary length scale rarely exceeds 10^{-3}. Let $\mathbf{u}$ be the horizontal velocity and ∇ the horizontal gradient operator. Further, we define f as the Coriolis parameter, p as the pressure, and ρ as the density. Also, ρ_0 is the reference density; w is the vertical velocity, and $\mathbf{k}$ is a unit vector in the vertical direction; d_t is the substantive derivative, and ∂_t is the local derivative with respect to time.

$$d_t\mathbf{u} + f\,\mathbf{k} \times \mathbf{u} + \nabla(p/\rho_0) = \mathbf{F} \tag{2.1}$$

$$\rho g + \partial_z p = 0 \tag{2.2}$$

$$\nabla \cdot \mathbf{u} + \partial_z w = 0 \tag{2.3}$$

$$\rho = \rho_0(1 - \alpha\theta) \tag{2.4}$$

$$d_t\theta = Q \tag{2.5}$$

Equations (2.1) and (2.2) are the equation of motion in the horizontal plane and the hydrostatic equation, respectively. Equation (2.3) is the equation of continuity and (2.4) is the simplified equation of state, which relates the density to an apparent temperature. The apparent temperature θ combines the buoyancy effects of both temperature and salinity. The parameter α in (2.4) is an expansion coefficient. Further $\mathbf{F}$ and Q are terms representing the closure approximations for unresolved small-scale motion in the momentum and apparent temperature equations. The use of a single buoyancy variable is sufficient to discuss many aspects of ocean dynamics, keeping in mind that a separate treatment of temperature and salinity is necessary for an accurate simulation of the role of the ocean in climate. We have adopted simple linear closure approximations,

$$\mathbf{F} = A_{\mathrm{MH}}\,\nabla^2\mathbf{u} + A_{\mathrm{MV}}\,\partial_z\,\partial_z\mathbf{u} \tag{2.6}$$

$$Q = A_{\mathrm{HH}}\,\nabla^2\theta + \partial_z(A_{\mathrm{HV}}\,\partial_z\theta) \tag{2.7}$$

where

$$A_{\mathrm{HV}} = \begin{cases} \infty, & \partial_z\rho > 0 \\ \text{const}, & \partial_z\rho < 0 \end{cases} \tag{2.8}$$

FIG. 1. Patterns of potential vorticity minus relative vorticity for the reference case of Cox and Bryan (1984). (a) The horizonal pattern near the surface. (b) A meridional vertical section 25° east of the western boundary. Units are 10^{-12} g cm^{-4} s^{-1}. [From Cox and Bryan (1984). Reproduced with permission from *Journal of Physical Oceanography*, a publication of the American Meteorological Society.]

TABLE I. PARAMETERS OF THE COX AND BRYAN (1984) MODEL REFERENCE CASE

Parameter	Symbol	Value
Resolution		
Longitude	$\Delta\lambda$	$1.2°$
Latitude	$\Delta\phi$	$1°$
Vertical	Δz	Variable (15 levels)
Lateral viscosity	A_{MH}	10^4 m^2 s^{-1}
Vertical viscosity	A_{MV}	10^{-3} m^2 s^{-1}
Lateral diffusion	A_{HH}	10^3 m^2 s^{-1}
Vertical diffusion	A_{HV}	0.3×10^{-4} m^2 s^{-1}
Wind stress	τ_0^*	0.1 Pascal
Equator to polar boundary temperature difference	$\Delta\theta^*$	$20°$C
Expansion coefficient	α	2.5×10^{-4} °C^{-1}

with parameters as shown in Table I. Equation (2.8) is a simple parameterization of convection. The vertical diffusion coefficient has a uniform background value for stable stratification and becomes infinite for the unstable case. This parameterization acts as a constraint to exclude unstable stratification in the model.

At the upper boundary,

$$w = 0 \tag{2.9}$$

$$A_{HV}\,\partial_z\theta = \mu\Delta z(\theta^* - \theta) \tag{2.10}$$

$$A_{MV}\,\partial_z\mathbf{u} = \tau^* \tag{2.11}$$

The rigid-lid condition given by (2.9) effectively filters out high-speed surface gravity waves. Equations (2.10) and (2.11) define the surface flux of buoyancy and momentum that drive the general circulation of the model. Three-dimensional numerical models are a unique tool for untangling the competing effects of wind-driving and buoyancy gradients. In (2.10) we have used a formulation introduced by Haney (1971) in which μ^{-1} is a time constant and Δz represents the thickness of the mixed layer. The following functions of latitude ϕ in radians specify the boundary conditions:

$$\theta^* = \Delta\theta^*(1 - 1.13\phi) + \theta_0 \tag{2.12}$$

$$\tau^* = \tau_0^* \begin{cases} 1.1\,\cos(4.77 - 5.46\phi) + 0.5, & \phi \geq 0.175 \\ 0.2 - 3.2\phi, & \phi \leq 0.175 \end{cases} \tag{2.13}$$

The model is bounded by two meridians separated by $60°$ of longitude, and mirror symmetry is assumed across the equator. A polar wall is placed at $65°$ of latitude from the equator. Other parameters are specified in Table I. Below the surface of the model, the lateral walls are taken to be insulating. A no-slip condition is specified on the lateral boundaries, and a free-slip condition is specified at the bottom boundary.

3. Zonally Averaged Transports of Mass, Heat, and Potential Vorticity

3.1. Mass Transport in the Meridional Vertical Plane

We are accustomed to thinking of the thermohaline circulation primarily as an overturning in the meridional vertical plane. For this reason it is useful to examine the pattern of circulation of the zonally integrated flow, keeping in mind that many complex details are lumped together in this process. The zonally integrated transport is divergence-free so that it can be described in terms of a transport stream function of the form

$$\partial_z \psi = - \int_0^{\lambda_L} \rho_0 va \cos \phi \, d\lambda \tag{3.1}$$

$$a^{-1}\partial_\phi \psi = \int_0^{\lambda_L} \rho_0 wa \cos \phi \, d\lambda \tag{3.2}$$

Here, λ_L is the longitude at the eastern boundary. Three cases are considered: one case without wind, driven by differential heating only; another case in which wind is included; and a third case in which wind has twice the amplitude of the previous cases. The first two cases form the basis of the study of thermocline ventilation and vorticity balance by Cox and Bryan (1984). Patterns of the transport stream function in the vertical meridional plane are shown in Fig. 2a–c. In these diagrams a different scale is used for the upper 1 km of the model ocean in order to show the details of the wind-induced transports near the surface. The case without wind is shown in Fig. 2a. The pattern of overturning is very simple. There is a broad upwelling region with transport upward, rather uniform with respect to latitude. Downward motion is concentrated in a narrow region close to the poleward wall. The pattern is very much like that obtained by Rossby (1965) in a laboratory experiment. In Rossby's experiment, fluid was confined in a container that was insulated along the sidewalls and bottom. For experimental convenience, the experiment was actually carried out for an inverted ocean, but we will describe the results for the physically equivalent case in which a horizontal temperature gradient is imposed on the fluid from above. In the laboratory experiment there are no effects of rotation. The flow induced by the imposed temperature gradient consists of a concentrated downwelling at the point of minimum temperature at the upper boundary and a broad upwelling over the interior of the container. A thermal boundary layer forms at the base of the upper plate as a simple analog of the ocean's thermocline in a nonrotating system.

The effect of the wind pattern on the meridional circulation is shown in

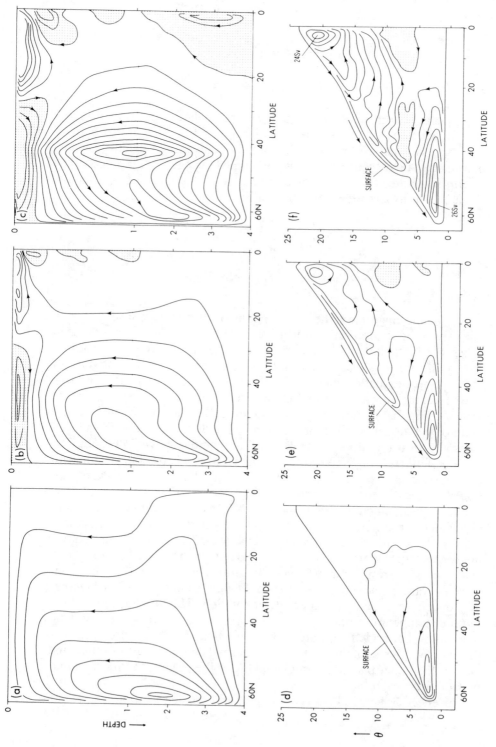

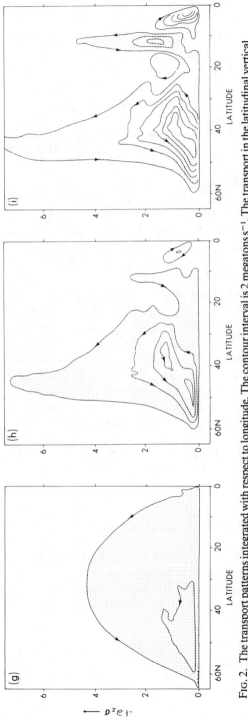

FIG. 2. The transport patterns integrated with respect to longitude. The contour interval is 2 megatons s⁻¹. The transport in the latitudinal vertical plane for the (a) no wind, (b) reference wind stress, and (c) two times the reference wind stress. (d) – (f) are the transport patterns in the θ latitudinal plane for the same three cases. (g) – (i) are the corresponding patterns of transport in the PV-latitudinal plane.

Fig. 2b. Ekman suction near the equator has the effect of creating an intense cell in which almost no motion existed in the case without wind. Roemmich (1983) has examined data for the Atlantic equatorial zone, confirming the existence of such a shallow overturning circulation. Roemmich found that the geostrophic inflow toward the equator in the thermocline was in good agreement with the upwelling required by Ekman suction. The wind-forced overturning adjacent to the equator is an extremely important feature in relation to the poleward heat transport. We will return to that point later. In addition, Ekman pumping causes downwelling in the subtropics and Ekman suction leads to upwelling at higher latitudes in the region of the subarctic gyre. Note that the effects of Ekman pumping and suction are not confined to the upper ocean. If we compare the patterns of Fig. 2a and 2b, it is possible to see that the stream function is also changed at lower levels in the same sense that one would expect from the wind-induced vertical motion near the surface. Deep upwelling is reduced by the wind in the subtropical gyre region and enhanced in the subarctic gyre region.

The same wind-induced features that show up in Fig. 2b are present in amplified form in Fig. 2c. The surface equatorial cell is much intensified and the area of stagnant flow at depth is enlarged. At the equator some peculiar overturning cells appear at depth. Our analysis indicates that these cells are due to the poor numerical resolution in the vertical direction in deep water. Since the fluid has a nearly uniform temperature below the thermocline, this numerical error does not have a serious effect on the heat balance. A significant new feature, however, is the closed cell in middle latitudes at the base of the thermocline. An examination of the three-dimensional flow patterns (not shown) indicates that the upper branch of this cell is associated with the western boundary current, while the lower branch is associated with water being injected into the thermocline in the interior.

3.2. Mass Transport in the Meridional Temperature Plane

Since convection guarantees that the vertical stability of the model ocean will be either neutral or stably stratified, one can define a coordinate system based on temperature instead of z. In such a system we can define new transport stream lines in the latitude–density plane equivalent to (3.1) and (3.2).

$$\partial_\theta \psi = -\int_0^{\lambda_L} \rho_0 v \, \partial_\theta z \, a \cos \phi \, d\lambda \tag{3.3}$$

$$a^{-1} \partial_\phi \psi = \int_0^{\lambda_L} \rho_0 \, d_t\theta \, \partial_\theta z \, a \cos \phi \, d\lambda \tag{3.4}$$

As shown in (2.13) the reference temperature specified at the surface decreases linearly with latitude. For weak flow the surface temperature is very nearly in equilibrium with the reference temperature. Thus the upper boundary is very nearly a straight, diagonal line sloping downward toward polar latitudes. Significant departures take place in Fig. 2e,f owing to the very vigorous western boundary current created by the wind-driven circulation. The pattern of flow for the pure heating case is very simple and regular. Deep water created at the polar boundary flows isothermally at the base of the thermocline toward the equator, feeding upward flow into the thermocline as it moves along.

The effect of Ekman suction at the equator is shown very dramatically in Fig. 2e,f. Mixing at the equator allows flow to move across isotherms gaining heat as it rises to the surface. Once at the surface, the waters move poleward, losing heat across the upper boundary. The poleward flow is largely Ekman transport near the equator, merging into a western boundary current in middle latitudes. At 45°N the upper flow is terminated at the point at which the western boundary current separates from the boundary. At this point the flow doubles back toward the equator and increases in temperature. This pattern appears to be due to overturning motion but in reality the return branch is the southward-moving surface flow in the interior of the subtropical gyre. Note that the return flow lies very close to a diagonal line connecting equatorial and polar temperatures in Fig. 2e,f. Since the equatorward interior flow is much less intense than the flow at the western boundary current, its temperature roughly corresponds to the specified reference temperature at each latitude rather than the western boundary current flow.

If we examine the upper two-thirds of the pattern in the strong wind case, Fig. 2f, it is apparent that cross-isothermal flow is confined to the surface and to the region just below the equator. Nearly horizontal transport lines in the temperature–latitude plane indicate that the interior flow is almost isopycnal. Only at the base of the pycnocline in the lower third of the diagram is there significant cross-isopycnal flow. At the base of the pycnocline the flow is weaker and mixing processes evidently play a larger role. The same tendency appears in Fig. 2e, but is not as clear cut. The important point brought out in Fig. 2f is that it is not necessary to invoke a nonuniform vertical diffusion to obtain a solution in which diapycnal flow in the upper thermocline is highly localized. The important factor is not the form of the vertical mixing, but the local ratio of vertical mixing to advection. This is perhaps the most significant point brought out by these calculations.

The transport diagrams in the temperature–latitude plane provide a convenient way to analyze the poleward heat transport, which is one of the most important features of our solutions from a climate standpoint. The heat transport across any latitude circle can be calculated by simply adding up the transports at different temperatures. Poleward heat transport is most effective for circulations in which the poleward and equatorward branches have very different temperatures. This is true of the wind-driven meridional overturning at low latitudes. It is not true for surface-intensified horizontal gyres. Surface heat balance calculations (Budyko, 1963; Hastenrath, 1980) indicate that poleward heat transport in the ocean in the Northern Hemisphere has a very different distribution with latitude than poleward heat transport in the atmosphere. Atmospheric poleward heat transport tends to have a maximum in mid-latitudes where cyclones play the largest role. Poleward heat transport in the ocean appears to be stronger in the lower latitudes. Figure 3a shows the poleward heat transport of the model for the three cases shown in

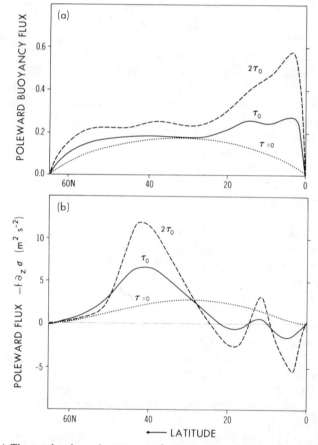

Fig. 3. (a) The total poleward transport of apparent heat in petawatts (10^{15} W) for the no-wind case (dotted line), the reference case (dashed line), and the high-wind case (solid line). (b) The corresponding curves for the transport of PV in units of square meters per square second.

Figure 2. We see that the pure heating case has a maximum in mid-latitudes. The effect of wind is to shift the maximum poleward heat transport toward lower latitudes due to the strong meridional overturning caused by Ekman transport away from the equator, compensated by the return flow of cooler waters at lower levels. The reference temperature of the surface boundary condition, which is a nearly linear function of latitude, is not particularly realistic. In reality, meridional gradients of surface temperature are rather weak in the tropics. If this factor had been taken into account, the poleward heat transport curves would have a somewhat different shape near the equator and the maximum would be less pronounced and perhaps shifted slightly poleward.

3.3. Potential Vorticity Transport Diagrams

As pointed out in the introduction, the potential vorticity has turned out to be an important variable for interpreting and diagnosing theoretical models and making comparisons between theory and observations. Two diagrams as shown in Fig. 1, taken from Cox and Bryan (1984), show the distribution of potential vorticity minus the relative component near the surface in the horizontal plane and the same quantity in the meridional plane at a longitude of $25°$, where $0°$ is the position of the western boundary. Figure 1b shows that the potential vorticity minus the relative component (henceforth referred to as PV) goes to zero at the equator where the Coriolis parameter is zero and also at the polar wall where the vertical stability vanishes. Here, PV, defined as $-f\partial_z\rho$, will always be positive due to the convective constraint of the model. Generally, PV is highest near the surface and decreases with depth, but the relation between PV and the z coordinate is not monotonic. The horizontal pattern of PV shown in Fig. 1a shows that the east–west variations may be large. These features must be kept in mind in the interpretation of diagrams similar to those of Fig. 2a–f, but with PV as the ordinate. In this case, transport across lines of constant PV is a measure of the zonally averaged generation or decay of PV. Thus Fig. 2g–i provides a measure of the total PV budget of the model. As in the previous diagrams, the case of pure heating has a very simple transport pattern. Low-vorticity water formed by convection at the polar wall is carried equatorward in the deep water and gradually gains PV by diffusion from above. Higher-PV waters near the surface are carried poleward and lose their vertical stability by convection as they are carried into regions of net surface cooling.

Wind introduces some complicated effects in the PV budget at lower latitudes. Note in Fig. 1b that PV has a subsurface maximum near the equator. Thus the surface Ekman transport away from the equator has a lower value of PV associated with it than the geostrophically balanced inflow at lower levels. At slightly higher latitudes PV is highest at the surface and the poleward Ekman transport under the Easterlies carries PV away from the equator. This regime is interrupted at $20°N$. Note that the horizontal vorticity pattern in Fig. 1a shows a pronounced tongue of high-PV water jutting out from the eastern boundary at this latitude. Over a limited span of latitude, the equatorward movement of this tongue dominates the poleward PV transport. At higher latitudes the poleward flow of high-PV water in the western boundary current is the most important factor. Poleward of $45°N$ convection decreases the potential vorticity of surface waters. Some of the details of this process are shown in the analysis of PV along trajectories in Cox and Bryan (1984).

The total poleward transport of PV is shown in Fig. 3b for the three cases under consideration. Unlike heat transport, the maximum PV transport takes place at higher latitudes. The dominant process is the transport poleward of high-PV waters by the western boundary current and the destruction of PV by convection in the subarctic gyre region.

4. PYCNOCLINE STRUCTURE

Theories of the ocean structure often bypass the difficult question of the origin of the ocean pycnocline. It is more common to assume that a basic stratification exists and to study the modification of that density structure by the effects of large-scale wind patterns. A major reason why the thermohaline circulation problem is considered so intractable is the lack of quantitative data on cross isopycnal (diapycnal) mixing. Various mechanisms have been proposed [see Garrett (1979) for a review], but measurements alone do not provide guidance as to which mechanisms dominate in different geographical regions and how they should be incorporated in a comprehensive model. In the absence of an accepted parameterization of vertical mixing, our approach has been to explore the consequences of a simple mixing hypothesis in detail and create the framework for more accurate prescriptions as they become available.

A convenient integral measure of the pycnocline penetration is a scale depth d defined as

$$d = \frac{1}{\rho_s - \rho_{00}} \int_{-H}^{0} (\rho - \rho_{00}) \, dz \qquad (4.1)$$

where ρ_s is the surface density and ρ_{00} the density at $z = -H$. Table II provides a comparison of observations and the models. The observed scale depth is calculated from globally averaged values of density referred to

TABLE II. PYCNOCLINE SCALE DEPTH $d^* + d'$ BASED ON THE
AREA-AVERAGED DENSITY PROFILE[a]

Study	Domain	Pycnocline depth scale $d^* + d'$
Observed		
Levitus (1982)	World Ocean	389
Bryan et al. (1982)	Sector	445
Present study	Sector	
$\tau = 0.0$		215
$\tau = \tau_0^*$		285
$\tau = 2\tau_0^*$		350

[a] In computing the scale depth the density referred to surface pressure is used.

surface pressure from the hydrographic atlas of Levitus (1982). For comparison, the scale depth is shown for the ocean component of a coupled ocean–atmosphere model used in carbon dioxide/climate response studies (Bryan et al., 1982; Spelman and Manabe, 1984). Also shown are the scale depths corresponding to the three cases considered in the previous section. Here, d^* is the scale depth due to heating alone and d' is the increase in depth due to wind.

The structure of the pycnocline in the meridional vertical plane is shown in Fig. 4. The figure is based on a longitudinal average over 12° in the middle of the basin. Without wind the pycnocline is rather featureless. The effect of wind is to produce a much more realistic downbowing of the pycnocline at high latitudes and an upbowing near the equator. As indicated in Table II the scale depth of the pycnocline is increased by approximately 30% when a wind pattern near the observed amplitude is imposed, and the scale depth is increased by 60% when the wind amplitude is doubled. For comparison the zonally averaged pattern of isopycnals for the Atlantic from Levitus (1982) are shown in Fig. 5. Superficially the agreement is favorable. A closer examination shows some interesting differences. In Table III the Brunt–Väissällä frequency in the model and in the Levitus atlas may be compared. It is obvious that the real ocean is more stratified near the surface and at depth than the model. One obvious factor is a single source for deep water in the model compared to multiple sources in the real ocean. Another possibility is that a uniform vertical mixing may prove to be inadequate for a really detailed simulation of the ocean's pycnocline.

Bryan and Cox (1967) made a comparison of simple scale theory and the results of numerical experiments. It is interesting to review these results and apply them to the higher-resolution numerical experiments of Cox and Bryan (1984). One definition of a scale velocity is based on the geostrophic relation differentiated with respect to z and combined with the hydrostatic

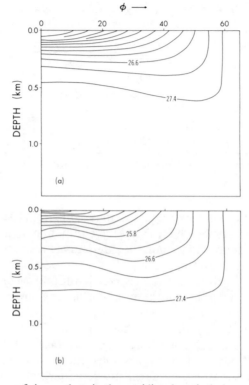

FIG. 4. The pattern of sigma–theta in the meridional vertical plane, averaged over an 8°
longitude belt in the middle of the basin. (a) No-wind case and (b) reference case. Sigma–theta is
equal to $(\rho - \rho_0) \times 10^{-3}$ in units of grams per cubic centimeter.

equation

$$V^* = g\alpha\, \Delta\theta^* d/2\Omega a \qquad (4.2)$$

Here, a is the radius of the Earth and $\Delta\theta^*$ is the total difference in reference
temperature between the equator and the polar boundary; Ω is the angular
velocity of the earth; d is the depth scale. Alternatively, the scale velocity may
be defined from the Sverdrup relation (Pedlosky, 1979), the balance between
vortex stretching and the beta effect. Let τ_0^*/L be a measure of the amplitude
of the wind curl in the subtropical gyre, and $2\Omega/a$ is a measure of beta:

$$V^{**} = \tau_0^*\, a/2\Omega L\, d\rho_0 \qquad (4.3)$$

In the case of no wind, a balance between advection and diapycnal mixing
must hold in the pycnocline. Therefore,

$$V^*/a = A_{\mathrm{HV}}/d^2 \qquad (4.4)$$

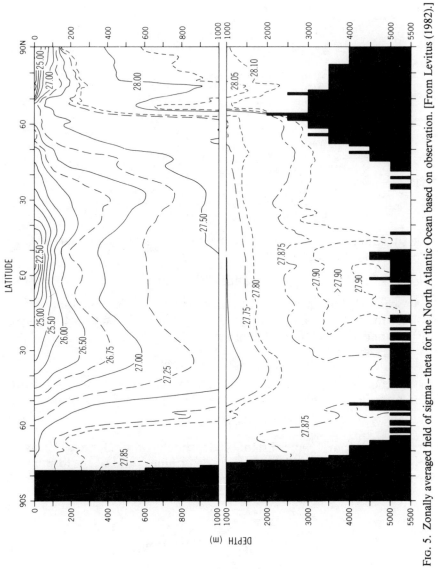

FIG. 5. Zonally averaged field of sigma–theta for the North Atlantic Ocean based on observation. [From Levitus (1982).]

TABLE III. BRUNT–VÄISÄLLÄ FREQUENCY IN
UNITS OF RADIANS PER HOUR

Depth (m)	Model	Observations (Levitus, 1982)
15	30.54	25.80
50	37.10	36.50
100	30.93	32.18
150	25.04	25.00
235	21.21	17.96
340	19.53	13.75
470	17.44	11.54
640	14.00	10.09
860	9.69	9.12
1130	5.65	7.76
1470	2.87	6.01
1880	1.41	4.42
2370	0.69	3.38
2950	0.47	2.90
3635	0.28	2.54

The substitution of V^* from (4.2) into the left-hand side of (4.4) gives the expression for the scale depth

$$d^{*3} = 2A_{HV}\Omega a^2/g\alpha\,\Delta\theta^* \tag{4.5}$$

In the case of wind acting on the thermocline we can derive another expression for the scale depth by setting the two definitions of scale velocity given by (4.2) and (4.3) equal to each other:

$$d^{**2} = \tau_0^* a^2/(\rho_0 g\alpha\,\Delta\theta^* L) \tag{4.6}$$

In the general case the scale depth might be expected to be some combination of (4.5) and (4.6). The experimental results shown in Table II suggest

$$d = c_1 + c_2\tau_0^* \tag{4.7}$$

Here c_1 and c_2 are two constants independent of wind stress. Using the no-wind and the normal-wind cases to determine c_1 and c_2, the formula can be used to predict the thermocline depth in the high-wind case. The linear fit is shown in Fig. 6.

5. TRANSIENT RESPONSE

The Earth's atmosphere cannot fully respond to any long-term change in external conditions without a major interaction with the ocean. Since the ocean has a heat capacity that is many times larger than the atmosphere, it is

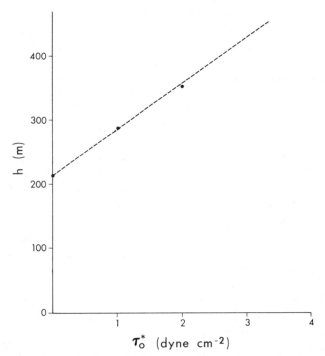

FIG. 6. The dependence of scale depth of the pycnocline on the strength of the surface wind stress. Dots represent the results of numerical experiments. The dashed line is a linear fit.

able to act as a climatic buffer. The response of the combined ocean–atmosphere system is a ponderous process, requiring many years for a new equilibrium to be approached. The pycnocline of the ocean shields the deep water of the ocean from direct contact with surface waters except by pathways originating at high latitudes. Since mixing across isopycnals appears to be a relatively weak process, the most direct interaction between surface and subsurface waters is through advection and mixing along isopycnals. The general outlines of the way in which deep waters of the World Ocean are refreshed by movements from surface outcrops along isopycnal surfaces have been recognized from water mass studies of the ocean [see Warren and Wunsch (1981) for a review]. A new element has been introduced by recently acquired data on anthropogenic tracers such as tritium and freons. The new tracers allow quantitative estimates of the rate of movement along vertical pathways that were not possible before.

An important, potential application of ocean models is in the study of climate transients due to external effects such as the buildup of atmospheric CO_2. The data sets on anthropogenic tracers provide a superb opportunity to test the competence of the ocean models to handle transient climate problems in which the uptake of CO_2 or a heat anomaly must be correctly predicted. First-order, one-dimensional models of tracer penetration are already in widespread use. The most useful model is that of Oeschger *et al.* (1975) in which the ocean's mixed layer is modeled by a well-mixed slab, underlain by a deep slab of uniform diffusivity. The model requires that the penetration of a surface-derived tracer increases as the square root of time.

Although this simple model has been very successful in fitting transient tracer data, it can only be considered a convenient mathematical construct considering the lack of physical similarity between model and prototype, the real ocean. Further progress demands a model that incorporates some of the actual processes of water mass formation in the ocean. A three-dimensional model could permit an estimate of the geographical distribution of tracer penetration and a comparison of dynamically active and passive tracers. One of the first attempts to use a three-dimensional model to study tracers was carried out by Holland (1971). Recently, attempts have been made to simulate the tritium invasion of the ocean following the bomb tests of the late 1950s and early 1960s (Sarmiento, 1983). We shall return to these tritium simulations in Section 6 after a brief summary of some more idealized experiments that compare the behavior of active and passive tracers in three-dimensional models.

Bryan and Lewis (1979) modeled the water mass distribution of the World Ocean using a multilevel model. Observed temperature, salinity, and wind stress as a function of season were imposed as boundary conditions at the surface. Starting with uniform temperature and salinity at all depths, the model was integrated until equilibrium was reached by using the distorted physics approach described by Bryan (Bryan *et al.*, 1984). The solutions were successful in simulating many of the major water mass features observed, particularly the intermediate waters of the Southern Ocean. A similar calculation has been reported by Meehl *et al.* (1982) and Han (1984). In a recent study Bryan *et al.* (1984) use a World Ocean model for response studies. The equilibrium solutions are perturbed by adding a uniform temperature increment to the specified temperature boundary condition at the upper boundary. Experiments were carried out with a globally uniform perturbation of plus and minus 0.5°C at the surface. The response to the changed boundary conditions was studied over a 50-year numerical integration, and compared with a control run for a dynamically inactive tracer.

To describe the results of the transient solutions, it is convenient to define a penetration scale depth based on the anomaly, which is analogous to the pycnocline scale defined by (4.1):

$$d'' = \frac{1}{\mu_s} \int_{-H}^{0} \mu \, dz \qquad (5.1)$$

TABLE IV. THE PENETRATION DEPTH OF SURFACE-
DERIVED HEAT ANOMALIES AND TRACERS SCALED BY
THE PYCNOCLINE SCALE DEPTH

Study	Case	10 year	40 year
Bryan *et al.* (1984)	−0.5°C	0.70	1.36
Bryan *et al.* (1984)	+0.5°C	0.49	1.04
Bryan *et al.* (1984)	Tracer	0.52	1.00
Bryan *et al.* (1982)	High CO_2		
Bryan *et al.* (1982)	Heat	0.65	1.55
Bryan *et al.* (1982)	Normal CO_2		
Bryan *et al.* (1982)	Tracer	0.50	0.98

In this case μ_s is the surface anomaly and μ the subsurface anomaly. Here, d'' exhibited the same square root of time dependence in the switch-on experiments as predicted by the box-diffusion model of Oeschger *et al.* (1975), although the physics of the three-dimensional and one-dimensional models are quite different. The effective global diffusion obtained by fitting the three-dimensional model results to the box-diffusion model is over five times that of the background vertical diffusion A_{HV} of the numerical model itself.

Values of penetration depth for the anomalies are given in Table IV scaled by the pycnocline depth. The penetration is given for 10 years and 40 years. For a square root of time dependence, the penetration depth at 40 years should be double that at 10 years. Most of the results follow this rule rather closely. A positive temperature anomaly of 0.5°C and a tracer behaved in essentially the same way, penetrating one-half of a pycnocline scale depth in a decade and a full scale depth in 40 years. A negative temperature anomaly penetrated considerably faster, and more detailed analysis shows that this is due to enhanced high-latitude convection.

Another study (Bryan *et al.,* 1982) allows a similar comparison of a dynamically active and passive tracer in a more realistic climatic context, but with an admittedly much more idealized geometry. A coupled atmosphere and ocean was contained in a 120° longitude global sector with mirror symmetry across the equator and cyclic boundary conditions at the meridional walls. One-half the surface area is occupied by ocean and the remainder by level land surface. The ocean is similar to that of Cox and Bryan (1984) described earlier except that it extends to the pole and does not have as high lateral or vertical resolution. The equilibrium climates corresponding to normal and four times normal atmospheric CO_2 have been described by Spelman and Manabe (1984). The results shown in Table IV are based on two numerical integrations starting from the normal CO_2 equilibrium climate. One case is a calibration run in which only a passive tracer is switched on at the surface and allowed to penetrate downward. In the other case, the

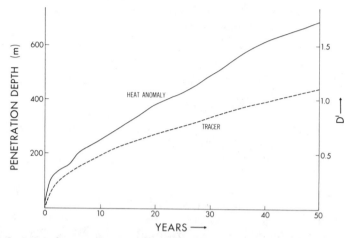

FIG. 7. Increase of penetration scale for the surface switch-on of a thermal anomaly (solid line) and a passive tracer (dashed line) based on the coupled ocean–atmosphere model of Bryan *et al.* (1982).

initial conditions are the same, but the atmospheric CO_2 was abruptly increased fourfold and the coupled system allowed to respond. The equilibrium response of sea-surface temperature is approximately 3.5°C in this case. Thus the effective positive temperature anomaly at the upper surface is much greater than the +0.5°C anomaly of Bryan *et al.* (1984). While one would expect that a more stable stratification would retard the rate of downward mixing of an anomaly, curiously enough, the large anomaly actually increases the rate of penetration. The time-dependent behavior is seen in Fig. 7. The heat anomaly consistently penetrated faster than the passive tracer. A more detailed analysis (Bryan and Spelman, 1985) shows that the dynamical feedback is through decreased high-latitude convection. In the model, heat uptake at low latitudes is not really affected by the rise in temperature that takes place there. On the other hand, since high-latitude convection ordinarily cools the ocean, a suppression of convection at high latitudes traps large amounts of heat below the surface. Figure 7 suggests that this mechanism may provide an important negative feedback to CO_2-induced climate change. The effect would be to slow down the response to increasing atmospheric CO_2 by augmenting the buffering effect of the ocean.

6. TRITIUM SIMULATIONS

The bomb tests of the late 1950s and early 1960s produced tritium in amounts greatly exceeding its natural abundance. This tritium was delivered to the surface of the ocean as water (HTO) and thus is an ideal tracer for exchange between the surface and interior. The processes involved in this exchange are of great relevance to predictions of CO_2 uptake by the oceans as well as the associated climate changes.

Measurements of tritium were made by the Geochemical Ocean Sections Study (GEOSECS) over the entire globe in the decade of the 1970s. These measurements are complemented by a series of other studies, particularly in the North Atlantic, where the data coverage for the period mid-1971 to mid-1973 is excellent [e.g., Sarmiento *et al.* (1982)]. The North Atlantic data have been used in model calibration study (Sarmiento, 1983), which will be reviewed here.

Sarmiento (1983) made use of currents from a model developed by Sarmiento and Bryan (1982) for the tritium simulation. This model covers the region between 20°S and 68°N in the Atlantic Ocean. It has 1° horizontal resolution and 12 levels in the vertical. The water mass properties of the model are damped to observed values at the surface and in deep water.

Figure 8 shows one of many comparisons made between the model simulation and observations. The data shown is from the GEOSECS West Atlantic section. The model succeeds in reproducing many of the important features of the data, such as the low equatorial concentrations and penetration, the Subtropical Underwater maximum at ~150 m in the region between ~10°N and ~30°N, the strong gradient region associated with the North Equatorial Current, and the deep penetration in high latitudes. The major failure of the model is the lack of penetration into the deeper part of the thermocline in the region between ~30°N and ~50°N. The reason for this is not well understood, though it may be related to some inadequacy in simulating cross-Gulf Stream/North Atlantic Current exchange.

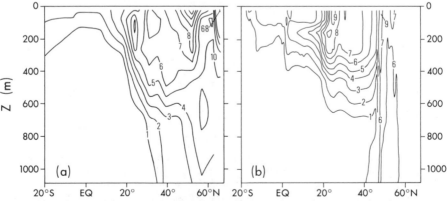

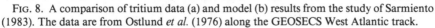

FIG. 8. A comparison of tritium data (a) and model (b) results from the study of Sarmiento (1983). The data are from Ostlund *et al.* (1976) along the GEOSECS West Atlantic track.

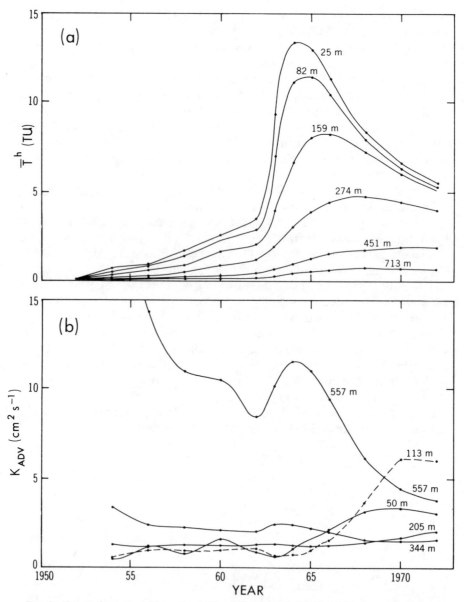

FIG. 9. Results from the tritium simulation of Sarmiento (1983). (a) Horizontally averaged tritium concentrations at various levels in the main thermocline as a function of time. (b) The contribution of vertical advection to the tritium penetration as expressed in the form of an "apparent" vertical diffusivity obtained by performing a horizontal average. (c) The same as (b), only for convective overturning processes. [From Sarmiento (1983). Reproduced with permission from *Journal of Physical Oceanography*, a publication of the American Meteorological Society.]

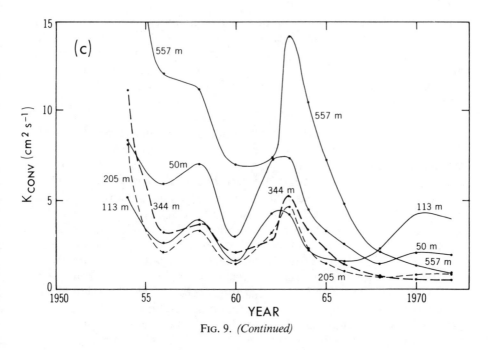

Fig. 9. *(Continued)*

One of the major points that was made by the simulation was the great importance of seasonal convection in addition to downward advection and mixing in tracer penetration. Figure 9 shows "apparent" vertical diffusivities calculated from the tritium simulation by averaging horizontally over the entire model domain as explained by Sarmiento (1983). The diffusivity provided by the model is 0.5 cm² s⁻¹. Clearly, this is completely overshadowed by the advective and convective contributions, with the convective contribution being the largest of all. The behavior of these terms is greatly variable with time as well as depth. A model such as Oeschger *et al.*'s (1975) box-diffusion model simply cannot simulate the model prediction without a vertical diffusivity exhibiting a complex behavior in both time and space.

7. SUMMARY

As new data become available, it is becoming increasingly apparent that the ocean circulation is at least as complicated as the circulation of the atmosphere and perhaps more so in certain respects. Analytic models have played a key role in providing essential ideas and will continue to do so, but judging by the experience of atmospheric scientists, numerical models will ultimately be the primary tool for quantitative analysis of ocean circulation. A major impediment to the inclusion of the thermohaline component of ocean circulation has been the lack of enough quantitative data on diapycnal mixing in the ocean thermocline. Convective mixing can be included using methods developed in atmospheric models, but mixing under stable conditions in the absence of strong large-scale shear is difficult to model with any confidence. In the high-resolution numerical experiments of Cox and Bryan (1984), vertical mixing is just approximated by a simple constant eddy diffusion. However, the solutions show that if wind driving is sufficiently strong, vertical mixing is only a dominant process in certain localized regions. Diapycnal flow in the model is largely confined to the surface, where boundary conditions are imposed, to the region directly below the equator, and to the base of the thermocline. Most of the central pycnocline corresponds to an ideal fluid. Diapycnal flow below the thermocline takes place in a region in which upwelling pinches the isopycnal up toward the surface. At the base of the pycnocline, mixing becomes important because the flow is weak and consequently the Péclèt number becomes small. The conclusion to be drawn from these solutions is that the effects of vertical mixing can be highly localized even for a very simple parameterization of vertical mixing, provided that the resolution of the model is good enough.

The globally averaged response to a tracer or thermal anomaly "switched on" at the upper surface is similar to the response of a diffusive slab, although the physical process of downward penetration is entirely different. The penetration is found to be approximately one-half the pycnocline scale depth after 10 years and a full scale depth after 40 years. A negative buoyancy anomaly has a much faster initial penetration than a passive tracer. A positive anomaly, on the other hand, penetrates at the same rate as the tracer at first, but at a slightly faster rate at later times.

Work is now in progress on a model of much greater resolution that can include the effect of mesoscale eddies. Some of the present results must be considered to be tentative until they can be confirmed with the eddy-resolving, three-dimensional model.

Acknowledgments

The authors warmly acknowledge the advice and encouragement they have received over the years from their colleagues at the Geophysical Fluid Dynamics Laboratory and the many visitors who participated in developing ocean models. Essential to this effort has been the laboratory's former director, Joseph Smagorinsky, who had the foresight to nurture ocean circulation modeling from its feeble infancy to its present state, which, if not yet mature, is at least in a state of robust adolescence.

The authors also wish to thank Martha Jackson, Michael Cox, and Sol Hellerman for their many contributions and long-term commitment to the work of the ocean circulation group at the laboratory.

REFERENCES

Bryan, K., and Cox, M. D. (1967). *Tellus* **19**, 54–80.
Bryan, K., and Cox, M. D. (1968). *J. Atmos. Sci.* **25**, 945–967.
Bryan, K., and Lewis, L. J. (1979). *JGR, J. Geophys. Res.* **84**, 2503–2517.
Bryan, K., Komro, F. G., Manabe, S., and Spelman, M. J. (1982). *Science* **215**, 56–58.
Bryan, K., and Spelman, M. J. (1985). *JGR, J. Geophys. Res.* (submitted for publication).
Bryan, K., Komro, F. G., and Rooth, C. (1984). "Climate Processes and Climate Sensitivity," Geophys. Monogr. No. 29. Am. Geophys. Union, Washington, D.C.
Budyko, M. I. (1963). "Guide to the Atlas of the Heat Balance of the Earth." Gidrometeorologicheskoe Izdatel'skoe, Leningrad.
Cox, M. D. (1970). *Deep-Sea Res.* **17**, 47–75.
Cox, M. D., and Bryan, K. (1984). *J. Phys. Oceanogr.* **14**, 674–687.
Garrett, C. (1979). *Dyn. Oceans Atmos.* **3**, 239–265.
Han, Y.-J. (1984). *Dyn. Oceans Atmos.* **8**, 141–172.
Haney, R. L. (1971). *J. Phys. Oceanogr.* **1**, 241–248.
Hastenrath, S. (1980). *J. Phys. Oceanogr.* **10**, 159–170.
Holland, W. R. (1971). *Tellus* **23**, 371–392.
Holland, W. R., Keffer, T., and Rhines, P. B. (1984). *Nature (London)* **308**, 698.
Levitus, S. (1982). "Climatological Atlas of the World Ocean," NOAA Prof. Pap. No. 13. U.S. Govt. Printing Office, Washington, D.C.
Luyten, J. R., Pedlosky, J., and Stommel, H. (1983). *J. Phys. Oceanogr.* **13**, 292–309.
Manabe, S., and Bryan, K. (1969). *J. Atmos. Sci.* **26**, 786–789.
Meehl, G. A., Washington, W. M., and Semtner, A. J. (1982). *J. Phys. Oceanogr.* **12**, 301–312.
Oeschger, H., Siegenthales, U., Schotterer, U., and Gugelmann, A. (1975). *Tellus* **27**, 168–192.
Ostlund, H. G., Dorsey, H. G., and Bresher, R. (1976). Data Rep. No. 5. Rosenstiel School Mar. Atmos. Sci., University of Miami, Coral Gables.
Pedlosky, J. (1979). "Geophysical Fluid Dynamics." Springer-Verlag, Berlin and New York.
Pedlosky, J. (1983). *J. Phys. Oceanogr.* **13**, 2038–2044.
Rhines, P. B., and Young, W. R. (1982). *J. Fluid Mach.* **122**, 347–367.
Roemmich, D. (1983). *J. Phys. Oceanogr.* **13**, 1534–1539.
Rossby, H. T. (1965). *Deep-Sea Res.* **12**, 9–16.
Sarmiento, J. L. (1983). *J. Phys. Oceanogr.* **13**, 1924–1939.
Sarmiento, J. L., and Bryan, K. (1982). *JGR, J. Geophys. Res.* **87**,(C1), 394–408.
Sarmiento, J. L., Rooth, C. G. H., and Roether, W. (1982). *JGR, J. Geophys. Res.* **87**(C10), 8047–8056.
Spelman, M. J., and Manabe, S. (1984). *JGR, J. Geophys. Res.* **89**(C1), 571–586.
Warren, B. A., and Wunsch, C. (1981). "Evolution of Physical Oceanography." M.I.T. Press, Cambridge, Massachusetts.

TROPICAL OCEANOGRAPHY

S. George Philander

Geophysical Fluid Dynamics Laboratory/NOAA
Princeton University
Princeton, New Jersey

1. Introduction

The principal currents in the tropical Pacific and Atlantic Ocean are zonal (Fig. 1). The westward South Equatorial Current to the south of 3°N is in the direction of the prevailing tradewinds, but the eastward North Equatorial Countercurrent, between 3°N and 10°N approximately, flows counter to the wind. Sverdrup (1947) in one of the early triumphs of dynamical oceanography, showed that the countercurrent is driven by the curl rather than the direction of the wind stress. The other major eastward current, the Equatorial Undercurrent, is driven by the eastward pressure force maintained by the westward trade winds (Charney, 1960). These currents are associated with large density gradients. For example, the eastward pressure force that drives the Equatorial Undercurrent is a consequence of large zonal density gradients: the western tropical Pacific Ocean has an unusually deep (~ 150 m) and unusually warm (~ 28 °C) mixed surface layer; along the South American coast the depth of the mixed layer practically vanishes and sea-surface temperatures can be as low as 18 °C. [See Fig. 4 of Philander and Rasmusson (this volume).]

The tropical currents are subject to considerable variability: some current reverse direction seasonally — the North Equatorial Counter Current in the Atlantic Ocean, for example (Garzoli and Katz, 1983) — and others disappear occasionally — the Equatorial Undercurrent during the 1982 El Niño, for example (Firing *et al.,* 1983; Halpern *et al.,* 1983). This variability implies large changes in the oceanic thermal field. The associated horizontal redistribution of heat in the upper ocean can completely change sea-surface temperature patterns as during El Niño events, for example. The character of this oceanic variability depends on the time scale of the wind changes, and

461

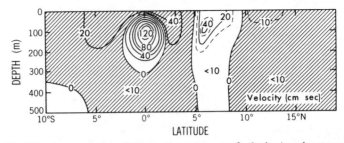

FIG. 1. Meridional cross section of the zonal component of velocity (centimeters per second) in the central Pacific. Shaded regions indicate westward flow. Near the equator the velocities are based on direct measurements; at higher latitudes geostrophic velocities relative to the flow at 1000 m were computed. [After Knauss (1963). Copyright 1963 by Wiley (Interscience).]

also on time scales intrinsic to the ocean. Of fundamental importance is the time it takes the ocean to adjust to a sudden and permanent change in wind conditions. Lighthill's (1969) seminal study of this problem was motivated by the generation of the Somali Current after the sudden onset of the south-west monsoons. He demonstrated that the adjustment time of the ocean decreases with decreasing latitude, so that the Somali Current can be gener-ated within a matter of weeks, whereas it would take on the order of a decade to generate the Gulf Stream from a state of rest in mid-latitudes (Veronis and Stommel, 1956). It is the rapid adjustment of the tropical ocean and the speed with which heat can be redistributed horizontally in the upper ocean that makes possible phenomena such as the interannual El Niño events in the Pacific, and the considerable seasonal changes in the circulations of the tropical Atlantic and Indian Oceans. The similarities and differences be-tween the three tropical ocean basins provide us with a wealth of information about the manner in which changes in the geometry of the ocean basin and changes in the forcing function affect the response. This response can be described deterministically because variability in the tropical oceans is pri-marily forced by the winds. Instabilities of the mean currents contribute to variability only in a narrow band of frequencies near a period of 3 weeks.

This chapter, because of the limited space available, is limited to a brief discussion of a central topic in tropical oceanography: the manner in which the ocean adjusts to the abrupt onset of winds that then remain steady. Sections 2 and 3 describe this adjustment to imposed zonal winds in a shallow-water and a continuously stratified ocean, respectively; in Section 4 the winds are meridional. For a discussion of a wider range of topics, the reader is referred to the review articles by Knox and Anderson (1985) and Cane and Sarachik (1983), who include an extensive list of references.

2. JETS AND WAVES

The eastward winds that prevail over the central Indian Ocean at the time of the equinoxes generate the intense oceanic jet shown in Fig. 2 (Wyrtki, 1973). This current has a number of curious features. Though there is nothing exceptional about the structure of the winds near the equator, the jet is only a few hundred kilometers wide and is centered on the equator. It accelerates at first but becomes steady after a few weeks even though the winds continue to provide eastward momentum to the ocean. Subsequently, the jet decelerates and reverses direction, though the winds never reverse direction.

To explain the behavior of the jet, an appealingly simple model of the tropical ocean will suffice. In the model, the interface between two layers of immiscible fluid, each of constant density, simulates the sharp and shallow tropical thermocline that separates the warm surface waters from the cold waters of the deep ocean. The upper layer has density ρ_1, has a mean depth H, and is bounded above by a rigid lid. The infinitely deep, motionless lower layer has density ρ_2. Linear hydrostatic motion in the upper layer is driven by the zonal wind stress τ^x, which acts as a body force. This motion is associated with a displacement η of the interface and is described by the shallow-water equations

$$u_t - fv + g'\eta_x = \tau^x/H \tag{2.1a}$$

$$v_t + fu + g'\eta_y = 0 \tag{2.1b}$$

$$g'\eta_t + C^2(u_x + v_y) = 0 \tag{2.1c}$$

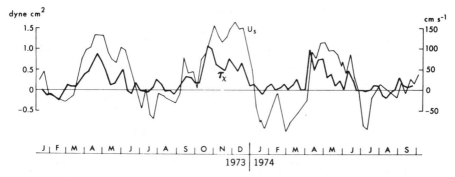

FIG. 2. The zonal velocity component at the surface and the zonal component of the wind stress as measured on the equator near Gan (70°E). [After Knox (1976).]

Here x and y measure distance in the eastward and northward (from the equator) directions; u and v denote the corresponding velocity components; t measures time and

$$f = \beta y, \qquad g' = [(\rho_2 - \rho_1)/\rho_2]g, \qquad C^2 = g'H \qquad (2.2)$$

The latitudinal derivative of the Coriolis parameter is β, and g is the gravitational acceleration. Reasonable numerical values are

$$(\rho_2 - \rho_1/\rho_2 = 0.002, \qquad H = 100 \text{ m}, \qquad h = 20 \text{ cm}, \qquad C = 140 \text{ cm/s}^{-1} \qquad (2.3)$$

Equations (2.1) can be reduced to a single equation

$$(V_{xx} + V_{yy})_t + \beta V_x - \frac{1}{C^2}V_{ttt} - \frac{f^2}{C^2}V_t = \frac{f}{C^2}\frac{\partial}{\partial t}\left(\frac{\tau^x}{H}\right) + \frac{\partial^2}{\partial_x \partial_y}\left(\frac{\tau^x}{H}\right) \qquad (2.4)$$

The motion induced by the sudden onset of spatially uniform zonal winds, which then remain steady, is initially independent of longitude provided that attention is confined to regions distant from the coasts. Far from the equator there is Ekman drift

$$V = -\tau^x/fH \qquad (2.5)$$

after an inertial period. If the winds are eastward then this motion at a right angle to the wind converges on the equator, implying that there is a distinctive equatorial region in which downwelling is intense. The width of this region can readily be inferred from a scale analysis of (2.4) and is the equatorial radius of deformation

$$\lambda = \sqrt{C/\beta} \sim 250 \quad \text{km} \qquad (2.6)$$

Since Eq. (2.1a) reduces to

$$U_t = \tau^x/H \qquad (2.7)$$

at the equator — recall that zonal variations are negligible — it follows that the equatorial zone is characterized by an accelerating jet in the direction of the wind. This jet is in geostrophic balance; its acceleration matches the steadily increasing latitudinal density gradient associated with the deepening of the equatorial thermocline caused by the convergent Ekman flow (Yoshida, 1959).

The motion described thus far is independent of longitude. To satisfy the boundary conditions at the meridional coasts $x = 0$ and L it is necessary to superimpose on the jet the free modes of oscillation of the ocean. Assume that the modes are of the form

$$v = V(y)e^{i(kx - \sigma t)}$$

then

$$V_{yy} + (\beta^2/C^2)(Y^2 - y^2)V = 0 \qquad (2.8)$$

where

$$Y^2 = [(\sigma^2/C^2) - k^2 - (\beta k/\sigma)](C^2/\beta^2)$$

Solutions to this equation are wavelike (oscillatory) in an equatorial zone of half-width Y, but are exponentially decaying poleward of latitudes $\pm Y$. In other words, wave propagation is possible only in an equatorial waveguide whose width Y has a maximum value

$$Y_{max}^2 = \sigma^2/\beta^2 + \beta^2/4\sigma^2 \qquad (2.9)$$

Figure 3 depicts this curve and shows that in extraequatorial latitudes inertia-gravity waves are separated from Rossby waves by a frequency band in which no free waves are possible. Near the equator there are waves at all frequencies.

An appropriate superposition of latitudinally propagating waves can form standing modes that are described by Hermite functions and whose dispersion relation is (Matsuno, 1966)

$$[(\sigma^2/C^2) - k^2 - (\beta k/\sigma)](C/\beta) = 2l + 1, \qquad l = 0,1,2, ... \qquad (2.10)$$

Particularly important in the oceanic adjustment are the low-frequency nondispersive Rossby modes with westward group velocities for which the dispersion relation (2.10) simplifies to

$$\sigma = -kC/(2l + 1), \qquad l = 1,2,3, ... \qquad (2.11)$$

The most rapid waves, associated with small values of l, are described by Hermite Functions of a low order and are strongly trapped about the equator. Those modes that extend into high latitudes are associated with large values of l, have low frequencies, and have small group velocities.

In addition to the waves described by the dispersion relation (2.10), there is a Kelvin wave that travels eastward nondispersively:

$$u = F(x - Ct) \exp(-y^2/2\lambda^2), \qquad v = 0 \qquad (2.12)$$

where F is an arbitrary function.

Let us return to the accelerating equatorial jet. It can be expressed in terms of the complete set of Hermite Functions that describe the natural modes of the ocean. These are the modes that ensure that the zonal velocity component vanishes at the coasts $x = 0$ and L. The modes excited at the western coast ($x = 0$) must have eastward group velocities. The short dispersive Rossby waves with this property play a negligible role in the oceanic adjustment. Of paramount importance is the Kelvin wave that, at $x = 0$, must have

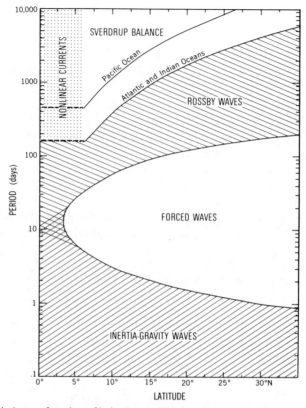

FIG. 3. Periods, as a function of latitude, at which inertia–gravity, Rossby, and no waves—in other words, only forced waves—are possible. At very long periods, which depend on the zonal extent of the basin, the equilibrium response to the wind is a Sverdrup balance except near the equator, where the currents are highly nonlinear.

a latitudinally integrated mass flux equal and opposite to that of the jet (Cane and Sarachik, 1976, 1977). This condition determines the function F in Eq. (2.12):

$$u^{\text{KELVIN}} = 0, \qquad\qquad\qquad\qquad\qquad \text{for} \quad t < x/C$$

$$u^{\text{KELVIN}} = \frac{0.84\tau^x}{C_\rho H}(x - Ct)\exp(-y^2/2\lambda^2), \qquad \text{for} \quad t > x/C$$

This equation describes a front, or bore, that is excited at the coast $x = 0$ at time $t = 0$ and that travels eastward at speed C. After it passes a point in the interior of the basin, the acceleration of the wind-driven jet, and the steady deepening of the thermocline, decreases abruptly. This happens because the Kelvin front introduces zonal gradients: in the momentum Equation (2.1a) for the conservation of mass, divergence of the zonal current now balances the meridional convergence. Figure 4 shows how dramatically the Kelvin wave front affects the flow.

The long nondispersive Rossby waves excited initially at the eastern coast $x = L$ travel westward at speeds $C/3$, $C/7$, $C/11$, . . . and have an effect on the flow similar to that of the Kelvin wave. The immediate neighborhood of the equator is influenced primarily by the most rapid wave ($l = 1$), which is also the most strongly trapped about the equator. This wave meets the Kelvin wave at $t = 3L/4C$, whereafter the equatorial jet starts to decelerate. Upon reaching the eastern coast the Kelvin wave front reflects partially as Rossby waves and partially as poleward travelling coastal Kelvin waves (Moore and Philander, 1977). The long Rossby waves, upon reaching the western coast, reflect as Kelvin and short Rossby waves. All these waves, and their further reflections, contribute to the oceanic adjustment, but from Fig. 5 it is evident that the adjustment within a radius of deformation of the equator is accomplished essentially in the time it takes a Kelvin wave to propagate eastward across the basin plus the time it takes the reflected Rossby wave to cross the basin, $L/C + 3L/C = 4L/C$ (Cane, 1979).

The Kelvin wave is confined to the narrow equatorial zone so that the oceanic adjustment outside this zone proceeds entirely from the eastern coast and is effected by Rossby waves. Far from the equator their speed is approximately $\beta C^2/f^2$ and at a given latitude the basin is in an adjusted state after a time $Lf^2/\beta C^2$ (Anderson and Gill, 1975). This time increases with increasing latitude and with an increase in the width of the ocean basin. Its value is shown in Fig. 3.

In an inviscid ocean the equilibrium response to spatially uniform zonal winds is a state of no motion with a zonal pressure that balances the winds: $\eta_x = \tau^x/C^2$. (In the absence of friction, oscillations about this state persist.) For mean currents to be present in the equilibrium state, processes that represent the mixing of heat must be taken into account (Yamagata and Philander, 1985). It is insufficient to include only the mixing of momentum. The dissipation attenuates the waves that effect the oceanic adjustment so that mean currents are present in the equilibrium state.

Winds that are confined to a band of longitudes can affect the ocean outside that band because of the waves that propagate away from the forced region (McCreary, 1976; Cane and Sarachik, 1976). Wind variations in the Pacific west of the dateline can alter oceanic conditions in the eastern Pacific. Ripa and Hayes (1981), Knox and Halpern (1982), and Eriksen et al. (1983) have observed the Kelvin waves excited by such wind changes.

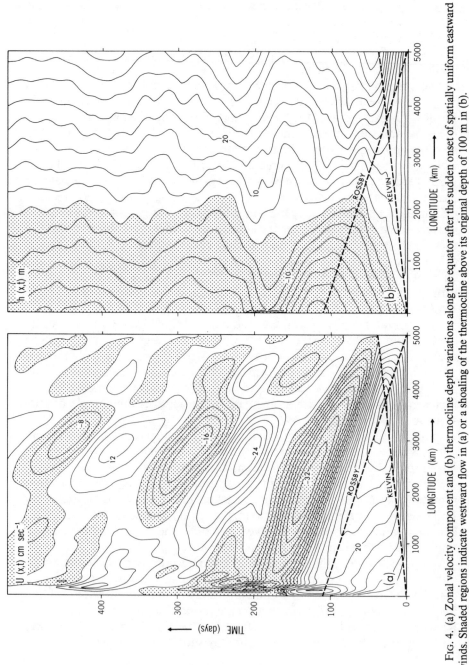

FIG. 4. (a) Zonal velocity component and (b) thermocline depth variations along the equator after the sudden onset of spatially uniform eastward winds. Shaded regions indicate westward flow in (a) or a shoaling of the thermocline above its original depth of 100 m in (b).

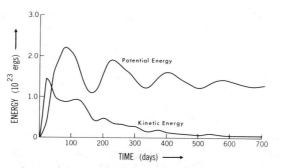

Fig. 5. Kinetic and potential energy in the band from 6°N to 6°S for the motion shown in Fig. 4.

The results described here suggest explanations for the measurements in Fig. 2. The initial acceleration of the jet probably stops when the passage of a Kelvin wave establishes zonal pressure gradients that balance the wind stress. The passage of a Rossby wave will cause a deceleration at a later stage. Measurements with drifting buoys in the eastern Indian Ocean do indeed seem to confirm this wave (Gonella *et al.,* 1981). In the central Indian Ocean, however, the deceleration can also be attributed to the relaxation of the eastward wind. If the winds turn off abruptly, the westward pressure force that the winds had maintained is unbalanced and accelerates the flow westward (Cane, 1980). Something similar happens in the Pacific Ocean when the westward trade winds, which normally maintain an eastward pressure force, relax. The unbalanced pressure force accelerates the equatorial currents eastward so that they transport warm water into the eastern Pacific (McCreary, 1976; Hurlburt *et al.,* 1976).

In general, wind fluctuations are not abrupt but are gradual. Suppose that the winds vary on a time scale long compared to the adjustment time of the ocean. The response will then be in equilibrium with the winds at all times. An example of such a response is the seasonal change in the zonal density gradient along the equator in the Atlantic that is practically in phase with the seasonally varying winds (Katz *et al.,* 1977). This suggests that the adjustment time for the equatorial Atlantic is less than the seasonal time scale, in agreement with the result in Fig. 3.

The shallow water model [Eq. (2.1)] is a powerful tool for studying the adjustment of tropical oceans. It is even capable of simulating, with reasonable success, observed sea-level fluctuations when forced with realistic winds (Busallacchi and O'Brien, 1981). (The sea level reflects changes in the depth of the thermocline.) The model has severe limitations, however, because of its simple vertical structure, and is incapable of coping with the Equatorial Undercurrent, for example.

3. The Equatorial Undercurrent

The Equatorial Undercurrent is a swift jet that flows eastward, just below the ocean surface, all along the equator. It extends vertically over a depth of 150 m approximately, is 300 km wide, and is continuous over a distance of more than 10,000 km in the Pacific Ocean and 5000 km in the Atlantic Ocean. The current is effectively a ribbon that marks the location of the equator. It disappears whenever the equatorial surface winds are eastward for a prolonged period — during the southwest monsoons in the Indian Ocean, and during the 1982–1983 El Niño event in the Pacific Ocean. This is consistent with the hypothesis that the Equatorial Undercurrent is driven by the eastward pressure force maintained by westward winds. The shallow-water model of Section 2, though it reproduces an eastward pressure force in response to westward winds, has too simple a vertical structure to simulate an undercurrent. Consider, therefore, a model that permits motion with a more complex vertical structure so that directly wind-driven currents are confined to a shallow surface layer, while currents at greater depths are driven by pressure gradients and by the divergence of the surface flow. In such a model the westward winds drive the surface layers at the equator westward while the deep geostrophic flow is equatorward in both hemispheres:

$$-fv + (1/\rho_0)P_x = 0 \qquad (3.1)$$

Near the equator the Coriolis parameter is vanishingly small and fails to balance the pressure force P_x, which therefore accelerates the convergent fluid eastward. The result is an Equatorial Undercurrent below the westward surface flow. The critical feature of this model, and of almost all models of the Undercurrent, is the difference between the vertical structure of the directly wind-driven surface currents and that of the zonal pressure force maintained by the wind. In Section 2, we found that waves excited at coasts establish the zonal density gradients. In a continuously stratified ocean these waves propagate horizontally and downward and can establish density gradients at depths greater than that of the wind-driven surface currents.

The horizontal structure of waves in a continuously stratified fluid is described by Eqs. (2.1) provided that the gravity wave speed C is regarded as a constant of separation that also appears in the equation for the vertical structure of the waves:

$$W_{zz} + (N^2/C^2)W = 0 \tag{3.2}$$

Here W is the vertical structure of the vertical velocity component—all variables are assumed to be separable—and N is the Brunt–Väisälä frequency of the fluid (Moore and Philander, 1977). Given the boundary conditions for the vertical velocity at the flat ocean floor and at the ocean surface, Eq. (3.2) yields an infinite number of eigenvalues C_n ($n = 0, 1, 2, \ldots$) and eigenfunctions W_n known as the baroclinic plus barotropic modes. For the barotropic mode the stratification of the ocean is unimportant: the horizontal currents are independent of depth and the gravity wave speed is $C_0 = (gH_0)^{1/2}$, where H_0 is the total depth of the ocean. For the baroclinic modes, C_n decreases as n increases. The small values of C_n—for the first mode $C_1 \sim 2.5$ m s^{-1}—reflect the very weak stratification of the ocean. The horizontal structure of each vertical mode is described by Eq. (2.1), where C assumes the appropriate eigenvalue. It follows that although each mode has the same waves, with the same dispersion relation, the wave speed is C, and the temporal scale and the spatial scale [which is the radius of deformation of Eq. (2.6)] are different for each mode.

The abrupt onset of zonal winds that act as a body force in a surface layer of depth H of a continuously stratified ocean drives meridional Ekman flow far from the equator and an accelerating zonal jet in an equatorial zone with $(ND/\beta)^{1/2}$. Here D is the depth of the thermocline. This motion is confined to the surface layers of the ocean and is very similar to the wind-driven jet described in Section 2. To satisfy boundary conditions at the coasts $x = 0$ and L waves are excited. The amplitudes of the waves are determined by projecting the wind-driven jet onto the vertical modes of the ocean and then onto the latitudinal modes associated with each vertical mode. As in the example discussed in Section 2, the most important waves for the adjustment are long nondispersive Rossby waves excited at the coast $x = L$, and Kelvin wave fronts excited at the coast $x = 0$. These waves introduce zonal density gradients in the surface layers and at greater depth. The existence of zonal pressure gradients below the surface layers permits the generation of an Equatorial Undercurrent as described earlier.

The adjustment of the upper layers of a stratified ocean is essentially the same as that of a shallow-water model (Section 2) because the first two modes, especially the second, accomplish most of the adjustment (Philander and Pacanowski, 1980). Hence, the time it takes for basinwide density gradients in the thermocline and the Equatorial Undercurrent to be established is approximately the time it takes a second-mode baroclinic Kelvin wave to propagate across the basin. For the Atlantic Ocean this is on the order of a

month. Below the equatorial thermocline, low-frequency motion corresponds to downward-propagating waves that travel at shallow angles to the
horizontal and give rise to zonal jets with short vertical scales (Luyten and
Swallow, 1976; McCreary, 1984).

4. THE SOMALI CURRENT

Shortly after the onset of the southwest monsoons over the western Indian
Ocean in May, an intense narrow jet — the Somali Current — appears along
the eastern coast of tropical Africa. The current has two branches: the southern one veers offshore near 4°N, where a wedge of cold surface waters
extends eastward; the northern one is part of a clockwise gyre between 4°N
and 10°N and is associated with intense upwelling, and hence cold surface
waters, near 10°N. Toward the end of August, the cold wedge near 4°N starts
to drift northward until it merges with the cold tongue near 10°N, at which
stage the Somali Current flows continuously along the northeast African
coast (Swallow *et al.,* 1983; Schott, 1983). The current disappears after the
onset of the northeast monsoons in November and is replaced by relatively
weak southward current. The clockwise gyre between 10°N and 4°N can,
however, persist below the ocean surface for a considerable time after the
onset of the northeast monsoons (Bruce, 1979).

The Somali Current is driven primarily by the winds parallel to the East
African coast. Along South America the winds are also parallel to the coast,
but there the wind-driven Peruvian Current is strikingly different from the
Somali Current. Whereas the Somali Current is narrow and intense — it can
reach speeds in excess of 2 m s^{-1} and its width is 0(100 km) — the Peruvian
Current is very broad [0(1000 km)] and is very slow [0(10 cm s^{-1})]. As it flows
toward the equator, this current gradually veers westward to feed the South
Equatorial Current (Fig. 1). It is associated with low sea-surface temperatures and is separated from the warm surface waters to the north of the
equator by a sharp front, along 3°N approximately. A numerical experiment
in which a model ocean is forced with spatially uniform northward winds
simulates many of the features of the Somali and Peruvian Currents and
confirms that, in spite of their differences, both of these currents are driven
primarily by the meridional component of the winds (Fig. 6).

Consider first the response of the oceanic interior — the region far from
coasts — to cross-equatorial (northward) winds. Near the surface, the motion is eastward in the northern hemisphere and westward in the southern
hemisphere. This Ekman drift, which intensifies with decreasing latitude
because the value of the Coriolis parameter decreases, attains its maximum
amplitude at a radius of deformation (~ 300 km) from the equator so that

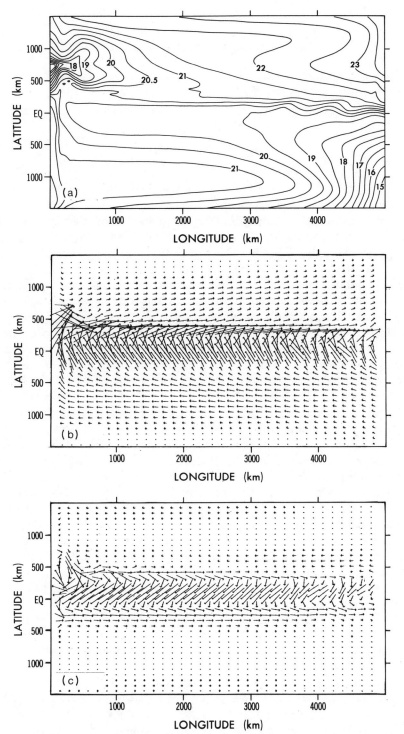

FIG. 6. Isotherms (°C) at a depth of 12.5 m (a) and horizontal velocity vectors at 12.5 m (b) and 62.5 m (c) in a multilevel primitive-equation oceanic model forced with spatially uniform northward winds that have persisted for 200 days, by which time the ocean is the equilibrium with the winds. [After Philander and Pacanowski (1981).]

there is an eastward jet near 3°N and a westward jet near 3°S. Equatorward of 3° latitude the Coriolis force fails to balance the wind stress τ^y and the meridional pressure gradient η_y becomes important (Moore and Philander, 1977):

$$fu + g\eta_y = \tau^y/H \qquad (4.1)$$

Nonlinearities advect the westward flow south of the equator into the northern hemisphere and intensify the eastward jet near 3°N (Cane, 1979) to such an extent that the latitudinal shear of the currents gives rise to unstable waves that are evident in the isotherms of Fig. 6 and in satellite photographs of the sea-surface temperature in the eastern tropical Pacific (Legeckis, 1977).

The oceanic response to northward winds is distinctive in a narrow zone along the meridional coasts of the basin. Motion in these coastal zones has many similarities with the motion driven by zonal winds near the equator. For example, winds parallel to a coast (or the equator) drive offshore (or meridional) Ekman flow, cause upwelling, and generate an accelerating coastal (or equatorial) jet whose width is the radius of deformation (Charney, 1955). If the winds are spatially uniform then coastal Kelvin waves, excited at the boundary of the force region, introduce alongshore variations. In particular, these waves introduce alongshore pressure gradients that balance the wind stress so that the acceleration of the jet stops and equilibrium conditions are established (Allen, 1976). This coastal jet is particularly intense near the equator along the western coast of a basin because it has to absorb the strong westward flow from the oceanic interior into the western coast near 3°S and transport it across the equator. Most of this fluid is lost to the eastward jet near 3°N, which can be so intense that the coastal jet practically separates from the coast near 3°N. Since the offshore flow near 3°N is strongly divergent while the onshore flow near 3°S is convergent, the cross-equatorial density gradient along the coast is associated with a pressure force in the direction of the wind. Dissipation is therefore important in the momentum balance of the coastal jet between 3°N and 3°S (Cox, 1976, 1979).

These results explain several features of the Somali Current, but not the northward drift of the southern tongue of cold water near 3°N, which, by late August, merges with the northern cold tongue near 10°N, where the winds parallel to the coast are exceptionally intense. The curl of the wind stress over the western part of the Indian Ocean appears to be responsible for this feature (Philander and Delecluse, 1983).

Along the eastern boundary of the ocean basin, the coastal current that transports water from 3°N (where there is an eastward jet) to 3°S (where there is a westward current) flows counter to the wind and is subsurface. (Its counterpart in the west is in the direction of the wind.) Long Rossby waves rapidly disperse the coastal features along the eastern boundary westward. (Short Rossby waves with small eastward group velocities are ineffective in dispersing phenomena along the western boundary of the basin eastward.) It is this difference in the properties of Rossby waves with eastward and westward group velocities that is principally responsible for the difference between the oceanic response to cross-equatorial winds along the eastern and western sides of an ocean basin. In Fig. 6 coastal features in the east are seen to disperse farther and farther westward the lower the latitude. The reason for this is the increase in long Rossby wave speed with decreasing latitude.

5. Discussion

This chapter describes how waves effect the adjustment of the ocean to a change in wind conditions. These waves propagate most rapidly near the equator so that the oceanic adjustment is the most rapid there. This result has important implications for models of the variability of the upper ocean. Over large parts of the subtropical oceans, one-dimensional models that take into account only the local fluxes of heat and momentum across the ocean surface are capable of realistic simulations of upper ocean variability and of sea-surface temperature changes on time scales of days to years. This is not true in the tropics, however, because there the rapid adjustment of the ocean implies that considerable amounts of heat can be redistributed horizontally in the upper oceans on time scales of weeks to months. This happens during El Niño, for example. It follows that models that take the three-dimensional structure of the tropical oceans into account are necessary to simulate its low-frequency variability. Fortunately, instabilities of the mean currents make only a secondary contribution to this variability, which is primarily forced by the wind and which can therefore be described deterministically. Models capable of simulating this variability are needed for studies of the interactions between the ocean and atmosphere and are now being developed.

Acknowledgments

I am indebted to Ms. J. Pege and Mr. P. Tunison for expert technical assistance in the preparation of this paper.

References

Allen, J. S. (1976). Some aspects of the forced wave response of stratified coastal regions. *J. Phys. Oceanogr.* **6,** 113–119.

Anderson, D. L. T., and Gill, A. E. (1975). Spin up of a stratified ocean with applications to upwelling. *Deep-Sea Res.* **22**, 583–596.

Bruce, J. G. (1979). Eddies off the Somali Coast during the Southwest Monsoon. *JGR, J. Geophys. Res.* **84**, 7742–7768.

Busalacchi, A. J., and O'Brien, J. J. (1981). Interannual variability of the equatorial Pacific in the 1960's. *JGR, J. Geophys. Res.* **86**, 10901–10907.

Cane, M. A. (1979). The response of an equatorial ocean to simple wind-stress patterns. I. Model formulation and analytic results. *J. Mar. Res.* **37**, 233–252.

Cane, M. A. (1980). On the dynamics of equatorial currents with application to the Indian Ocean. *Deep-Sea Res.* **27**, 525–544.

Cane, M. A., and Sarachik, E. S. (1976). Forced baroclinic ocean motions. I. *J. Mar. Res.* **34**(4), 629–665.

Cane, M. A., and Sarachik, E. S. (1977). Forced baroclinic ocean motions. II. *J. Mar. Res.* **35**, 395–432.

Cane, M. A., and Sarachik, E. S. (1983). Equatorial oceanography. *Rev. Geophys. Space Phys.* **21**, 1137–1148.

Charney, J. G. (1955). The generation of oceanic currents by winds. *J. Mar. Res.* **14**, 477–498.

Charney, J. G. (1960). Non-linear theory of a wind-driven homogeneous layer near the equator. *Deep-Sea Res.* **6**, 303–310.

Cox, M. D. (1976). Equatorially trapped waves and the generation of the Somali Current. *Deep-Sea Res.* **23**, 1139–1152.

Cox, M. D. (1979). A numerical study of Somali Current eddies. *J. Phys. Oceanogr.* **9**, 311–326.

Eriksen, C. C., Blumenthal, M. B., Hayes, S. P., and Ripa, P. (1983). Wind-generated equatorial Kelvin waves observed across the Pacific Ocean. *J. Phys. Oceanogr.* **13**, 1622–1640.

Firing, E., Lukas, R., Sades, J., and Wyrtki, K. (1983). Equatorial Undercurrent disappears during 1982–1983 El Niño. *Science* **222**, 1121–1123.

Garzoli, S. L., and Katz, E. J. (1983). The forced annual reversal of the Atlantic North Equatorial Countercurrent. *J. Phys. Oceanogr.* **13**, 2082–2090.

Gonella, J., Fieux, M., and Philander, G. (1981). Mise en évidence d'ondes Rossby équatoriales dans l'Océan Indian an moyen de bouées derivantes. *C. R. Hebd. Seances Acad. Sci., Ser. B* **292**, 1397–1399.

Halpern, D., Hayes, S., Leetmaa, A., Hansen, D., and Philander, G. (1983). Oceanographic observations of the 1982 warming of the tropical Pacific. *Science* **221**, 1173–1175.

Hurlburt, H. E., Kindle, J. C., and O'Brien, J. J. (1976). A numerical simulation of the onset of El Niño. *J. Phys. Oceanogr.* **6**, 621–631.

Katz, E., Belevitsch, R., Bruce, J., Bubnov, V., Cochrane, J., Duing, W., Hisard, P., de Mesquita, A., Miller, L., and Rybnikov, A. (1977). Zonal pressure gradient along the equatorial Atlantic. *J. Mar. Res.* **35**(2), 293–307.

Knauss, J. S. (1963). The Equatorial Current system. *In* "The Sea" Vol. 1 (M. N. Hill, ed.), Vol. 1, pp. 235–252. Wiley (Interscience), New York.

Knox, R. A. (1976). On a long series of measurements of Indian Ocean equatorial currents near Addu Atoll. *Deep-Sea Res.* **23**, 211–221.

Knox, R. A., and Anderson, D. (1985). Recent advances in the study of low latitude circulations. *Deep-Sea Res.* (in press).

Knox, R. A., and Halpern, D. (1982). Long range Kelvin wave propagation of transport variations in Pacific Ocean equatorial currents. *J. Mar. Res.* **40**, Suppl., 329–339.

Legeckis, R. (1977). Long waves in the eastern equatorial Pacific; a view from a geostationary satellite. *Science* **197**, 1177–1181.

Lighthill, M. J. (1969). Dynamic response of the Indian Ocean to the onset of the southwest monsoon. *Philos. Trans. R. Soc. London, Ser. A* **265**, 45–93.

Luyten, J., and Swallow, J. (1976). Equatorial Undercurrents. *Deep-Sea Res.* **23,** 1005–1007.
McCreary, J. P. (1976). Eastern tropical ocean response to changing wind systems with application to El Niño. *J. Phys. Oceanogr.* **6,** 632–645.
McCreary, J. P. (1984). Equatorial beams. *J. Mar. Res.* **42,** 395–430.
Matsuno, T. (1966). Quasi-geostrophic motions in equatorial areas. *J. Meteorol. Soc. Jpn.* **2,** 25–43.
Moore, D. W., and Philander, S. G. H. (1977). Modeling of the tropical oceanic circulation. *In* "The Sea" (M. N. Hill, ed.), Vol. 6, pp. 319–361. Wiley (Interscience), New York.
Philander, S. G. H., and Delecluse, P. (1983). Coastal currents in low latitudes (with application to the Somali and El Nino Currents). *Deep-Sea Res.* **30,** 887–902.
Philander, S. G. H., and Pacanowski, R. C. (1980). The generation of equatorial currents, *JGR, J. Geophys. Res.* **85,** 1123–1136.
Philander, S. G. H., and Pacanowski, R. C. (1981). The oceanic response to cross-equatorial winds (with application to coastal upwelling in low latitudes). *Tellus* **33,** 201–210.
Ripa, P., and Hayes, S. (1981). Evidence for equatorially trapped waves at the Galapagos Islands. *JGR, J. Geophys. Res.* **86,** 6509–6516.
Schott, F. (1983). Monsoon response of the Somali current and associated upwelling. *Prog. Oceanogr.* **12,** 357–381.
Sverdrup, H. U. (1947). Winddriven currents in a baroclinic ocean with application to the equatorial currents in the eastern Pacific. *Proc. Natl. Acad. Sci. U.S.A.* **33,** 318–326.
Swallow, J. C., Molinari, R. L., Bruce, J. G., Brown, O. B., and Evans, R. H. (1983). Development of near surface flow pattern and water mass distribution in the Somali Basin in response to the southwest monsoon of 1979. *J. Phys. Oceanogr.* **13,** 1398–1415.
Veronis, G., and Stommel, H. (1956). The action of variable wind-stress on a stratified ocean. *J. Mar. Res.* **15,** 43–69.
Wyrtki, K. (1973). An equatorial jet in the Indian Ocean. *Science* **181,** 262–264.
Yamagata, J., and Philander, S. G. H. (1985). The role of damped equatorial waves in the oceanic response to winds. *J. Oceanogr. Soc. Jpn.* (in press).
Yoshida, K. (1959). A theory of the Cromwell Current and equatorial upwelling. *J. Oceanogr. Soc. Jpn.* **15,** 154–170.

SIMULATION OF MESOSCALE OCEAN VARIABILITY IN MID-LATITUDE GYRES

WILLIAM R. HOLLAND

National Center for Atmospheric Research
Boulder, Colorado

1. INTRODUCTION

Over the course of the past three decades, oceanographers and meteorologists have made great progress in developing an understanding of large-scale oceanic and atmospheric phenomena. This progress has resulted from a balanced scientific approach that has involved better and better observational descriptions of the large-scale circulations in both media as well as more and more sophisticated models of these flows.

The meteorologists have always been relatively rich in observations: a good description of the atmospheric general circulation exists. The oceanographers, however, due to the very much greater difficulty in observing the interior of the ocean, have had to make do with very sketchy descriptions of behavior. This has led to models being used in somewhat different ways. The atmospheric scientist could attempt to "simulate" developing atmospheric flows and check the prediction against reality. They could also make use of models to study idealized circumstances in order to delve into basic dynamical questions without constraining themselves to realistic simulations. This combination of predictive and theoretical studies has played an important part in understanding the atmosphere.

The oceanographer has for the most part had to use the second of these approaches. Large-scale temperature and salinity fields, as well as the quasi-steady three-dimensional distributions of other properties, have been constructed by observational oceanographers for more than half a century. The broadbrush picture of the major water masses of the World Ocean is well in

ADVANCES IN GEOPHYSICS, VOLUME 28A

hand. However, an understanding of the underlying dynamical reasons for these distributions has not been reached. This is because the velocity field, in contrast with the property distributions, is not only hard to measure but is highly time dependent. Only by use of sophisticated models, in conjunction with broadbrush observations, can we hope to eventually reach a level of understanding at all commensurate with the atmospheric dynamicist.

It is convenient for some purposes to think of the ocean as being quasi-steady. Although we now recognize that the circulation is often strongly turbulent, steady-state models that attempt to explain the nearly permanent property distributions are an important component of any modeling strategy. In such a model the effects of eddies have to be "parameterized" in terms of mean-flow quantities in order to close the mathematical problem.

An alternative approach is to explicitly include eddy motions, at least on some space and time scales. Such models require much greater horizontal resolution to take into account the instability properties of the larger-scale circulation, which gives rise to mesoscale eddies on the spatial scale of the Rossby radius of deformation. In the oceanic context this means resolutions of 20 km or even finer are required. This is the fundamental trade-off between eddy and noneddy models.

Time-dependent forcing at the surface of the ocean by both wind and thermohaline components (e.g., seasonal effects) may be needed to satisfactorily explain broad-scale water mass properties in either of these kinds of models. Thus the oceanographer has had to think in terms of a hierarchy of models from steady-state ones through transiently forced (but laminar) ones up to fully turbulent ones. The first completely parameterizes eddies, the second includes forced transients only, and the third includes internally generated eddies (quasi-geostrophic turbulence) as well. Each allows a focus on different fundamental aspects of the problem and each requires a different array of data to test conclusions and pass judgment on the degree of realism in its behavior.

It is worth discussing what is meant by "the general circulation of the ocean." The term general circulation, applied to the atmosphere, is defined by the "Glossary of Meteorology" to mean "the complete statistical description of atmospheric motions over the earth." The Glossary goes on to point out that "these statistics include not only the temporal and spatial *mean* conditions but also higher-order statistics that measure the spatial and temporal *variability* of the flow." This concept lays emphasis on the fact that we may observe and model components of the circulation even though we cannot possibly encompass all of the time and space scales in any description. It is clear that we can study only a restricted subset of the actual flows and that the atmosphere and oceans might best be described for some purposes in terms of their time and space statistics. That is, if in some idealized world (for example, the computer) a complete description were known for the velocity $v = v(x,t)$ and density $\rho = \rho(x, t)$, then all statistical moments could theoretically be calculated. However, a summary description of reduced complexity that would be achievable observationally might involve time averaging (in the atmosphere both time and zonal averaging are useful) that allows one to define certain basic observed statistical properties—$[v]$, $[\rho]$, $[v'^2]$, etc. Here, in the oceanic context, the brackets are meant to imply time averages. These would provide a basis for testing models, not in a "prediction" mode (because adequate ocean data do not yet exist), but in a "statistical" mode (for which the long-term means—$[v]$, $[T]$, $[S]$, and certain statistics such as $[T'^2]$ and eddy kinetic energy $[u'^2 + v'^2]/2$—could be tested against observations). For the past several years this has been the goal of modelers looking at mesoscale eddy problems in mid-latitude gyre scale circulation models. A discussion of this work and a forecast of its future are the aims of this chapter.

2. The Observations

During the past decade the physical oceanographic community has carried out extensive observational programs to examine the nature of the eddy field and related mean circulation in mid-latitude ocean basins. This work has involved new analyses of older data, such as the extensive temperature and salinity data available in world data centers, as well as the collection of new observations by new kinds of instruments and observing systems. Analyses of these data to look specifically at the variability in the ocean has been extraordinarily fruitful, and the broadbrush geography of this variability has begun to emerge, at least in those regions (the North Atlantic, North Pacific, and parts of the Circumpolar Current) in which the oceanographic community has focused its efforts.

Let us illustrate the basic nature of the problem by examining two maps of the North Atlantic prepared by Dantzler (1977). Figure 1a shows the region of the main subtropical gyre in terms of the time-averaged depth of the 15°C isotherm based on the approximately 60,000 XBT records available to Dantzler in the mid-seventies. The well-known features of the gyre are apparent, including the thermal front of the Gulf Stream as a western boundary current and its eastward extension and a broad Sverdrupian flow that closes the clockwise circulation on the east and south. It is this kind of large-scale mean circulation that theoreticians have traditionally tried to reproduce with their models.

Figure 1b shows the variability of this same surface in terms of the rms depth displacement of the 15°C isotherm. This kind of construction shows a

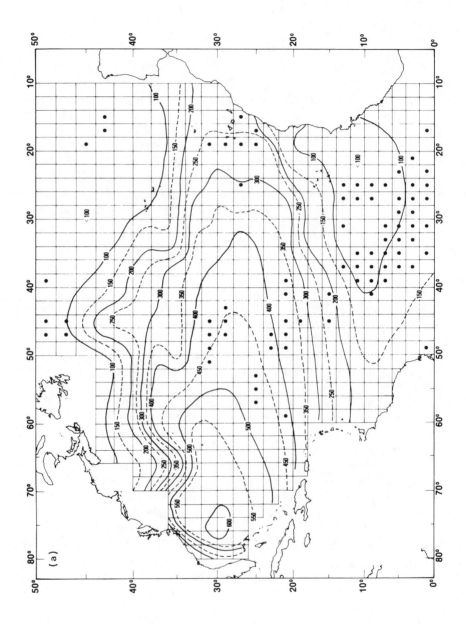

(a)

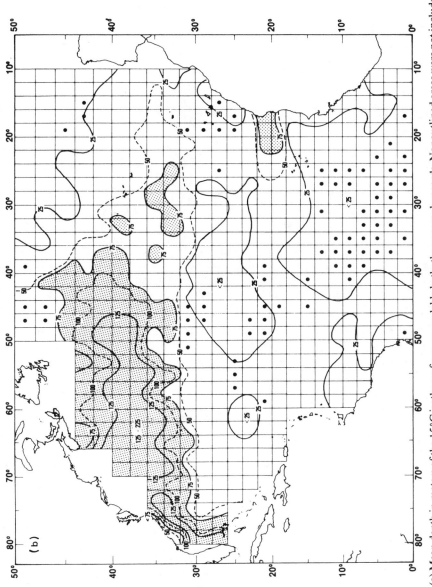

FIG. 1. (a) Mean depth in meters of the 15°C isotherm from expendable bathythermograph records. Nonoutlined areas were not included in the study. [====, isobaths (m); ●, fewer than four observations.] (b) Root-mean-square displacement in meters from the mean depth of the 15°C isotherm. Contour interval is 25 m rms [====, isopleths of constant rms displacement (m); ●, fewer than four observations.] [From Dantzler (1977). Reproduced with permission from *Journal of Physical Oceanography*, a publication of the American Meteorological Society.]

483

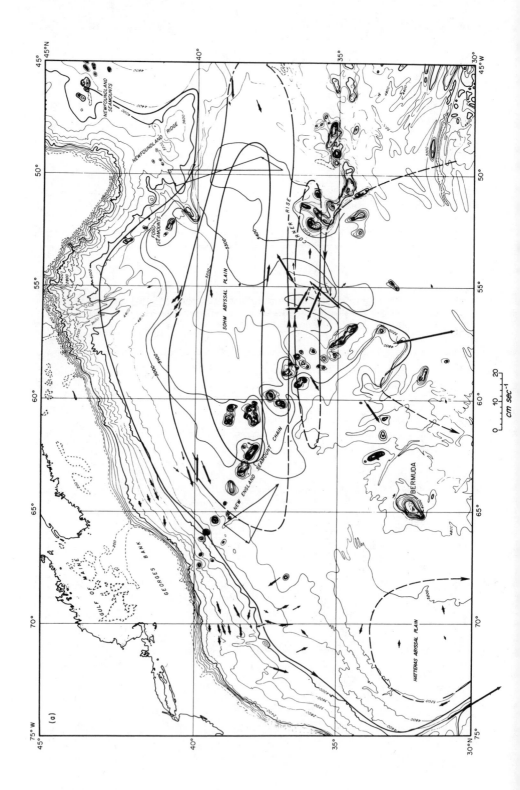

(a)

cm sec⁻¹

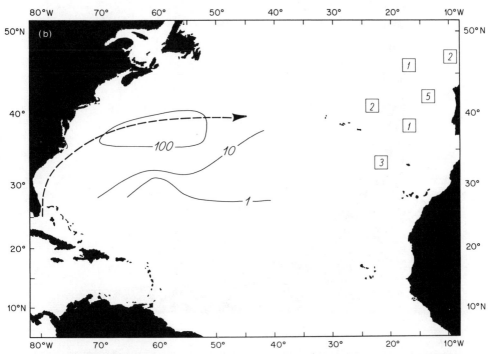

FIG. 2. (a) Suggested scheme for the deep circulation in the Western North Atlantic (on opposite page). Each contour is about 10×10^6 m^3 s^{-1}. Dashed parts are meant to suggest less certainty. [From Hogg (1983). *Deep-Sea Research* **30,** A note on the deep circulation of the western North Atlantic: Its nature and causes. Reprinted with permission. Copyright 1983 Pergamon Press, Ltd.] (b) Order of magnitude contours of abyssal eddy kinetic energy (in centimeters squared per second squared). [From Schmitz (1984).] The heavy dashed line is the locus of maximum kinetic energy for the time-averaged flow at the sea surface, as taken from Fig. 6 in Wyrtki *et al.* (1976).

different aspect of the "oceanic general circulation" in this region. Here the focus is on the transient character of the flow and, by comparison with the "mean flow" suggested by Fig. 1a, the relationship of one to the other. Here we see the broad outlines of the horizontal structure of the variability field, at least for this particular field. It reveals the very high variability of the Gulf Stream region and very much lower variability south of 30°N and east of 40°W. The region of maximum rms displacements around 38°N latitude extends from the western boundary far to the east.

Even though this early attempt could show only the broadest of relationships between mean and eddy fields, it illustrates the new perspective that has been at the heart of gyre scale eddy-resolved ocean circulation modeling — the ocean circulation as being describable in terms of mean quantities plus

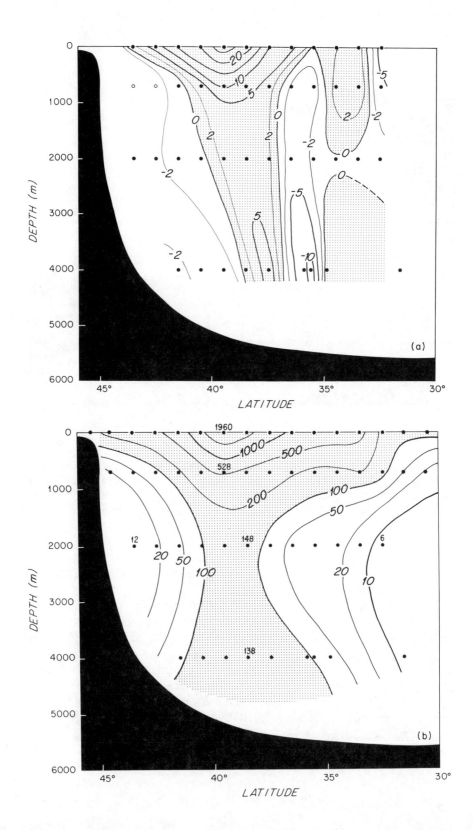

statistical moments of various kinds. The modeler thus has a whole host of descriptors of the general circulation to try to simulate and, if successful, a whole new set of dynamical problems concerned with eddy–mean-flow interaction to unravel.

Since the mid-seventies when several analyses of this kind were carried out [e.g., Wyrtki *et al.* (1976), Dantzler (1976), Bernstein and White (1977)], new observations have been made that describe the nature of mean and eddy signatures of the large-scale circulation. These involve many kinds of instrumentation — current meters, surface and SOFAR floats, satellite observations, XBT measurements from ships of opportunity, as well as standard hydrography from oceanographic ships. The particular focus of many of these programs has varied, but all have contributed strongly to the description of the circulation as a more or less turbulent system, with the variability being as important a consideration for many purposes as the time-averaged flow itself. Schmitz *et al.* (1983) give a complete review of these attempts to map mesoscale variability in mid-latitude oceans, and the volume "Eddies in Marine Science" surveys these results (Robinson, 1984).

Figures 2–4 show several examples of eddy and mean-flow "geography." The first of these, Fig. 2a, shows a construction of deep mean currents based on mooring data in the western North Atlantic (Hogg, 1983). The data are still rather sparse but the large-scale pattern of the deep horizontal mean currents is beginning to emerge. Fig. 2b shows the deep eddy kinetic energy field in the North Atlantic basin based on long-term current meter mooring data (Schmitz, 1984). Maximum eddy kinetic energies (at 4000 m) are found under the eastward extension of the Gulf Stream. The eddy energy levels vary by two orders of magnitude over the subtropical gyre, forming a clear pattern related to Gulf Stream instabilities and penetration into the interior.

Figure 3 shows constructions based on a mix of different instruments (surface drifters, SOFAR floats, current meter data) of the vertical structure of mean zonal velocity and eddy kinetic energy along 55°W (Richardson, 1983, 1984). These sections show for the first time the vertical and horizontal structure of eddy kinetic energy and the related zonal flow at a single longitude.

FIG. 3. (a) Contoured mean zonal velocity section (centimeters per second) along 55°W and through the Gulf Stream from drifters, floats, and current meters. Eastward velocity is shaded. Dots indicate centers of boxes used in calculating velocity except at 4000 m, where they show current meter locations. The bottom profile is from 55°W; the average bottom profile between 50–60°W is shifted southward from this by about one degree in latitude. [From Richardson (1985).] (b) Contoured section along 55°W of eddy kinetic energy (per unit mass). High eddy kinetic energy and its gradient coincide with the deep mean Gulf Stream and bounding countercurrents. [From Richardson (1983). Reproduced with permission from *JGR, Journal of Geophysical Research* **88**, 2705–2709, copyright by the American Geophysical Union.]

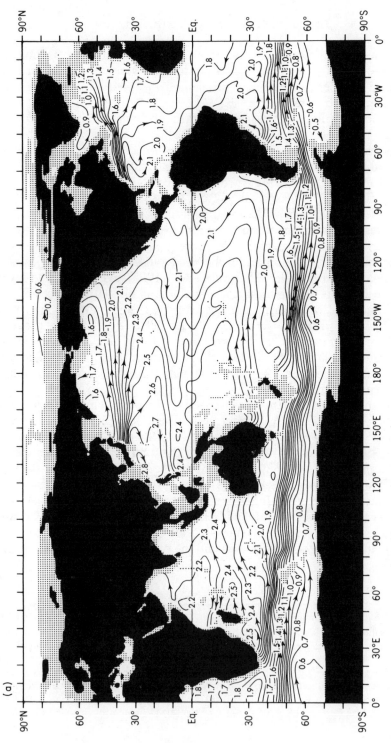

(a)

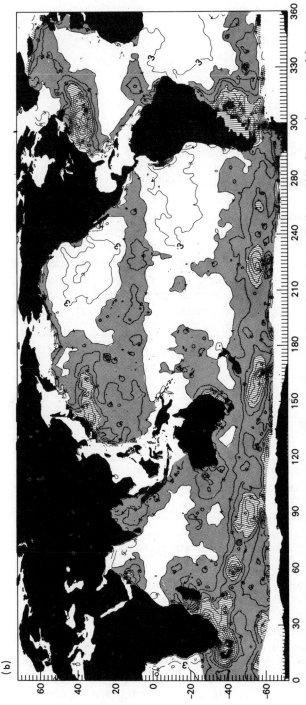

FIG. 4. (a) Global dynamic topography relative to 2000 dbar determined from historical data (Levitus, 1982). Contour in geopotential meters (m² s⁻²) describe the major surface circulation patterns. Comparison with Fig. 4b shows high correlation between intense flow and mesoscale sea-height variability. (b) Global mesoscale sea-height variability measured by the SEASAT altimeter, September 15 to October 10, 1978. The North Atlantic and North Pacific are dominated by the highly energetic Gulf Stream and Kuroshio systems that extend seaward nearly 4000 km. In the Southern Hemisphere the Agulhas Current below Africa and the Falkland/Brazil Current confluence off South America are clearly apparent. High variability due to the Antarctic Circumpolar Current extends in a nearly continuous band around the polar oceans, with isolated maxima coinciding with major topographic ridges and plateaus. Owing to the predominance of values less than 4 cm in mid-ocean, the north equatorial current systems in both the Atlantic and Pacific can be seen as zonal bands of higher variability. (White areas, 0–4 cm; stippling, 4–7 cm; cross hatching, >7 cm.) [From Cheney *et al.* (1983). Reproduced with permission from *JGR, Journal of Geophysical Research* **88**, 4343–4354, published by the American Geophysical Union.]

Finally, Fig. 4 shows the global structure of sea-surface height and its variability. Since the geoid is as yet not well known enough to allow satellite altimeters to determine the mean sea-surface height field, we cannot show such a map. However, constructions based on a level of no motion hypothesis and the time-averaged density field, such as that in Fig. 4a (Levitus, 1982), have long been used by oceanographers to represent sea-surface topography. Figure 4b shows the global variability of sea-surface height based on the SEASAT satellite altimeter (Cheney *et al.*, 1983). Even though the time series on which this world map is based is very short, virtually all of the eddy-rich areas stand out and their relationship to the mean field is established. Future satellites can be expected to much better define these areas and to allow one to examine secular change, space and time spectra, and other aspects of sea-surface height variability in the global ocean.

These different kinds of data (horizontal maps and vertical sections; temperature, horizontal velocity, sea-surface heights; etc.) illustrate the novel perspectives being gained about the ocean circulation and its variability. Each of these quantities describes a different aspect of the circulation and will test different ideas or model results concerning the dynamical causes and interrelationships involved in establishing these patterns.

3. EDDY-RESOLVED OCEAN MODELS

Numerical models capable of reproducing the internal instability processes responsible for much of the eddy variability in mid-latitude gyres have only recently evolved. The first numerical experiments of this kind were carried out by Holland and Lin (1975a,b). Other studies soon followed, stimulated by the observations found during the MODE Experiment and intending to examine the eddy–mean-flow interactions in closed gyres (Semtner and Mintz, 1977; Robinson *et al.*, 1977; Holland, 1978; Semtner and Holland, 1978). These studies suggested some of the possible mechanisms and some of the kinds of behavior to be found in eddying oceans. Here we will not review these studies; this has been done in several places (Holland *et al.*, 1983; Schmitz *et al.*, 1983). Instead, we will look at more recent and largely unpublished work that focuses on the comparison of model results with observations and makes use of these comparisons to extend the calculations to address the most relevant dynamical questions. This means focusing on the discrepancies in the model calculations as well as the successes in order to determine the extent to which the particular numerical experiments are relevant to actual ocean gyres.

3.1. Two-Layer Experiments

Let us first examine a calculation using a two-level quasi-geostrophic model for an ocean basin that is 4000 km square. It has simple sinusoidal wind forcing that drives two gyres of circulation. This was one of the numerical experiments in Holland (1978), the one that Schmitz and Holland (1982) compared with observations from the deep North Atlantic.

Figure 5a shows the time-averaged stream function for the flow in the

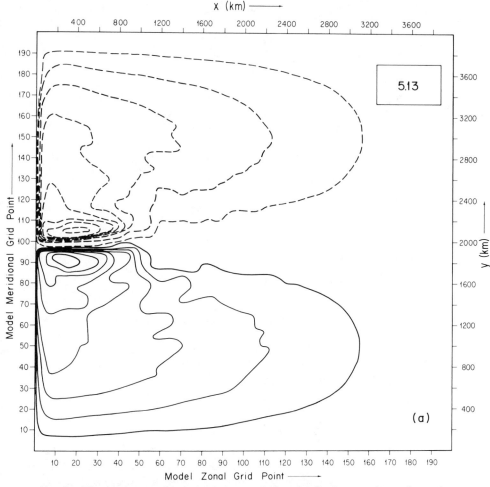

FIG. 5a. The time-averaged mass transport stream function for the upper layer of a two-layer numerical experiment (13) driven by a simple cosine wind stress. The basin is 4000 km square and the layers are 1000 m (upper) and 4000 m (lower) in thickness. Solid lines indicate clockwise circulation, dashed lines counterclockwise circulation. About 30×10^6 m^3 s^{-1} circulate around each surface gyre.

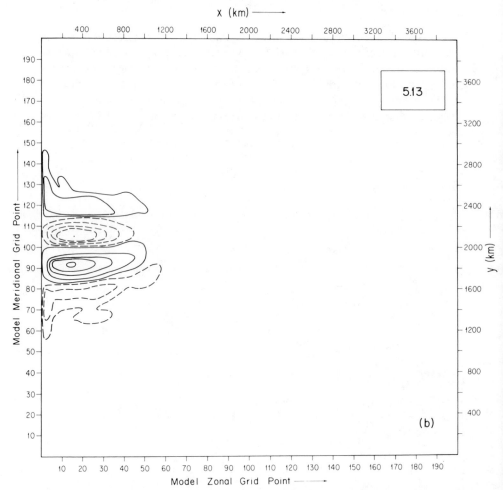

FIG. 5b. The time-averaged mass transport stream function for the lower layer of experiment 13. Maximum velocities in the eastward jet at 10 cm s^{-1}; the deep clockwise gyre transports 25×10^6 m^3 s^{-1} in the recirculation region.

upper layer. The southern half of this domain is intended to be a simple analogue to the North Atlantic subtropical gyre in its wind forcing amplitude and domain size. In addition there exists a second gyre on the north that is not realistic but is convenient for producing a Gulf Stream-like jet that extends eastward into the interior. This kind of calculation is carried out by turning on the wind stress (driving the upper layer) at time = 0; the ocean spins up from rest, eventually reaching a statistical equilibrium. The following analyses are based on a 5-year time series saved during this equilibrium stage.

Although meandering strongly in its instantaneous state, the mean east-ward Gulf Stream jet that results forms a thin northern wall for the subtropical gyre. Later we shall see some pictures of transient flows, but here we shall look only at time-averaged states. A large part of the gyre structure at the sea surface is dictated by the curl of the wind stress—a simple Sverdrup flow

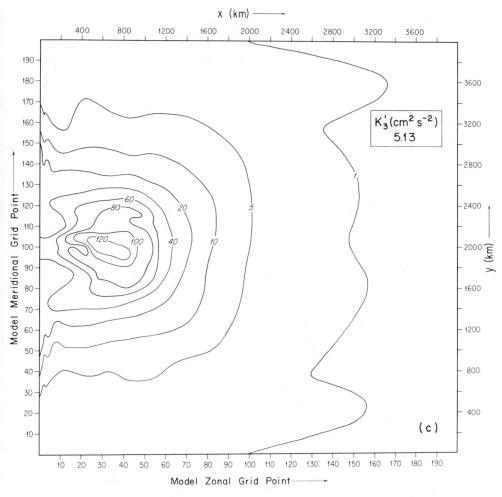

FIG. 5c. The pattern of abyssal eddy kinetic energy (selected contours as shown). The maximum eddy energy (per unit mass) is 125 cm^2 s^{-2} found under the intense surface Gulf Stream jet.

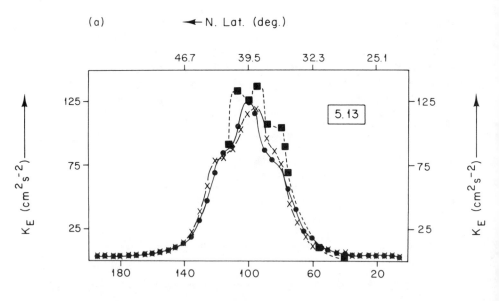

Fig. 6a. Abyssal kinetic energies (K_E, cm² s⁻²) as a function of model meridional grid point and observed latitude: solid squares denote data along 55°W; dots are used for model run 13 results 600 km from the western boundary; Xs for results 800 km from the western boundary.

exists in much of the interior. But it is modified enormously in the region of the Gulf Stream by eddy–mean-flow interactions and by inertial recirculation. [See Holland and Rhines (1980) and Harrison and Holland (1981) for a more complete discussion of eddy effects in various parts of a smaller basin case.]

The time-averaged stream function in the lower layer is shown in Fig. 5b. Under the surface Gulf Stream there exists an eastward flow of about 10 cm s⁻¹ and, fairly tightly confined to it, a return (westward) flow on both sides. There is a hint of a somewhat weaker gyre farther north and south of this. This quasi-geostrophic model has no built-in frictional mechanisms (vertical friction) to couple layers together. The only way in which the deep ocean is driven is by the eddies from above. In fact, for cases with strong enough lateral friction such that a steady state is reached, the flow is entirely confined to the upper layer; the lower layers are motionless. Only the presence of eddies can cause a downward transfer of zonal momentum and energy associated with the eddy processes that drive these deep jets (Holland and Rhines, 1980).

Finally, let us look at a picture of eddy kinetic energy in the deep ocean in order to see something of the flavor of this particular statistic (Fig. 5c). In this simple model maximum eddy kinetic energies of 120 cm² s⁻² are found, much like the maximum amplitudes found under the Gulf Stream (Schmitz, 1976). The high-energy regions correspond roughly to the region of significant mean flows, especially in terms of the scale of eastward penetration into the ocean interior. We shall return to this point later.

Let us now focus on this geographical structure of variability and the associated mean flows much in the spirit of the observations presented in Section 2 in order to compare these spatial distributions. Schmitz and Hol-

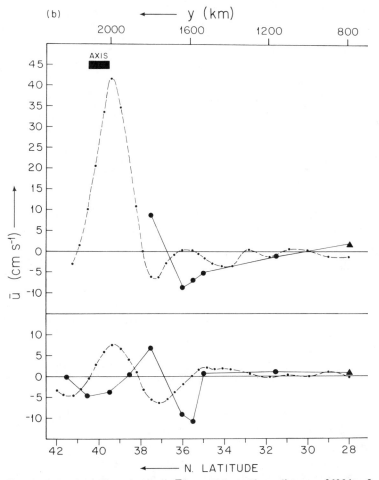

FIG. 6b. Mean zonal velocity component $\bar{u}$ for model run 13 at a distance of 600 km from the west coast, along with observations along 55°W. The model latitude y origin has been chosen (approximately) to line up with the axis of the Gulf Stream at the southern end of its observed range. (●——●, data; ·– –·, 5.13; top, upper layer; bottom, lower layer.)

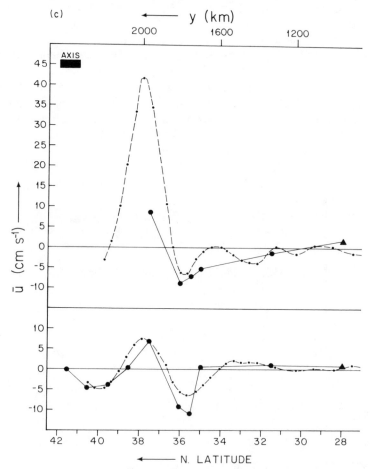

FIG. 6c. Mean zonal velocity component $\bar{u}$ for model run 13 at a distance of 600 km from the west coast, along with observations along 55°W. The model latitude y origin has been arbitrarily chosen to maximize (approximately) the similarity with data. The bar labeled axis denotes the observed climatological range for the Gulf Stream (●——●, data; ·− −·, 5.13; top, upper layer; bottom, lower layer.)

land (1982) took the highly idealized experiment shown in Fig. 5 to compare with observations based on long-term current meter mooring data from the Western North Atlantic. The reader is referred to that paper for details of the comparison. Basically, they found that while the meridional structure of eddy kinetic energy and of the mean zonal flows indicated in Fig. 5b,c were quite realistic in some respects, the zonal penetration scale of both the eddy and mean patterns was much too restricted in the model to the vicinity of the western boundary. This is most clearly seen by comparing the zonal and meridional scales apparent in Figs. 2a,b and 5b,c (note the domain size in Fig. 5 is 4000 km on a side).

Schmitz and Holland (1982) make their case using several perspectives. Here we summarize the results in Fig. 6. Figure 6a shows observations and several model meridional sections of deep eddy kinetic energy. Amplitude and structure are reasonably good, at least for the sections chosen. (The model sections are all from the extreme western side of the basin, through the intense part of the meandering eastward jet.) Figure 6b,c shows two perspectives on the mean zonal currents along 55°W and from a model section only a few hundred kilometers from the western side of the basin. Again amplitude and meridional structure show some interesting correspondences between model and data. The eastward jet and westward recirculation are reproduced by the model, but an interesting offset between the historical axis of the surface Gulf Stream and the observed deep eastward flow is highlighted as an important property of the North Atlantic at 55°W since the model results show no such offset. The model is, of course, very simple, but this point illustrates one of the main purposes of this kind of intercomparison — to identify those basic features of the observed flow not found in the calculations and then to investigate what is missing from the

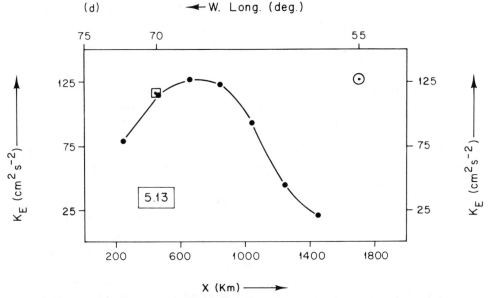

FIG. 6d. Maximum abyssal eddy kinetic energy (K_E) (in centimeters squared per second squared), near the Gulf Stream as a function of zonal coordinate for model run 13 plotted with solid dots connected by lines. 70°W data are denoted by an open square and 55°W data by an open circle surrounding small dots. [From Schmitz and Holland (1982).]

model that might be responsible. This is one way that models can be used to isolate the important dynamical processes and balances occurring in the ocean. Figure 6d illustrates the fundamental discrepancy identified by Schmitz and Holland (1982) for the calculation of Fig. 5 — the lack of a sufficient penetration scale for the eddy field (and as already suggested the mean currents as well). The model eddy energy along the course of the eastward jet reaches similar amplitudes near the western side of the basin, but falls off much too rapidly toward the east.

Holland and Schmitz (1985) have been investigating this penetration-scale question in a number of different kinds of numerical experiments. The basic question is what sets the penetration scale in these simple oceans? Figures 7–9 show results from several numerical experiments that give a clue to what establishes this characteristic of the experiments. The upper diagrams in each figure are mean upper- and lower-layer stream function, while the lower diagrams are eddy kinetic energy in the upper and lower layers. Figure 7 shows these fields, redrawn and scaled somewhat differently, for the experiment shown in Fig. 5 (call this experiment 13). Figures 8 and 9 show similar fields from two auxiliary experiments (25 and 28), the first with the lateral friction coefficient increased from that in case 13 (in this case "biharmonic" friction is used and the case 25 coefficient is 10 times larger than that of case 13) and the second with a uniform bottom topographic slope (shoaling northward at the rate of 1.7 m km^{-1} in the lower layer of the model). All other parameters have been kept the same as those in 13. The obvious result that stands out in these figures is that the eastward penetration scale has been increased markedly in experiments 25 and 28 over that in 13 for all the fields, that is, for both mean and eddy quantities. The latter two experiments are much more Atlantic-like in this respect than is 13. Note the rather counterintuitive result that increased friction leads to greater eastward penetration!

Energetic and other analyses show what has happened here (Holland and Schmitz, 1985). Both enhanced lateral friction and northward shoaling topography tend to stabilize the flow somewhat (linear analysis would suggest this). The eddies, which are the basic brake on the mean circulation, have reduced ability to counter the inertial tendency for overshoot of the kind investigated by Veronis (1966), and the mean jets extend eastward. There is thus a subtle balance between the instability processes that tend to tear the jet apart (i.e., restrict its penetration) and another tendency for inertial processes to carry the stream right across the basin. The interesting thing is that this stabilizing tendency does not change the eddy energies very much; the amplitudes are nearly as big in experiments 25 and 28 as they were in 13, but the eddy patterns are filling out a much bigger part of the domain.

These results suggest that anything that changes the nature of the instability of the thin Gulf Stream jet will alter the penetration scale for the Gulf Stream. In these models this means not only changing physical parameters and including new or different physics, but also changing such things as vertical resolution of the model. Schmitz and Holland (1982) suggested the need for enhanced vertical resolution to give a proper penetration, but it is now clear that all stabilizing/destabilizing effects conspire together to give a particular result as far as penetration. Holland and Schmitz (1985) discuss the two-layer situation in some detail, but as we shall see in the following section, the inclusion of more layers in the vertical not only changes the nature of the penetration aspect of the solutions, but also introduces some new physical behavior not found in two layers.

3.2. Three-Layer Experiments

As mentioned earlier, Schmitz and Holland (1982) suggested that higher-vertical-resolution experiments might lead to a more realistic penetration scale. At the time of their work, only a few three-layer experiments had been run. Now, however, many such cases have been examined and rather exciting new results found (Holland, 1985a,b). The penetration aspect of these experiments is one interesting focus of that work, but much more important, (1) multiple source regions for eddies are found, and (2) vast regions of the interior ocean become homogenized in terms of the potential vorticity distributions. While the details of these findings may be found in Holland (1985a,b) and in Holland *et al.* (1984), here we shall examine the essence of these results by looking at a single three-layer quasi-geostrophic experiment.

The interested reader is directed to the preceding papers for a complete discussion of the quasi-geostrophic equations and the detailed dynamical reasons for the behavior found in these experiments. Here, let us simply examine a sequence of pictures from a three-layer numerical experiment that has a single gyre of steady wind forcing. The wind has a simple cosine dependence to give a wind curl over a certain range of latitudes and then constant wind stress on the north and south flanks. This will produce a simple gyre of circulation in the interior of the ocean much like a subtropical ocean gyre with no subpolar gyre to its north. In any case, this forms a Gulf Stream that meanders eastward as shown in Fig. 10. Both instantaneous and mean pictures of the stream function are shown.

There are some new things happening here. First, the whole southern flank of the subtropical gyre also is unstable now (Holland, 1985b). It is baroclinically unstable, the waves propagating westward with typical space and time scales for a mesoscale eddy field. As shown by energetic analyses, this eddy field derives its energy from the potential energy stored in the bowl shape of

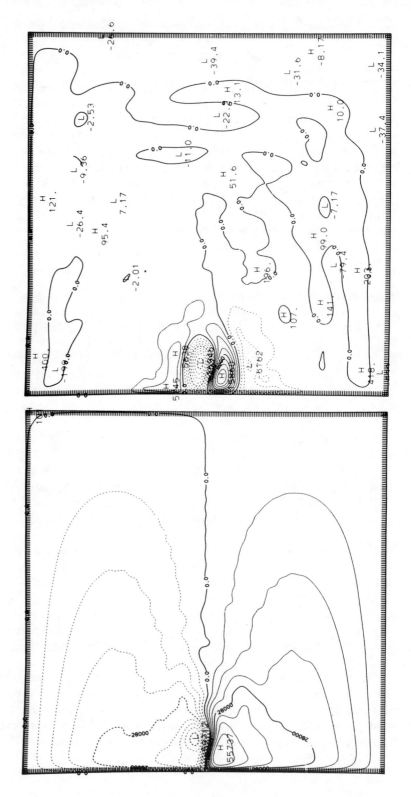

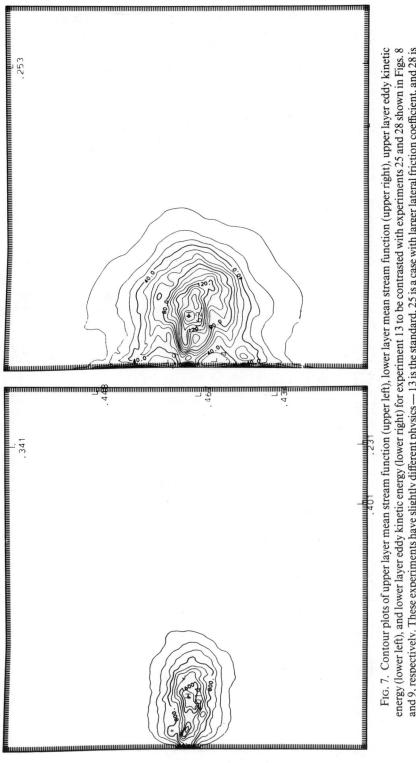

FIG. 7. Contour plots of upper layer mean stream function (upper left), lower layer mean stream function (upper right), upper layer eddy kinetic energy (lower left), and lower layer eddy kinetic energy (lower right) for experiment 13 to be contrasted with experiments 25 and 28 shown in Figs. 8 and 9, respectively. These experiments have slightly different physics — 13 is the standard, 25 is a case with larger lateral friction coefficient, and 28 is a case with a gently sloping bottom topography that shoals from south to north. Note the greater eastward penetration of mean jet and eddy energy in the latter two cases. The maximum eddy energies in the regions of instability are 2000 cm^2 s^{-2} (upper layer) and 125 cm^2 s^{-2} (lower layer) for case 13.

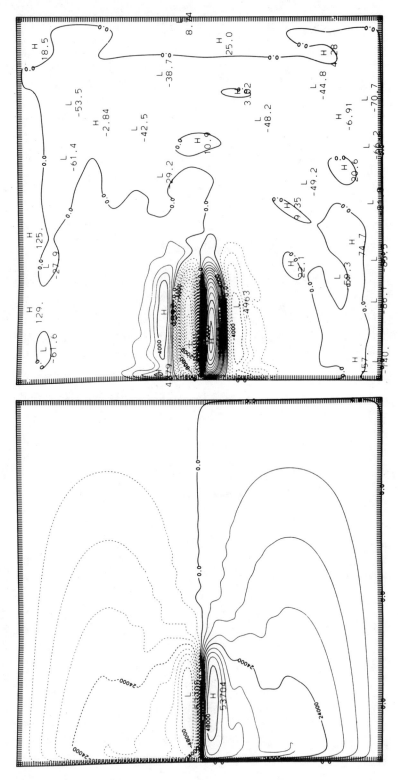

502

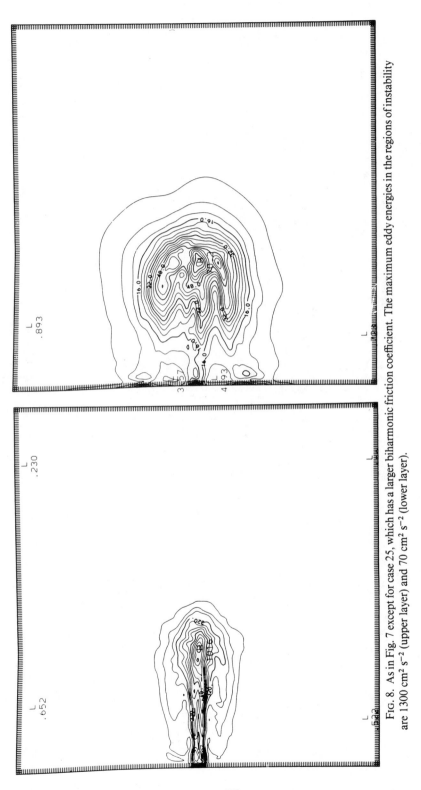

FIG. 8. As in Fig. 7 except for case 25, which has a larger biharmonic friction coefficient. The maximum eddy energies in the regions of instability are 1300 cm² s⁻² (upper layer) and 70 cm² s⁻² (lower layer).

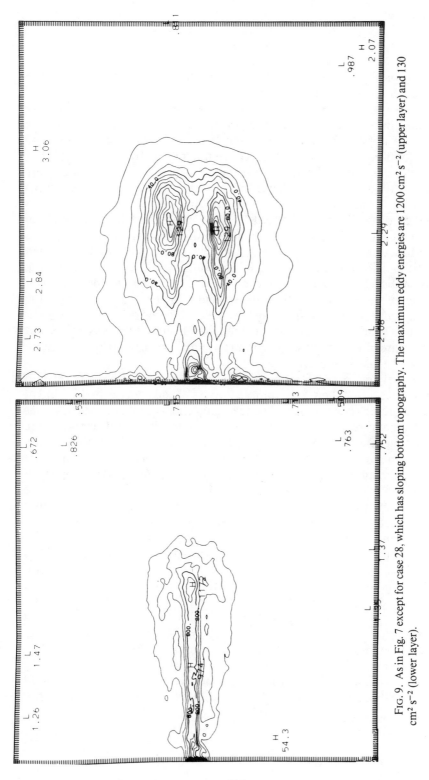

FIG. 9. As in Fig. 7 except for case 28, which has sloping bottom topography. The maximum eddy energies are 1200 cm² s⁻² (upper layer) and 130 cm² s⁻² (lower layer).

the subtropical gyre, where the thermocline slopes up toward the equator. The Gulf Stream region is unstable (as in the two-layer case) in a rather complex way—both lateral shear instability and baroclinic instability are important in this region. Local and global energy budgets suggest roughly equal contributions from these two "mechanisms." Together they conspire to put a lot of eddy energy into the ocean in that region. In fact, in these kinds of calculations, the Gulf Stream often meanders vigorously, occasionally shedding a ringlike feature both northward and southward into the westward return flow. In the upper layer, the circulation fills out the entire domain defined by the wind curl (the Sverdrup flow). In the middle layer (which in this particular calculation represents 300–1000 m depth), the instantaneous stream function is that shown in Fig. 10b. The mid-depth Gulf Stream is in the same location and penetrates as far eastward as its surface manifestation, but the anticyclonic gyre is much more tightly confined to the northwest quadrant of the basin. On the southern flank of the subtropical gyre the eddies are the dominant signal below the surface layer. Under the Gulf Stream and nearby, there are well-defined time-averaged flows as before, but since they are of smaller amplitude than the eddy signal, they do not show up well in these instantaneous maps.

There are two aspects of this numerical experiment to focus on. One has to do with the fact that there are multiple sources of eddy energy in this kind of basin. Figure 11 shows a map of eddy kinetic energy in the middle layer, as one representative picture. There are very high levels of eddy energy in the Gulf Stream extension region, analogous to that found in the two-layer case, but now, in contrast to earlier two-layer cases, there is a minimum at the middle of the subtropical gyre and a secondary maximum of eddy energy on the southern flank. This is clearly due to a simple baroclinic instability as the Sverdrup flow turns to the west. Given the vertical shear, linear stability theory actually pinpoints the region in which this instability will exist. The eddies fill out the basin all the way across to the western wall.

The other thing that happens has to do with potential vorticity distributions and strong mixing regions in the middle layer of this same experiment. Figure 12 shows a map of potential vorticity in this layer. Essentially, in the region where the Gulf Stream is going eastward, rapid mixing occurs, dictated by the shape of the gyre, and the potential vorticity homogenizes over a very large part of the domain (Holland, 1985a). Interesting kinds of structures occur on the edges of these highly homogenized regions, governed by the advection of potential vorticity around the gyre.

These vast regions of well-mixed potential vorticity have now been found in many eddy-active regions of the World Ocean. Maps based on density data (allowing the construction of linearized potential vorticity) have been drawn. Figure 13 (Holland *et al.,* 1984) shows an example from the North

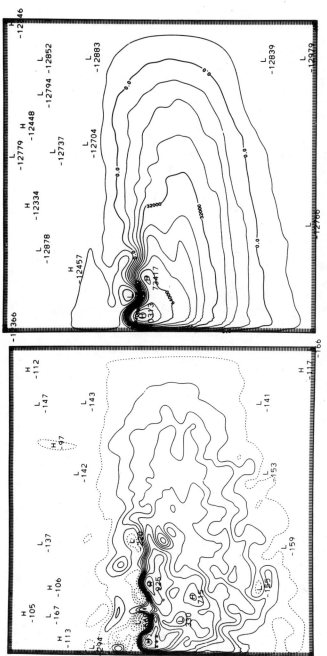

FIG. 10a. The mass transport streamfunctions (left — instantaneous; right — time-averaged) for the upper layer (0–300 m) of case 3L-12. The upper layer is driven by a single gyre of wind forcing with $T = -T_0 \cos[\pi(y - y_1)/(y_2 - y_1)]$ for $y_1 < y_2$, and $T = +T$ for $y > y_2$. Here $y_1 = 800$ km and $y_2 = 2800$ km are the distances north of the southern boundary. The maximum transports in the mean pictures are 27, 30, and 28×10^6 m³ s⁻¹, respectively. Note that the upper layer alone transports all the mass needed to satisfy the Sverdrup condition and that the contribution from the lower layers is an eddy-driven component that enhances the net transport by a factor of three.

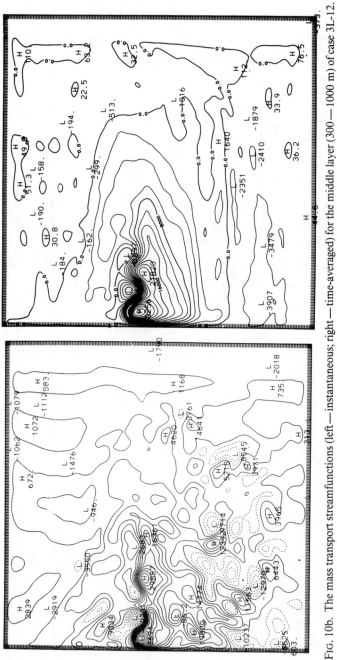

FIG. 10b. The mass transport streamfunctions (left — instantaneous; right — time-averaged) for the middle layer (300 — 1000 m) of case 3L-12.

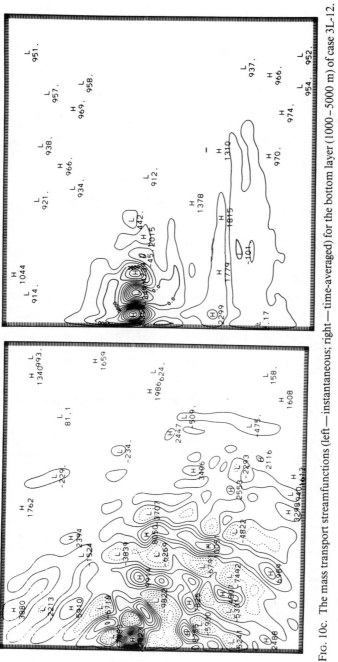

Fig. 10c. The mass transport streamfunctions (left—instantaneous; right—time-averaged) for the bottom layer (1000–5000 m) of case 3L-12.

509

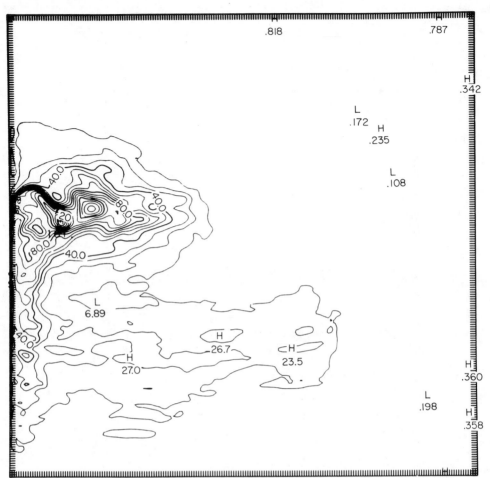

FIG. 11. The eddy kinetic energy pattern in the middle layer of experiment 3L-12. The maximum values in the Gulf Stream region reach about 150 cm² s⁻². There is a secondary maximum on the south flank of the subtropical gyre and a well-defined minimum in between.

FIG. 12. The pattern of mean potential vorticity in the middle layer of experiment 3L-12 shown as (a) a horizontal map and (b) a perspective drawing. The potential vorticity is defined here (i.e., in the quasi-geostrophic model) as $Q = \text{LAP PSI} + f(y) + \text{STRETCHING TERM}$. Note the large pool of homogenized potential vorticity and the plumelike structure associated with advective effects on the eastern side of the nearly constant region. Note also the dominance of planetary vorticity in the regions distant from intense eddy influence. Such homogenization effects occur in the middle layers of all numerical experiments, but the details of the structures depend on eddy and mean circulation influences. [From Holland (1985b).]

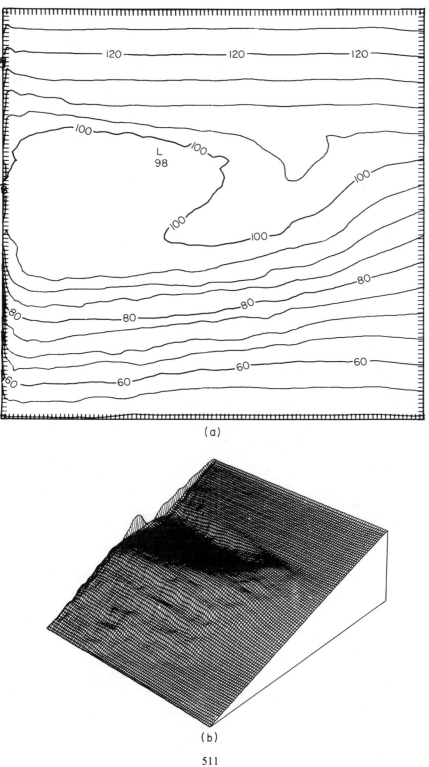

(a)

(b)

511

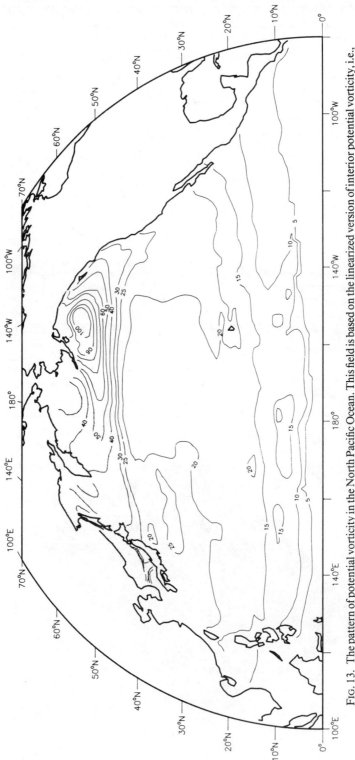

FIG. 13. The pattern of potential vorticity in the North Pacific Ocean. This field is based on the linearized version of interior potential vorticity, i.e., $Q = f(y) \times \partial\sigma/\partial z$ since the relative vorticity component is unknown. This Q requires only a knowledge of the density field. [From Holland *et al.* (1984). Reprinted with permission from *Nature (London)* **308**, 698–705. Copyright © 1984 Macmillan Journals Limited.]

Pacific. Note the very large region in which the potential vorticity is absolutely constant and the plumelike feature moving around the periphery much like the model feature in Fig. 12.

It is important to realize what this implies about the shape of the gyre in these regions. The separation between density surfaces must be changing at just the right rate with longitude to cancel the effect of the changing Coriolis parameter. This places an enormous constraint on the shape of the gyre in these regions in which the potential vorticity is constant.

3.3. Eight-Layer Experiments

Let us conclude our discussion of eddy-resolved quasi-geostrophic model studies by showing some recent results from numerical experiments with much greater vertical resolution (Holland, 1985c; Holland et al., 1984). This is important because two- and three-layer results show a strong dependence on vertical resolution and because new observations are beginning to focus on the vertical structure of eddy and mean-flow quantities (Schmitz, 1978; Richardson, 1983, 1984). With eight vertical levels, the vertical distributions of eddy and mean currents and the vertical structure of various processes begins to be adequately defined. The cases to be discussed here again use very simple rectangular basins and sinusoidal wind forcing so that results can be related to earlier work and will be as simple as possible.

Figure 14 shows the stream function at three levels (out of eight), namely at 150 m, 850 m, and 1750 m, spanning the main thermocline. The upper level shows the subtropical gyre as before, but now we can see more clearly what is happening in terms of vertical structure of mean currents. There are two spatial scales associated with recirculation in the middle and deep layers. One can be described as a very tight confinement of the flow near the Gulf Stream. It exists from top to bottom (it is all you see in the deep layers) and is made up of an eastward Gulf Stream jet and a tight recirculating westward component of the flow on either side. The scale of penetration into the interior in this experiment is quite large, reaching nearly 2500 km from the western boundary. In the middle layers the broad basin-filling Sverdrup gyre at the sea surface becomes more and more confined with depth to the northwest quadrant of the subtropical gyre. The middle panel of Fig. 14 shows what is left of the broad gyre at the 850-m level. About 40% of the transport in the eastward jet reaches some distance out into the interior, while the rest is in the very tight recirculation region. At greater depths only the tight recirculation remains. The baroclinic signal tends to die away with depth, leaving only the barotropic flow at the deepest levels. As mentioned earlier, all of these structures, except for the very broad one right at the sea surface, are intimately tied to the eddy field. The strength of the circulation at

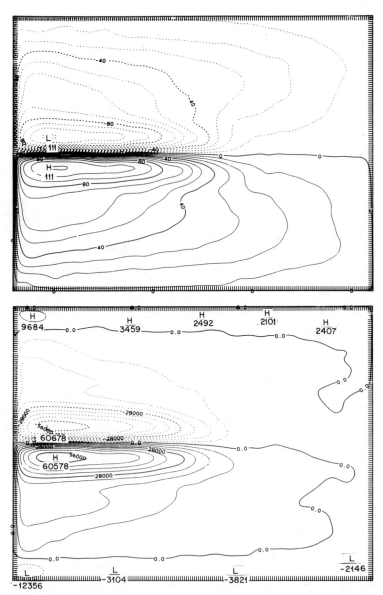

FIG. 14. The mean mass transport stream functions at three levels (150, 850, and 1750 m from top to bottom) in an eight-layer experiment called 8L-2. The levels are the first, third, and fifth in the model and indicated the main features of the flow at the surface, in the main thermocline, and in the deep ocean. Note the Sverdrup gyres at the top, the two distinct scales of flow at middle depths, and the barotropic recirculation gyres below the thermocline.

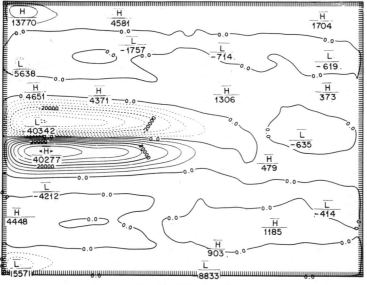

FIG. 14. *(Continued)*

middle and deep levels and the structure there are governed by eddy – mean-flow interactions associated with instability mechanisms and important eddy forcing in the vicinity of the Gulf Stream.

Let us examine north – south vertical sections of mean zonal velocity and eddy kinetic energy from this eight-layer experiment analogous to those constructed by Richardson (1983, 1984), reproduced earlier as Fig. 3. Figure 15 shows the full north – south extent of the basin (2800 km) and the full depth range (5000 m). The model fields at the eight levels in the model have been interpolated in the vertical to construct these sections.

The mean zonal flow at a mid-longitude is shown in Fig. 15a and can be compared with that constructed by Richardson (1984) along 55°W. The mean surface Gulf Stream flows at about 55 cm s^{-1} in the model calculation but only about half this value at 55°W. These are, of course, time averages over the vigorously meandering Gulf Stream, and so these values will be considerably less than instantaneous values. In both model and observations the flow decreases from this jet maximum both north and south in a characteristic fashion. Figure 3a shows an apparent tilt in the jet axis with depth, described also by Hogg (1983), in which the maximum of the surface current is significantly north of that in the deep ocean. This figure also clearly shows the westward return flow mentioned earlier. There is not very much indication of a return flow on the north side of the deep jet maximum, but there are relatively strong westward flows (> 10 cm s^{-1}) on the south, suggesting a somewhat asymmetrical gyre structure not present in this particular model

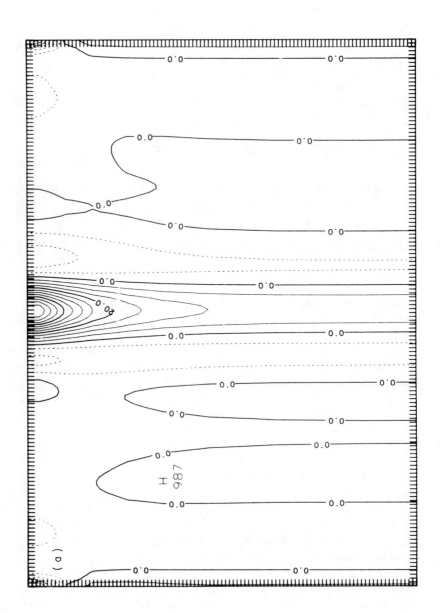

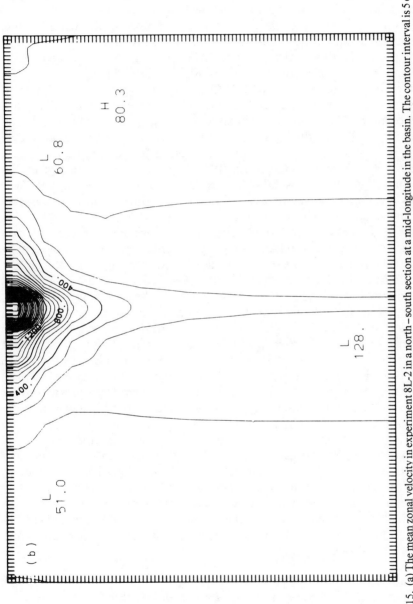

FIG. 15. (a) The mean zonal velocity in experiment 8L-2 in a north–south section at a mid-longitude in the basin. The contour interval is 5 cm s⁻¹, showing a surface jet maximum of 55 cm s⁻¹, a deep eastward flow of about 8 cm s⁻¹, and deep westward recirculating flows of 6 cm s⁻¹. (b) The eddy kinetic energy in experiment 8L-2 in a north–south section at a mid-longitude in the basin. The entire depth range — 0 to 5000 m — is shown. The contour interval is 100 cm² s⁻², the surface maximum is about 2900 cm² s⁻², and the bottom maximum is about 160 cm² s⁻².

simulation. Note that the model westward flows are about 6 cm s^{-1} in this section. It may be that the continental slope on the north needs to be taken into account in the models to achieve this kind of asymmetry, but there are other possible reasons as well, including asymmetry in the wind forcing, bottom topography, thermohaline forcing, and so forth.

Figure 15b shows a vertical section of eddy kinetic energy in the eight-layer calculation. Compare these results with Fig. 3b. The eddy energy levels are too big everywhere in this domain (although not completely out of line) and the structures are quite similar. The eddy kinetic energy in the Gulf Stream reaches almost 2000 cm^2 s^{-2}, while the model suggests 2900 cm^2 s^{-2}. The vertical structure near the stream is quite realistic and the deep energy level about right. Away from the stream, however, the eddy minimum at depth found at 20–25°N [see Richardson (1983)] is not apparent, although earlier two- and three-layer cases did produce such a feature. At this stage all these issues are not resolved; there are simply not enough eight-layer cases to rationalize all these kinds of features.

The focus here is on both the vertical and the horizontal structure of eddy kinetic energy and their relation to mean currents. The data do not seem to suggest a vertical tilt in the pattern of eddy kinetic energy in Fig. 3b like that in the mean flow. This suggests that some of what is seen in the observations of mean currents might be due to causes not present in the model (e.g., thermohaline forcing), whereas most of what is seen in the observations of eddy kinetic energy is included (i.e., Gulf Stream instability and downward propagation of eddy energy). In addition, Richardson (1984) has pointed out that the location of the deep mean zonal flow has undergone a shift of more than 200 km (a secular trend) when three 9-month deployments of current meter moorings are treated separately. The three separate profiles all show a deep Gulf Stream bounded by two countercurrents, but the location of the eastward jet has moved considerably over a 2-year period.

Finally, let us examine one last figure to emphasize the extent to which eddy energy penetrates eastward across the gyre in this eight-layer numerical experiment. Figure 16 shows a zonal section, coinciding with the latitude of the mean Gulf Stream, showing a contour plot of eddy kinetic energy. The surface maximum extends eastward more than halfway across the basin essentially unchanged, suggesting the possibility that there is a region of eddy generation along the path of the Stream that is zonally invariant in the western half-basin.

4. SPECULATIONS AND CONCLUSIONS

The results and discussions so far show something of the recent history of eddy resolved mid-latitude ocean model development and application over

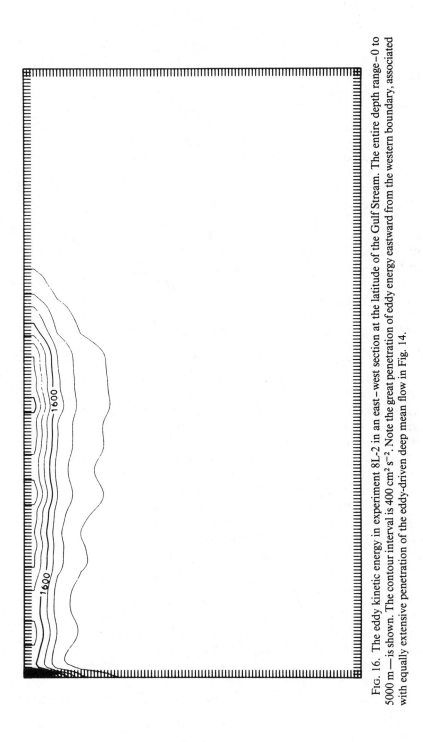

FIG. 16. The eddy kinetic energy in experiment 8L-2 in an east–west section at the latitude of the Gulf Stream. The entire depth range–0 to 5000 m —is shown. The contour interval is 400 cm² s⁻². Note the great penetration of eddy energy eastward from the western boundary, associated with equally extensive penetration of the eddy-driven deep mean flow in Fig. 14.

the past few years. For the first time, observations are providing a major guide to this development. The models are not only pursuing idealized but dynamically important questions, but they are also addressing questions directly relevant to the observations. The "successes" and "failures" both contribute considerable insight into not only how the models work, but also how the ocean works. The physics needed to reproduce the major features of the mean circulation and the distributions of various eddy statistics are becoming clear. This, coupled with the new techniques coming online to observe the turbulent ocean in all its richness of space and time scales, makes for optimism that the basic dynamical nature of large-scale ocean circulation will be unravelled in the coming years.

Given this statement of optimism on the part of the author, let me also reiterate that models such as those described here, indeed all models, involve enormous compromises that color the results that are found. It is incumbent upon the researcher to fully understand this point and not to begin to see his model as "the ocean." These constructions can at best only crudely represent the real system and should be seen as a mere guide to understanding actual oceans.

With these preliminaries let me mention a few of the problems and speculate on some of the findings in this work. Little has been said here about numerical issues (or indeed about the physical choices that have gone into the numerical experiments). For most of the studies presented here the basin is nearly 4000 km square and the horizontal grid resolution is 20 km. A typical Gulf Stream ring is 150 or 200 km across. The basic mesoscale eddy field has that kind of dimension to it but the western boundary currents, which are quite thin, are not resolved very well. A number of studies to examine whether this is critical have been done, but the issue is by no means settled. For the sequence of experiments discussed here, the western boundary current is quite passive and its detailed structure not apparently critical, but there are other examples in which, for a certain parameter range, the flow going northward in the western boundary current is itself unstable. In those cases the boundary current will sometimes spontaneously separate from the western wall and penetrate into the interior at a latitude well south of the zero of the wind stress curl. This suggests that there is a Gulf Stream separation problem that is not presently understood very well.

The details of potential vorticity homogenization are not yet very well understood, especially for higher vertical resolution like the eight-level case discussed earlier, but broad homogeneous regions occur with a simple depth dependence related to the bowl slope of the gyre. See the discussion by Holland *et al.* (1984) relating these model results to both theory and observations of the potential vorticity distributions.

Let me speculate about the nature of our understanding of the potential vorticity homogenization process and the differences between the North Atlantic and North Pacific as suggested by this kind of model calculation. These oceans are really quite different. The North Pacific is essentially an ocean where little outcropping of density surfaces occurs on the northern side of the subtropical gyre, while the North Atlantic middle level density surfaces all outcrop on the north side of that subtropical gyre. This suggests that the North Pacific might be considered more of a "quasi-geostrophic" ocean in the sense that thermodynamic processes at the sea surface play a lesser role and the eddy processes a greater role in modifying the internal potential vorticity distributions. In contrast, the North Atlantic has many density surfaces coming to the sea surface, allowing surface forcing to directly influence the interior of the ocean — i.e., the eddies might play a less dominant role here. This is consistent with the hypothesis that both surface forcing along isopycnal surfaces of the kind suggested by Luyten *et al.* (1983) and eddy influences of the kind discussed by Rhines and Holland (1979), Holland and Rhines (1980), and Rhines and Young (1982a,b) are important for modifying the oceanic interior and particularly for setting the large-scale potential vorticity distributions.

In these numerical experiments, it is only the eddy field that influences the deep ocean interior, but in the North Atlantic (and in primitive equation models in which outcropping surfaces occur) the potential vorticity (or other properties) can also be carried along density surfaces from the sea surface into the interior. This suggests that by comparing potential vorticity maps from various ocean basins, in particular the North Atlantic and North Pacific, we might be able to sort out eddy-driven effects from surface-density-driven effects.

Finally, it would be useful to introduce more realistic bottom relief into these calculations. However, this is not straightforward, because the present quasi-geostrophic models are limited to small-amplitude topographic variations. In the North Atlantic topographic features extend virtually from top to bottom. Note the topography indicated in Fig. 3 along 55°W. Several preliminary calculations with idealized topography have been done, but these have not been systematically studied. This is an extremely important problem in that we need some understanding of the role played by topography, both small-scale roughness and larger-scale features like the mid-Atlantic ridge and continental slopes, upon eddy – mean-flow interactions.

There are other processes left out of the models discussed here that should be mentioned. First, variations in static stability in mid-latitude gyres are quite large, and outcropping density surfaces and frontal structures in the Gulf Stream ubiquitous. The quasi-geostrophic models, which do not include these physics correctly, may not give accurate results. Even more important, the forcing of the ocean by thermohaline processes cannot easily be incorporated into such models. Consequently, we will eventually need to do calculations with very-high-resolution primitive equation models with realistic topography, wind forcing, and thermal forcing.

Before that stage is reached, however, this simpler class of models needs further exploitation. The quasi-geostrophic model has shown a remarkable ability to model many aspects of eddy–mean-flow interactions and has reproduced semiquantitatively many features of the oceanic general circulation—a general circulation described in terms of both its temporal mean and its variability. Even with the simpler physics and the high computational efficiency involved, many of the dynamical processes occurring in these models are still not well understood. Further analyses and new experiments are needed to understand fully the workings of these analogs to the turbulent ocean.

References

Bernstein, R. L., and White, W. B. (1977). Zonal variability in the distribution of eddy energy in the mid-latitude North Pacific Ocean. *J. Phys. Oceanogr.* **7**, 123–126.

Cheney, R. E., Marsh, J. G., and Beckley, B. D. (1983). Global mesoscale variability from collinear tracks of SEASAT altimeter data. *JGR, J. Geophys. Res.* **88**, 4343–4354.

Dantzler, H. L. (1976). Geographic variations in intensity of the North Atlantic and North Pacific oceanic eddy fields. *Deep-Sea Res.* **23**, 783–796.

Dantzler, H. L. (1977). Potential energy maxima in the tropical and subtropical North Atlantic. *J. Phys. Oceanogr.* **7**, 512–519.

Harrison, D. E., and Holland, W. R. (1981). Regional eddy vorticity transport and the equilibrium vorticity budgets of a numerical model ocean circulation. *J. Phys. Oceanogr.* **11**, 190–208.

Hogg, N. G. (1983). A note on the deep circulation of the western North Atlantic: Its nature and causes. *Deep-Sea Res.* **30**, 945–961.

Holland, W. R. (1978). The role of mesoscale eddies in the general circulation of the ocean-numerical experiments using a wind-driven quasi-geostrophic model. *J. Phys. Oceanogr.* **8**, 363–392.

Holland, W. R. (1985a). The homogenization of potential vorticity in mid-latitude gyres. (In preparation.)

Holland, W. R. (1985b). Multiple sources of eddy energy in mid-latitude gyres. (In preparation.)

Holland, W. R. (1985c). The vertical structure of eddy-resolved ocean circulation. (In preparation.)

Holland, W. R., and Lin, L. B. (1975a). On the generation of mesoscale eddies and their contribution to the oceanic general circulation. I. A preliminary numerical experiment. *J. Phys. Oceanogr.* **5**, 642–657.

Holland, W. R., and Lin, L. B. (1975b). On the generation of mesoscale eddies and their contribution to the oceanic general circulation. II. A parameter study. *J. Phys. Oceanogr.* **5**, 658–669.

Holland, W. R., and Rhines, P. B. (1980). An example of eddy-induced ocean circulation. *J. Phys. Oceanogr.* **10**, 1010–1031.

Holland, W. R., and Schmitz, W. J., Jr. (1985). On the penetration scale of model midlatitude jets. *J. Phys. Oceanogr.* (in press).

Holland, W. R., Harrison, D. E., and Semtner, A. J., Jr. (1983). Eddy-resolving models of large-scale ocean circulation. *In* "Eddies in Marine Science" (A. R. Robinson, ed.), Chapter 17, pp. 379–403. Springer-Verlag, Berlin and New York.

Holland, W. R., Keffer, T., and Rhines, P. R. (1984). Dynamics of the oceanic general circulation: The potential vorticity field. *Nature (London)* **308**, 698–705.

Levitus, S. (1982). *In* "Climatological Atlas of the World Ocean," NOAA Prof. Pap. No. 13. U.S. Govt. Printing Office, Washington, D.C.

Luyten, J., Pedlosky, J., and Stommel, H. (1983). The ventilated thermocline. *J. Phys. Oceanogr.* **13**, 292–309.

Rhines, P. B., and Holland, W. R. (1979). A theoretical discussion of eddy-driven mean flows. *Dyn. Atmos. Oceans* **3**, 289–325.

Rhines and Young (1982a). A theory of wind-driven ocean circulation, I. Mid-ocean gyres. *J. Mar. Res. 40(Suppl),* 559–596.

Rhines and Young (1982b). Homogenization of potential vorticity in planetary gyres. *J. Fluid Mech.* **122**, 347–368.

Richardson, P. L. (1983). A vertical section of eddy kinetic energy through the Gulf Stream system. *JGR, J. Geophys. Res.* **88**, 2705–2709.

Richardson, P. L. (1985). Average velocity and transport of the Gulf Stream near 55°W. *J. Mar. Res.* **43**, 83–111.

Robinson, A. R., ed. (1984). "Eddies in Marine Science." Springer-Verlag, Berlin and New York.

Robinson, A. R., Harrison, D. E., Mintz, Y., and Semtner, A. J. (1977). Eddies and the general circulation of an idealized oceanic gyre: A wind and thermally driven primitive equation numerical experiment. *J. Phys. Oceanogr.* **7**, 182–207.

Schmitz, W. J., Jr. (1976). Eddy kinetic energy in the deep western North Atlantic. *JGR, J. Geophys. Res.* **81**, 4981–4982.

Schmitz, W. J., Jr. (1978). Observations of the vertical distribution of low frequency kinetic energy in the western North Atlantic. *J. Mar. Res.* **36**, 295–310.

Schmitz, W. J., Jr. (1984). Abyssal eddy kinetic energy in the North Atlantic. *J. Mar. Res.* **42**, 509–536.

Schmitz, W. J., Jr., and Holland, W. R. (1982). A preliminary comparison of selected numerical eddy-resolving general circulation experiments with observations. *J. Mar. Res.* **40**, 75–117.

Schmitz, W. J., Jr., Holland, W. R., and Price, J. F. (1983). Mid-latitude mesoscale variability. *Rev. Geophys. Space Phys.* **21**, 1109–1119.

Semtner, A. J., and Holland, W. R. (1978). Intercomparison of quasigeostrophic simulations of the western North Atlantic circulation with primitive equation results. *J. Phys. Oceanogr.* **8**, 735–754.

Semtner, A., and Mintz, Y. (1977). Numerical simulation of the Gulf Stream and mid-ocean eddies. *J. Phys. Oceanogr.* **7**, 208–230.

Veronis, G. (1966). Wind-driven ocean circulation. Part 2. Numerical solution of the non-linear problem. *Deep-Sea Res.* **13**, 31–55.

Wyrtki, K., Magaard, L., and Hager, J. (1976). Eddy energy in the oceans. *JGR, J. Geophys. Res.* **81**, 2641–2646.

MODELING CIRCULATION AND MIXING IN ESTUARIES AND COASTAL OCEANS

Alan F. Blumberg*

Dynalysis of Princeton
Princeton, New Jersey

AND

Li-Yauw Oey†

Geophysical Fluid Dynamics Program
Princeton University
Princeton, New Jersey

1. Introduction

In recent years knowledge of the physical oceanography of estuaries and continental shelves and experience on how to model them numerically have expanded considerably. While some of this expansion is due to increased scientific curiosity, most of it can be attributed to an awakened public environmental concern. Throughout history, estuarine and coastal waters have been a hub of human activities related to commerce, as well as a dumping ground for a variety of waste products. These waters have been observed to be remarkably resilient to natural and many man-created events; however, the increased demand on them has shown that they are in a rather delicate balance and often are quite fragile (Officer *et al.,* 1984). The ever-increasing utilization of these waters calls out for a better understanding of, and predictive capability for, the circulation and mixing processes in response to both natural and man-made forcings. It seems clear that the ultimate objective should be the development of a marine forecast model for estuarine and coastal ocean circulation of potential use to such diverse human activities as

* Present address: HydroQual, Inc., Mahwah, New Jersey.
† Present address: Skidaway Institute of Oceanography, Savannah, Georgia.

525

coastal shipping, commercial fishing, offshore dumping, and oil and gas exploration and recovery. The model should be capable of simulations on synoptic through seasonal time scales of currents, sea-surface elevations and distributions of temperature, salinity, and other chemical constituents.

The focus in this article is on the estuaries, those semienclosed coastal bodies of water (bays, rivers, inlets, sounds, fjords, and lagoons) that have a free connection to the open ocean and contain a mixture of seawater and freshwater derived from land drainage (Cameron and Pritchard, 1963) and shallow coastal waters within a few hundred kilometers off the coast, usually within the shelf break. The physical processes that control circulation and mixing in the estuarine and coastal ocean regions are closely related to those of the ocean. There are some important differences, however. The presence of land boundaries is perhaps the strongest constraint on the observed motion. The hydrodynamical processes are characterized by internal deformation radii (Rossby radius) of 5 to 15 km and topographic horizontal scales ranging from 1 km in the estuaries to 100 km on the continental shelves. The depths are typically less than 100 m so that the effects of winds and surface heating/cooling can extend throughout the water column. The importance of the tides with their large modulation of the water level and currents is illustrated through the production of intense levels of near-bottom turbulence by currents scrubbing against the bottom that can penetrate well into the interior of the water column. Winds, tides, density gradients, and large-scale circulation off the continental shelf are the driving forces for circulation and need to be properly accounted for in a numerical forecast/simulation model.

A review of recent advances in the numerical hydrodynamic modeling of estuaries and coastal regions is presented herein. Turbulence mixing processes and their various parameterizations will only be briefly discussed; the reader is referred to Blumberg (1985) for a more complete review. So many numerical models have been developed in the past decade that only a survey with representative examples of the model classes can be provided here. The comprehensive, three-dimensional circulation model developed by Blumberg and Mellor (1980) and applied extensively by the authors and their collaborators at Princeton University and Dynalysis will be used as a framework for distinguishing one model type from another. This paper begins with a discussion of the major issues of estuarine and coastal ocean circulation modeling and is followed by the survey of existing models. The limitations of these models are discussed, and some suggestions for model improvement are offered. In the last section, unresolved questions are discussed and recommendations are put forth for what new knowledge is needed to answer these questions.

2. Some Problems

The most crucial factor limiting the development of a truly predictive circulation model is a lack of a comprehensive observational data base for model initialization, boundary condition specification, and model result assessment and for providing insight into the fundamental processes that drive the circulation and mixing. How well a model will simulate depends critically on how accurately the boundary conditions and the initial state are known. Meteorologists, despite enormous quantities of detailed global atmospheric data, have long ago identified the acquisition of data as the foremost problem in atmospheric prediction. No estuarine or coastal ocean model has been fully verified due to the paucity of data. Despite significant advances in our understanding of estuarine and coastal ocean physics made over the past three decades (Beardsley and Boicourt, 1981; Allen et al., 1983), many of the dynamic and thermodynamic processes controlling the baroclinic as well as the barotropic circulation have yet to be completely quantified. The precise mechanisms that transport salt and momentum and the role of winds, tides, and freshwater discharges in this transport remain unanswered. Through the work of Elliott (1978), the classical two-layered, tidally averaged, estuarine circulation pattern described first by Pritchard (1952) is now viewed as only one state in a very complex circulation system. Additional data analyses by Dyer (1977) and Pritchard (1978) indicate that significant three-dimensional variations exist and that three-dimensional modeling is required, together with more high-quality observations that sample both the mean and turbulent parts of the motion.

Another problem is that of model resolution. The estuaries and coastal regions are physically small in comparison with the atmosphere and oceans. The models, however, use as many computer resources since the degree of detail required is substantial. The model resolution must be fine enough to include islands, coastal promentories, embayments, canyons, and other topographic features so that the circulation induced by the feature is properly captured in the model simulation. Often, estuarine and coastal circulation models require the use of the largest and fastest of computers to preserve the necessary detail. When these resources are not available, due to economic constraints, it has been typical to see the system simplified to the extent of omitting important physical mechanisms responsible for the circulation.

An inadequate parameterization of small-scale turbulence, that is, of vertical mixing, is the last problem to be addressed here. Most models use an eddy viscosity approach in which the mixing coefficients are related to local and often global measures of the flow characteristics. These models, if given sufficient data for calibration, can produce reasonable results. However, these models are not entirely satisfactory since their basic formulation is valid only for the circumstances in which they are calibrated and lack universality of application. Rather impressive results have been obtained, however, with the use of second-moment closure models of small-scale turbulence. These closure models have been developed [see Mellor and Yamada (1982) for a review] such that mixing or the inhibition of mixing of an oceanic property, for example, momentum, heat, and salt, can be predicted with considerable confidence. The closure models solve dynamic equations for the mean flow variables and turbulence correlations. The requisite model constants are determined through an analysis of carefully chosen laboratory experiments and are not site-specific parameters.

3. Models and Model Results and Interpretations

In the following sections some of the more recent developments in estuarine and coastal ocean modeling will be described. The one-dimensional, cross-sectionally averaged models so widely used in the analyses of engineering works will not be covered because the predictive ability and future utility of these models are rather limited. The interested reader is referred to Odd (1981) for more information.

For illustrative purposes, the present discussion will concentrate on the estuarine and coastal ocean circulation model (henceforth denoted as ECOM) developed by Blumberg and Mellor (1980). The model is three-dimensional with prognostic variables being the three components of velocity, temperature, salinity, turbulence kinetic energy, and turbulence macroscale. The density, vertical eddy viscosity, and vertical eddy diffusivity are also calculated. The model responds to surface wind stress, heat flux, and salinity flux and to the specification of tidal forcing, freshwater discharge, and other lateral boundary conditions. As such, the model addresses mesoscale phenomena, that is, flows characterized by 0.5- to 300-km length scales and tidal-yearly time scales (Beardsley and Boicourt, 1981). The analytical turbulence closure scheme developed by Mellor and Yamada (1974) to model small-scale turbulence has been incorporated. The model also incorporates a σ-coordinate system such that the number of grid points in the vertical is independent of depth so that the dynamically important surface and bottom Ekman layers across the entire sloping shelf can be adequately resolved. Recently, a curvilinear coordinate system has also been introduced into the model so that complex coastline geometries can be more readily accommodated (Blumberg and Herring, 1983). A complete description of the governing equations and numerical techniques can be found in Blumberg and Mellor (1985b).

3.1. Two-Dimensional Vertically Integrated Models

There are instances in which a simplification in the governing equations is permissible. The relevant equations can be reduced from the three-dimensional set to become the vertically integrated two-dimensional equations of momentum and mass conservation, most notably exploited by Leendertse (1967) and Heaps (1969) in seminal papers. Two-dimensional models have been used extensively for predicting storm surge in the North Sea (Nihoul, 1978; Peregrine, 1981), for investigating wind-driven and tidally induced circulation in lakes and bays (Imasato et al., 1975; Sugimoto, 1975; Tee, 1976; Yanagi, 1976; Yasuda, 1980), for studying water exchange through straits (Awaji et al., 1980) and for simulating oil spill trajectories in harbors (Hires et al., 1983). The results of the last studies should be viewed with caution since Lagrangian descriptions often depend on vertical structure in the horizontal velocity field, and conclusions derived from a vertically integrated model may not always be reliable (Ianniello, 1977, 1979).

A vertically integrated model, the barotropic portion of ECOM, has also been used to predict tides in the Chesapeake Bay, the Delaware Bay, and New York Harbor (Blumberg, 1977a,c; Henn, 1983; Oey et al., 1985), and the mean storm-induced circulation in the Middle Atlantic Bight (Blumberg and Kantha, 1985). The model results have been compared extensively with available observations and the agreement is generally good. To demonstrate the more general utility of this model, it has been used to simulate the eddy-shedding characteristics of the Loop Current in the Gulf of Mexico. The model was configured with a 25-km horizontal grid resolution and run in a reduced gravity mode [the free surface now represents the deviation of a pycnocline from a level surface; see Gill (1983)]. Figure 1 illustrates that strong eddies are shed periodically. Clearly visible is the Loop Current penetrating far into the Gulf, developing an eddy and then as the eddy begins traveling westward, the generation of another. A thorough investigation of the eddy-driven circulation in the Gulf has been performed by Hurlburt and Thompson (1980), who used a similar reduced gravity model approach.

The vertically integrated model is popular since it is relatively straightforward to program and can produce physically interesting results with only modest computational demands. Its major deficiencies are the absence of any vertical structure and the need for a simplistic parameterization of the bottom stress. For tidal and storm surge predictions, the quadratic (or linear) bottom stress parameterization together with a constant friction coefficient can often lead to significant phase errors. There is evidence that a three-dimensional model that resolves the vertical shear in the horizontal velocity and computes the bottom stress gives improved tidal prediction (Oey et al., 1984, Part II). On continental shelves, excluding the very-near-shore region

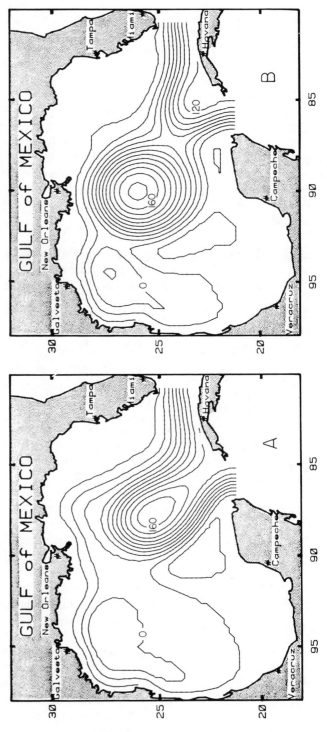

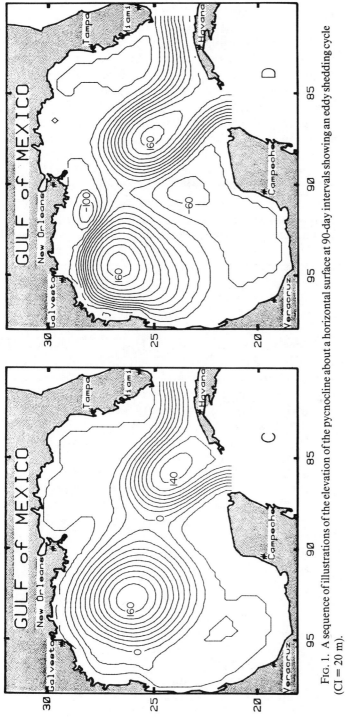

Fig. 1. A sequence of illustrations of the elevation of the pycnocline about a horizontal surface at 90-day intervals showing an eddy shedding cycle (CI = 20 m).

of thickness on the order of the baroclinic Rossby radius (5–15 km), the fluctuating currents generated by wind are predominantly barotropic (Allen,
1975; Kundu *et al.*, 1975; Beardsley and Boicourt, 1981), and the use of a
vertically integrated model should be a good approximation. In estuaries,
one is often interested in predicting horizontal dispersion of salt (or contami-
nant), produced by a combination of the vertical shear in the horizontal
velocity and vertical turbulent diffusion of salt [see, for example, Fischer *et
al.* (1979)]. With a vertically integrated model this dispersion process must
be empirically represented. An accurate representation is often difficult
since the vertical structure of velocity and vertical turbulent mixing processes are complex and depend, for example, on time-dependent wind forcing. One therefore adjusts the dispersion coefficients to match the computed
horizontal salinity structure with observations. The coefficients are only
valid under the particular conditions of observation and their validity under
general conditions is questionable.

3.2. Two-Dimensional Models with Vertical Structure

The most important difference between the various models that resolve
vertical structure lies in the parameterization of vertical turbulent mixing
processes. To the best of the authors' knowledge, all published models use, in
one form or another, an eddy diffusivity formulation to relate various turbulence correlations to the mean velocity and density fields. The turbulence
energy and length scales and the dependency of mixing on vertical stratification and shear are different. Bowden and Hamilton (1975) experimented
with various algebraic expressions of the eddy diffusivity as a function of
water depth and magnitude of the depth-mean current and found that the
formulation with the eddy diffusivity varying over a tidal cycle gave the best
agreement between model results and salinity observations in the Mersey
estuary. The parameters in their algebraic expressions were chosen empirically to fit a particular set of data. Extrapolation of these parameters, the
reader should note, to other estuaries or even to the same estuary under
different tidal stage, wind forcing, or river runoff can lead to unrealistic
predictions.

A coastal ocean simulation by Blumberg and Mellor (1980) that uses a
second-moment turbulence closure model is illustrated in Fig. 2. The
bathymetry of a transect normal to the coast off Tiana Beach, Long Island,
New York, was digitized with (1-km horizontal spacing and 21 vertical
points). All alongshore gradients have been neglected in this application of
the ECOM model. Figure 2 illustrates the differences in the coastal ocean
response after 12 hr to an imposed alongshore (upwelling favorable) wind
stress of 1 dyn cm^{-2} for homogeneous and stratified conditions. In both

simulations one can observe the formation of a near-shore coastal jet. The role of stratification is readily apparent in reducing the thickness of the surface Ekman layer. Attention is directed to the development of a thin bottom layer, manifest there only by the fact that bottom temperature has mixed vertically by use of turbulence closure scheme.

Other models that compute turbulence kinetic energy are those of Johns (1978) and Smith and Takhar (1981). Johns concludes that the friction coefficient used in the parameterization of bottom stress in a vertically integrated model varies significantly over a tidal cycle. Since bottom friction affects the tidal phase and amplitude, one must choose its value carefully when predicting tides using a vertically integrated model. Smith and Takhar found, because of the absence of cross-channel velocity shear in a two-dimensional (vertical plane) model, that even with a better prediction of turbulence diffusion, an appropriate value of the longitudinal dispersion coefficient is still required to correctly predict the residual circulation and salinity intrusion. On the other hand, Blumberg (1977b, 1978) neglected the longitudinal dispersion terms and, with an algebraic eddy diffusivity model, found good agreement with observed residual circulation and salinity intrusion in the Potomac River.

The condition under which a given estuary may be well approximated by a two-dimensional vertical-plane model can be obtained by using the Hansen and Rattray (1965, 1966) stratification–circulation diagram. Given the observed nontidal current near the water surface and the observed top-to-bottom salinity difference, this diagram gives the relative strength of the density-induced circulation in the vertical plane in comparison with the two-dimensional horizontal circulation. For a partially mixed and a well-mixed estuary, the diagram has been shown by Oey (1984) to be valid under arbitrary variations of wind stress, freshwater discharge, width, depth and eddy diffusivities, and dispersion coefficients along the estuary. Often, the circulation and salt transport in elongated estuaries with smooth lateral boundaries and small cross-channel topographic variation can be calculated with a two-dimensional model. In general, a good prediction of turbulence mixing and a good cross-channel resolution are important to a realistic simulation. On the continental shelf, a two-dimensional (vertical plane) model can provide useful physical insights and checks on theoretical analysis; however, there is mounting observational evidence that three-dimensionality is important (Allen and Kundu, 1978). Thus, ultimately one must seek a synoptic scale resolving, three-dimensional numerical model of coastal dynamics and kinematics. With the advent of modern array processing computers and with the ever-accelerating amount of observations taken in estuarine and coastal waters, the time has finally come to implement three-dimensional models, not just for research purposes, but also as a practical prediction tool.

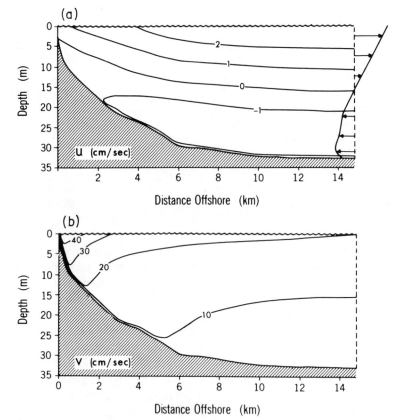

FIG. 2. The response of a homogeneous (a, b) and stratified (c–f) coastal ocean to an alongshore, upwelling favorable (directed into the plane of the paper) wind stress. The cross-shore velocity is denoted as u (positive offshore) and the alongshore velocity as v (positive into the plane of the paper). The initial temperature distribution is denoted as T_0.

3.3. Three-Dimensional Models

Three-dimensional estuarine and coastal ocean modeling is still in its infancy when compared to the state of the art in oceanic and atmospheric modeling. The pioneering work has been that of Leendertse and Liu [see Liu and Leendertse (1978) for a review] with model simulations of the three-dimensional velocity, temperature, and salinity structure in Chesapeake Bay, San Francisco Bay, and in more recent unpublished work the coastal waters around Alaska. Tide- and wind-driven currents appear quite well simulated; however, the viability of the baroclinic portion of the model has never been firmly established, since only simulations of less than 3 days' duration have been conducted. The model used an equation for turbulence kinetic energy and specified a turbulence length scale as a function of the distance from

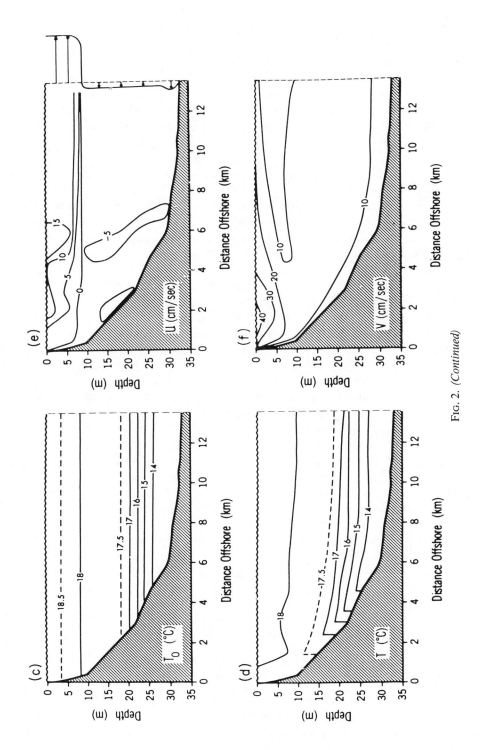

FIG. 2. (Continued)

bottom and surface boundaries. Another early model was due to Caponi (1976), who proposed a three-dimensional model of an estuary and applied it to the Chesapeake Bay. Constant eddy diffusivity coefficients were used to parameterize vertical turbulence mixing. Tee (1979, 1982), neglecting stratification, used a linear set of equations and separated the vertical deviations of the currents from their vertical averages. The resulting set of equations could be solved efficiently for various vertical algebraic eddy viscosity formulations. Some agreement with observations was obtained in the Bay of Fundy during a period of weak stratification for a suitable choice of the vertical eddy viscosity function. Owen (1980) used a Galerkin technique in the vertical and a finite-difference grid in the horizontal to compute the three-dimensional tidal current in the Bristol Channel. Algebraic eddy viscosity formulas were used and some agreements with observed currents were obtained. Stratification was not considered in the model. In an extension to the approach taken by Owen, Gordon (1982) has been able to include baroclinicity in a model of Narragansett Bay. A three-dimensional model with eddy diffusivities dependent on the local Richardson number has been developed by Wang (1982) to study shelf circulation around islands. The equations of motion were cast in cylindrical coordinates to achieve a better representation of an island geometry than could have been obtained by using rectangular coordinates.

A real-time simulation of the Hudson–Raritan estuary using real wind forcing, river and sewage discharges, and sea-level forcing applied along the open boundaries has been recently completed by Oey et al. (1984). The calculation run with the ECOM model covers July through September 1980 and uses grid boxes of size $0.53 \text{ km} \times 0.53 \text{ km} \times 1 \text{ m}$ in a modeled region of $35 \text{ km} \times 35 \text{ km} \times 10 \text{ m}$. The grid resolution is believed to be fine enough so that horizontal dispersion processes could be well simulated in the model; therefore, the horizontal diffusivity coefficients were set equal to zero. A statistical analysis of the simulation shows that at high wave number k, the model predicts correctly the two-dimensional k^{-3} energy spectrum. Sample results are shown in Fig. 3. The rather high value of the computed salinity during the ebb phase in Fig. 3c is attributed to the neglect of a freshwater source south of Sandy Hook in the model calculation. The generally flat part of salinity distribution during this ebb phase is simulated well, however, and is caused by the ebbing of generally less saline water that flows along the right-hand bank from Raritan River and trapped in Sandy Hook Bay. The predicted subtidal response conforms well with observations taken during the simulation period. Oey et al. (1984) also analyzed the salt fluxes and circulation in the estuary and showed how they are affected by subtidal forcings due to local and nonlocal winds and the neap-spring tide variation. Observational evidence that subtidal forcings are important in estuaries have been reported by Weisberg (1976), Elliott (1978), Wang and Elliott (1978), Pape and Garvine (1982), and Walters (1982).

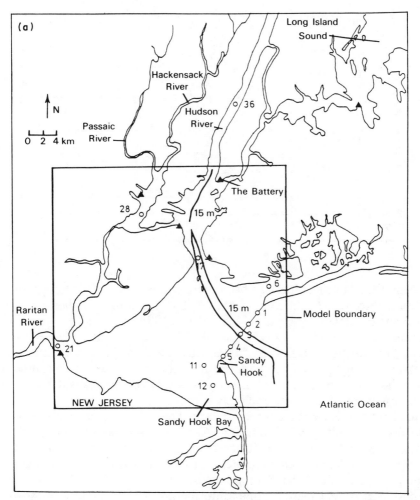

FIG. 3. Results from a numerical simulation of the Hudson–Raritan estuary. (a) The model domain. Rivers, narrow channels, and straits are extended beyond the model region as two-dimensional (vertical plane) waterways. (National Ocean Survey, August 1980; current meter station, O; tide gage station, ▲.) (b) A time–depth contour of subtidal longitudinal velocity (centimeters per second, positive ebbing) during August at a station located 12 km due west of NOS Station 4. The top panel shows the classical two-layer estuarine flow during a calm period with surface ebbing and bottom flooding waters. Around 18:00 on August 19, there was an up-estuary wind of magnitude 0.5 dyn cm^{-2}, lasting approximately 3 days. The direction of flow in each layer is now reversed (bottom panel). (c) Comparison with observation of the calculated longitudinal velocity (top panel, positive ebbing) and salinity (bottom panel) during 2 days in August 1980 at NOS Station 5. The depth at this station is 12 m below mean low water (MLW), and meter depth is 4.6 m below MLW. (------, observed; ——, calculated.) (d) Same as (c) but now for NOS Station 36 in the Hudson River. The depth at this station is 17 m below MLW, and meter depth is 4.9 m below MLW (------, observed; ——, calculated.)

(Continued on next page.)

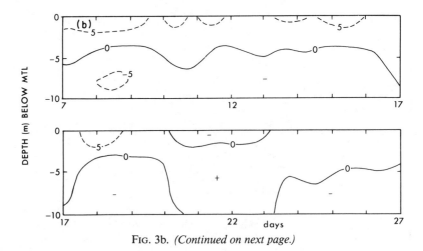

FIG. 3b. *(Continued on next page.)*

The ECOM model has also been used to simulate the circulation in the Gulf of Mexico (Blumberg and Mellor, 1985) and the Middle and South Atlantic Bights (Blumberg and Mellor, 1980, 1983). Consider first the model simulation of the circulation in the Middle Atlantic Bight, shown in Fig. 4. The horizontal resolution is 25 km, and there are 11 grid points in the vertical. Climatological temperature and salinity distributions are used for initialization and open boundary conditions. Geostrophically derived, vertical gradients of horizontal velocity with a condition of no flow at 2000 m are also used along the open boundary. The most obvious feature of the results is the Gulf Stream behavior off Cape Hatteras and the southward flow along the shelf. The spatial structure of the isotherms and isohalines are properly simulated. A major conclusion from this research effort was that the relatively cold and fresh inflow current from the North Atlantic, the upper part of which is entrained into the northern boundary of the Gulf Stream and the lower part of which becomes the Western Boundary Undercurrent, plays a dominant role in the general circulation. This current may well be the baroclinic mechanism responsible for the separation of the Gulf Stream from the continental shelf. In the Gulf of Mexico, comparison of the three-dimensional model (50-km horizontal resolution and 16 vertical levels) results with observational data indicates that the model seems to reproduce the large-scale features of the circulation such as the variability, intensity, and areal extent of major current systems. The seasonal variation of the mixed layer and thermocline compares well, but not perfectly, with climatology. In the South Atlantic Bight simulation, the model (25-km horizontal resolution and 21 vertical levels) has produced results that are in substantial agreement with our general understanding of the circulation.

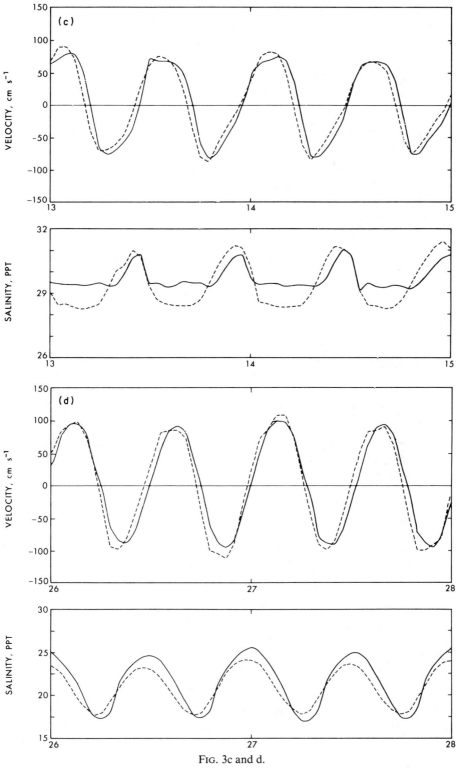

Fig. 3c and d.

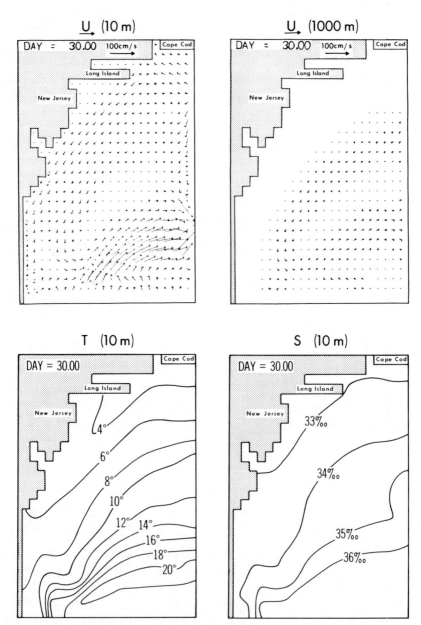

FIG. 4. The simulated 10- and 1000-m depth circulation patterns, temperature, and salinity distributions from a model of the Middle Atlantic Bight. The initial thermodynamic fields are February climatology and the results are after a 30-day spin-up period.

T (1000 m)   S (1000 m)

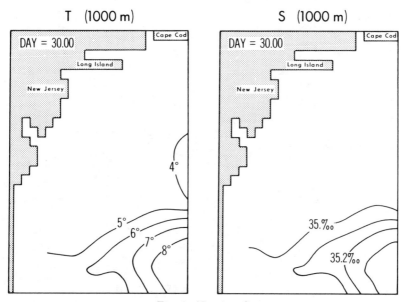

FIG. 4. *(Continued)*

The surface and bottom currents on the continental shelf (the model domain encompasses the deeper offshore waters as well) for periods of weak and strong winds are illustrated in Fig. 5. The circulation of the shelf south of ∼ 31°N seems to consist of the persistent cyclonic feature suggested by Blanton *et al.* (1981) and the calculated southward flow offshore of the Carolina Capes is in agreement with drifter inferred currents. The vertical distribution of the currents indicates that a strong baroclinic response exists.

Three-dimensional, prognostic model experiments with the ECOM have also been conducted (Blumberg and Mellor, 1985b) to investigate some of the characteristics of upwelling and eastern boundary currents. The model basin has a continental shelf slope with characteristics typical of northern California. Alongshore variation in topography is not considered. The response of the temperature and alongshore velocity distributions to an upwelling favorable, 1-dyn cm^{-2} wind stress is illustrated in Fig. 6. The initial response to the onset of the winds is the classical Ekman surface offshore flow and the compensating onshore flow at depth. Intense coastal upwelling is found within the forcing zone. As time progresses, the onshore circulation decreases in strength and the flow becomes markedly three-dimensional. The equatorward jet is confined to the coastal region. As found by a number of previous investigators and corroborated in this simulation, a poleward undercurrent develops below the thermocline over the slope region (∼ 250-m depth) by the generation and propagation of coastal trapped waves.

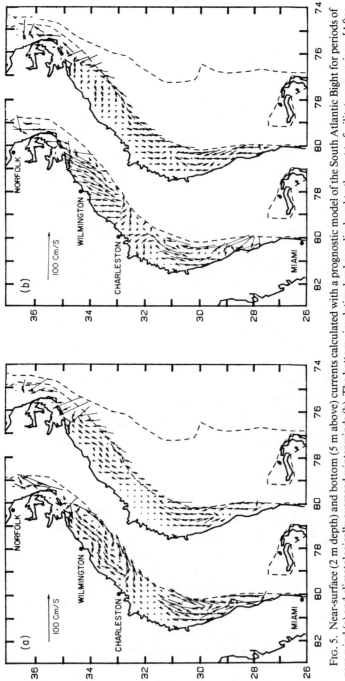

Fig. 5. Near-surface (2 m depth) and bottom (5 m above) currents calculated with a prognostic model of the South Atlantic Bight for periods of zero wind (a) and climatologically averaged winter winds (b). The bottom circulation has been displaced to the east to facilitate comparison. [After Blumberg and Mellor (1983). Reproduced with permission from *JGR, Journal of Geophysical Research* **88**, 4579–4592, copyright by the American Geophysical Union.]

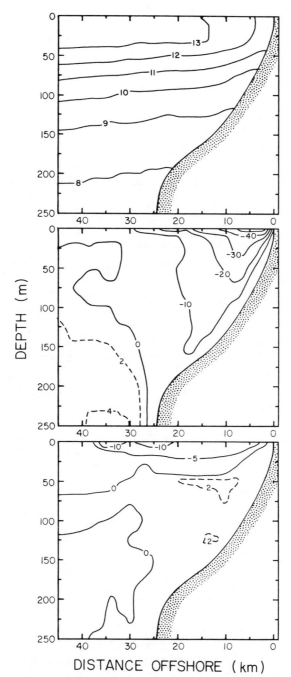

FIG. 6. The model simulations of temperature (°C), alongshore velocity (centimeters per second, negative in the direction of the wind), and cross-shore velocity (centimeters per second, positive onshore) after 60 hr from a three-dimensional model upwelling experiment. The vertical section is near the northern edge of the wind-forcing zone.

4. FUTURE DIRECTIONS AND CONCLUDING REMARKS

Recent simulations with numerical models have provided much insight about the future directions required to gain a deeper understanding of, and obtain a better predictive capability for, the dynamics and kinematics of estuaries and coastal waters. Second-order turbulence closure models appear to offer sufficient predictive power so that further turbulence model development in the next five years or so is expected to be minimal. The uncertainty in using these models in coastal waters lies in the uncertainty of the value of the bottom roughness parameter z_0. Grant and Madsen (1979) have shown that the bottom shear stress is considerably enhanced in the presence of oscillatory currents due to swells with periods of 10 to 20 sec. The corresponding z_0 values are typically an order of magnitude larger than the observed physical bottom roughness. The roughness should therefore be carefully determined from available observations prior to any application of the model to a particular coastal region.

An important objective of future modeling efforts should be a careful evaluation and validation of the numerical model results. In addition to the customary synoptic comparison of model results with observations, effort must also be made to compare the simulated subtidal physics with observations. As a result of the lack of comprehensive synoptic data, it is becoming increasingly apparent that one of the most convincing demonstrations of the skill of model prediction need be statistical in character. Statistical techniques should be developed to provide an objective measure of the similarities and differences between observational and computational data. Comparisons of spectral distribution similar to those proposed by Bedford and Babajimopoulous (1980) and Schwab (1983) for verifying lake transport models need to be considered.

The estuarine and continental shelf regions are the principal areas where land runoff is mixed with salty oceanic water. The strong coupling that develops can influence the circulation in both the estuary and shelf regions. This calls for coupling models of both regions. Two difficulties must be overcome. One is in proper specification of the open boundary conditions on the shelf. Ideally, one would need observed sea level at these open boundaries in conjunction with a scheme similar to that proposed by Blumberg and Kantha (1985) that permits waves impinging on the boundary to be transmitted without reflection. Another difficulty is that the offshore wind stress should be used over the shelf region instead of the nearest land-based observing site as is commonly done. If no offshore measurements are available, one should extrapolate the coastal wind stress offshore in a manner suggested, for example, by Weisberg and Pietrafesa (1983).

In models of coastal waters with complex bathymetry, fine-grid resolution is essential. Most of the estuarine and coastal models currently in use do not have enough grid resolution. As a result, important physical processes, for example, salt dispersion, are not directly simulated and *ad hoc* assumptions about the longitudinal dispersion processes must be used. This limits the generality of a model and often obscures the physics. In continental shelf regions in which baroclinic effects are important, fine cross-shelf grid spacing that resolves the baroclinic Rossby radius is required. Numerical models with variable grid spacing would be most appropriate in this case.

ACKNOWLEDGMENTS

The authors would like to acknowledge the contributions made by Joseph Smagorinsky to our investigations of estuarine and coastal ocean circulation. It was through his sustained interest that the three-dimensional model described in this article came to fruition. Ample computer resources and a creative research environment were generously made available. A debt of gratitude is also owed to George L. Mellor for his many substantive ideas concerning the model development and applications. Discussions with H. James Herring and Lakshmi H. Kantha over many years have contributed significantly to our modeling efforts. Support for this work was provided to AFB by the Dynalysis program for Independent Research and Development (IRD) and to LYO by the Visiting Scientist Program of Princeton University/NOAA, Grant 04-7-022-44017, and by the Office of Sea Grant of NOAA, Grant 81-AA-D-0065, Project R/E-3.

REFERENCES

Allen, J. S. (1975). *J. Phys. Oceanogr.* **5**, 300–325.
Allen, J. S., and Kundu, P. K. (1978). *J. Phys. Oceanogr.* **8**, 13–27.
Allen, J. S., Beardsley, R. C., Blanton, J. O., Boicourt, W. C., Butman, B., Coachman, L. K., Huyer, A., Kinder, T. H., Royer, T. C., Schumacher, J. D., Smith, R. L., Sturges, W., and Winant, C. D. (1983). *Rev. Geophys. Space Phys.* **21**(5), 1149–1181.
Awaji, T., Imasato, N., and Kunishi, H. (1980). *J. Phys. Oceanogr.* **10**, 1499–1508.
Beardsley, R. C., and Boicourt, W. C. (1981). *In* "Evolution of Physical Oceanography" (B. A. Warren and C. Wunsch, eds.), pp. 198–233. MIT Press, Cambridge, Massachusetts.
Bedford, K. W., and Babajimopoulos, C. (1980). *J. Hydraul. Div., Am. Soc. Civ. Eng.* **106**, No. HY1, 21–38.
Blanton, J. O., Atkinson, L. P., Pietrafesa, L. J., and Lee, T. N. (1981). *Deep-Sea Res.* **28A**, 393–405.
Blumberg, A. F. (1977a). *J. Hydraul. Div., Am. Soc. Civ. Eng.* **103**, No. HY3, 1–10.
Blumberg, A. F. (1977b). *J. Hydraul. Div., Am. Soc. Civ. Eng.* **103**, No. HY3, 295–310.
Blumberg, A. F. (1977c). *Chesapeake Sci.* **18**(3), 319–323.
Blumberg, A. F. (1978). *Estuarine Coastal Mar. Sci.* **6**, 209–215.
Blumberg, A. F. (1985). *In* "Physics-Based Environmental Modelling: Lakes, Reservoirs and Artificial Impoundments" (W. G. Gray, ed.). Am. Soc. Civ. Eng., New York, (to be published).

Blumberg, A. F., and Herring, H. J. (1983). "Dynalysis of Princeton," Rep. No. 81. Dynalysis of Princeton, Princeton, New Jersey.

Blumberg, A. F., and Kantha, L. H. (1985). *J. Hydraul. Eng.*, **111**, No. 2, 237–255.

Blumberg, A. F., and Mellor, G. L. (1980). *In* "Mathematical Modelling of Estuarine Physics, Proceedings of an International Symposium" (J. Sunderman and K.-P. Holz, eds.), pp. 203–219. Springer-Verlag, Berlin and New York.

Blumberg, A. F., and Mellor, G. L. (1983). *JGR, J. Geophys. Res.* **88**, 4579–4592.

Blumberg, A. F., and Mellor, G. L. (1985). *Isr. J. Earth Sci.* (to be published).

Blumberg, A. F., and Mellor, G. L. (1985). *In* "Three-Dimensional Shelf Models, Coastal and Estuarine Sciences" (N. Heaps, ed.), Vol. 5. Am. Geophys. Union, Washington, D.C. (to be published).

Bowden, K. F., and Hamilton, P. (1975). *Estuarine Coastal Mar. Sci.* **3**, 218–301.

Cameron, W. M., and Pritchard, D. W. (1963). *In* "The Sea, Ideas and Observations on Progress in the Study of the Seas" (M. N. Hill, ed.) Vol. 2, pp. 306–324. Wiley (Interscience), New York.

Caponi, E. A. (1976). *Adv. Geophys.* **19**, 189–310.

Dyer, K. R. (1977). *In* "Estuaries, Geophys., Environ." (Geophys Study Comm., eds.), pp. 22–29. Nat. Acad. Sci., Wash., D.C.

Elliott, A. J. (1978). *Estuarine Coastal Mar. Sci.* **6**, 285–299.

Fischer, H. B., List, E. J., Koh, R. C. Y., Imberger, J., and Brooks, N. H. (1979). "Mixing in Inland and Coastal Waters." Academic Press, New York.

Gill, A. E. (1983). "Atmosphere-Ocean Dynamics." Academic Press, New York.

Gordon, R. B. (1982). Ph.D. Thesis, Dep. Ocean Eng., University of Rhode Island, Kingston.

Grant, W. D., and Madsen, O. S. (1979). *JGR, J. Geophys. Res.* **84**, 1797–1808.

Hansen, D. V., and Rattray, M. (1965). *J. Mar. Res.* **23**, 104–122.

Hansen, D. V., and Rattray, M. (1966). *Limnol. Oceanogr.* **11**, 319–325.

Heaps, N. S. (1969). *Philos. Trans. R. Soc. London, Ser. A* **265**, 93–137.

Henn, D. S. (1983). M.S. Thesis, Dep. Mech. Aerosp. Eng., Princeton University, Princeton, New Jersey.

Hires, R. I., Oey, L.-Y., and Mellor, G. L. (1983). *Civ. Eng. Pract. Des. Eng.* **2**, 585–625.

Hurlburt, H. E., and Thompson, J. D. (1980). *J. Phys. Oceanogr.* **10**, 1611–1651.

Ianniello, J. P. (1977). *J. Mar. Res.* **35**, 755–786.

Ianniello, J. P. (1979). *J. Phys. Oceanogr.* **9**, 962–974.

Imasato, N., Kanari, S., and Kunishi, H. (1975). *J. Oceanogr. Soc. Jpn.* **31**, 15–24.

Johns, B. (1978). *J. Phys. Oceanogr.* **8**, 1042–1049.

Kundu, P. K., Allen, J. S., and Smith, R. L. (1975). *J. Phys. Oceanogr.* **5**, 683–704.

Leendertse, J. J. (1967). "Aspects of a Computational Model for Long-Period Water-Wave Propagation" RM-5294-PR. Rand Corp., Santa Monica, California.

Liu, S.-K., and Leendertse, J. J. (1978). *Adv. Hydrosci.* **11**, 95–164.

Mellor, G. L., and Yamada, T. (1974). *J. Atmos. Sci.* **31**, 1791–1806.

Mellor, G. L., and Yamada, T. (1982). *Rev. Geophys. Space Phys.* **20**, 851–875.

Nihoul, J. C. J. (1978). "Hydrodynamics of Estuaries and Fjords" *Elsevier Oceanogr. Ser. (Amsterdam)* **23**.

Odd, N. V. M. (1981). *In* "Transport Models for Inland and Coastal Waters" (H. B. Fischer, ed.), pp. 39–62. Academic Press, New York.

Oey, L.-Y. (1984). *J. Phys. Oceanogr.* **14**, 629–645.

Oey, L.-Y., Mellor, G. L., and Hires, R. E. (1984a). *Estuarine, Coastal Shelf Sci.* (in press).

Oey, L.-Y., Mellor, G. L., and Hires, R. E. (1984b). "A Three-Dimensional Simulation of the Hudson-Raritan Estuary. Parts I, II, and III," Tech. Reps. Geophys. Fluid Dyn. Program, Forrestal Campus, Princeton University, Princeton, New Jersey.

Owen, A. (1980). *J. Phys. Oceanogr.* **10**, 1290–1302.

Pape, E. H., III, and Garvine, R. W. (1982). *JGR, J. Geophys. Res.* **87**(C10), 7955–7970.
Peregrine, D. H. (1981). "Floods due to High Winds and Tides." Academic Press, New York.
Pritchard, D. W. (1952). *J. Mar. Res.* **11**, 106–123.
Pritchard, D. W. (1978). *In* "Estuarine Transport Processes" (B. Kjerfve, ed.), pp. 1–10. Univ. of South Carolina Press, Columbia.
Schwab, D. J. (1983). *J. Phys. Oceanogr.* **13**, 2213–2224.
Smith, T. J., and Takhar, H. S. (1981). *Estuarine, Coastal Shelf Sci.* **13**, 27–45.
Sugimoto, T. (1975). *J. Oceanogr. Soc. Jpn.* **31**, 1–14.
Tee, K.-T. (1976). *J. Mar. Res.* **34**, 603–628.
Tee, K.-T. (1979). *J. Phys. Oceanogr.* **9**, 930–944.
Tee, K.-T. (1982). *Estuarine, Coastal Shelf Sci.* **14**, 27–48.
Walters, R. A. (1982). *J. Phys. Oceanogr.* **12**, 658–668.
Wang, D.-P. (1982). *J. Phys. Oceanogr.* **12**, 605–617.
Wang, D.-P., and Elliott, A. J. (1978). *J. Phys. Oceanogr.* **8**, 225–232.
Weisberg, R. H. (1976). *J. Phys. Oceanogr.* **6**, 721–736.
Weisberg, R. H., and Pietrafesa, L. J. (1983). *JGR, J. Geophys. Res.* **88**(C8), 4593–4610.
Yanagi, T. (1976). *J. Oceanogr. Soc. Jpn.* **32**, 199–208.
Yasuda, H. (1980). *J. Oceanogr. Soc. Jpn.* **35**, 241–252.

MODELING SEA-ICE DYNAMICS

W. D. Hibler, III

U.S.A. Cold Regions
Research and Engineering Laboratories
Hanover, New Hampshire

1. Introduction

Large areas of polar oceans are covered with a thin, variably thick layer of ice formed mainly from freezing seawater and accumulated snowfall. While very thin compared to the oceans and atmosphere, sea ice can substantially modify the air–sea heat and momentum exchanges. In addition, melting and freezing of sea ice create variations in the sea-surface salt fluxes that affect the ocean circulation. These exchange characteristics are strongly affected by the fact that the sea-ice cover is dynamic rather than static. As a consequence, understanding the dynamic characteristics of this ice cover is important for understanding air–sea interaction in the polar regions and for determining the role sea ice plays in climatic change.

Investigation into the role of sea-ice dynamics in air–sea interaction has, until recently, received relatively little attention in the climate community. As a consequence, appreciation for the complexities and unique nature of this polar geophysical fluid, apart from its thermodynamic insulating character and high albedo, has been slow to develop. In this chapter an attempt is made to enhance this appreciation by examining the nature of sea-ice dynamics and discussing the dominant characteristics of a dynamic sea-ice cover vis-à-vis air–sea interaction. Particular emphasis is placed on examining momentum transfer through the sea-ice cover and how stresses within the ice may modify this transfer. In addition, results from numerical studies of a dynamic thermodynamic sea-ice model are discussed in order to illustrate the role of sea-ice dynamics in the air–sea interaction. It is hoped that

ADVANCES IN GEOPHYSICS, VOLUME 28A

this review will substantiate the need for increased attention to sea ice at institutions engaged in research related to the atmosphere and oceans.

2. Theory of Sea-Ice Dynamics

A prominent feature that distinguishes sea ice formed in the polar regions from the ice formed in small lakes or ponds is its motion. This motion and the attendant deformation cause heat, salt, and momentum exchanges between the atmosphere and ocean to be quite different from those that would occur for a static ice cover. The term "sea-ice dynamics" encompasses the physics that determine the evolution of sea-ice motion. In practice, the ice motion and thermodynamics are intrinsically related. For example, winter rates of freezing depend on the distribution of ice thicknesses, which in turn depend on ice transport patterns. The ice transport, on the other hand, is modified by the ice thickness distribution (especially the thin-ice percentage).

For purposes of numerical models, the main features of the dynamics of this coupled system may be characterized by the following elements: (1) a momentum balance describing ice drift in response to air and water stresses, Coriolis force, internal ice stress, inertial forces, and ocean currents; (2) an ice rheology that relates ice stress to ice deformation and strength; (3) an effective mass balance describing the dependence of ice thickness characteristics on growth, decay, and ice drift; and (4) an ice strength dependent on the ice thickness and floe size. In discussing these four elements, sea ice will be assumed to comprise a two-dimensional continuum. Such a continuum description does not, however, rule out representing rapidly changing ice conditions. Nonlinear ice rheologies alone, for example, can introduce discontinuities into the ice-velocity field, even though the forcing fields and sea-ice cover may be initially rather smooth.

2.1. Momentum Balance

The momentum balance describes the forces that determine drift and deformation of sea ice. Considering a sufficiently large collection of floes so that the average drift may be well defined, to a good approximation the momentum balance is given by

$$m\, D_t\, \mathbf{u} = -mf\, \mathbf{k} \times \mathbf{u} + \tau_a + \tau_w + \mathbf{F} - mg\, \nabla H \qquad (2.1)$$

where $D_t = (\partial/\partial t + \mathbf{u} \cdot \nabla)$ is the substantial time derivative, m is the ice mass per unit area, $\mathbf{k}$ is a unit vector normal to the surface, $\mathbf{u}$ is the ice velocity, f

is the Coriolis parameter, τ_a and τ_w are the forces due to air and water stresses, H is the elevation of the sea surface with respect to the geoid, and $\mathbf{F}$ is the force due to variations in internal ice stress. In this formulation, τ_w denotes the frictional drag due to the relative movement between the ice and the underlying ocean. In applications in which one is concerned with ice drift over periods of time large compared with inertial periods, the air and water stresses can be estimated from integral boundary layers with constant turning angles (McPhee, 1979; Brown, 1980; Leavitt, 1980):

$$\tau_a = c_a'(\mathbf{U}_g \cos \phi + \mathbf{k} \times \mathbf{U}_g \sin \phi) \tag{2.2}$$

$$\tau_w = c_w'[(\mathbf{U}_w - \mathbf{u}) \cos \theta + \mathbf{k} \times (\mathbf{U}_w - \mathbf{u}) \sin \theta] \tag{2.3}$$

where $\mathbf{U}_g$ is the geostrophic wind (assumed to be much larger than $\mathbf{u}$), $\mathbf{U}_w$ the geostrophic ocean current, c_a' and c_w' the air and water drag constants, and ϕ and θ the air and water turning angles. In the deep ocean both currents and sea-surface tilt can be well estimated from geostrophic considerations by setting H equal to the dynamic height and computing currents by $\mathbf{U}_w = gf^{-1}\mathbf{k} \times \nabla H$, where g is the acceleration due to gravity. In general both c_a' and c_w' are nonlinear functions of the winds and currents. The most commonly used formulation is a quadratic parameterization, where

$$c_a' = \rho_a c_a |\mathbf{U}_g| \tag{2.4}$$

$$c_w' = \rho_w c_w |\mathbf{U}_w - \mathbf{u}| \tag{2.5}$$

with c_a and c_w being dimensionless drag coefficients [with typical values of 0.0012 and 0.0055, respectively (McPhee, 1980)]. There are also a variety of other nonlinear boundary layer formulations.

Observations and dimensional analysis show that the force balance is mostly among the air and water stresses, the Coriolis force, and the ice interaction force. Measurements show water and air stresses to be about 0.1 $\mathrm{N\ m^{-2}}$. For 3-m-thick ice moving at 0.1 $\mathrm{m\ s^{-1}}$, the Coriolis force is about 0.05 $\mathrm{N\ m^{-2}}$ and is commensurate with the wind and water stresses. Inertial forces, in contrast, are smaller. However, the acceleration term can be significant in inertial oscillations where the acceleration and Coriolis force balance. For most applications the momentum advection term $(\mathbf{u} \cdot \nabla \mathbf{u})$ is very small since velocity changes of 0.1 $\mathrm{m\ s^{-1}\ km^{-1}}$ would be needed for a 0.1-$\mathrm{N\text{-}m^{-2}}$ force.

The relative roles of wind and ocean currents depend on the time scale of interest. Over the span of several days or less, steady current effects are normally quite small (several percent relative to the wind-driven components) (Hibler and Tucker, 1979; Thorndike and Colony, 1982). However, current and tilt effects are significant over several months since the wind effects tend to average out (Hibler and Tucker, 1979). Also, in relatively shallow regions, barotropic currents can significantly affect ice drift over short time periods.

The remaining term in the momentum balance is the ice interaction. It is difficult to directly measure the ice stress, so numerical model calculations for both the Arctic (Hibler, 1979; Hibler and Walsh, 1982; Hibler and Bryan, 1984) and the Antarctic (Hibler and Ackley, 1983) must be relied on to show that ice stress is a significant term in the momentum balance, even far from shore. This conclusion is consistent with residual estimates in the Beaufort Sea by Hunkins (1975), where all the terms in the momentum balance were estimated from direct measurements. The highly nonlinear nature of ice interaction does not allow a simple correlation between ice stress and winds, ocean currents, sea-surface slope, or acceleration.

2.2. Sea-Ice Rheology: A Highly Nonlinear Medium

Determining the constitutive law for sea ice has been a major problem in geophysical fluid dynamics. Much of the reason for this is the highly irregular nature of ice floes and the complex coupling between thermodynamics, mass balance, and motion. Significant progress has been made in understanding this rheology by emphasizing the similarities between granular media and sea ice (Coon, 1974). In addition, there are many analogs in statistical mechanics theory. The main aspects of sea-ice rheology currently in question are: (1) the parameterization of shear rupture and compressive failure, (2) the relative magnitudes of shear and compressive strengths, (3) the presence (if any) of effective pressure due to random bumping of floes, (4) the dependence of ice strength on ice thickness and floe size characteristics, and (5) the relative role of collisions versus prolonged contact stresses in the ice rheology. These questions are important for understanding the way the ice responds to external forcing and for understanding the behavior of the coupled air–ice–ocean system.

If sea ice is considered to be a two-dimensional isotropic continuum, the most general constitutive law applicable to nonelastic deformation [see, e.g., Malvern (1969)] can be written in the form

$$\sigma_{ij} = 2\eta\dot{\epsilon}_{ij} + \left[(\zeta - \eta)\left(\sum_k \dot{\epsilon}_{kk} \right) - P \right]\delta_{ij} \tag{2.6}$$

where σ_{ij} is the depth-integrated horizontal stress tensor, $\dot{\epsilon}_{ij}$ is the horizontal strain rate tensor assumed to be independent of depth, and $\delta_{ij} = 1$ if $i = j$ or 0 if $i \neq j$. In Eq. (2.6), η, ζ, and P are, in general, functions of the two invariants of the two-dimensional strain rate sensor. These invariants can be taken as the principal values of ice strain rate tensor or alternatively as $\Sigma_k \dot{\epsilon}_{kk}$ and

$\Sigma_{ij}\, \dot{\epsilon}_{ij}\dot{\epsilon}_{ij}$. To obtain an internal ice force for the momentum balance of Eq. (2.1), the stress tensor is differentiated as

$$F_j = \sum_i \frac{\partial \sigma_{ij}}{\partial x_i} \qquad (2.7)$$

2.2.1. Linear versus Nonlinear Behavior. A particular problem in early developments in ice dynamics was the degree of linear-versus-nonlinear behavior of the ice rheology. In a linear rheology, the stress tensor is a linear function of the strain rates. By using the general isotropic formulation in Eq. (2.6), η, ζ, and P would be constants independent of strain rate for a linear rheology. Early efforts to approximate the ice interaction made use of linear rheologies without a pressure term. Laikhtman (1964), for example, proposed a linear Newtonian viscous model employing only a shear viscosity (η finite; $\zeta = 0$) that was easy to deal with numerically and was subsequently used by a variety of authors (Egorov, 1970; Doronin, 1970) to carry out empirical–numerical studies with application to ice forecasting. A similar shear–viscosity-only model was used by Campbell (1965) in a basinwide mean arctic ice drift simulation. Theoretical and numerical studies using a more "general" linear viscous law containing both bulk ζ and shear η viscosities have successfully simulated observed ice drift and deformation far from shore, over both short-time intervals (Hibler, 1974) and a seasonal cycle (Hibler and Tucker, 1979). Best estimates of the viscosity magnitudes yielded values of the order of 10^{12} kg s^{-1}, with the bulk viscosity ζ about twice as large as the shear viscosity η. In a seasonal study, Hibler and Tucker (1979) showed that these viscosities vary in a regular seasonal manner.

However, while generally performing well far from shore, the linear viscous rheology has a major problem. In particular, accurate simulations of the central pack require viscosities quite different from those needed to simulate near-shore behavior (Hibler *et al.*, 1974; Rothrock, 1975a). For example, viscosities (two-dimensional) ranging between 10^{11} and 10^{12} kg s^{-1} are needed to model pack-ice behavior far from shore (Hibler, 1974; Hibler and Tucker, 1979). Near shore, however, the needed viscosities may be as small as 10^8 kg s^{-1} (Hibler *et al.*, 1974). In very small channels they can be as small as 10^5 kg s^{-1} (Sodhi and Hibler, 1980). Such variations suggest that inclusion of some type of nonlinear dependence of stress on the strain rate is necessary.

The other extreme possibility of a linear law is to approximate the ice interaction only by a pressure term, with the pressure having no dependence on strain rate. Such a rheology was assumed by Roed and O'Brien (1981) for the ice margin. When this rheology was coupled to a Coriolis force and to a simple continuity equation for the ice compactness, geostrophic adjustment tended to cause a jetlike effect to appear at the ice edge in the absence of water

drag. The main problem with such a rheology is that the ice will expand and
do work on itself without external forcing. As a consequence, it is not possible to apply energetic consistency conditions that can be used with plastic or
viscous rheologies.

2.2.2. Plastic Flow. To avoid the inherent deficiencies in linear viscous
rheologies, Coon (1974) proposed a plastic rheology for sea ice based on an
analogy to granular media. In a plastic constitutive law the stress state of the
ice is presumed to be independent of the magnitude of the strain rate. Such a
law allows highly nonlinear behavior, which is helpful in explaining ice flow
both near and far from shore (Hibler *et al.,* 1974). In addition, it contains a
simple way to specify a low tensile strength concurrently with a high compressive strength. A plastic law also has the attractive feature that a rate-inde-
pendent stress is consistent with assuming that the work done in ice deformation is primarily due to ridging. In particular, the energy expended in ridging
would be expected to be independent of the rate of ridge building. By assuming that ridging occurs due to shear deformation as well as convergent deformation (Thorndike *et al.,* 1975; Rothrock, 1975b), this concept can be
extended into a complete explanation (in terms of ridging and frictional
losses) of all energy dissipated during plastic flow [see Hibler (1984a) for a
more complete discussion]. It is also possible to argue that such plastic
rheologies applied to the marginal sea-ice zone by considering inelastic collisions among a large number of small floes induced by mean ice deformation
(Bratchie, 1984).

To illustrate the nature of a plastic sea-ice rheology, it is convenient to
consider the state of stress by using the principal stress components σ_1 and σ_2
of the stress tensor. The stress state is defined by a point having coordinates
(σ_1, σ_2) and will lie on a graph such as that shown in Fig. 1. If the ice were
described by a linear viscous rheology allowing only shear or uniform divergence, then the stress state would fall on the lines shown in Fig. 1, $\sigma_1 = -\sigma_2$
or $\sigma_1 = \sigma_2$, respectively. For the ideal plastic rheology, the stress state is
divided into two categories: (1) it lies within some fixed yield curve such as
the ellipse shown in Fig. 1 or (2) it lies at a point on the yield curve and can
never lie on a point outside the curve. In the first category, the sea ice is
assumed to have no deformation ($\dot{\epsilon}_{ij} = 0$ for all i and j) or to deform elastically. In the second category, the sea ice is assumed to deform with a strain
rate tensor having principal axes given by the "normal flow rule" (Malvern,
1969). This rule gives a relation between the stress state at a given point on
the yield curve and the strain rates by insisting that the ratio of the principal
components of the strain rate is the same as the ratio of the components of a
vector normal to the yield curve at the given stress point. The normal flow
rule arises out of classical plasticity theory under which the material is

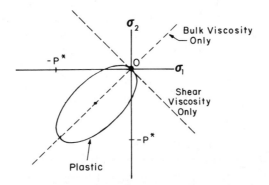

FIG. 1. Allowable stress states for a linear viscous rheology with either a bulk or shear viscosity and for an ideal rigid plastic rheology with an elliptical yield curve. The stress states are plotted as a function of the principal components of the two-dimensional stress tensor. For plastic flow, the stress state lies on the solid curve with the location dictated by the ratio of the strain rate principal components. For example, the stress state for pure shearing deformation is located at the ends of the semiminor axis of the ellipse and at 0 for isotropic expansion. For rigid motion the stress state lies inside the yield curve. In all cases, negative values of σ_1 and σ_2 represent compressive stresses and positive values tensile stresses.

assumed to behave elastically inside the yield curve. Under these conditions, if one assumes that the second law of thermodynamics holds (via the Drucker postulate that the work done by an external agency during a cycle of loading and unloading is nonnegative), then the associated flow rule follows [see Goodier and Hodge (1958, pp. 58–60)]. However, it should be noted that for sea ice, where such elastic behavior is doubtful, the normal flow rule is no longer a necessary consequence of the Drucker postulate.

Probably the best available smooth yield curve for sea ice is an ellipse as proposed by Hibler (1977) (see Fig. 1). The area within this curve where rigid motion occurs allows only small tensile stress and limited compressive stress. When the stress reaches the yield curve, sea-ice deformation begins to occur. Applying the normal flow rule to this curve yields (Hibler, 1977) values for the η, ζ, and P in Eq. (2.6) of

$$P = P^*/2 \qquad (2.8)$$

$$\zeta = P^*/2\Delta \qquad (2.9)$$

$$\eta = \zeta/e^2 \qquad (2.10)$$

where

$$\Delta = \left[(\dot{\epsilon}_{xx}^2 + \dot{\epsilon}_{yy}^2)\left(1 + \frac{1}{e^2}\right) + \frac{4}{e^2}\dot{\epsilon}_{xy}^2 + 2\dot{\epsilon}_{xx}\dot{\epsilon}_{yy}\left(1 - \frac{1}{e^2}\right) \right]^{1/2} \qquad (2.11)$$

and where $-P^*$ is the maximum compressive stress allowed and e the ratio of the semimajor and semiminor axes of the ellipse. Note that a given stress can be produced by various combinations of strain rates, so that strain rate is not a unique function of stress. In simple physical terms, the yield curve of Fig. 1 simply encloses the stress regime that a large-scale sea-ice field can maintain without tensile rupture, compressive failure, or other forms of deformation.

Simulations using plastic rheologies have reproduced many aspects of sea-ice dynamics. Near-shore simulations by Pritchard et al. (1977) have shown the capability of plastic rheology to model relatively stationary behavior under stress. With respect to basinwide seasonal simulations, Hibler (1979) has shown that in addition to producing near-shore shear-zone effects, a plastic rheology yields geographical ice thickness buildup and ice outflow from the Arctic Basin that agree well with observations. Some of these results will be discussed later in the chapter.

2.2.3. Some Examples of Plastic Flow. To help illustrate the relative behavior of various assumed rheologies and their effects on ice drift, it is useful to analyze a special one-dimensional case of the momentum balance employing only a linear water drag term cu, an external constant wind stress τ, and a one-dimensional ice stress σ,

$$cu - (\partial/\partial x)(\sigma) = \tau \tag{2.12}$$

Assume that ice occupies the region bounded by rigid walls at $x = 0$ and $x = L$. Let us now examine the linear viscous case in which $\sigma = \zeta(\partial u/\partial x)$, with ζ a constant. Substituting this expression for σ into Eq. (2.12) gives

$$cu - \zeta(\partial^2 u/\partial x^2) = \tau \tag{2.13}$$

A solution of Eq. (2.13) utilizing the boundary conditions $u(0) = u(L) = 0$ is

$$u = \frac{\tau}{2c\,\sinh(\lambda L)}[(e^{-\lambda L} - 1)e^{\lambda x} + (1 - e^{\lambda L})e^{-\lambda x}] + \frac{\tau}{c} \tag{2.14}$$

where $\lambda = (c/\zeta)^{1/2}$.

Let us now consider a one-dimensional rigid plastic rheology with constant strength. For our plastic rheology we shall assume that $\sigma = -P$ for $\partial u/\partial x < 0$ and $\sigma = 0$ for $\partial u/\partial x > 0$. These assumptions define a rigid plastic rheology (in one dimension) with no tensile strength. A solution for this case may be constructed by noticing that (1) for any deformation $\sigma = -P$ while for no motion $0 \geq \sigma \geq -P$ and that (2) the maximum force expected is at the right-hand boundary. With these considerations in mind, we see first that if $\tau L < P$ no motion of any kind will occur and the system will be rigid. If, on the other hand, $\tau L > P$ then motion can occur for a σ satisfying the preceding plastic assumptions and $\sigma(L) = -P$. Integrating Eq. (2.12) from x to L we have

$$\int_x^L (cu - \tau)\, dx = -P - \sigma(x) \tag{2.15}$$

However, we also must have $\partial u/\partial x = 0$ except at the boundary, otherwise $\sigma(x) = -P$ and Eq. (2.12) cannot be satisfied, since there would be no stress gradient and hence no internal ice force. Therefore u is a constant, as is τ, and we obtain

$$\sigma(x) = -P + (cu_0 - \tau)(x - L) \tag{2.16}$$

The value of u_0 may be obtained by noting that the total force acting on the rigid block is $-cu_0 L + \tau L - P$, and since there is no acceleration

$$u_0 = (\tau L - P)/cL \tag{2.17}$$

This analysis is also easily extended to include nonlinear water drag terms. Using the notation of Eqs. (12.2) and (12.3), the steady-state momentum balance for this one-dimensional system is

$$\rho_a c_a U_g^2 = \rho_w c_w u^2 - \partial \sigma / \partial x \tag{2.18}$$

By the same methods as employed in the linear case, for a constant wind the solution for this system is

$$u = \sqrt{[\rho_a c_a U_g^2 - (P/L)]/\rho_w c_w} \tag{2.19}$$

if $P < \rho_a c_a U_g^2 L$, and $u = 0$ otherwise. For a numerical comparison relevant to the Arctic Basin we take $L = 2.5 \times 10^3$ km, which is the scale of the Arctic Basin, and $P = 8.25 \times 10^4$ N m^{-1}, an empirical best-fit ice strength for 3-m-thick ice in the Arctic Basin in winter (Hibler and Walsh, 1982). Using these numbers, together with the drag coefficients defined earlier, we obtain a comparison of free drift and drift with ice interaction as shown in Fig. 2. Note that for large wind speeds there is little difference between free drift and the rigid/plastic solution, whereas for smaller wind speeds the difference is very marked, with the rigid/plastic system totally stopping. One difference from the linear water drag case is that the slope of the ice-drift rate versus wind speed decreases asymptotically to the free drift slope for large geostrophic wind speeds. In the one-dimensional linear water drag case, the free drift and plastic solutions would be parallel but would have different x-axis intercepts.

A mirror reflection of this figure holds for negative ice velocities. Consequently, if one were to force this model with a zero mean Gaussian distribution of wind speeds and then fit the results with a linear model, the effect of the ice interaction would be to reduce the ratio of ice drift to wind speed. This

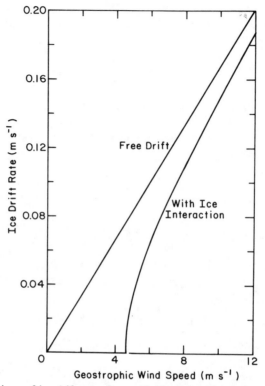

FIG. 2. Comparison of ice drift rates for an idealized one-dimensional system with and without plastic-ice interaction. Quadratic boundary layers were used and for the ice interaction case typical strength and length scales relevant to the Arctic Basin were assumed.

ratio would, however, be dependent on the variance of the wind speeds, with smaller variances yielding more of a slope reduction. These considerations are relevant to linear correlations of ice-drift rates with winds (Thorndike and Colony, 1982) that yield relatively slight reductions of the linear regression parameters in winter. This simple analysis suggests that part of the reason for such results may be the increased intensity and hence variance of winds in winter.

2.3. Ice Thickness Distribution and Thickness–Strength Coupling

2.3.1. Governing Equations. In the cases analyzed above, the behavior of ice dynamics under constant strength conditions has been examined. However, in reality the ice strength is related to the ice thickness characteristics in some way. The thickness characteristics, in turn, affect the air–sea heat exchanges [see, e.g., Maykut (1978)]. A model for this thickness–strength relationship in terms of ridging and a multiple-level ice thickness distribution was presented by Thorndike et al. (1975). With this multiple-level approach the ice strength is related to the ridge-building process, and as such may be particularly applicable to the central Arctic Basin. [For interested readers a more detailed discussion and critique of this multilevel formulation are given in Hibler (1984a).] However, near the ice margin, where individual floes are more pronounced, such a multiple-thickness formulation may not apply.

A simple two-level formulation for modeling the ice thickness distribution has been proposed by Hibler (1979) that captures many of the essential features of thickness–strength coupling and modification by dynamics of the air–sea heat exchange. The basic concept is that because of its low strength and high growth rates, many of the dynamic and thermodynamic characteristics of sea ice are dominated by the thin ice. Consequently, the ice thickness distribution may be approximately characterized by breaking it into two parts, thick and thin. This is done by dividing the ice cover into an area A (called the compactness), which is covered by thick ice, and a remaining area $(1 - A)$, which is covered by thin ice.

For the mean ice thickness per unit area h and compactness A, the following continuity equations apply:

$$\partial h/\partial t = -\partial(uh)/\partial x - \partial(vh)/\partial y + S_h \tag{2.20}$$

$$\partial A/\partial t = -\partial(uA)/\partial x - \partial(vA)/\partial y + S_A \tag{2.21}$$

where $A < 1$, u is the x component of the ice-velocity vector, v is the y component of the ice-velocity vector, and S_h and S_A are thermodynamic terms. While Eq. (2.20) is a simple continuity equation for ice mass (characterized by the mean thickness h), with thermodynamic source and sink terms, Eq. (2.21) is somewhat more complex. By including the restriction that $A < 1$, a mechanical sink term for the areal fraction of ice has been added to a simple continuity equation for the ice concentration. This sink term turns on when $A = 1$ (i.e., no open water left) and under converging conditions removes enough ice area through ridging to prevent a further increase in A. Although the sink term does not change the ice mass, it can cause the "thick" ice thickness to increase by allowing h to increase while A does not. Note that this restriction does not affect the conservation of ice mass, which is explicitly guaranteed by Eq. (2.20).

In the two-level simulation results reported later in this chapter, the thermodynamic terms S_A and S_h are given by

$$S_h = f(h/A)A + (1 - A)f(0) \qquad (2.22)$$

$$S_A = \begin{cases} (f(0)/h_0)(1 - A), & \text{if } f(0) > 0 \\ 0, & \text{if } f(0) < 0 \end{cases}$$

$$+ \begin{cases} 0, & \text{if } S_h > 0 \\ (A/2h)S_h, & \text{if } S_h < 0 \end{cases} \qquad (2.23)$$

with $f(h)$ the growth rate of ice of thickness h and h_0 a fixed demarcation thickness between thin and thick ice.

The S_h term specifies that the net ice growth or melt is given by the sum of the ice grown on open water plus the additional growth over the portion of the cell covered by thick ice, which is estimated to be that of ice of constant thickness h/A. For melting conditions, the same sum is used, which is equivalent to assuming that the heat absorbed by open water will horizontally mix and melt additional ice until the mixed layer returns to freezing. The S_A term characterizes the way in which growth and decay change the relative areal extents of thin and thick ice. The idea is that the areal fraction of thin ice will decrease rapidly under freezing conditions and increase slowly under melting conditions. For freezing conditions, the fraction of open water $(1 - A)$ is allowed to decay exponentially with a time constant of $h_0/f(0)$, which gives the first term in Eq. (2.23). In Arctic simulations, $h_0 = 0.5$ m is used, while for Antarctic simulations h_0 is set equal to 1.0. This larger Antarctic value is based on field observations (Ackley et al., 1980; Gow et al., 1982) that suggest that frazil ice formation may well prolong ice production in open water regions. Setting $h_0 = 1.0$ parameterizes this by causing open water to be removed more slowly by growth. The second term in the S_A equation accounts for melting. Its magnitude is derived by assuming that the thick ice is uniformly distributed between 0 and $2(h/A)$ in thickness and that it all melts at the same rate.

To couple the ice strength to the ice thickness characteristics, the ice strength P^* is taken to be a function of compactness and thickness according to

$$P^* = P_0 h \exp[-C(1 - A)] \qquad (2.24)$$

where P_0 and C are fixed empirical constants and h is in meters. This formulation makes the strength strongly dependent on the amount of thin ice (characterized by the compactness A), while also allowing the ice to more slowly strengthen as it becomes thicker. The constant C is taken to be 20, which causes the strength to be very small when the fraction of open water is 15% or larger.

2.3.2. Ramifications of Thickness–Strength Coupling. Thickness–strength coupling causes modeled large-scale spatial variations of thickness to be determined often more by mechanical considerations than by thermodynamics. This feature is illustrated by Figs. 3 and 4, which are taken from a multiple-thickness seasonal equilibrium simulation (Hibler, 1980) of the Arctic Basin ice cover. Very similar results are obtained by using a two-level thickness distribution (Hibler, 1979). As can be seen from Fig. 3, the dynamics introduces a marked change in spatial contours of ice thickness as compared with the thermodynamic simulations. Basically, the ice-velocity field (its mean annual values are shown in Fig. 4) tends to thicken ice by convergence and concomitant ridging off the Canadian Archipelago while thinning the ice off the Alaskan and Siberian coasts. (It should be noted that daily velocities will differ substantially from the mean annual values.) The shape and magnitudes of the simulated thickness contours (Fig. 3) agree well with observed estimates (Fig. 5). The results considering only thermodynamic effects are very similar to those obtained by Washington *et al.* (1976) and Parkinson and Washington (1979); while their thermodynamic simulations yield realistic thickness magnitudes, their spatial variations do not agree well with observations.

The essential physics of the buildup is that as the ice thickens due to convergence it becomes stronger and reduces the ice-velocity field convergence. If no ice interaction were assumed, the ice would build up essentially without bound. The main issue for climatic studies here is that the maximum thicknesses can be significantly affected and are determined by mechanical as well as thermodynamic considerations. An important footnote is that this reduction in ice-velocity convergence is not necessarily concomitant with a reduction in ice-drift rate.

In addition to ice buildup, on smaller scales thickness–strength coupling can lead to a number of fluctuating effects, such as kinematic waves. Some of these effects depend on the nonlinear ice interaction and the nonlinear coupling between ice strength and thickness characteristics.

An example of such fluctuating effects is illustrated in Figs. 6 and 7 [for more details, see Hibler *et al.* (1983)]. Figure 6 shows ice-velocity/time series at points progressively further from a wall in an idealized simulation, while Fig. 7 shows compactness profiles at different times. In this simulation the two-level coupled equations discussed previously were integrated for 18 hr at time steps of 15 min on a 9×9 grid. The initial conditions consisted of 10% open water together with a mean ice thickness of 0.5 m. To simplify analysis, the ice strength is taken to depend only on the compactness, not on the ice thickness:

$$P = (0.5 \text{ m})P^*e^{-C(1-A)} \qquad (2.25)$$

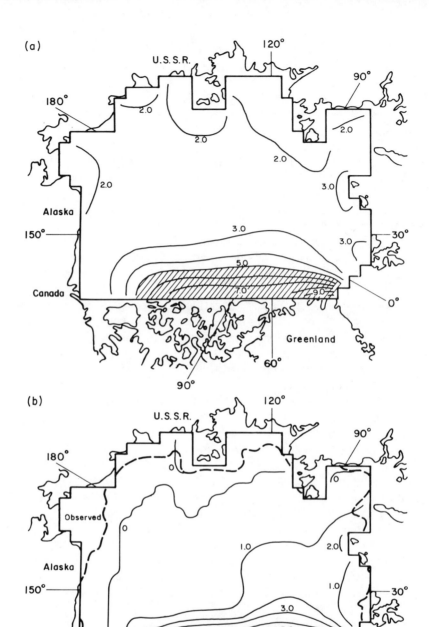

FIG. 3. Average (a) April and (b) August thickness contours (meters) for the fifth year of a multilevel dynamic-thermodynamic simulation. Thickness contours for (c) April and (d) August for a "thermodynamics-only" simulation. [From Hibler (1980).]

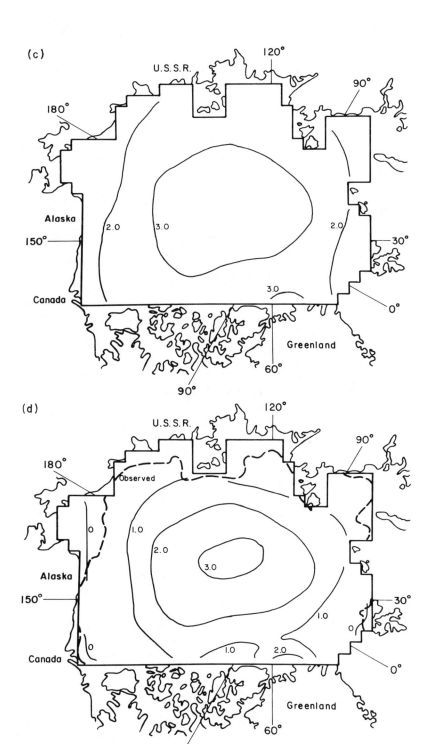

FIG. 3. *(Continued)*

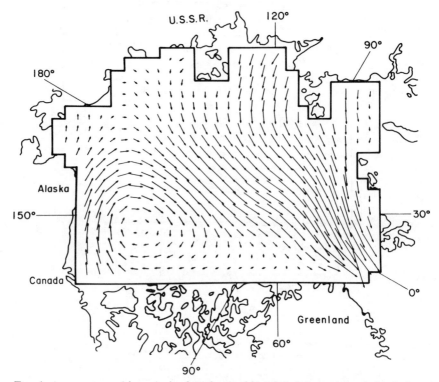

FIG. 4. Average annual ice-velocity field for the fifth year of the multilevel simulation. A velocity vector one grid space long represents 0.02 m s⁻¹. [From Hibler (1980).]

In addition, the turning angles and Coriolis parameter were set equal to zero. A constant wind speed of 9.23 m s⁻¹ in the positive x direction was used.

As can be seen from Fig. 6, even though the forcing is fixed, points nearest the boundary first slow down and then speed up. The initial slowing down of the ice near the coast is due to the ice becoming stronger as the compactness decreases (see Fig. 7). However, the region of low compactness eventually becomes large enough to accumulate an adequate wind fetch to overcome the differential of plastic stresses between the rigid boundary on one side and the less compact ice on the other. When this happens, the near-shore ice begins to drift faster, although not faster than the initial drift rates.

Note that nearest the coast there are also small fluctuations in the ice velocity. These waves arise from the fact that the velocity of ice is balanced in part by the stress gradient, while the stress gradient is maintained by a convergence of the ice-velocity field. As a consequence, a perturbation of either one of these quantities can cause a wave to propagate down the stress gradient slope. This wave can naturally develop in the evolution of the

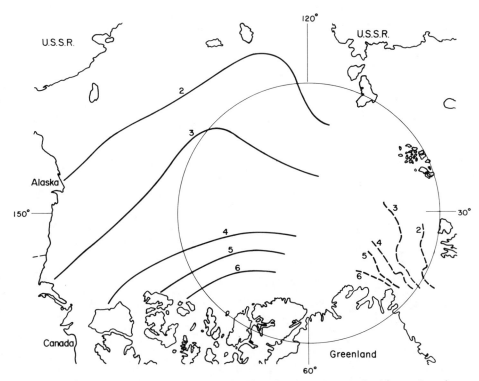

FIG. 5. Approximate contours (m) of observed ice thickness values obtained from submarine sonar data (LeSchack, private communication). The solid contours were obtained by LeSchack from a composite analysis of both summer (1960, 1962) and winter (1960) data, whereas the dashed contours are from April 1977 data. (From Hibler, 1980.)

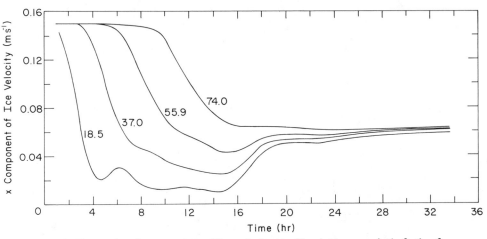

FIG. 6. Time series of x component of ice velocity at grid points progressively farther from right-hand boundary of buildup experiment. The grid points used were centered in the y direction, and the distances from the right-hand boundary are labeled. ($P^* = 20$ N m^{-2}, $C = 30$.)

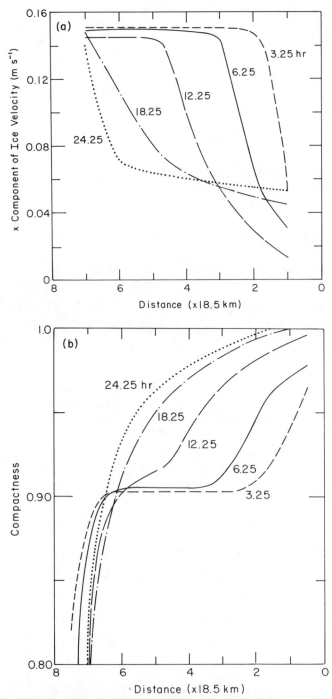

FIG. 7. (a) Compactness and (b) velocity profiles at different times in a numerical buildup experiment. The profiles were taken from grid cells centered in the y direction. ($P^* = 20\,\mathrm{N\,m^{-2}}$, $C = 30$.)

system since the initial buildup can be out of equilibrium with regard to kinematic waves (when the dependence of strength on compactness is non-linear). Such a kinematic wave is apparent in Fig. 6, most notably at hour 6 in the velocity/time series of the point nearest the coast. Tests at smaller time steps verified that this wave was not a numerical artifact. However, while this wave is noticeable in the velocity/time series, its effect on the compactness profiles is not major (see Fig. 7b). It is possible that continual excitation of such waves may be responsible for observed mesoscale sea-ice fluctuations and may affect the oceanic boundary layer characteristics.

3. The Role of Sea-Ice Dynamics in the Atmosphere– Ocean System

To help illustrate the role of sea-ice dynamics in air–sea interaction and climatic change, some selected results from numerical model simulations are discussed. The model studies include simulation of both the Arctic and Antarctic ice cover. In addition, some selected results from a coupled ice–ocean model of the Arctic–Greenland and Norwegian Seas are briefly de-scribed.

Except for the Arctic results shown later in Fig. 10 the model used to carry out seasonal simulations is the two-level dynamic thermodynamic model of Hibler (1979). In addition to the basic equations for the model discussed earlier, a thermodynamic code is employed. This code consists of the time-independent thermodynamic sea ice model of Semtner (1976), with the effects of snow cover approximated by allowing the ice-surface albedo to be an estimated snow value (0.75) when the calculated surface temperature of the ice is below freezing, and that of snow-free ice (0.66) when the surface temperature is at the melting point [see, e.g., Manabe and Stouffer (1980)]. The albedo of the open water is taken to be 0.1. Heat storage in the ocean is accounted for by utilizing a motionless mixed layer with a fixed depth of 30 m. The main atmosphere driving fields for the model consist of daily geostrophic wind fields and surface air temperatures and humidities.

3.1. Effect of Sea-Ice Dynamics on Simulated Seasonal Sea-Ice Cycles

A dominant effect of dynamics in Arctic simulations is to cause the spatial variations of thickness to be determined more by mechanical considerations than by thermodynamics, a feature that is in agreement with observational submarine sonar data. This characteristic was discussed earlier and is illus-trated in Figs. 3 and 5. It is notable that this type of mechanical buildup can

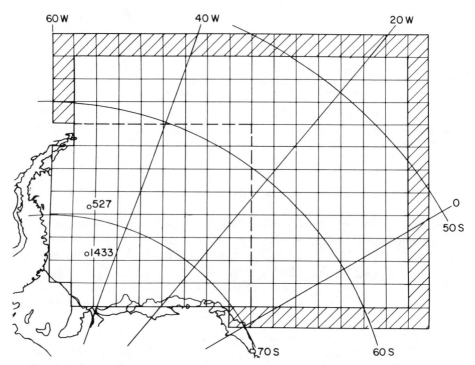

FIG. 8. Grid used for numerical simulations of the Weddell Sea pack ice. Hatched grid cells represent open boundaries. Open circles denote initial positions of two drifting buoys (on 1 January 1979) that supplied surface temperature data for the reanalysis. [From Hibler and Ackley (1983).]

also play a critical role in the sensitivity of simulated ice thicknesses to atmospheric warming. The essential concept here is that under warming conditions, the ice interaction can modify the ice-velocity field in regions of ice convergence, thus allowing greater thickness buildup than would occur without thickness–strength coupling. The importance of this effect for the Weddell Sea pack ice was studied by Hibler (1984b) by comparing simulations employing a fully coupled model to simulations using a fixed-ice-velocity model that did not contain ice interaction feedback effects (i.e., the ice-velocity fields do not change if "warmer" temperatures are used). The results showed that using a fixed velocity field, rather than allowing the ice-velocity field to be modified by ice interaction, causes the ice thickness to decrease more under a warming (especially in summer).

In addition to ice thickness buildup, ice dynamic effects can also modify the simulated ice edge. Such an effect is particularly pronounced in simulations of Antarctic sea ice as shown in Figs. 8 and 9. Figure 8 shows the grid used for a seasonal simulation of the Weddell Sea pack ice model (Hibler and Ackley, 1983), while Fig. 9 shows simulated and observed ice coverage averaged over the whole grid from a hierarchy of simulations (Hibler, 1984b). The ice coverage is basically the sum of areas of all grid cells covered by ice of any thickness. All models include a spatially and temporally varying heat flux from the ocean with an average of about 13 W m^{-2}.

The model results shown in Fig. 9 are for a fully coupled dynamic–thermodynamic model, a static thermodynamics-only model, and a static model with *in situ* leads. In the "leads-only" model, the leads are specified to be uniform spatially with values equal to the spatially averaged daily results from the full model. As can be seen, a complete inclusion of sea-ice dynamics causes a more complete seasonal cycle in much better agreement with observation than either the leads-only case or the full model. There are two reasons for the larger seasonal cycle in the case of the full model. One is an increased heat absorption due to leads. However, a second reason is the presence of advection effects, which tend to shift the whole ice edge into open water and thus reduce the extent. This is particularly pronounced where the edge is not zonally symmetric.

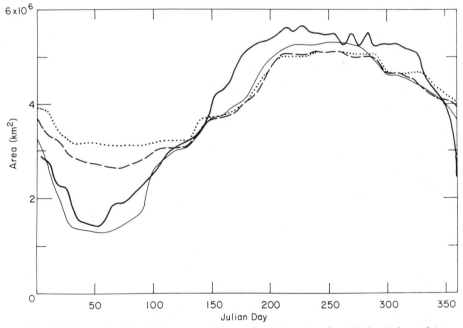

FIG. 9. Time series of spatially averaged ice area for a hierarchy of model simulations of the Weddell Sea pack ice. (Control temperatures: thin line, full model; heavy line, observed; dotted line, thermo only; dashed line, leads only.) [From Hibler (1984b).]

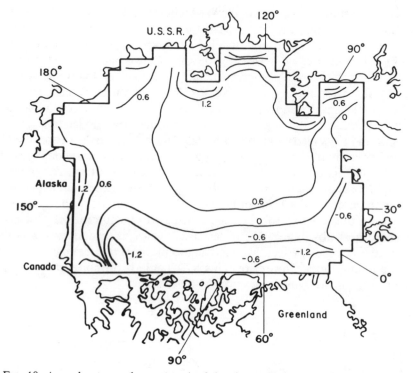

FIG. 10. Annual net growth contours (at 0.6-m intervals) for a multiple-thickness-level dynamic thermodynamic simulation of the Arctic Basin ice cover. [From Hibler (1980).]

While ice transport can modify the ice extent, a perhaps more dominant effect of ice transport is to modify the net seasonal growth. Figures 10 and 11 show net ice growth from simulations of the Arctic Basin ice cover by Hibler (1980) and simulations of the Weddell Sea pack ice by Hibler and Ackley (1983). In the static-leads-only or thermodynamics-only models, the net growth is zero in a seasonal simulation since all the ice growth is balanced by melt. However, with advection included there are major changes, with much of the ice growth taking place in regions of ice divergence and the ice melt occurring near the ice edge or in regions of ice convergence. In the Weddell Sea, for example, much of the ice growth occurs in southern parts of the grid, with ice melt occurring farther north. In the Arctic, much of the ice growth occurs in the shelf regions, with ice melt occurring near the Canadian Archipelago, where the ice is very thick due to mechanical ridge formation. This imbalance in ice growth is especially important in oceanographic simulations since it represents a major modification in the surface salt flux characteristics. It could also possibly affect the atmospheric circulation in that regions of high growth represent regions of net atmospheric heat gain, while regions of ice melt probably represent regions of net atmospheric heat loss.

While not so obvious from the ice extent plots, it is also good to remember that the sea-to-air heat exchanges will be substantially larger in a dynamic ice cover than in a thermodynamics-only ice cover. This is illustrated in Fig. 12, which shows the net ice growth for the same three Antarctic sea-ice models discussed earlier. As can be seen, the increased seasonal swing of both the full model and the leads-only model yields a sea-to-air heat loss about five times larger than the thermodynamics-only model.

Inclusion of sea-ice dynamics also causes a decrease in the coherence time scale of simulated ice thicknesses (Walsh *et al.*, 1984). This is illustrated in Fig. 13, which shows the autocorrelation function for the total monthly averaged ice mass simulated over the Northern Hemisphere from a full dynamic thermodynamic model and from a thermodynamics-only model. The simulated record spans 20 years and has the average annual seasonal cycle removed. As can be seen, there is much less coherence in time when dynamics are added, indicating that thickness anomalies can be more rapidly removed or modified. This result may be particularly relevant to the effect of sea-ice anomalies on long-range forecasts.

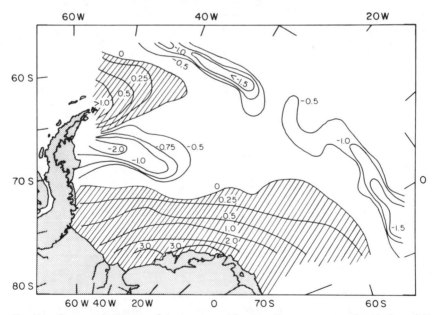

Fig. 11. Contours in meters of the net annual ice growth over an annual cycle for a fully coupled dynamic thermodynamic model of the Weddell Sea pack ice. [From Hibler and Ackley (1983).]

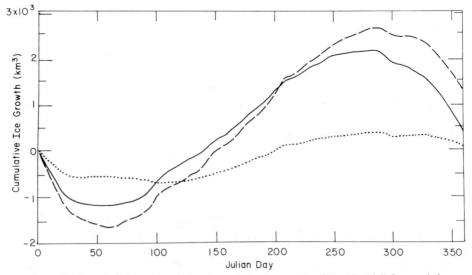

FIG. 12. Cumulative ice growth for three different models of the Weddell Sea pack ice. Control temperatures: solid line, full model; dashed line, fixed leads; dotted line, thermo only. (From Hibler, 1984b.)

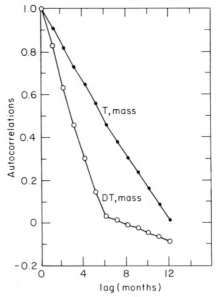

FIG. 13. Autocorrelations of departure from monthly mean ice mass over a 20-yr period for the whole domain covered by a Northern Hemisphere sea-ice model. Results are shown for a full dynamic thermodynamic simulation (DT) and for a thermodynamics-only simulation (T). [Drawn from data in Walsh *et al.* (1984).]

3.2. Some Results from an Ice–Ocean Model

Because of the close coupling between the ice and ocean in polar regions, it is helpful in analyzing ice dynamics effects to model both the ice and ocean concurrently. As an initial step in this direction, Hibler and Bryan (1984) constructed a diagnostic ice–ocean model and used it to carry out a series of seasonal simulations of the Arctic, Greenland, and Norwegian Seas. This model includes the full three-dimensional circulation of the ocean and hence differs from previous models of the seasonal cycle of Arctic sea ice where the ocean has been approximated either by a fixed-depth motionless mixed layer (Washington *et al.,* 1976; Parkinson and Washington, 1979; Hibler, 1980; Hibler and Walsh, 1982; Manabe and Stouffer, 1980), with possibly a small constant heat flux from the deeper ocean or by a one-dimensional, variable-thickness mixed layer (Pollard *et al.,* 1983).

This ice–ocean model was constructed by coupling the two-thickness-level thermodynamic sea-ice model (Hibler, 1979) with a multilevel baroclinic ocean model (Bryan, 1969). The sea-ice model supplies heat flux, salt flux, and momentum exchange boundary conditions for the top of the ocean. The ocean model, in turn, supplies current and heat exchange information to the ice model. Since the concern here was to examine the effect of ocean circulation on sea ice, observed oceanic temperature and salinity data (Levitus, 1982) were used to weakly force the ocean model so that its equilibrium time scale is similar to that of the ice model (3 to 5 yr). This "diagnostic" method allows the ocean model to be forced to available climatological ocean data while at the same time allowing considerable adjustment in the upper ocean due to the effects of ice–ocean interaction. In addition, the barotropic mode of the ocean is fully simulated so that temporally varying currents due to surface stress fluctuations are part of the model predictions. The basic idea here is to specify the ocean circulation over climatic time scales while modeling the shorter-term fluctuations.

Some of the main results from the model simulations are shown in Figs. 14 through 16. Figure 14 compares observed ice buoy (Thorndike and Colony, 1980) drift to simulated results, both with and without the ocean model included. Although of considerable magnitude, the ocean currents are smaller than the ice drift, and in buoy-drift comparisons they account for less than 50% of the net ice drift. While not apparent from this figure, more detailed analysis shows both the ice motion and current structure to have considerable temporal variability. The variability in the ice motion occurs everywhere, while the main current variability is in shallower regions or near rapid topographic variations.

An important feature of this coupled ice–ocean model is the modification by the ice interaction of the wind stress transferred into the ocean. This effect

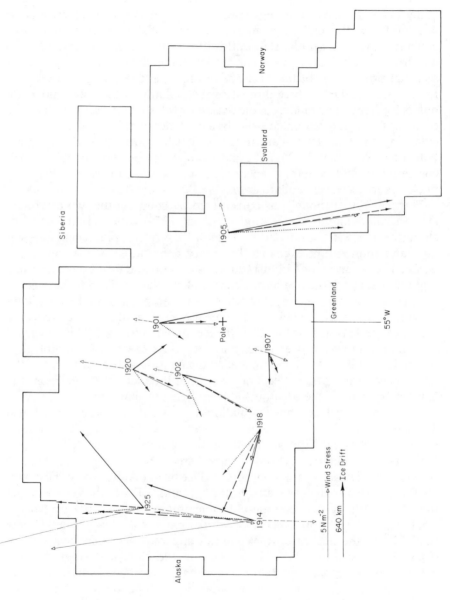

is particularly pronounced on long time scales since large fluctuations in wind stress tend to average out. As shown in Fig. 14 the ice interaction at the buoy locations has a magnitude comparable to the mean wind stress. Also, while in most cases the ice stress opposes the wind stress, it can combine with the wind stress or be at right angles to the ice drift due to the configuration of the land boundary and the ice edge.

Probably the most noticeable effect of the modeled ocean circulation is to greatly improve the ice margin simulation (Fig. 15a). This improved ice margin is due to the large oceanic heat flux from the deeper ocean into the upper mixed layer in this region (Fig. 16). The heat flux occurs primarily in winter; analysis shows that much of the enhancement is due to deep convection, which brings up warm water and prevents ice formation in early winter. This convection explains the absence of ice in the full model simulation far from the ice margin.

Near the ice margin a similar physics applies, but the precise location of the ice edge becomes more sensitive to the surface salt balance and to lateral effects in the oceanic circulation. The sensitivity simulations shown in Fig. 15b, for example, indicate that the freshwater flux from melting at the advancing ice edge tends to seal off the ice margin to upward oceanic heat flux and allows a farther advance than would otherwise occur. A sensitivity simulation without lateral motion in the ocean (Fig. 15b) also tends to produce a more excessive edge at the end of one year, since the lateral transport of heat to both the deep and upper layers is missing. This latter result demonstrates the difficulty of simulating the seasonal cycle of sea ice when using only a one-dimensional mixed-layer model.

4. Concluding Remarks

The dynamical nature of the polar sea-ice cover substantially modifies air–sea momentum, heat, and salt exchanges. As a consequence, sea-ice dynamics plays a pivotal role in air–sea interaction in polar regions. Simulation results reviewed here have indicated the complexity of different dynamical effects and the role they can play in air–sea interaction. This complexity makes it difficult to guess the correct *ad hoc* dynamical modification to add

---

FIG. 14. Long-term averages of simulated and observed drift rates of ice buoys, wind stress, and force due to ice interaction at the location of ice buoys. Drift rates have been converted to distances by multiplication by time. The time intevals used were February–November for buoys 1901 and 1902, March–September for buoy 1905, May–November for buoy 1907, and March–November for the remaining buoys. (---▷, ice stress; ——▷, wind stress; ——▶, actual buoy drift; ···▶, ice model only drift; ——▶, fifth year ice ocean model drift.) [From Hibler and Bryan (1984).]

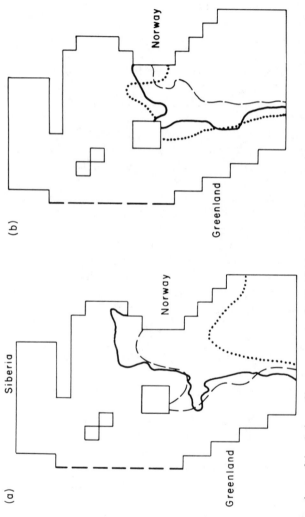

FIG. 15. Comparisons of simulations of ice concentration and ice thickness. (a) February 50% concentration limits from fully coupled ice–ocean model (dashed line) and for an ice-only model (dotted line), which included a fixed-depth mixed layer. The observed limit (solid line) is taken from fleet weather (Suitland, Maryland, U.S. Navy) charts for the end of February. (b) Simulated 0.005-m thickness contours for day 360 for a full ice–ocean model, a "motionless" ocean model, and a coupled ice–ocean model with no salt fluxes due to freezing and melting. The "motionless" model (dashed line) and no-salt simulations (dotted line) were run for only one year and were initialized to ice thickness and ocean fields at the end of the fourth year of the full diagnostic model simulation (solid line). [From Hibler and Bryan (1984).]

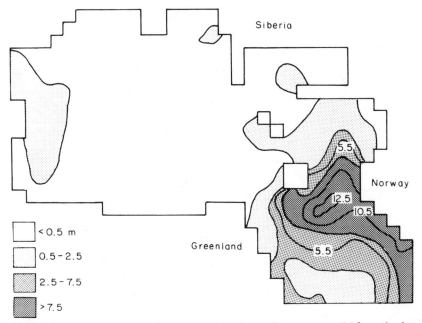

FIG. 16. Average annual heat gained by the upper layer of the ocean model from the deeper ocean and by lateral heat transport. The contours are in terms of the melting capacity of the heat in meters of ice per year. For comparison, a melt rate of 1 m of ice per year is equivalent to 9.57 W m⁻². [From Hibler and Bryan (1984).]

to climate models. Instead, they emphasize the importance of including a more realistic treatment of dynamics vis-à-vis a fully coupled dynamic–thermodynamic model. Such models exist, and while more demanding of computer time than static models, are much faster computationally than present atmospheric GCMs. Thus, there seems to be much potential for investigating the role of sea ice in climate in the near future.

ACKNOWLEDGMENTS

Much of the modeling work described here was made possible by aid and support from scientists at the GFDL during two sabbatical stays there. I would particularly like to thank Dr. Kirk Bryan, Dr. Syukuro Manabe, Mr. Michael Cox, and Mr. Michael Spelman. Comments on this manuscript by Dr. Kirk Bryan were also appreciated.

Last but not least, I would like to thank Dr. Joseph Smagorinsky for his unstinting support of work reviewed here both during my stays at the GFDL and at other times. It has made a difference. This review was supported in part by the Office of Naval Research.

References

Ackley, S. F., Gow, A. J., Buck, K. R., and Golden, K. M. (1980). Sea-ice studies in the Weddell Sea aboard USCGC Polar Sea. *Antarct. J. U.S.* **15**(5), 84–86.

Bratchie, I. (1984). Rheology of an ice-floe field. *Ann. Glaciol.* **5**, 23–28.

Brown, R. A. (1980). Planetary boundary layer modeling for AIDJEX. *In* "Sea Ice Processes and Models" (R. S. Pritchard, ed.), pp. 387–401. Univ. of Washington Press, Seattle.

Bryan, K. (1969). A numerical method for the study of the circulation of the world oceans. *J. Comput. Phys.* **4**, 347–376.

Campbell, W. J. (1965). The wind-driven circulation of ice and water in a polar ocean. *J. Geophys. Res.* **70**, 3279–3301.

Coon, M. D. (1974). Mechanical behavior of compacted arctic ice floes. *J. Pet. Technol.* **26**, 466–470.

Doronin, Yu. P. (1970). On a method of calculating the compactness and drift of ice floes. *Tr. Arkt. Antarkt. Nauchno. Issled. Inst.* **291**, 5–17; *AIDJEX Bull. (Engl. Transl.)* **3**, 22–39 (1971).

Egorov, K. L. (1970). Theory of drift of ice floes in a horizontally heterogeneous wind field. *Probl. Arkt. Antarkt.* **34**, 71–78; *AIDJEX Bull. (Engl. Trans.)* **6**, 37–45 (1971).

Goodier, J. N., and Hodge, P. G., Jr. (1958). "Elasticity and Plasticity." Wiley, New York.

Gow, A. J., Ackley, S. F., Weeks, W. F., and Govoni, J. (1982). Physical and structural characteristics of Antarctic sea ice. *Ann. Glaciol.* **3**, 113–117.

Hibler, W. D., III (1974). Differential sea ice drift. II. Comparison of mesoscale strain measurements to linear drift theory predictions. *J. Glaciol.* **13**, 457–471.

Hibler, W. D., III (1977). A viscous sea ice law as a stochastic average of plasticity. *JGR, J. Geophys. Res.* **82**, 3932–3938.

Hibler, W. D., III (1979). A dynamic thermodynamic sea ice model. *J. Phys. Oceanogr.* **9**, 815–846.

Hibler, W. D., III (1980). Modeling a variable thickness sea ice cover. *Mon. Weather Rev.* **108**, 1943–1973.

Hibler, W. D., III (1984a). "Ice Dynamics," USACRREL Monogr. National Technical Information Service, U.S. Dept. of Commerce Springfield, Va. 84-3.

Hibler, W. D., III (1984b). The role of sea-ice dynamics in modeling CO_2 increases. *In* "Climate Processes and Climate Sensitivity," Geophys. Monogr. No. 29, Maurice Ewing Ser. No. 5, (J. E. Hansen and T. Takahashi, eds.) pp. 238–253. Am. Geophys. Union, Washington, D.C.

Hibler, W. D., III, and Ackley, S. F. (1983). Numerical simulation of the Weddell Sea pack ice. *JGR, J. Geophys. Res.* **88**, 2873–2887.

Hibler, W. D., III, and Bryan, K. (1984). Ocean circulation: Its effect on seasonal sea ice simulations. *Science* **224**, 489–492.

Hibler, W. D., III, and Tucker, W. B. (1979). Some results from a linear viscous model of the Arctic ice cover. *J. Glaciol.* **22**, 293–304.

Hibler, W. D., III, and Walsh, J. E. (1982). On modeling seasonal and interannual fluctuations of Arctic sea ice. *J. Phys. Oceanogr.* **12**, 1514–1523.

Hibler, W. D., III, Ackley, S. F., Crowder, W. K., McKim, H. W., and Anderson, D. M. (1974). Analysis of shear zone ice deformation in the Beaufort Sea using satellite imagery. *In* "The Coast and Shelf of the Beaufort Sea" (J. C. Reed and J. E. Sater, eds.), pp. 285–296. Arctic Institute of North America, Montreal, Canada.

Hibler, W. D., III, Udin, I., and Ullerstig, A. (1983). On forecasting mesoscale ice dynamics and buildup. *Ann. Glaciol.* **4**, 110–115.

Hunkins, K. (1975). The oceanic boundary layer and stress beneath a drifting ice floe. *JGR, J. Geophys. Res.* **80**, 3425–3433.

Laikhtman, D. L. (1964). "Physics of the Boundary Layer of the Atmosphere" (Engl. Trans.) U.S. Dept. of Commerce, Washington, D.C.

Leavitt, E. (1980). Surface-based air stress measurements made during AIDJEX. *In* "Sea Ice Processes and Models" (R. S. Pritchard, ed.), pp. 419–429. Univ. of Washington Press, Seattle.

Levitus, S. (1982). "Climatological Atlas of the World Oceans," NOAA Prof. Pap. No. 13. U.S. Govt. Printing Office, Washington, D.C.

Malvern, L. E. (1969). "Introduction to the Mechanics of a Continuous Media." Prentice-Hall, Englewood Cliffs, New Jersey.

McPhee, M. G. (1979). The effect of the oceanic boundary layer on the mean drift of pack ice: Application of a simple model. *J. Phys. Oceanogr.* **9**, 388–400.

McPhee, M. G. (1980). An analysis of pack ice drift in summer. *In* "Sea Ice Processes and Models" (R. S. Pritchard, ed.), pp. 62–75. Univ. of Washington Press, Seattle.

Manabe, S., and Stouffer, R. (1980). Sensitivity of a global climate model to an increase of CO_2 concentration in the atmosphere. *JGR, J. Geophys. Res.* **85**, 5529–5554.

Maykut, G. A. (1978). Energy exchange over young sea ice in the central Arctic. *JGR, J. Geophys. Res.* **83**, 3646–3658.

Parkinson, C. L., and Washington, W. M. (1979). A large-scale numerical model of sea ice. *JGR, J. Geophys. Res.* **84**, 311–337.

Pollard, D., Batteen, M. L., and Han, Y. J. (1983). Development of a simple upper-ocean and sea ice model. *J. Phys. Oceanogr.* **13**, 754–768.

Pritchard, R. S., Coon, M. D., and McPhee, M. G. (1977). Simulation of sea ice dynamics during AIDJEX. *J. Pressure Vessel Technol.* **99J**, 491–497.

Roed, L. P., and O'Brien, J. J. (1981). Geostrophic adjustment in highly dispersive media: An application to the marginal ice zone. *J. Geophys. Astrophys. Fluid Dyn.* **18**, 263–278.

Rothrock, D. A. (1975a). The steady drift of an incompressible Arctic ice cover. *JGR, J. Geophys. Res.* **80**, 387–397.

Rothrock, D. A. (1975b). The energetics of the plastic deformation of pack ice by ridging. *JGR, J. Geophys. Res.* **80**, 4514–4519.

Semtner, A. J. Jr. (1976). A model for the thermodynamic growth of sea ice in numerical investigations of climate. *J. Phys. Oceanogr.* **6**, 379–389.

Sodhi, D. S., and Hibler, W. D., III (1980). Nonsteady ice drift in the Strait of Belle Isle. *In* "Sea Ice Processes and Models" (R. S. Pritchard, ed.), pp. 177–186. Univ. of Washington Press, Seattle.

Thorndike, A. S., and Colony, R. (1980). "Arctic Ocean Buoy Program," Data Rep. University of Washington, Seattle.

Thorndike, A. S., and Colony, R. (1982). Sea ice motion in response to geostrophic winds. *JGR, J. Geophys. Res.* **87**, 5845–5852.

Thorndike, A. S., Rothrock, D. A., Maykut, G. A., and Colony, R. (1975). The thickness distribution of sea ice. *JGR, J. Geophys. Res.* **80**, 4501–4513.

Walsh, J. E., Hibler, W. D., III, and Ross, B. (1984). A model simulation of 20 years of Northern Hemisphere sea ice fluctuations. *Ann. Glaciol.* **5**, 170, 176.

Washington, W. M., Semtner, A. J., Parkinson, C., and Morrison, L. (1976). On the development of a seasonal change sea-ice model. *J. Phys. Oceanogr.* **6**, 679–685.

INDEX